The
Order Primates
An Introduction

M. E. Stephens • J. D. Paterson
University of Calgary

KENDALL/HUNT PUBLISHING COMPANY
2460 Kerper Boulevard   P.O. Box 539   Dubuque, Iowa 52004-0539

Contents

iv

Preface

The University of Calgary has graduation requirements which force social science students to master a few science courses and science students to endure social science courses. Modern students seem reluctant to venture into the realms of other faculties but are required to do so.

The introductory course in primatology offered by the Department of Anthropology has developed a reputation among cautious students as a "less mathematical" science option for social science majors and as a less "airy fairy" social science option for science majors. Since it has no prerequisites it tends to attract a large enrollment. This causes several problems for the instructors. The classes contain two groups of students with different interests and backgrounds. They lack a common vocabulary and frequently have little real interest in the subject.

No text has yet proved adequate for such a diverse grouping of students. We have concluded that the most appropriate option is to teach with a collection of readings. The readings may be a mix of light and popular pieces to stimulate interest and to ease the social science students into the field combined with some more serious "scientific" articles. The jargon and theories in the serious papers can then be explained and discussed in lectures.

In organizing a course which presents information about an order of mammals containing approximately 200 species one may easily overwhelm students. It becomes necessary to select examples from the multitude and, since this is an anthropology course, human primates will tend to receive greater attention. However, the course is designed to lead to humans in a gradual manner.

The readings in this book follow the basic course format. Note that the book reflects taxonomic classification and starts with the distantly related primates and ends with humans. First, introductory material on such basics as evolutionary theory, taxonomy and classification, with an application of both to a section on primate evolutionary history is presented.

The second section of the book then selects primate species to illustrate aspects of biology, ecology and behavioural ecology. The selection of species presented begins with humans' most distant primate kin, the Prosimian/Strepsirhines and Platyrhine examples of the Anthropoid/Haplorhine. Social science students will be happier to refer to the latter as "new world monkeys".

Part three of the book continues to illustrate biological aspects of primate life with examples drawn from the Catarrhines (old world monkeys and apes).

Part four segues into a transition between the biology of non-human primates and the biological perspectives on humans. This section focuses upon apes and other primate models for understanding general primate behaviour and/or primate aspects of human behaviour.

The fifth part of the book focuses on human primates. The four sections leading to this concluding component enable students to consider humans both as primates and biological organisms. Many of our social science students must be eased into this concept. Fortunately the term "human primate" is not as traumatic as "human animal".

This book will be used by several different instructors at the University of Calgary. It is unlikely that all of the readings or material will be used in any single section of the course. Many of our colleagues expressed amazement that two individuals as dissimilar as the editors could collaborate on a text. The diversity of the editors mirrors the diversity of the field of primatology. For that reason it seemed honest not to worry about the tonal differences in the introductions to various sections of the book. They reflect honest, but respected, differences. We hope that the selections will enable students to appreciate the myriad possibilities of primate studies.

We also express our gratitude to the primatologists, anthropologists, paleontologists, zoologists, psychologists, ethologists, and journalists who actually researched and wrote most of this volume. Finally, we thank our respective spouses who would have no trouble accepting the fact that humans are also primate animals.

M. E. Stephens
J. D. Paterson
University of Calgary

PART 1

Overviews and Theory

Evolution

James D. Paterson

The topic of evolution and matters of evolutionary theory are very complex, and a fully detailed discussion of them is beyond the capacity of this text. Indeed a full discussion of the issues within evolutionary theory is sufficient to fill several volumes of this size. The purpose here is not to lead the student through this mass, but only to provide some entry into the literature, provide a basic set of the major concepts, and perhaps to lead to further inquiries on the student's part.

There are three current meanings of the word "evolution" according to Thompson (1982) and Poirier (1987). The original use of the word was merely to indicate "change over time", without any consideration of process. The second meaning as Poirier (1987) states "seems at first only to be a statement about process: that organisms are related by

descent through common ancestry, a process that produces the shared structural and behavioral patterns seen in change over time." The third meaning of the word is a combination of the first two with the implication of a particular explanatory process, that of the Darwinian natural selection model.

Evolution, in a rigid technical sense for modern usage, is defined as the change in the genetic makeup of populations of organisms from generation to generation. It is no more complex than that. Thus any and all aspects of change, due to whatever causes, known or unknown, are considered evolutionary change if they affect the genetic structure of the population. It is entirely proper to speak of the evolution of domestic animals and plants, since they are "changed genetically" from their wild ancestors. However, the mecha-

1

nism by which domestic animals are "evolved" differs from that of their wild relatives, in this case the "evolution" is by means of artificial selection by the humans who control these populations.

Evolution is not a metaphysical, religious, cultural or social phenomenon. The colloquial application of the term evolution to any one of these categories is a gross abuse and misuse of the word. Religious, cultural and social phenomena may indeed change over time and from generation to generation, but under the definition of evolution which is used here, none of these constitutes an evolutionary development. The gene pools have not been affected directly, although populational genetics may be affected strongly by non-genetic forces in a society. Human populations in most areas of the world have had their gene pools modified as a result of conquests, attempts at genocide, and preferential selectional patterns of leaders, but these have not been more than the side effects of non-evolutionary and ephemeral developments.

Evolution is a process: an ongoing phenomenon that continually changes the genetic makeup of populations. It ultimately results in the continued success or eventual extinction of the population. While some of the causes of evolutionary change are random, the results of evolution are not. Evolution is a process that applies to populations rather than to individuals *per se*. It is the population that evolves, NOT the individual. The population is not the only unit of evolution, since genetic change can spread from population to population within the same "species". Populations within a species DO differ from each other and according to the degree of differentiation may be categorized as "subspecies" or "races" (although a more appropriate label may be "gens" or "demes"). Usually there is some degree of reduction in reproductive success between subspecies, a phenomenon which may indicate a potential for eventual separation into distinct species. Part of the differentiation may be due to environmental factors and local adaptation. Species which show marked differences between populations, but no reduction of reproductive success, (such as *Homo sa-*

piens sapiens) are referred to as polytypic.

EVOLUTIONARY THEORY

The "theory" of evolution is concerned with how these changes in genetic makeup occur, what effect they have on living populations, and how fossil populations arose, developed, and disappeared. There is no question about whether or not evolution actually exists. FOR THERE TO BE NO EVOLUTION, EVERY GENERATION WOULD HAVE TO BE EXACTLY THE SAME, *GENETICALLY*, AS THE PREVIOUS GENERATION. There could be no loss or addition of genes to the pool, although if loss was allowed, but not addition, the result would eventually be a population with virtually no variation in appearance. Such a population would have most of the characteristics of a group of clones, or a tissue culture in the laboratory.

Theories of evolution have been common since the middle of the eighteenth century, and like most other western science have some points of origin, or commonalities with, earlier Greek philosophies.

Some processes must be defined, since they form the ground in which must of the discussion of the evolutionary mechanisms is set. See Figure 1 for illustrations of the following processes.

Anagenesis

The process of one species evolving into another along the same lineage is called anagenesis or phyletic evolution. This was the main model employed in Darwin's work, and is often assumed to go along with a model of continual slow but constant "adaptive" change in the lineage. This is, however, a substantially arbitrary perception, and Dawkins (1986) sets forth a viewpoint which provides a great variation in evolutionary rate, while still maintaining allegiance to Darwinian natural selection.

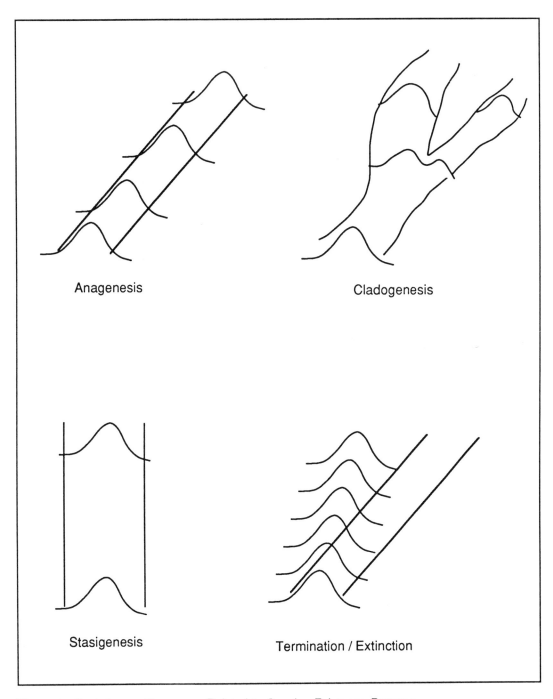

Anagenesis

Cladogenesis

Stasigenesis

Termination / Extinction

Figure 1: Evolutionary Processes Related to Species Existence Patterns

Some taxonomists and many paleontologists consider it convenient to divide a lineage into time segments. Especially when enough change over time has occurred, and it may be appropriate to give the segments different species names. It must be recognized that the arbitrariness of the process, if considered in its most outrageous form would require the placement of parents and offspring into different species. It may be more appropriate to conceptualize these divisions as relativistic and a species may extend up and down time only so far as reproductive viability could theoretically extend from the reference individual—in exactly the same manner as the "rassenkreis", or race-circle, model of species diversity.

Phyletic evolution is accepted as a real phenomenon by many researchers even though there is no direct evidence to support it. However, the division of a lineage into temporal species is somewhat arbitrary and depends as much on the history of fossil discoveries as on the fossils themselves.

Cladogenesis

Cladogenesis is the splitting of one lineage into two or more sublineages or new lineages. In this pattern of speciation, one ancestral species gives birth to two or more descendent species. The splitting is theorized, by phyletic gradualists to take a substantial amount of time to occur and can generally happen only when populations are geographically, or spatially, isolated from each other. When there is a geographic separation, it is possible for differences in selection or drift to result in true reproductive isolation. The reproductive isolation may be genetic—interbreeding no longer produces fertile offspring, morphological—interbreeding is no longer physically possible, or behavioural—interbreeding no longer occurs because of different mating seasons, or different signals for recognizing sexually receptive mates.

It is more difficult for cladogenesis to occur in wide ranging populations than for those which have very local habits, for two reasons. First, wide ranging populations are generally more often in contact with each other. There are fewer sources of geographic isolation, and genes move freely between populations. Second, wide ranging species often utilize many different resources, so that when physical isolation does occur, it takes a long time for reproductive isolation to result from selective mechanisms.

Great morphological differences between populations can only evolve after speciation, and therefore after reproductive isolation. They are a consequence, rather than a cause of speciation. During and just after the process of speciation, populations of the two species may be virtually indistinguishable. The punctuational perspective, to be considered later in this section, sees speciation as a relatively rapid process, but the mechanisms by which it occurs are still unknown.

Stasigenesis

The special case of stasigenesis must be examined, since the concept of stasis in a lineage will arise later. The model is a special (some would say the general) case of anagenesis in which there is virtually no morphological change taking place in the lineage. As a consequence, there can be no recognition of differentiated morphospecies. The lineage remains structurally the same, if not identical over extremely long periods of time.

The classic environment in which stasigenesis takes place is the deep sea habitat. For example, sharks of various lines, in some cases, represent 200 to 300 million years with limited or virtually no change. The genus *Carcharodon* is represented by a 250 million year old species—*Carcharodon megalodon*, and by the living *Carcharodon carcharas* otherwise known as the Great White Shark. The two species do not differ significantly in morphology, but only in size.

Termination—A Special Case of Extinction

The special case of termination is another variant of anagenesis which may take place as a lineage lags behind in adapting to changing environment. In this process, the genetic range of the species, and the rate of incorporation of new genetic structures, is limited and unable to provide for adaptation to the new conditions. The species becomes "maladapted" to the new environment and consequently becomes extinct—"terminated"—in the area. The only option for such a species lies in migration or shift of range to environments under which survival is possible, if such relocation is impossible, then extinction must inevitably occur.

A SHORT DISCOURSE ON PROGRESS IN EVOLUTION

The concept of progress in evolution is a confusing one. Whether it is the religious advocate claiming that he is "above the animals", or a philosopher expounding on Bergsonian "élan vital", or a taxonomist declaring that a particular characteristic is apomorphic / derived / advanced, they all hold differing concepts of "progress". The religious advocate may mean that "he" (personally) or maybe the human species, was specially created at a higher level than the animals, the philosophy of Bergson implies a teleological force which drives evolution towards a greater degree of perfection, while the taxonomist is merely stating his belief that the characteristic under examination appears later in the history of the lineage, reflecting a changed state with respect to an earlier condition. Part of the confusion is built into the English language, and part of it derives from an inadequate distinction between "absolute" and "relative" varieties of "progress".

A key to understanding is to recognize that absolute progress is Spencerian not Darwinian. Herbert Spencer published a paper in 1852 in which he outlined a model of "social and human evolution" and ranked all other societies as to their approach to the highest level which had been achieved, that of the Victorian British society. He saw this progress in *abso-

lute*, not relative terms. Victorian England was the highest form of society, it was an "absolute good" to which all others might aspire. Unfortunately, after the publication of Darwin's 1859 volume, the biological concept of evolution, and *relative* progress became confused in the minds of many people with the social evolution and absolute progress of Spencer. This led to the absurd and abhorrent "Social Darwinism" of the late nineteenth century and its adoption by the capitalists of North America, the fascists of central Europe, and the bolsheviks of Russia. It is important to recognize the distinction between Spencer's and Darwin's concepts of progress, they are not the same, and cannot be construed to be so under any circumstances. One is teleological, directed towards a conceptualized end, while the other is relativistic, driven from the outside through the processes of adaptation to the environment.

A quotation from Simpson in his conclusion to a review article on the concept of progress in evolution presents an eloquent statement of its nature.

> "Some organisms are better than their ancestors or than some of their relatives at doing certain things in certain ways. Some oysters are better at being oysters than their ancestors. Some trees are better at living on mountain tops than others. We are doubtless better at being men than *Australopithecus* was, although I go along with Haldane far enough to believe that monkeys are better at being monkeys than we would be even if we tried. It is also true that sometimes whole groups have been carried by selection to a point where their great expansion into various adaptive zones became possible, a progressive feature of evolution. . . . That is the explanation, in unduly broad terms, of the spread of dominant groups from time to time.
>
> With such examples it is perfectly reasonable to say that improvement has factually occurred and that there is therefore evolutionary progress. The progress is, however, ad

hoc in every case. Our ancestors' progress was not the oysters', the trees', or the monkeys', nor was theirs ours. Since we are humans, after all, the most interesting and important progress is progress toward us, but let us not mistake this for a general phenomenon.

Probably the most important result of this somewhat dispersive inquiry is negative: there is no innate tendency toward evolutionary progress and no one, overall sort of such progress. We cannot sit back and assume that natural selection will lead to progress for us, or for anything else. We cannot even assume that prolongation of past progress would continue to be progress." Simpson (1974 pp. 50–51)

Ayala (1977) confirms this perspective by stating: "Needless to say, organisms are more or less progressive depending on what criterion of progress is used. By certain criteria, flowering plants are more progressive than many animals." Thus making the point that progress, like beauty, is in the eye of the beholder. Again this perspective represents a relativistic concept of progress.

A common fallacy, one which frequently befuddles people, and even evolutionary biologists on occasion, is an acceptance of a scale of simple to complex as representing "progressive change". In a logical sequence, simple to complex does represent one type of progression, but directionality is not part of the sequence as an innate characteristic. The directionality, when specified, may just as well be "complex to simple" along the sequence. Indeed one of the commonly recognized philosophies in modern engineering sees three phases of development in which an initial idea works, perhaps well, but is a bit crude and deficient in some aspects, followed by a second phase with a complex assemblage of over-engineered solutions to the inadequacies of the first stage, and finally follows a simple, uncomplicated device designed properly to do the job without the defects found in either of the first two stages. In other words, a crude idea followed by a "Rube Goldberg" device, followed by a simple, clean solution. Evolution can not always be considered as an engineering exercise, but very frequently the principles of engineering are implicit in the evolutionary pattern. As a result, the evolutionary pattern may not reflect a 'simple to complex' directional gradient, but often does.

Is progressive evolution needed? Some modern evolutionists now argue that the notion of increasing complexity must be divorced from the notion of selection or fitness. Increases in complexity, long accepted as a major indicator of progressive or advantageous, change, may follow automatically from the way in which the epigenetic system operates. Complexity probably should not be conceived as a measure of fitness, but as a measure of the information content of developmental building instructions. It will not necessarily increase as a function of optimization. Phenotypic changes will not occur randomly, but will depend on the existence of alternative developmental pathways that can accommodate them. At issue is the probability of the occurrence of changes in different directions.

What has been called "progress", then, is quite probably the product of a host of factors, only one of which is the natural selection of individuals belonging to single lineages. And evolution is NOT MERELY PROGRESSIVE CHANGE! It is doubtful that a competent post-modern evolutionary theory would need to avail itself of the concept of progressive evolution.

Behaviour and Natural Selection

As Mayr has often pointed out (Mayr 1960, 1963, 1970) behaviour is the first point at which the environmental conditions can act as selective pressures on any organism. In the evolutionary sense, an organism is constantly being subjected to a multitude of environmental pressures. That evolution may be driven primarily by the interaction of behaviour and ecological circumstances has been strongly argued by Geist (1972) in an article in which he concludes that the majority of the defining mammalian characteristics of the therapsid (mammal-like) reptiles can be attributed to this process. If the selective pressure is of an acute form, offering the organism an immediate or short term option of survive or die, it is the levels of cognition, self awareness or learned tradition which provide the first response. In this sense, being self aware, cognitive, and having a set of learned responses may be the critical difference between escaping from a selection mechanism, such as a predator, or becoming the predator's dinner. Conversely, a self aware, cognitive, traditionally behaving predator also must respond to selective pressure, and perform effectively at taking prey. These behavioural responses, on either side, may or may not be supported by physiological variations on a continual or response basis, but the genetic level would not be directly involved. However, it must be recognized that if the organism is selected out of the gene pool there may be some effect on the gene frequencies in the pool, but the effect is relatively greater for a small population than for a large one. If selective pressures are more of a chronic, continuing form, the responses of the organisms may be more generally involved at the behavioural and physiological levels. If these two layers, acting in a feedback relationship are able to strike new balances with the changed environmental conditions, for each individual organism, then the population can continue to exist in the same area over a lengthy time period without significant changes in the gene pool, although some change in morphology may occur if that is associated with the appropriate physiological response.

THE GENOME AND GENETICS

Every eukaryote cell, the basic type of cell from which multicellular organisms are formed, has a complex structure which may be derived from an ancient symbiotic fusion. Structures such as chloroplasts in plants and mitochondria in animals seem to have once been independent cells (Margulis, 1981). As a result each eukaryotic cell has genetic information in at least two locations, within the nucleus resides the host cell genome, and in the mitochondria resides the mitochondrial DNA (mtDNA).

The nuclear genome is the repository of the major collection of information for the structuring of the cell and for the operation of all internal processes. The information appears to be in the form of code. The genetic code, as deciphered by Watson and Crick (1953) is straightforward and based upon the four base compounds—Adenine, Thymine, Guanine, and Cytosine—which are linked to the sugar and phosphate backbone of the molecule. A set of three base pairs codes for a particular amino acid, but because there are four bases involved, there are 64 possible triplets which can specify among only 20 amino acids, thus the system has a very substantial degree of redundancy. This redundancy helps to maintain stability of function, for mutations which change the code triplet, but do not result in coding for a different amino acid, are effectively neutral in that no effects are seen. The codes of the genomic system have been the subject of intensive research, but the details remain, in large part, a mystery (John and Miklos, 1988).

To employ a mechanistic analogy, it is possible to compare the information of the genome to that in a computer systems program. (This has also been a common theme in science fiction novels, for an excellent example see : *Code of the Lifemaker* by James P. Hogan). The genome is functionally like a computer code, but a "compiled" code which has been converted from a programing language into "binary", and we, as humans, have had a multitude of problems in the "de-compiling" of it, in order to make the code intelligible. In comparison with a computer program, the data in the genome as presented by John and Miklos (1988), can be seen to have lots of "comments" imbedded in it, it has "self-modifying units" which operate on the structure of the genome, but rarely have

7

any external significance, and has been corrupted over millennia with "worms" and "viruses" acquired from numerous sources. Some resources have been damaged and made non-functional. The code also seems to hold large numbers of conditional statements, what a programmer might see as "if—then" loops. Some of the code appears to be "pseudo—hardware" in that it contains the information for constructing the cell, while other parts of the code are directly involved with operation. Surprisingly, the code is also interactive, various "epigenetic" factors from outside of the cell are involved in determining the courses of internal program execution (conceptually this view is descended directly from Waddington). While this analogy of the genome to a computer program may be considered as quite fanciful, much of the design and operation of the genomic program does appear to parallel the binary codes for our silicon machines, certainly not in detail, but perhaps in general conceptualization.

MECHANISMS FOR THE GENERATION OF VARIATION

For any system of evolutionary change to operate, whether that evolution proceeds by natural selection or any other mechanism, there must be a process or set of processes which generate variations. It is well recognized that every individual organism is at least potentially unique, that some degree of variation in virtually all characteristics occurs within each species. Some of that variation is due to differences in the genome, and some portion of it is due to variable epigenetic factors. The internal variations within the genome have traditionally been looked at as the most important sources of variability. The mechanisms for generating variation are numerous, but the oldest and most important one recognized is mutation.

Mutation

Mutation is the direct change of genetic material resulting from physical, radiational, or chemical influences. A multitude of factors can cause mutations (that is: can be "mutagens") and such influences from the environment are all pervasive, continuous, and regularly contribute to the pool of mutated genes. The changed genes may be inherited, but only if they occur at appropriate points in the germinal cell lines in the gonadal tissues. Mutation is a random process, it is not possible to accurately predict what mutations will occur under what influences, but there are some consistencies. An observable mutation generally alters part of what is usually a very complicated process—the interrelated steps that lie between the genetic code for a characteristic and the actual development of that characteristic. Hence the most likely effect of a perceptible random change is that the process will work imperfectly or not at all. However, while the majority of such mutations are deleterious, there is the rare and unusual one which is beneficial to the organism containing it—but it may occur as rarely as 1 out of a billion mutations, or more frequently, depending upon the molecular system affected. Only an extremely small proportion of mutations are added to the gene pool as advantageous genetic changes. Even further reducing the likelihood of this type of occurrence is the requirement that the mutation must take place in the gonadal tissue related to production of reproductive cells if it is to have any chance of being passed on. Mutations that take place in somatic cells of adult organisms have absolutely no impact on evolution, although these are often considered to be important in the aging process for individual organisms. Thus the number of mutations permanently added to a population is small and generally results in no observable differences in either the average or the variation of particular characteristics. Yet this new material, these "evolutionary novelties" ultimately provides the basis for future evolutionary change.

Mutation may have an additional impact however, in directing change. The probable effect of most mutations is the reduction, or incomplete development, of the characteristic controlled by the mutated genetic material. Of course, reduction is a likely consequence only if the characteristic is polygenic and if its growth involves a complex series of steps, each of which is dependent on the previous steps proceeding correctly. If the characteristic is under single gene control, then a reduction mutation would probably have the effect of completely eliminating the feature. If the selection for a feature is relaxed, so that it no longer matters whether or not the characteristic is present in the organism, mutations causing reduction will not be selected against, and eventually the feature may be lost throughout the population. Because reduction is the consequence of a large number of mutations, and because in a polygenic trait mutations in most of the many controlling genes will have the same effect of reduction, REDUCTION OF THE CHARACTERISTIC IS THE LIKELY CONSEQUENCE OF MUTATION WHEN THERE IS RELAXED SELECTION. This has been called the "probable mutation effect" by C. L. Brace (1963).

The simplest mutational change involves the removal, insertion, or addition of a single base pair of the DNA molecule. Because of the manner in which DNA is constructed, a mutagenic force which removes a base nucleotide from only one strand of the molecule is unlikely to have any mutational effect. The molecule will be repaired at the damaged site, replacing the missing nucleotide with an identical unit, since this will be the only unit which will match with the undamaged side of the strand. This automatic repair mechanism serves to keep the number of actual mutations at a low level, hence conserving genetic information and inducing stability in the genome.

Mutations naturally occur in more than just the structural gene set, and mutations may take quite different forms.

Relative Growth and Heterochrony

The two terms "relative growth" and "heterochrony" are frequently confused, primarily because they refer to changes within the processes of ontogeny or individual development. Relative growth refers to ontogenetic changes in body proportions, while heterochrony refers to changes in the sequential operations of development. The former may be the result of genetic change in controller genes, such as the case for the "achondroplasia" or limb shortening which has been found in many mammals, both on individual bases due to mutational change, and in the whole species due to evolutionary processes. However, relative growth may also be the result of epigenetic factors such as the amounts of trace materials, the overall food availability, and such esoteric problems as the appropriate surface to volume ratio for a particular thermal environment. Thus epigenesis plays a strong role in ontogenetic development, and changes in proportion may be due to environmentally induced "somatic adaptation". Where the modification of regulatory genes can be established, an evolutionary change in the structure of the organism can be accepted, although such developments tend to be allometric or scaled proportion changes.

Heterochrony, as an evolutionary change in the sequence of development tends to be more dramatic and significant as an event. The changes to an organism under such circumstances may provide far reaching effects both within the structure of the animal, and within the ecosystem it inhabits. The most widely known form of heterochrony is paedomorphosis (Gould 1977).

Paedomorphosis—Progenesis, Neoteny, and Hypermorphosis

The terms paedomorphosis, which includes progenesis and neoteny, and hypermorphosis have been extensively used by Gould (1977) to deal with heterochronic changes in ontogenetic development. The implicit understanding which

Gould (1977) and Stanley (1979) apply to these cases is that they are strictly controlled by genetic mechanisms. Progenesis is the acceleration of sexual maturity with respect to the rest of ontogeny. This results in the organism achieving reproductive capacity before it has completed its growth schedule. In this sense, almost all primates can be viewed as positively progenetic to some degree, as mammals are in general, but at least the genus *Erythrocebus*, the patas monkey, displays negative progenesis, delaying sexual maturity in the male until full growth is attained. Neoteny, unlike some of the popular definitions, is considered by Gould (1977) and Stanley (1979) to only represent the retardation of somatic development with respect to the onset of the reproductive phase of life. This latter can range from a retardation of a limited set of structural features all the way to a complete juvenalization of the animal. The alternate term, hypermorphosis, means the extension of ontogeny, usually through the process of lengthening a developmental phase prior to sexual maturation. The clearest situation in which hypermorphic changes would be visible is when an extension of the infant or juvenile phases results in overall size enlargement.

These various processes can result in substantial change in the morphology of the organism, though the impacts are directly related to the intensity of the process changes which occur. It is instructive to note the linking of these three processes to the phenomenon of sexual maturation. The advent of sexual reproductive capacity in most organisms signals the actual end of growth, or at least the immanence of growth termination. For most species of mammals the two are linked loosely, while for insects and many other invertebrates, the final metamorphosis and reproductivity are locked together.

Mosaic Evolution

Mosaic evolution is a perspective which naturally follows from both natural selection and genomic turnover processes. Mosaic evolution is the independent change of different parts of the phenotype of an organism. The principle behind this is recognizable in that changes in a particular part of the organism may affect the survival and/or reproduction of the whole organism. Pleiotropic genes may be responsible for mosaic evolution in some circumstances but the two patterns are not necessarily linked. Mosaic evolution of major anatomical units is especially obvious in the hominid lineage. The broad chest with laterally orientated arms is shared with the African hominoids, while the pelvic and pedal changes associated with habitual erect bipedal locomotion is a unique evolution of the early hominid lineage. The third component of the mosaic is the expansion of cranial capacity coupled with skull remodelling and dental reduction. The three phases overlap to a degree in temporal sequence, but each proceeded at its own pace, and apparently independent of each other.

Population Genetics

Population Definition The "population" in the previously provided definition of evolution, is a group of organisms that regularly breed together. The population may be the entire species, but is more likely to be a subunit, a "deme" which is a local breeding population. The total collection of the genes in a population are referred to as its "gene pool", and consequently, evolution can be seen as CHANGE IN A GENE POOL FROM GENERATION TO GENERATION. The changes may be due to the introduction of a new gene into the pool, either through genomic process in situ, or via importation from a nearby population, but most commonly the changes are statistical—changes in the relative frequencies of the genes already present in the pool. Note that the frequency of a particular gene is a simple measure of how often it occurs. It can be thought of as the proportion of individuals who carry that gene, out of the total of all individuals in the gene pool. Thus it may be seen that the actual course (or direction) that evolutionary change takes depends in part upon the genes already present in the pool.

Population genetics is primarily concerned with the charting of the pattern of gene distribution present in various populations, and with the patterns of change in gene frequencies which may occur. Chief among the primary tools of population genetics are the multitude of statistical procedures of analysis and extrapolation.

Hardy-Weinberg Equilibrium

Two investigators early in the twentieth century observed consistencies in the pattern of frequencies of gene alleles and independently derived the same mathematical ratios for the pattern. Hardy and Weinberg independently formulated a rule which is now one of the basics of population genetics. The mathematics of the Hardy-Weinberg Ratio deal quite straightforwardly with the case for two alleles, which normally means there are three possible genotypes, and are detailed in very comprehensible form by Maynard-Smith in Chapter 3 of his "Evolutionary Genetics" (Maynard-Smith, 1989). What is the most important aspect for evolutionary theory is the fact that a calculation of Hardy-Weinberg ratios over several generations indicates that a stabilizing function is at work in all populations. There are only a few circumstances which can substantially distort the ratios from generation to generation. These fall into the recognized categories of:

1) Selection between zygote formation and sampling time.
2) Non-random mating.
3) Populational mixing (may also be due to sampling from more than one population).
4) The genotypes differ in probability of selection to the sample.

Thus factors which weight the probabilities for different genotypes may be applied within the mathematics to follow the effects of micromutational short term evolutionary development. However the predominant effect of the Hardy-Weinberg ratios is to suggest that normal patterns will maintain a stable genetic structure in the shorter time frame.

Founder Effect

Migration may result in evolution whenever individuals enter (immigrate) or leave (emigrate) a population, since they either introduce new genetic material or remove some from the gene pool. Migration usually acts in conjunction with selection or drift in order to effect populational change. Genetic changes introduced into a small population as the result of new individuals arriving are subject to the selection process, and may be retained or eliminated according to their value. If the migrants form a large portion of the population, the changed genes may not need to be very advantageous in order to be retained, idiosyncracies and deleterious genes may even be retained. When individuals leave a population, the reasons for their leaving might result in selection for certain characteristics in the migrating group. An example of this may be the explorer or pioneer mode proposed by Geist as part of his "dispersal hypothesis" (Geist 1971)—larger, heavier, better armed, more aggressive forms are found in many "pioneering" species during their expansion phases.

When some portion of a population moves out of contact with the parental population, it opens the possibility of the founding population pursuing a course of allopatric speciation. As discussed in the taxonomic section, the perspective of Hennig (1966) suggests that both the emigrating and the resident portions of the species will develop along distinct lines into new species. This pattern would only be likely if the populations were small, the emigrating and residing portions had distinctly different gene frequencies, and especially if some unique genes went with each group.

Drift—The Sewell Wright Effect

Drift is a random change not due to selection, mutation, or migration. By its very definition, drift implicitly requires that the genes concerned be selectively neutral, the results of their molecular processes are without advantage or disadvantage to the organisms carrying them. It is often termed the "Sewell Wright Effect" after its descriptor (Wright, 1931) and is basically a product of the random sampling of the genes of the parent population for the development of the next generation. Not all genes will be represented at the same frequencies from generation to generation, just as not all data is represented in a random sample drawn from a universe. Drift is a phenomenon primarily of small samples. The sample may be the result of migration from a larger population (over space), in which case it is often confounded with the "Founder Effect", or it may be the next generation of that population (over time), in which case it is associated with the "Sewell Wright Effect". One might expect that evolutionary change due to drift would be completely random. However, while the process is random, the result of the process may not be. The effect of drift is the fluctuation of gene frequencies. One result which does not appear to be random, yet certainly is, might be to eliminate genes that appear in low frequencies. If the random up and down fluctuation sends the frequency of a gene to "0" in the next generation, then that gene is forever lost to the population. Conversely, if a gene exists at high frequency in a population, the random fluctuation might bring it to a frequency of 1.00. This latter case is termed "fixation" of the gene, but at the same time it represents the loss of all other variants. This process of loss of genetic material in small populations can have substantial and very visible effects—one of these is that the members of small populations tend to have many "look-alikes" due to loss of genetic variation. Another common effect of drift is to increase variability between isolated populations. Because of the randomness of the process, different genetic material is lost in each group subjected to drift.

The Bottleneck Effect
An evolutionary mechanism suggested by Stanley (1975, 1979) has been termed the "bottleneck effect". If an entire species is reduced to the point that only a few

individuals, at most a very small portion of the population, survives, then the genetic composition of the species may be radically modified. This restriction process is seen as a "bottleneck" through which the species passes and may be "reborn". If the process is repeated several times, the cumulative effect might be a new species. Stanley (1979) suggests that bottlenecking is unlikely to occur with any degree of frequency, and that this process is of relatively little importance as an evolutionary mechanism. What Stanley does not seem to consider is some larger scale aspects which may be associated with the appearance of bottlenecking in a species.

SELECTIONAL MECHANISMS

Natural selection in the Darwinian and Neo-Darwinian models is a straightforward pairing of two processes, selective death and selective reproduction. Selective death carries with it the implication that this is death before reproductive capacity is engaged, otherwise it would have no evolutionary effect. This is a process of weeding out those individual organisms which are defective in some way. It should not be considered that this is an optimising process selecting only the "best", but in reality it is selection against those individuals which are "not adequate" to the requirements for survival in the particular environment. It has been the normal case in evolutionary theory over the past century that this has been viewed as an optimising process, and one which leads to "improvement in adaptation", but as will be argued later, a more appropriate view is to see it as a stabilizing function. Selective reproduction is considerably more complex, since a multitude of factors come into play in determining whether or not a particular individual is able to pass on their genes to more than, less than, or the average number of offspring.

Selection results in individuals having differing numbers of offspring survive to reproductive status. Those individual organisms which have more surviving offspring than others thus have their genes represented in higher frequencies in sequential generations. This change in gene frequency is, as has been noted, the essence of evolution. There are many factors which come into play in the processes of selection and the rate of change can be anything from blindingly fast to infinitesimally slow. An example from Wolpoff (1980) may be useful—:"Yet how fast is this change? To use round figures, the average cranial capacity of human ancestors two million years ago is about 500 cc,. . . . Today, again using round figures, average cranial capacity is about 1,500 cc. . . . The rapid increase, then, is 1000 cc in two million years—a tripling of capacity. On the average the increase per year is 1000/2,000,000 or only 1/2000th of a cc. If the average length of a generation is taken as twenty years, the "rapid" change is 1/100th of a cc per generation! The change per generation is so small that if it is still in progress today, it could not be measured." At the other end of the scale, selection appears to have effected the adaptation of various arthropods to poisonous chemicals and many bacteria to drugs in periods of a decade or less.

In sum, selection results in changes in the gene pool by changing the frequencies of various genes. The genes of individuals with more surviving offspring are more frequent in the next generation, while the genes of those with fewer surviving offspring are less frequent. Changing gene frequencies within a population may result in changing frequencies of morphological characteristics. Since most characteristics are polygenic, and their final form is influenced by the action of many genes, new frequencies can actually result in novel characteristics through combinations that could not occur before. The major effect of all this selection is to eliminate variations over the long term and hence to result in a pattern of stability or a slow tracking of environmental changes.

Changes in the gene pool, may only be produced by natural selection if the genes under consideration are involved in the production of observable traits or characteristics of the organism. These may be buffered against the selective pressures of the environment to a greater or lesser degree.

THE SPECIES LEVEL—MACROEVOLUTION AND SPECIES ORIGINS

The concept of Macroevolution as distinct from Microevolution has become popular and controversial during the past two decades. The intention of those who espouse the separation of Macro from Micro is to make distinct the impressions and feelings of many paleontologists that there are differing processes operating at the two levels. However, not everyone is an advocate of the macroevolutionary perspective, John Maynard Smith, after the 1980 conference on the topic, wrote in Nature (volume 289, 8 Jan. 1981, p 13) that "one does not know whether one is studying the habits of taxonomists or of evolving taxa". The process of macroevolution is expected, by those who are its advocates, to only be concerned with the "quantum" shift between species, rather than to deal with the changing genetic complement of a species. Thus Macroevolution takes as its field of attention the process or processes of speciation and higher level change. Surprisingly for many students of evolution and paleontology, Charles Darwin, though he utilized the phrase "Origin of Species" in the title of his masterwork, did not engage in discussion of the processes by which species came into being.

Phyletic Gradualism and Punctuated Equilibria

The terms Phyletic Gradualism and Punctuated Equilibria have become major buzzwords in the jargon of evolutionary theory during the 1980's. The two terms have come to be representational of the two contesting viewpoints of what are frequently referred to as "Darwinian" and "non-Darwinian" evolution. Both the gradualist and punctuationist perspectives have long histories in the field, but the major change in their relationships occurred with the publication and subsequent popularity of Eldredge and Gould's 1972 paper "Punctuated Equilibria: An Alternative to Phyletic Gradualism". This paper for the first time placed the arguments against the "evolution by means of Natural Selection" perspective on a firm footing.

Phyletic Gradualism, the name created by Eldredge and Gould in 1972, is nothing more than the traditional view of Neo-Darwinism and the New Synthesis, that evolution proceeds in a slow and gradual pace over geologic time with evolutionary novelty being very slowly integrated into the genetic structure of a species. The attempt to emphasize this perspective, an emphasis upon slow change in a single phyletic lineage as contrasted with the "stuttering" pattern of the punctuational perspective, resulted in the use of "phyletic gradualism" as term of mild opprobrium, or as a "strawman argument" as it was perceived by Dawkins (1986). Whether the academic arguments are valid or not, the essence of the position is that of a New Synthesis orientation towards slow and gradualistic change within a lineage leading to the transformation of one species into a successor species. The problem of cladogenesis or the generation of several species from a single ancestral form is not often of central focus, but when it does assume center stage, the general perception is that only the pattern of allopatric speciation is of relevance.

Punctuated Equilibria is a renovation, enhancement, and expansion of the original concepts of macro-mutational jumps, quantum evolution, and Richard Gold-schmidt's "hopeful monsters". In part the model of punctuated equilibria is derived from the perceptions of several paleontologists that the fossil record, particularly for many marine invertebrates, is represented by a pattern of sudden appearance of new species followed by the species remaining essentially unchanged over very long time spans. This pattern of a sudden transformation followed by long stability provides a picture of evolution proceeding by "fits and starts" or as a "stuttering" pattern of sudden arrival of new species—a punctuation—followed by a stable existence—equilibria. This pattern has been labelled as "rectilinear evolution" by Stanley (1975) see Figure 2 for an illustration of the difference from traditional tree structures. The early idea, initially set out by Darwin (1859), of the gaps in the fossil record being taken as "accidents of preservation" is rejected under this regime, and the gaps or breaks are considered to be real phenomena. While most of the argument associated with the punctuated equilibria model has been centered around the possible mechanism of punctuation, the major source of evidence for its support comes from the paleontological picture of stability. If the picture of long terms of stability and in many cases survival of species over millions of years without significant change, other than perhaps a generalized increase in size to accord with Cope's law, is valid, the association of natural selection with the origin of species is invalidated. Under such a regimen, Darwinian natural selection becomes a stabilizing mechanism without a role in generating evolutionary novelty, and it is necessary to search elsewhere for the speciation mechanism.

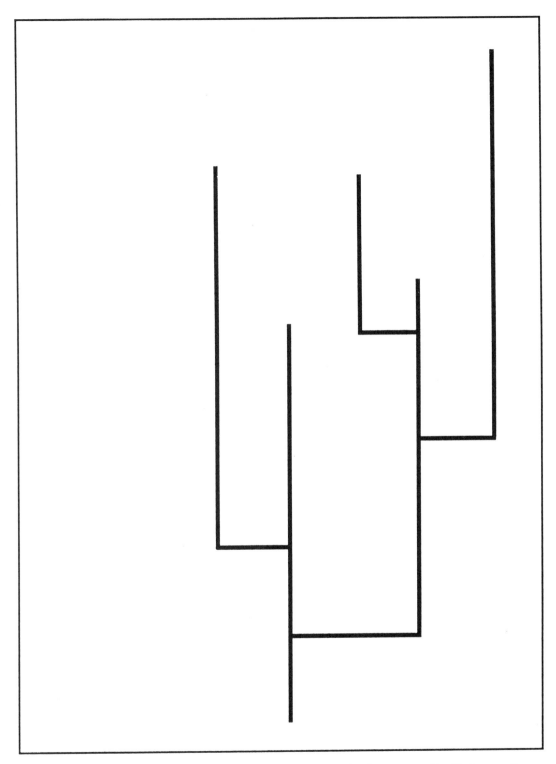

Figure 2: Rectilinear Evolution Pattern as perceived under the Punctuated Equilibria paradigm.

REFERENCES CITED

Ayala, F. J.
1977 Philosophical Issues. In Dobzhansky, T., Ayala, F. J., Ledyard Stebbins, G., and Valentine, J. W. (eds) Evolution. W. H. Freeman, San Francisco.

Brace C. L.
1963 Structural Reduction in Evolution. American Naturalist 97: 39–49.

Darwin, C.
1859 On the Origin of Species by Means of Natural Selection, or the Preservation of Favored Races in the Struggle for Life. John Murray, London

Dawkins, R.
1986 The Blind Watchmaker. W. W. Norton and Co. Inc. New York

Eldredge, N. and Gould, S. J.
1972 Punctuated Equilibria: An Alternative to Phyletic Gradualism. In Schopf, T. J. M. (ed) Models in Paleobiology. Freeman and Cooper, San Francisco

Geist, V.
1972 An ecological and behavioural explanation of mammalian characteristics and their implication to Therapsid evolution. Z. Säugetierkunde 37: 1–5.

1971 On the relation of social evolution and dispersal in ungulates during the Pleistocene, with emphasis on the old world deer and the genus Bison. Quaternary Research 1: 283–315.

Gould, S. J.
1977 Ontogeny and Phylogeny. The Belknap Press of Harvard University Press, Cambridge, Massachusetts.

Hennig, W.
1966 Phylogenetic Systematics. University of Illinois Press.

Hogan, J. P.
1983 Code of the Lifemaker Ballantine Books, New York.

John, B., and Miklos, G. L. G.
1988 The Eukaryote Genome In Development and Evolution. Allen and Unwin, London.

Margulis, L.
1981 Symbiosis in Cell Evolution. W. H. Freeman, San Francisco.

Maynard-Smith, J.
1981 Macroevolution. Nature, 289 (8) January 1981, p 13.

1989 Evolutionary Genetics. Oxford University Press.

Mayr, E.
1960 The emergence of evolutionary novelties. In Tax, S. (ed) Evolution after Darwin. University of Chicago Press. p 349–380.

1963 Animal species and evolution. Harvard University Press.

1970 Populations, Species, and Evolution. Harvard University Press.

Simpson, G. G.
1974 The Concept of Progress in Organic Evolution. Social Research 41 (1): 28–51.

Spencer, H.
1852 A Theory of Population, Deduced from the General Law of Animal Fertility. Westminster Review 57: 250–268.

Stanley, S. M.
1975 A Theory of Evolution Above the Species Level. Proc. Nat. Acad. Sci. USA 72 (2): 646–650.

1979 Macroevolution: pattern and process. W. H. Freeman, San Francisco, Calif.

Thompson, K.
1982 The meaning of evolution. American Scientist 70: 529–531.

Poirier, F. E.
1987 Understanding Human Evolution. Prentice Hall, Inc. Englewood Cliffs, New Jersey.

Waddington, C. H.
1957 The strategy of The Genes. Allen and Unwin, London.

Watson, J. D., and Crick, F. H.
1953 A structure for deoxyribose nucleic acid. Nature 171:737.

Wolpoff, M.
1980 Palaeoanthropology. Knopf, New York

Wright, S.
1931 Evolution in Mendelian Populations. Genetics 16, 97–159.

Huxley's Evidence as to Man's Place in Nature—A Century Later

William L. Straus, Jr.

In January of 1863, less than four years after the appearance of Charles Darwin's *On the Origin of Species*, Thomas Henry Huxley published three essays collectively entitled *Evidence as to Man's Place in Nature*. One of these, *On the Relations of Man to the Lower Animals*, was devoted to the thesis that man's closest living relatives are the anthropoid apes, particularly the gorilla and chimpanzee. This obviously had a tremendous impact on the thought of the Western world of that time, favorably stimulating some individuals and gravely offending others.

It is true that the publication of *On the Origin of Species* in November of 1859 had set the stage; but it must be noted that in *The Origin* Darwin seems studiously to have avoided any considerations of man's kinship. Indeed, his only mention of this problem is that in the future "light will be thrown on the origin of man and his history." It was not until 1871 that he published *The Descent of Man*, building upon the groundwork erected by Huxley eight years earlier.

Huxley declared that "the question of questions for mankind—the problem which underlies all others, and is more deeply interesting than any other—is the ascertainment of the place which Man occupies in nature and of his relations to the universe of things." For this, "some knowledge of man's position in the animate world is an indispensable preliminary."

There was no doubt in Huxley's mind that man's closest living relatives are the anthropoid apes (i.e., gorilla, chimpanzee, orang-utan, and gibbon). He believed, moreover, that the ape which "most nearly approaches man, in the totality of its organization, is either the Chimpanzee or the Gorilla" (it must be noted that he used the term "ape" to include not only the anthropoid apes but also the monkeys of both the Old and New Worlds). Indeed, he went so far as to claim that "whatever part of the animal fabric—whatever series of muscles, whatever viscera might be selected for comparison—the result would be the same—the lower Apes and the Gorilla would differ more than the Gorilla and the Man." In support of this tenet he stressed in particular the evidence of skull, dentition, hand, foot, and brain. Thus, for the skull, he noted that "the differences between Man and the Gorilla are of smaller value than those between the Gorilla and *some* [italics mine] other Apes." Inclusion of the word

Reprinted from William A. Strauss, Jr., "Huxley's Evidence as to Man's Place in Nature—A Century Later", pp. 161–167, in *Medicine, Science and Culture*, Edited by Lloyd Stevenson and Robert P. Multhauf, The Johns Hopkins Press, Baltimore, Maryland, 1968.

"some" preserves the validity of this statement. As for the teeth, his statement that "greatly as the dentition of the highest Ape differs from that of Man, it differs far more widely from that of the lower and lowest Apes" is not open to serious challenge. When one turns to the hand and foot, however, Huxley's arguments wither in the face of modern evidence. Thus the hand of man has a greater over-all resemblance to the hands of Old World monkeys than to the hand of any of the anthropoid apes (see, for example, Straus 1949). In fact, in many respects the hands of the anthropoid apes exhibit clear evidence of evolutionary structural and functional regression. As for the foot, undeniably there are striking resemblances between man and the anthropoid apes. Notwithstanding, the lack of an opposable great toe in man—this being in contrast to all other primates—represents an enormous anatomicophysiological gulf that separates him from the anthropoid apes and one that is far wider than any pedal difference separating the latter and the monkeys. A historical perspective is called for here. Respecting the foot, Huxley clearly was influenced by reports, prevalent in his day, that the great toe of uncivilized and barefooted men "retains a great amount of mobility, and even some sort of opposability." Thus he obviously believed that the foot of primitive man bridged the gulf between the feet of apes and civilized man. In other words, there would actually exist, in the living primates, a distinct gradation from the opposable to the nonopposable great toe. It is well known that the great toe of modern man may, under some circumstance, be capable of considerable "mobility"; but the notion that it is ever possessed of any degree of true "opposability" has long since been abandoned. As for the anthropoid-ape brain, while admitting its morphological approximation to that of man, it is now difficult to agree with Huxley's appraisal—which was based on gross morphology—that, "regarded systematically, the cerebral differences, of man and apes, are not of more than generic value—his Family distinction resting chiefly on his dentition, his pelvis and his lower limbs."

For Huxley, the anthropoid apes are "blurred copies" of man. Consequently, he concluded with a paraphrase of his earlier statement, namely, that "whatever system of organs be studied, the comparison of their modifications in the ape series leads to one and the same result—that the structural differences which separate Man from the Gorilla and the Chimpanzee are not so great as those which separate the Gorilla from the lower apes." Nevertheless, he believed—and this has sometimes been ignored—that "the structural differences between Man and the Man-like [i.e., anthropoid] apes certainly justify our regarding him as constituting a family apart from them," although "there can be no justification for placing him in a distinct order."

This statement is shortly followed by a rather curious passage: "Perhaps no order of mammals presents us with so extraordinary a series of gradations as this [the order Primates]—leading us insensibly from the crown and summit of the animal creation down to creatures, from which there is but a step, as it seems, to the lowest, smallest, and least intelligent of the placental Mammalia. It is as if nature herself had foreseen the arrogance of man, and with Roman severity had provided that his intellect, by its very triumphs, should call into prominence the slaves, admonishing the conqueror that he is but dust." As Wood Jones (1929) has pointed out, this passage implies uniserial evolution of the order Primates, culminating in man. It is a sort of evolutionary *Scala Naturae*, comprising a belief in "missing links" between the extant members of the series. This statement, together with other similar remarks, some of which I have cited, makes it obvious that Huxley believed man to have evolved from some type of genuine anthropoid ape. Indeed, he clearly implies that this ancestor was most closely allied to the gorilla and chimpanzee.

The zoologist, St. George Mivart, a distinguished contemporary of Huxley, was unable to accept the latter's conclusion. He stated (1873) that "it is manifest that man, the apes, and Half-apes cannot be arranged in a single ascending series of which man is the term and culmination." It is noteworthy in this connection, however, that Huxley did recognize the alternative possibility that man and the anthropoid apes might represent existing ramifications of a common, more primitive stock. This generally has been overlooked.

Thus, as I have noted elsewhere (Straus 1949), Huxley was the godfather, if not the father, of the theory that man evolved from an anthropoid ape. It is true that this theory was not actually initiated by him, having been hinted at by earlier philosophers and scientists, such as De Maillet and Buffon in the eighteenth century and Lamarck early in the nineteenth century (see Eiseley 1958). But it was Huxley who first marshaled evidence in its support and who first presented it in true scientific fashion.

Some of Huxley's statements now appear rather extravagant. But, as I have already noted, he must be viewed in proper historical perspective. The available evidence, scanty though it may now seem, in general supported his definite conclusions. Moreover, and this is of the greatest importance when one examines his writings, he was engaged in a great intellectual battle for the acceptance of not only the principle of organic evolution but—and this is a prime concern here—of man's evolution from a lower primate. His chief opponent was the great zoologist, Richard Owen; and it was to Owen, especially, that he was addressing his remarks, as is obvious when reading *On the Relations of Man to the Lower Animals*. No quarter was given in their battle. It is not surprising, therefore, that Huxley at times now seems to have been dogmatic and overhasty.

The scientific influence of *Man's Place in Nature* was tremendous. During the first half of the present century, Huxley's concept that man evolved from a true anthropoid ape became the orthodox theory of human descent. For example, the eminent anthropologist, Franz Weidenreich (1943), pronounced that "the result of the analysis of man's zoological character, first undertaken by Thomas Huxley . . . still stands firm: the organization of the human body, whether studied as a whole or in detail, is that of an anthropoid. No fact has become known which has the power to shake this statement." Three years later, he echoed this conviction by stating that Huxley had "settled, once and for all, the question of the special place of man in the zoological system," so that, "if the human form has gradually evolved from a simian one, the type from which it originated must have had the general appearance of an anthropoid and shown a corresponding organization of body and skeleton" (Weidenreich 1946). Moreover, Huxley's thesis that man is most closely allied to the gorilla and chimpanzee led to the assumption that man and the African great apes arose from a common ancestor apart from the other Old World primates. Schwalbe (1923), Elliot Smith (1924), Weinert (1932), Gregory (1934), and Keith (1934) all were outspoken proponents of this view.

This theory that derived man from a true anthropoid ape was developed in detail by, among others, such eminent scientists as the British anatomist Arthur Keith (1891, 1923, 1934) and the American paleontologist William Gregory (1916, 1927, 1934). They went further than Huxley in their speculations, however. They assumed that, since man evolved from a genuine anthropoid ape, said ancestor must have been an arboreal animal that hung and progressed by means of its arms—thus, to use a term popularized by Keith, it was a "brachiator." All of the existing anthropoid apes practice brachiation, although admittedly in different degrees. This includes even the gorilla, at least when he is young. Indeed, Gregory (1934) declared that man is "a made-over brachiator adapted to life on the ground," while Keith and others uttered similar statements. At the present time, Sherwood Washburn (1950, 1963) is perhaps the leading proponent of this theory, which retains much of its earlier popularity.

Meanwhile, another theory of human origin was being developed. This, it is important to note, does not deny man's close relationship to the anthropoid apes. However—and herein it differs fundamentally from the Keith-Gregory concept derived obliquely from Huxley—it envisages the common ancestor of man and the anthropoid apes as an animal that was essentially a monkey, rather than a true anthropoid ape. Hence this common ancestor—and herein resides the basic difference between the two theories—was not a true brachiator, since it lacked the specializations common to animals of that category. This latter concept had its real inception from the studies of the French paleontologist, Marcellin Boule (1911–13, 1921), and has since been developed and has gained a number of adherents, including the present writer (see Straus 1947, 1949, 1962; also, Buettner-Janusch 1966). In fairness to Huxley, it must be recognized that he regarded the origin of man from a primate that was more primitive than the anthropoid apes as a possibility, although he did not embrace this concept.

But, to return more precisely to Huxley, some of the recent researches in molecular biology—namely, those of Klinger *et al.* (1963) on chromosomes, of J. and V. Buettner-Janusch (1964) on hemoglobins, and of Goodman (1962, 1963) on serum proteins—have been interpreted as supporting Huxley's view that man is more closely related to the gorilla and chimpanzee than to the other extant anthropoid apes, the orang-utan and gibbon. Goodman (1963), merely on the basis of his serological studies, has actually proposed that the two African great apes be included within the family of man, the Hominidae.

In a recent paper, Simpson (1966), evidently strongly influenced by the molecular data noted above, definitely states that man "is most particularly related to chimpanzees and gorillas" and that he had a common ancestor with the African great apes "after their ancestry had become distinct from that of the other living apes." He emphasizes, however, in contrast to many proponents of the anthropoid-ape theory, that this common ancestor was "less specialized" than either the chimpanzee or the gorilla. Consequently, I must note, acceptance of the close relationship of man and the African anthropoids has no bearing on the precise nature of man's ancestors; hence it has no bearing on the question of whether they were or were not true brachiators. In fact, as Simpson states, "More precise evidence as to relationships and as to the course of anatomical change in the human ancestry must come from fossils."

It is thus clearly evident that Huxley's essay initiated an important and fruitful line of biological thought and research, and that today, more than one hundred years after its publication, its major thesis—that man is most closely related to the anthropoid apes and, perhaps, particularly to the gorilla and chimpanzee—is generally accepted. And, what is even more important, no single publication has provided a greater stimulus for the investigation of man's place in nature.

REFERENCES

BOULE, MARCELLIN, 1911–13, L'Homme Fossile de La Chapelle-aux-Saints. *Ann. Paléontol.*, 6:109–72; 7:85–192; 8:1–76.

_____, 1921, *Les Hommes Fossiles*. Paris: Masson & Cie.

BUETTNER-JANUSCH, JOHN, 1966, *Origins of Man*. New York: John Wiley & Sons.

BUETTNER-JANUSCH, JOHN, and BUETTNER-JANUSCH, VINA, 1964, Hemoglobins of Primates. In *Evolutionary and Genetic Biology of Primates*, ed. John Buettner-Janusch, vol. 2, pp. 75–90. New York-London: Academic Press.

DARWIN, CHARLES, 1859, *On the Origin of Species by Means of Natural Selection*. London: J. Murray.

_____, 1871. *The Descent of Man, and Selection in Relation to Sex*. 2 vols. London: J. Murray.

EISELEY, LOREN, 1958, *Darwin's Century*. Garden City, N.Y.: Doubleday & Co.

ELLIOT SMITH, G., 1924, *The Evolution of Man*. Oxford: The University Press.

GOODMAN, MORRIS, 1962, Immunochemistry of the Primates and Primate Evolution. *Ann. N.Y. Acad. Sci.*, 102:219–34.

_____, 1963, Man's Place in the Phylogeny of the Primates as Reflected by Serum Proteins. In *Classification and Human Evolution*, Ed. Sherwood L. Washburn, pp. 204–34. Chicago: Aldine Publishing Co.

GREGORY, WILLIAM K., 1916, Studies on the Evolution of the Primates. *Bull. Amer. Mus. Nat. Hist.*, 35:239–355.

_____, 1927, How Near Is the Relationship of Man to the Chimpanzee-Gorilla Stock? *Quart. Rev. Biol.*, 2:549–60.

_____, 1934, *Man's Place Among the Anthropoids*. Oxford: Clarendon Press.

HUXLEY, THOMAS H., 1863, *Evidence as to Man's Place in Nature*. London: Williams & Norgate.

KEITH, ARTHUR, 1891, Anatomical Notes on Malay Apes. *J. Straits Br. Roy. Asiat. Soc.*, 23:77–94.

_____, 1923, Man's Posture: Its Evolution and Disorders. *Brit. Med. J.*, 1:451–54, 499–502, 545–48, 587–90, 624–26, 669–72.

_____, 1934, *The Construction of Man's Family Tree*. London: Watts & Co.

KLINGER, HAROLD P., HAMERTON, JOHN L., MUTTON, DAVID, and LANG, ERNST M., 1963, The Chromosomes of the Hominoidea. In *Classification and Human Evolution*, ed. Sherwood L. Washburn, pp. 235–42. Chicago: Aldine Publishing Co.

MIVART, ST. GEORGE, 1873 *Man and Apes.* London: Robert Hardwicke.

SCHWALBE, G., 1923, Die Abstammung des Menschen und die ältesten Menschenformen. In *Kultur d. Gegenwart*, pt. 3, sect. 5: *Anthropologie*, pp. 223–338. Leipzig-Berlin: B. G. Teubner.

SIMPSON, GEORGE GAYLORD, 1966, The Biological Nature of Man. *Science*, 152:472–78.

STRAUS, WILLIAM L., JR., 1947, The Riddle of Man's Ancestry. *Amer. J. Phys. Anthrop.*, n.s., 5:243. (Abstract.)

_____, 1949, The Riddle of Man's Ancestry. *Quart. Rev. Biol.*, 24:200–23.

_____, 1962, Fossil Evidence of the Evolution of the Erect, Bipedal Posture. *Clinical Orthopaedics*, 25:9–19.

WASHBURN, S. L., 1950, The Analysis of Primate Evolution with Particular Reference to the Origin of Man. *Cold Spring Harbor Symposia on Quant. Biol.*, 15:67–78.

_____, 1963, Behavior and Evolution. In *Classification and Human Evolution*, ed. Sherwood L. Washburn, pp. 190–203. Chicago: Aldine publishing Co.

WEIDENREICH, FRANZ, 1943, The Skull of Sinanthropus pekensis: A Comparative Study on a Primitive Hominid Skull. *Paleontol. Sinica*, n.s., D., no. 10 (whole s. no. 127):229 pp.

_____, 1946, *Apes, Giants, and Man.* Chicago: University of Chicago Press.

WEINERT, HANS, 1932, *Ursprung der Menschheit.* Stuttgart: Ferdinand Enke.

WOOD JONES, FREDERIC, 1929, *Man's Place Among the Mammals.* New York: Longmans, Green & Co.

Distributional Strategies

Jared M. Diamond
——————— *University of California, Los Angeles* ———————

INTRODUCTION

Study of distributions of plant and animal species may be relevant to understanding distributions of human populations for two reasons. At a general level many of the types of questions, methods, models, and concepts characteristic of plant and animal studies recur in anthropology. In some specific situations similar selective forces may have operated on plant or animal and human populations, with similar consequences.

In this article I discuss what is meant by a distributional strategy, what selective forces ultimately determine it, and what properties of a species subject to these forces are the proximate causes of the species distribution. These general considerations will then be illustrated by several types of distributional patterns of Melanesian bird species. Finally I shall mention some human distributional patterns that may be understood in similar terms.

STRATEGIES

When we talk of 'distributional strategy', the root 'distribution' has a familiar meaning: the distribution of a species is simply its pattern of abundance in space and time. The use of the word 'strategy' however, needs some justification in this context. Normally, i.e. in human contexts, a strategy connotes three elements: the operation of thought processes, a preconceived goal, and a weighing of alternative means of achieving this goal in order to assess which means is most suitable. Recently ecologists and biogeographers have found it profitable to discuss plant and animal species as if they too adopted strategies. For instance a modern ecologist unashamedly reasons, 'A bird species of unstable habitats must adopt a strategy of rapid reproduction'. Or: 'A high ratio of search time to pursuit time is an optimal foraging strategy for a predator on large, hard-to-capture prey'.

Until recently, such anthropomorphic reasoning about plants and animals was considered dangerous and naive. It is now clear that the language of strategy is a profitable shorthand for describing both evolutionary phenomena and behavioral phenomena. At the evolutionary level species and individuals vary in their adaptations; the adaptations of some species (or individuals) permit them to leave more offspring than other species in a particular situation; the former species therefore come to outnumber the latter in that situation. Thus one can describe evolution as having goals, such as long survival or large number of surviving offspring. The probability of achieving these goals is a function of biological adaptations, which are analogous to the alternative means of achieving goals. The weighing of alternative strategies is made by natural selection rather than by thought processes. When we say that 'a bird species of unstable habitats must adopt a strategy of rapid reproduction', this is shorthand for something like the following: 'Species and individuals vary in their reproductive rates. The more unstable the habitat, the higher is the probability of local extinction or death due to random factors. Also, the smaller the population, the higher is the probability of local extinction due to random factors. The higher the reproductive rate, the briefer is the period between arrival of a few colonists at a vacant piece of habitat and the achievement of a large population size saturating this habitat. Extinction probabilities are higher during this interval than when a large population is achieved. The longer this interval and the fewer the pieces of suitable habitat at any moment, the higher is the likelihood that a species may happen to disappear from all habitat pieces simultaneously. Therefore in unstable habitats natural selection leads to preferential survival of species with high reproductive rates'.

Once one understands that the one sentence about strategy stands for these seven sentences of lengthy prose the language of strategy greatly facilitates discussion. Similar reasoning applies to behavioral strategies of single individuals. When we say that a clam whose shell is tapped closes its shell in order to protect itself from predators, we do not imply that the clam consciously envisions a scenario involving starfish and decides accordingly on a course of action more likely to result in its survival than alternative courses. Instead we imply that the clam's nervous system is programmed genetically (or sometimes in higher species, programmed through learning experiences in early life) and that such programs are closely related to survival probability (Mayr 1974).

The widespread acceptance of the meaning and potential value of strategic thinking in ecology is due largely to the work of the late Robert MacArthur (e.g. 1958, 1972), and has proved a liberating force.

DISTRIBUTIONAL STRATEGIES OF SOME BIRD POPULATIONS

What selective forces ultimately determine the relative values of different strategies, and what types of choices do strategies entail? In general terms the ultimate determinants of a species' strategy are the physical parameters of its environment, such as temperature, light, water, and minerals; the resource production spectrum, such as (for a frugivorous bird) the relative production rates of fruits of different sizes and hardness; the biological matrix of other species which prey on, compete with, and feed the given species; and the fluctuations of all these parameters in space and time. These selective forces shape the species' properties which are the proximate causes of its distributional pattern. Among these properties are: the foraging technique (e.g. for an insectivorous bird, whether it catches insects by sallying, hovering, plucking, or gleaning); the resource utilisation function (e.g. for a frugivorous bird, what proportions of fruits of different sizes and hardness it selects in its diet); the life table, i.e. the birth and death probabilities as a function of age; the abundance in the steady-state; the 'fundamental niche', i.e. the values of the above parameters in the absence of competing species that utilize some of the same resources or that behave aggressively towards the given species; and the 'actual niche', i.e. the values of the above parameters as a function of the competing species pool.

To illustrate the meaning of these general considerations, let us consider some types of distributional strategies among Melanesian bird species.

Supertramps

In the Bismarck Archipelago just east of New Guinea live two very similar species of flycatchers: the Golden Whistler (*Pachycephala pectoralis*) and the Black-tailed Whistler (*Pachycephala melanura*). Both are of similar size and appearance, catch insects by similar plucking movements, and occupy a fairly similar range of habitats. Of several hundred Melanesian islands that have been well explored ornithologically, none supports both species of whistler. Instead, their distributions form a complicated checkerboard (Fig. 1). The two species often occur to the mutual exclusion of each other on islands only a few miles apart. In general the Golden Whistler is found on the larger islands, while the Black-tailed Whistler is found on small islands or on islands recently defaunated by the volcanic explosions and tidal waves that occur frequently in this part of the world.

The Black-tailed Whistler is typical of a group of a dozen species called supertramps (Diamond 1974, 1975). Taxonomically these are varied (pigeons, honeyeaters, flycatchers, a white-eye, a thrush, and a starling), but all appear to share essentially the same distributional strategy. They reproduce rapidly: one pair has been observed to raise six broods in six months! They do not limit their reproduction but continue to breed rapidly even after their populations have saturated an island. The excess juveniles fly away, often over the ocean, in search of unoccupied habitats. The supertramps are not especially well adapted to any one particular habitat, but instead are moderately adapted to a wide range of conditions: from sea level to the summits of mountains, from coral atolls without fresh water to the perpetually dripping moss forest, from savannah to rainforest, from open sun to the deep shade of the forest interior, from near the ground to the forest canopy. Although supertramps multiply rapidly

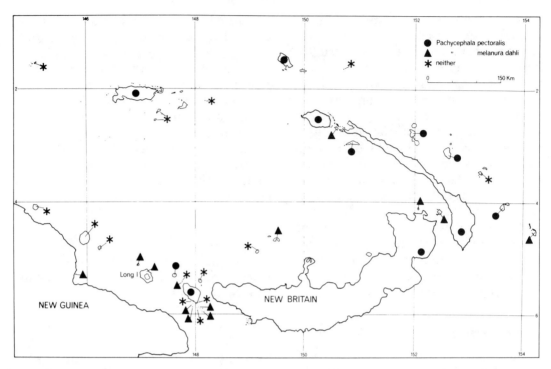

Figure 1. Checkerboard distributions of *Pachycephala* flycatcher species on islands of the Bismarck archipelago. Islands whose flycatcher faunas are known are designated by • (the over-exploiter *Pachycephala pectoralis* resident), ▲ (the supertramp *Pachycephala melanura dahli resident),* or ✳ (neither of these two species resident). Note that no island supports both species, and that almost all islands with • are larger than almost any island with ▲, except for the medium-large Long Island, devastated by a volcanic explosion two centuries ago and recolonised by *Pachycephala melanura* (from Diamond 1975, with permission of Harvard University Press).

and become abundant when resources are abundant, they may be more prone than other bird species to starve when resource levels are low.

The supertramp strategy is appropriate to existence on small islands. Since any plant or animal faces a finite risk of extinction due to population fluctuations, and this risk increases with decreasing population size (MacArthur and Wilson 1967), populations on small islands go extinct frequently (Mayr 1965; Diamond 1969). A strategy for existence on small islands must therefore include three ingredients: sending out many colonists, so as rapidly to recolonize islands on which there have been recent extinctions; reproducing rapidly, so that a recently arrived colonist pair can quickly fill an island with offspring and reduce the initially very high risk of population extinction; and maintaining an abundant population. Supertramps do generate many colonists because of the rapid breeding of adults and instinctively programmed dispersal of juveniles, most of whom are doomed to failure but a few of whom strike it rich by finding an empty island. Their rapid breeding also minimizes the period during which a growing colonist population is smallest and exposed to highest risk of extinction. The supertramps' abundant populations and ability to occupy any habitat help reduce risk of extinction in the steady-state. For the same reasons supertramps are among the first birds to colonise and fill islands that have been defaunated by volcanic explosions or tidal waves (Diamond 1974). The supertramps keep one step ahead of extinction: by the time another tidal wave or explosion strikes or another small-island population fluctuates out of existence, the dispersing juveniles have already assured the survival of the species by finding other recently emptied islands. However the supertramps are excluded from larger, older, or more stable islands by superior competitors, as will now be discussed.

Overexploiters

The Golden Whistler is typical of a group of species whose strategy is in many respects opposite to the supertramp strategy. Birds such as the Golden Whistler raise few broods and regulate their breeding closely. They are usually habitat specialists, very well adapted to some narrow range of habitats and absent from others. They cannot increase their numbers very rapidly when resources are abundant, but they manage to survive better than supertramps when resources are scarce. They are suspected of overexploiting their resources to gain a competitive advantage over species like supertramps (Diamond 1974, 1975). That is, birds like the Golden Whistler may catch insects so efficiently as to depress sustainable yields of insects, thereby starving out the Black-tailed Whistler. They may also devote much energy to aggressive behaviour. The price however, is that Golden Whistlers cannot maintain as high population densities as can Black-tailed Whistlers. In other cases, the dispersing juvenile supertramps that bombard the shores of all islands of the New Guinea region are excluded from the larger islands because of low resource levels caused not just by one competitor but by a constellation of competitors, each a habitat specialist. For instance, the supertramp fruit dove *Ptilinopus solomonensis*, which occupies all habitats of recently exploded volcanoes, is replaced on older islands by the combination of *Ptilinopus rivoli* in the mountains, *Ptilinopus superbus* in lowland forest, and *Ptilinopus insolitus* in lowland second-growth.

I have described the supertramp strategy and the overexploiter strategy in qualitative terms. The reader who wishes to see how these anecdotal interpretations actually emerge from mathematical models and detailed analyses of community structure will find such models and analyses in the following papers: MacArthur and Wilson (1967:Chapter 4) for analysis of extinction probabilities as a function of population size and of life-table parameters; Levins and Culver (1971) and Horn and MacArthur (1972) for analysis of frequency of occurrence in checkerboard distributions as a function of competitive ability and dispersal rates; and Diamond (1975) for analysis of the overexploiter strategy in terms of population growth rate, resource harvesting rate, susceptibility to starvation, and capacity for self-regulation of abundance.

27

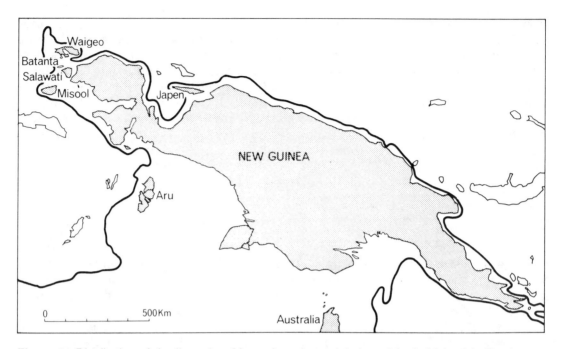

Figure 2. Distribution of the flycatcher *Monarcha telescophthalmus* (shaded islands). The heavy line is the contour of 200 m ocean depth, which is very close to the 100 m contour. The whole area within the heavy line formed a single landmass at times of lower sea level during the Pleistocene. Thus, present-day islands within this line are 'land-bridge islands'. Note that this flycatcher now occurs on every large (>450 sq km) land-bridge island named on the map, but on no oceanic island nor on any small land-bridge island, not even ones within a few hundred yards of New Guinea. The cockatoo *Proboneiger aterrimus* has the same distribution. Both species are capable of normal flight, and the cockatoo is a strong flier (from Diamond 1975, with permission of Harvard University Press).

Land-bridge Relict Populations

And intriguing distributional pattern in many animal species, and one that was duplicated by the Aboriginal population of Tasmania (below), is encountered on so-called land-bridge islands. During the Pleistocene, when much water was locked up in glaciers, sea level was at least 100 m lower than at present. Consequently, islands that now are separated from a continent by shallow water less than 100 m deep formed part of the adjacent continent during the Pleistocene. Examples of such 'land-bridge islands' are Britain off Europe, Trinidad off South America, Fernando Po off Africa, Borneo, Formosa, and Ceylon off Asia, and Aru off New Guinea.

Ever since the science of zoogeography was founded by Alfred Russell Wallace (1876), codiscoverer of evolution with Darwin, it has been realised that the distinction between land-bridge islands and oceanic islands (islands that never had land-bridges to continents) is important in understanding distributions of species that have difficulty dispersing over the ocean (see Darlington 1957:Chapter 8, for details). For example flightless mammals like the rhinoceros, tiger, elephant and gibbon occur on the large Indonesian islands that had Pleistocene land-bridges to Asia, but are absent from islands beyond the 100 m ocean contour. The obvious interpretation is that these mammals walked to Borneo, Java, or Sumatra over dry land more than 10,000 years ago and have persisted since.

Fig. 2 exhibits a similar distributional pattern for a New Guinea bird species, the Frilled Monarch (*Monarcha telescophthalmus*). This flycatcher occurs today on all seven of the large islands (> 450 sq km in area) that had Pleistocene land-bridges to New Guinea, but is on no smaller land-bridge island nor on any oceanic island regardless of size. Dozens of other New Guinea bird species are similarly absent from all oceanic islands, and are present on varying numbers of large land-bridge islands (Diamond 1972, 1973). For example the Beautiful Fruit-Dove (*Ptilinopus pulchellus*) is on four of the seven large land-bridge islands. The New Guinea Harpy Eagle (*Harpyopsis novaeguineae*) is on not a single land-bridge or oceanic island and is confined to New Guinea itself. Virtually all of these bird species are physically easily capable of flying to dozens of islands from which they are absent. The Harpy Eagle for instance, may soar 160 km overland each day in the course of its normal foraging, yet is absent from large islands a few kilometers from New Guinea. Most of these species must have been present on most land-bridge islands when they formed part of New Guinea. Why are they now absent from varying numbers of large land-bridge islands and all small ones? And why don't they now simply fly to these islands and to the oceanic islands?

If one accepts for the moment as an unexplained but given fact that these bird species refuse to fly across water gaps, then their differing distributions can be understood in terms of differing extinction probabilities. A species isolated on an island for 10,000 years runs a finite risk of extinction due to population fluctuations and environmental catastrophes. Simple mathematical models (MacArthur and Wilson 1967; Leigh 1975) lead to the prediction that extinction probability increases with decreasing population size and with increasing temporal coefficient of variation of population size. Extinction probability also increases with decreasing reproductive potential, since a slowly reproducing species whose population was reduced by one disaster may be finished off by a second disaster happening before its population has recovered. In agreement with these predictions, most of the bird species that survived on few or none of the large New Guinea land-bridge islands fall into one or more of four categories: species with low population densities because of large territory requirements (e.g. the Harpy Eagle); species with low population densities because of specialized habitat requirements; species with high coefficients of variation of abundance because of dependence on spatially and temporally patchy food supplies; and species of low reproductive potential (possibly true of most of the species). On New Guinea land-bridge islands smaller than about 130 sq km practically no bird population survives 10,000 years in isolation, and all species on small land-bridge islands are derived from recent over-water colonists.

Similar considerations underlie the differential survival of mammal species stranded on land-bridge islands. The best analysed case (Brown 1971) is provided not by islands in the ocean but by virtual islands of habitat. Out of the Great Basin Desert of Nevada and Utah rise 17 mountain ranges whose upper slopes support pinyon-juniper woodlands now isolated from each other by the 'sea' of desert surrounding the base of each mountain. At times of cooler Pleistocene climates, when the woodland descended to lower elevations and was continuous over the Great Basin, small woodland mammals must have had a continuous distribution. When rising temperatures drove the woodland up the mountains, the woodland mammals became stranded on their mountain tops as on land-bridge islands, and numerous populations have gone extinct in the last 10,000 years. As with birds of New Guinea land-bridge islands, the smallest mountain tops have lost the most mammal species, and the species that naturally live at low population densities (carnivores, large species, species of specialized habitats) have survived on the fewest mountain tops.

For these small mammals of woodland, dispersal across desert is virtually a physical impossibility. In contrast dispersal across a few kilometers of water would be a trivial effort for most New Guinea bird species. The failure of so many species to colonize oceanic islands or to recolonize land-bridge islands on which populations disappeared must be due to a behavioural program, about whose underlying selective forces we can only speculate. Colonizing success depends on many attributes, of which ability or willingness to fly across water is only one. For instance colonists must also have high reproductive potential, or they will be unlikely to survive the initial colonizing phase of low abundance or to recover from occasional population crashes. If dispersing juveniles of a species initially varied with respect to genes that programmed them for or against crossing water, the relative frequencies of these genes would come to depend on the subsequent colonizing success of the juveniles. If most juveniles that flew across water failed to found successful populations, the water-crossing gene would be selected out of existence, and the surviving population would consist of individuals programmed not to cross water. This may be what has happened among the land-bridge relict bird species, most of which are doomed by low reproductive potential to be poor colonists. In short, behavioural characteristics, such as the tendency to disperse, are subject to natural selection, just as are morphological characteristics (cf. Wilson 1975).

DISTRIBUTIONAL STRATEGIES OF SOME HUMAN POPULATIONS

In this final section we consider three problems of human distributional strategies analogous to the cases discussed for Melanesian birds.

Human Supertramps

In archipelagoes where many competing species are present, Melanesian bird supertramps are confined to small or remote islands and excluded from large islands. As one proceeds successively eastwards into the Pacific from New Guinea to the Bismarcks, then the Solomons, then the New Hebrides, then Fiji, bird species become fewer. Supertramps then begin to occupy large islands, because there are now fewer competitors. For instance the pigeons *Macropygia mackinlayi* and *Ptilinopus solomonensis* are confined to small islands of the New Guinea region and the Bismarcks but are on large and small islands of the Solomons. The pigeon *Ducula pacifica* is on small outlying islets of the Bismarcks and Solomons but is on large and small islands of the New Hebrides.

Among human groups, the Polynesians exhibit a similar distribution. As far east as the Fiji archipelago, the people of the large islands are mainly Melanesians, but Polynesians occur on small or outlying islands (e.g. Rennell and Nukumanu in the Solomons and Tikopia in the Santa Cruz group). At the time of European discovery Melanesians had not yet reached the more remote archipelagoes of the Pacific (Samoa, Tahiti, Hawaii, New Zealand) and here Polynesians settled large islands as well as small islands. Polynesians resemble supertramp bird species and differ from Melanesians in at least one attribute, superior overwater dispersal ability. It would be interesting to examine just how Melanesians excluded Polynesians from large islands wherever the distributions of the two groups overlapped. One also wonders whether Polynesians and Melanesians contrast in other traits distinguishing supertramps from overexploiters, such as population growth rate and self-regulation of population. The analogy may be weakened by the fact that Polynesians had passed their peak colonizing or 'supertramp' phase before European discovery.

A somewhat similar situation arises in the straits between New Guinea and New Britain (Fig. 3). Long Island in these straits underwent a cataclysmic volcanic explosion about two centuries ago. The bird fauna that has re-established itself on Long Island consists of supertramps plus species from the Bismarck islands of Tolokiwa, Umboi, Sakar and New Britain, to the east. The paucity of colonists derived from New Guinea is striking, since New Guinea is 20 times larger and several times closer to Long Island than is New Britain. The explanation for this pattern seems to be that many New Guinea species rarely cross water gaps, but that all New Britain species were initially derived by overwater colonization from New Guinea and were thus preselected from New Guinea's pool of superior colonists. Since the explosion man has also recolonized Long Island, beginning about a century ago. As true of Long Island's birds, the human colonists have mainly come from Tolokiwa, Umboi, Sakar, and New Britain. Few people have arrived from the much larger populations on the New Guinea mainland, clearly visible only 50 km from Long Island. The people of the small Bismarck islands are much better seafarers than those of the New Guinea coast, so much so that Bismarck people were still acting as the sea-going traders for the adjacent part of the New Guinea coast until a few decades ago. It may be that something similar to the so-called taxon cycle that Wilson (1961) described for colonizing Melanesian ants also operates for peoples of the Pacific. According to this formulation, colonists are preferentially drawn from populations of high growth rate but low competitive ability, such as populations of coasts and of 'stepping-stone' islands. After colonists establish themselves on a

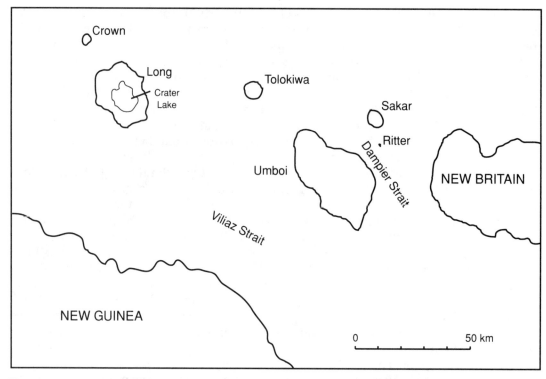

Figure 3. Map of Long Island and vicinity, near New Guinea. The human population and fauna of Long Island were destroyed in a volcanic explosion two centuries ago. Birds and man have recolonised Long mainly from Tolokiwa, Umboi, Saker, and New Britain, not from New Guinea, despite New Guinea's proximity and much greater area. This differential colonisation is not due to prevailing winds and currents, which reverse direction twice a year.

large island, they gradually withdraw into the island's interior and lose their dispersal ability and high growth rate. In genetic terms this cycle involves a switch from so-called r selection to so-called K selection (MacArthur and Wilson 1967).

Adaptive Significance of Population Self-Regulation

Species differ in the extent to which they self-regulate their population density. We have noted that overexploiters are thought to self-regulate much more than do supertramps, and that the adaptive value of self-regulation is higher in stable habitats than in unstable habitats.

Humans practise a wide range of customs that have the effect of limiting population growth, such as infanticide, sexual taboos during lactation, restrictions on who can marry whom or on who can marry at all, etc. In some situations intertribal differences in self-regulatory practices have been suggested as being of adaptive significance. For example Wagley (1969) compared social structure and resilience in two Tupi speaking Amerindian tribes of Brazil, the

Tapirapé and the Tenetehara. The latter have survived the shock of European contact and disease well and are now nearly as numerous as when discovered three centuries ago. Within 40 years of contact, the former people declined in numbers by 90%, their social structure disintegrated, and extinction seemed likely soon to follow. The technologies of these tribes are similar, but their social practices related to population regulation and population density are quite different. The Tapirapé restrict family size to three children (not more than two of the same sex), practice infanticide, observe a complex set of food taboos, and have a complex ceremonial life that cannot function in a village of less than 200 people and that impedes formation of new villages. In contrast the Tenetehara do not limit family size. Their social structure makes it easy for groups to split off and found new villages, and they were even initially more numerous than the Tapirapé. In biological language one can describe the Tapirapé as having low reproductive potential, low resilience (i.e. ability to recover only slowly from a population decline), high ability to self-regulate, and adaptations suitable to a very stable environment and low maintained population density, while the Tenetehara tend towards the opposite qualities. These differing strategies may help explain why the Tenetehara recovered from the mortality due to European-introduced diseases, while the Tapirapé population crashed and did not re-bound.

The Tasmanians: A Human Land-bridge Relict Population

A human distributional pattern similar to Fig. 2 has been discussed by Jones (also in Golson 1972:381–2). Off the southeast corner of Australia is a series of islands that lie in the shallow waters of Bass Strait and that formed part of the Australian mainland during the Pleistocene (Fig. 4). At the time of European discovery the only inhabited islands were the largest one, Tasmania, plus some smaller islands very close to Tasmania.

The paperback canoe-rafts of the Aborigines were inadequate for reaching more distant, medium-sized islands, such as Flinders and King. These two islands have yielded archaeological remains of man probably dating from Pleistocene land-bridge times, but not from more recently. The population of Tasmania itself was at least several thousand, but the largest of the recently uninhabited islands could not have supported more than 500 people, given its area and assuming population densities as on Tasmania. The obvious interpretation is that when rising sea levels inundated most of Bass Strait, the only island on which the stranded human population was large enough to maintain itself indefinitely was Tasmania. The populations on the smaller islands fluctuated out of existence, or else consciously abandoned the islands at time of land-bridge severance, and the limited water-crossing abilities of the Tasmanisns prevented recolonization.

This situation may have been almost unique in the modern world, since the recent peoples of other land-bridge archipelagoes had boats sufficient to permit recolonization of islands of which populations transiently disappeared. However the archaeological record from areas like the Greater Sunda Islands and the

33

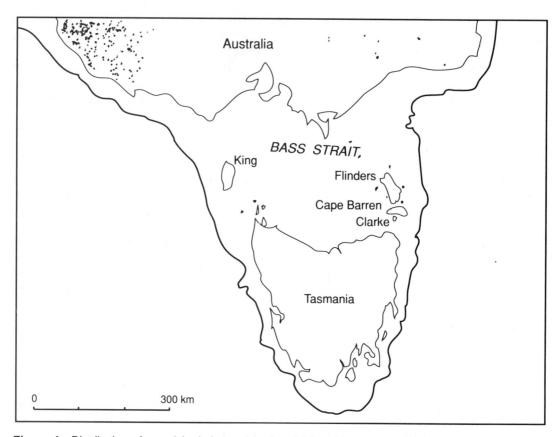

Figure 4. Distribution of man (shaded areas) in the vicinity of Bass Strait (separating southeastern Australia from Tasmania), at the time of European discovery. The heavy line is the contour of 100 m ocean depth. All the area within the heavy line formed a single landmass during Pleistocene times when sea level was lower. In modern times native Australians occurred only on the two largest fragments of this former landmass, Australia and Tasmania, although there is archaeological evidence of man on the smaller islands in the Pleistocene. Men spread over the Bassian Shelf when it was above water, but the populations that post-Pleistocene flooding left stranded on the smaller islands (e.g. Flinders, King, Cape Barren, Clarke) fluctuated out of existence or abandoned the islands, and recolonisation over all but the narrowest water gaps was impossible. Many animal and plant species (e.g. the Spotted Quail-Thrush *Cinclosoma punctatum*) have the same distribution, and presumably for the same reason.

Japanese archipelago may yield evidence of similar patterns, existing at times when man's water-crossing technology was less well developed than it was among primitive peoples recently extant.

ACKNOWLEDGEMENTS

I thank Drs. Sharon Kaufman-Diamond, John Terrell and Rhys Jones for suggestions.

34

REFERENCES

Brown, J. 1971 Mammals on mountaintops: nonequilibrium insular biogeography. *American Naturalist* 105:467–78

Cody, M. L. and J. M. Diamond (eds) 1975 *Ecology and evolution of communities.* Cambridge (Mass.): Belknap Press of Harvard University Press

Darlington, P. J. 1957 *Zoogeography: the geographical distribution of animals.* New York: Wiley

Diamond, J. M. 1969 Avifaunal equilibria and species turnover rates on the Channel Islands of California. *Proceedings of the National Academy of Sciences, U.S.A.* 64:57–63

1972 Biogeographic kinetics: estimation of relaxation times for avifaunas of southwest Pacific islands. *Proceedings of the National Academy of Sciences, U.S.A.* 69:3199–3203

1973 Distributional ecology of New Guinea birds. *Science* 179:759–69

1974 Colonization of exploded volcanic islands by birds: the supertramp strategy. *Science* 184:803–6

1975 Assembly of species communities. In Cody and Diamond 1975:342–444

Golson, J. 1972 Land connections, sea barriers and the relationship of Australian and New Guinea prehistory. In D. Walker (ed.) *Bridge and barrier: the natural and cultural history of Torres Strait*:375–97. Canberra: Australian National University, Research School of Pacific Studies, Department of Biogeography and Geomorphology, Publication BG/3

Horn, H. S. and R. H. MacArthur 1972 Competition among fugitive species in a Harlequin environment. *Ecology* 53:749–52

Leigh, E. G., Jr. 1975 Population fluctuations, community stability, and environmental variability. In Cody and Diamond 1975:51–73

Levins, R. and D. Culver 1971 Regional coexistence of species, and competition between rare species. *Proceedings of the National Academy of Sciences, U.S.A.* 68:1246–8

MacArthur, R. H. 1958 Population ecology of some warblers of northeastern coniferous forests. *Ecology* 39:599–619

1972 *Geographical ecology.* New York: Harper and Row

and E. O. Wilson 1967 *The theory of island biogeography.* Princeton: Princeton University Press

Mayr, E. 1965 Avifauna: turnover on islands. *Science* 150:1587–8

1974 Teleological and teleonomic: a new analysis. *Boston Studies in the Philosophy of Science* 14:91–117

Wagley, C. 1969 Cultural influences on population: a comparison of two Tupii tribes. In A. P. Vayda (ed.) *Environment and cultural behavior.* Garden City (N.Y.): Natural History Press

Wallace, A. R. 1876 *The geographical distribution of animals.* London: Macmillan

Wilson, E. O. 1961 The nature of the taxon cycle in the Melanesian ant fauna. *American Naturalist* 95:169–93

1975 *Sociobiology: the new synthesis.* Cambridge (Mass.): Belknap Press of Harvard University Press

Systematics and Taxonomy

James D. Paterson

The topics of systematics and taxonomy, like those of evolutionary theory, have developed into very complex fields, and a fully detailed discussion of them is beyond the capacity of this text. The purpose of these notes is to provide the student with some entry into the literature, a basic understanding of the area, and perhaps to stimulate interest in further reading.

The term "taxonomy" is derived from two Greek words which effectively translate as "law of arrangement". It can be defined in modern usage as "the theory and practise of classifying organisms". That such an activity is required as a means to order our knowledge of the organic world can be understood from the opening paragraph of the first chapter of Ernst Mayr's Principles of Systematic Zoology (Mayr, 1969).

> "The amount of diversity in the living world is staggering. About 1 million species of animals and half a million species of plants have already been described, and estimates on the number of still undescribed living species range from 3 to 10 million. An estimate of half a billion for the extinct species is consistent with the known facts."

Raup and Stanley (1971) go on to point out that 850,000 of the known animal species are insects, only 8,600 are birds, and about 6,000 are mammals. They further note that approximately 130,000 fossil species had been identified and described at that time, a figure representing a mere 8.7 percent of the known living species, and perhaps less than 3 percent of the possible number of living forms. Ultimately they note that Simpson's calculations of 1952, which were based upon the first application of the mathematical model of a "survivorship curve", suggested that the total number of distinct species which have lived on Planet Earth since life became established here may number somewhere between the limits of 50 million and 4 billion (4,000 million). In the period since Raup and Stanley's estimate, palaeontology has continued to add known species at a high rate. A current estimate might be that 140,000 to 170,000 species may be on the rolls of 1990. It is, however, obvious that the discipline of taxonomy has a great deal of work ahead of it (Only 4 billion species to go!). In order to maintain that mass of knowledge in some organized, useful fashion, its practitioners must utilize an appropriate set of theories and methodologies.

TAXONOMIC THEORY

There has been substantial change within the theoretical frameworks of the disciplines concerned with taxonomy over the past thirty years, yet some major syntheses have remained as standard texts throughout. Among the most significant basic works have been Simpson's Principles of Animal Taxonomy (1961), a treatise on the field by one of the prominent mid twentieth century taxonomists, and Mayr's Principles of Systematic Zoology (1969), still one of the most useful textbooks and guides for the practitioner of the discipline. Much of the recent theory and its ramifications will be considered later, but in order to understand the discussions, it is necessary to begin with some definitions.

These definitions are derived from many sources, but principly Simpson, Mayr, Eldredge, Cracraft, and Groves.

Systematics

Simpson (1961) provides this definition: "Systematics is the scientific study of the kinds and diversity of organisms and of any and all relationships among them." Mayr suggests a simplified version: "systematics is the science of the diversity of organisms". In either version it can be seen that systematics is a supra-inclusive class, with all aspects of biology subsumed under it since data from any and all branches of the biological sciences contribute to it. Systematics is unique in biological study with its dominant concern with diversity, and as such, deals with populations, species and higher taxa, rather than just with individual organisms or organic structures.

Zoological Classification

Mayr (1969) notes that classification partially overlaps with taxonomy, and is used in two differing ways. Even though Simpson's definition (1961) is: "Zoological classification is the ordering of animals (organisms) into groups, or sets, on the basis of their relationships, that is, the construction of associations by contiguity, similarity, or both." Mayr notes that this is coincident with what he terms *beta taxonomy* to distinguish it from *alpha taxonomy* (see Taxonomy, below). The second mode of use for the term is as a designation for the products of the activity of the taxonomist, which may be "classifications" of particular groups of organisms.

Zoological Nomenclature

"Zoological nomenclature is the application of distinctive names to each of the groups recognized in any given zoological classification." (Simpson, 1961). The rules and procedures governing this part of the discipline are under control of the International Code of Zoological Nomenclature as adopted by the International Congress of Zoology. The nomenclatural system in use is a derived form of the Linnaean binomial naming procedure.

Taxonomy

Simpson (1961) defines taxonomy as: "the theoretical study of classification, including its bases, principles, procedures, and rules" thus divorcing it from the practical aspects of classification and nomenclature, and making it a theoretical field. Mayr (1969) more pragmatically, as noted above, defines it as: "the theory and practise of classifying organisms" and implicitly accords it the status of *alpha taxonomy;* he therefore must utilize the term *beta taxonomy* to specify the same activity that Simpson labels as "classification".

Folk Taxonomy

A folk taxonomy is a classification (or beta taxonomy) which is held by a local group of humans as a part of their cultural heritage. It may reflect a high degree of correlation with a scientific taxonomy, but has been produced and maintained as part of the society's traditional adaptation to the local environment. The study of folk taxonomies is properly the realm of the anthropologist and linguist, and hence will not be considered in any detail.

THE FRAMEWORKS FOR CLASSIFICATION

Every human society holds a framework for classification of the plants and animals sharing their habitat. These folk taxonomies can be extremely precise, detailed knowledge sets, especially when the people concerned are hunters and gatherers. Though it may be that females may have a different classification than males, if their subsistence activities are split along sex role lines. The study of such folk taxonomies has been an activity for a few anthropologists and linguists over the past decades, and biologists on collecting expeditions often make use of the knowledge sets of local guides in their initial classifications. Traditional european folk taxonomy is undoubtedly one of the starting points from which the modern scientific taxonomy has evolved. Since the study of folk taxonomy is rightly the domain of ethnology, it will not be examined further.

Two ancient classification schemes in european thought which are allied with folk taxonomies, are the "teleological" and the "ecological". Both of these tend to merge into vernacular usage. The teleological classificatory system, according to Simpson (1961), defines "sets" of organisms which must not be considered to be taxa. These classifications are based upon an organism's usefulness or lack of it, to the human population. As such these systems are culturally relativistic, and anthropocentric; what may be considered as useful and valuable in one society may be regarded as unusable, irrelevant, or disgusting in another. As examples of teleological sets we might list: draught horses, meat animals, pets, vermin, pests, weeds, flowers, shade trees, ornamental shrubs, lodgepole pines, stringy-bark and paper-bark gums, etc. Teleological classification is of no use to the scientific investigator, but it is commonly employed by non-taxonomists. The ecological scheme has a slightly more rigorous base. According to Simpson (1961), it defines sets, again not taxa, in line with criteria such as the communities in which the organisms live, or environmental factors. A set of examples of these are the categories of: swamp plants, forest insects, alpine plants, arctic foxes, polar bears, savanna baboons, desert gazelles, etc. These are in common colloquial use, but would not be suited for a formal taxonomy.

There are two frameworks upon which modern classifications may be built or ordered. These are "keys" and "hierarchies", both of which make use of the concepts of levels layered one above the other, though each framework is organized for a distinctive purpose.

Keys

Simpson defines a key as: "a systematic framework for zoological classification, which is generally used for identification purposes rather than anything else, and which has a sequence of classes at each level of which more restricted classes are formed by the overlap of two or more classes at the next higher level." In other terms, a key is a tool for the identification of individual organisms, a mechanism to find the named taxon to which the sample or test organism belongs. A key can be viewed as an inverted pyramid which progressively narrows down towards the identification of an organism with a particular taxon. It assumes that a previously established hierarchy and taxa exist. An example provided by Simpson (1961) starts by recognizing a group of "bears" which contains animals of several colours, and then by the application of individual colour criteria, it becomes possible to separate "black bears, brown bears, and white bears", and then further divisions on other criteria may be applied until identification is achieved.

As a brief example, a rough key to the genera of new world monkeys is provided as Figure 1. Far more detailed and extensive keys may be found in the work of Philip Hershkovitz (1977, 1983, 1987, and others). These keys (Hershkovitz 1983, 1987) provide detailed discrimination down to the levels of subspecies for the genera *Aotus* and *Pithecia*, though for the latter, the investigator must make an *a priori* recognition of sex, since the keys are distinct for males and females.

Hierarchies

In contrast, Simpson defines a hierarchy as: "a systematic framework for zoological classification with a sequence of classes or sets at different levels in which each class except the lowest includes one or more subordinate classes." Thus a hierarchy is a multi-level pyramid which is progressively more inclusive, aggregating more and more taxa together as it approaches the apex. The current use of a hierarchy is to show the relationships be-

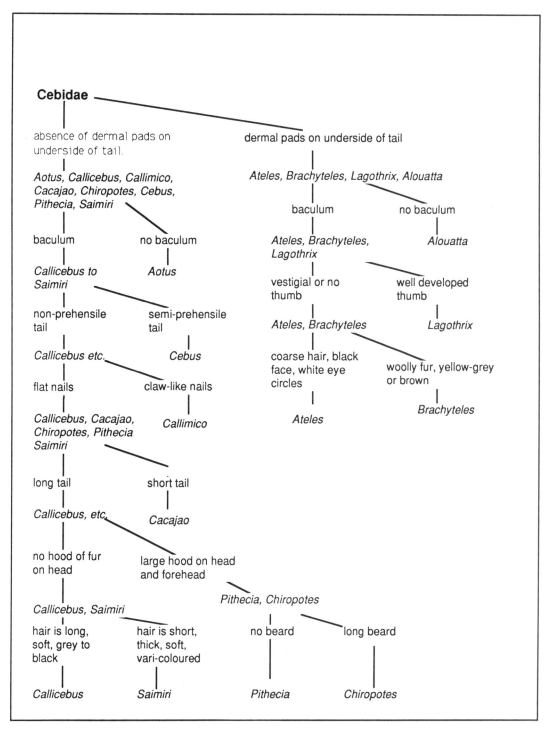

Figure 1a: An Identification Key for Male New World Monkeys—the genus breakdown for the Cebidae. Callitrichids are separated from Cebids by dental formula: 2 1 3 2 for the former, 2 1 3 3 for the latter.

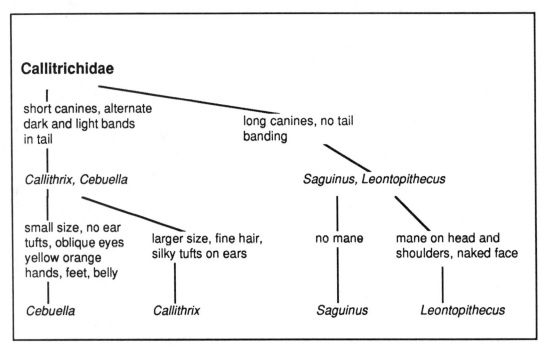

Callitrichidae

short canines, alternate dark and light bands in tail

long canines, no tail banding

Callithrix, Cebuella

Saguinus, Leontopithecus

small size, no ear tufts, oblique eyes yellow orange hands, feet, belly

larger size, fine hair, silky tufts on ears

no mane

mane on head and shoulders, naked face

Cebuella

Callithrix

Saguinus

Leontopithecus

Figure 1b: An Identification Key for Male New World Monkeys—the genus breakdown for the Callitrichidae.

tween different entities, and secondarily to reflect the evolutionary pattern of their development. Substantial misunderstanding of the form of a hierarchy is a common error. It is surprising how often an otherwise rigorous researcher makes the error of contrasting "hominids" with the "hominoids" without recognizing that the former category, the "hominids", are included within the latter "hominoids".

The Linnaean Hierarchy

Carl Linnaeus (1707–1778), spent his working life at the University of Upsalla in Sweden, Writing in Latin under the name Carolus Linnaeus, he is the author of the hierarchical system used in modern biology. The taxonomic hierarchy employed in zoological classification and adopted by general agreement among zoologists has been derived from the standardized version elucidated in definitive form in the 10th edition of *Systema Naturae* published in 1758. His work became sufficiently famous throughout Europe that he was eventually raised to the

Swedish nobility, with a consequent nominal change to Carl von Linné. Linnaeus originally set out his hierarchy with just 5 levels. It is now common to utilize at least seven (phylum and family are commonly added) and to dispense with Linnaeus' use of "Empire" for the whole world of material phenomena. It should be noted that Linnaeus was a devoutly religious man, and hence made use of the concept of a "Great Chain of Being" which ran from slime moulds to a "supreme being" in the form of the Judaeo-Christian "God". Thus the region above the "Empire" was occupied by incorporeal entities. The minimum list of levels employed in the late 20th century is:

Kingdom
  Phylum
    Class
      Order
        Family
          Genus
            Species

In some sectors of biological science, there are numerous additional levels utilized. The terms "super", "sub", and "infra" can be added as prefixes to create additional categories, and commonly the extras of "cohort", between class and order, and of "tribe", between family and genus, are used for mammals. The expanded hierarchy used by Simpson in his classification of the mammals (1945) uses 21 levels (in **boldface** below). A complete utilization of all possible and prefixed levels would yield 34, as in the following listing. This is substantially more than would be expected to be needed in practice.

Superkingdom
Kingdom
Subkingdom
Infrakingdom
  Superphylum
  Phylum
  Subphylum
  Infraphylum
    Superclass
    Class
    Subclass
    Infraclass
      Supercohort
      Cohort
      Subcohort
      Infracohort
        Superorder
        Order
        Suborder
        Infraorder
          Superfamily
          Family
          Subfamily
          Infrafamily
            Supertribe
            Tribe
            Subtribe
            Infratribe
              Supergenus
              Genus
              Subgenus
              Infragenus

Superspecies
Species
Subspecies
Infraspecies

To the present time, some of these potential levels have never been employed. Groves (personal communication, 1989) notes that he has yet to see the use of supergenus, infrafamily, infratribe, or infraspecies. Yet with all of these levels available, some are not satisfied. McKenna (1975) through the assumption of a rigidly cladistic formal taxonomy based on universal dichotomization, felt it necessary to add the following: Legion, with super, sub and infra levels between Subclass and Infraclass; Magnorder between Cohort and Superorder; Grandorder, and Mirorder between Superorder and Order; and Parvorder between Infraorder and Superfamily. A more useful, and more justifiable addition is that of *Plesion,* a proposal of Patterson and Rosen (1977) which is endorsed by Groves for "an unranked quasi-taxonomic category, to be inserted at the appropriate level so as not to disturb a pre-existing classification" (Groves, 1989). The concept is a flexible, but not well defined term, which Groves suggests is most suited to the denotation of a group displaying limited diversity.

In order to keep the situation under control for introductory students, two examples of a taxonomy of the primates are presented as Figures 2 and 3. The first of these is a fairly traditional one as provided by Conroy (1990), and the second is a somewhat more rigorous one based upon cladistic analyses by Groves (1989).

History and Usefulness

Since Linnaeus' establishment of the hierarchical scheme, it has come to be the only generally accepted ordering of organic life. While most of his theory and philosophy has been rejected, the hierarchy and the associated binomial nomenclatural system (see below) now forms the accepted system. The hierarchy provides an ordered mechanism, in its current guise, for understanding the relationships of the various lifeforms on Earth. It also

Figure 2: Taxonomy of Living Primates (after Conroy 1990).

Order	Suborder	Infraorder	SuperFamily	Family	Subfamily	Tribe	Common Names
Primates	Anthropoidea	Catarrhini	Hominoidea	Hominidae Pongidae Hylobatidae			Gibbons Apes & Humans
			Cercopithecoidea	Cercopithecidae	Cercopithecinae	Papionini	Guenons Baboons
						Cercopithecini	
					Colobinae		Colobus & Langurs
		Platyrrhini	Ceboidea	Callitrichidae	Callimiconinae		Marmosets
					Callitrichinae		
				Cebidae	Cebinae Alouattinae Aotinae Atelinae Pithecinae		Cebid monkeys
	Prosimii	Tarsiiformes	Tarsioidea				Tarsiers
		Lorisiformes	Lorisoidea		Lorisinae		Lorises Pottos
					Galaginae		Galagos
		Lemuriformes	Lemuroidea	Lemuridae Indriidae Daubentonidae Cheirogaleidae			Lemurs

Order	Suborder	Infraorder	Section	SuperFamily	Family	Subfamily	Tribe	Common Names
Primates	Haplorhini	Simiiformes	Catarrhini	Hominoidea	Hominidae	Homininae	Hominini	Humans
							Panini	Chimpanzees
							Gorillini	Gorillas
						Ponginae		Orangutans
					Hylobatidae			Gibbons & Siamangs
				Cercopithecoidea	Cercopithecidae	Cercopithecinae		Guenons
						Papioninae		Baboons & Macaques
					Colobidae	Colobinae		Colobus & Langurs
						Nasalinae		Nasalis
			Platyrrhini		Callitrichidae	Callimiconinae		Marmosets
						Callitrichinae		Marmosets
					Cebidae Alouattidae Aotidae Atelidae Pithecidae			Cebid monkeys
		Tarsiiformes			Tarsiidae			Tarsiers
	Strepsirhini	Lemuriformes			Cheirogaleidae			Dwarf Lemurs
					Indriidae	Indriinae		Indriids
					Lemuridae			Lemurs
					Lorisidae	Galaginae		Galago
						Lorisinae	Lorisini	Loris
							Perodictini	Potto
		Chiromyiformes			Daubentoniidae			Aye - Aye

Figure 3: Taxonomy of Living Primates (Constructed from listings in Groves 1989).

43

serves as a guide to the history of the evolution of life, while the nomenclatural system provides an unequivocal mechanism to refer to specific taxa and clusters of taxa within that hierarchy. It must be admitted that in spite of problems with the hierarchy in some ways, and a few biologists who are dissatisfied with the binomial nomenclature, wishing to have it changed, or at least modified, these devices remain as the most useful mechanisms yet developed to organize and recognize the relationships of organic life.

Basics of Nomenclature

A phylogenetic or evolutionary classification must provide two things to the biological community—it must give an absolutely accurate reference to particular creatures without fear of error, and it is expected to give an indication of their phylogenetic relationship to other creatures. It therefore represents an ordering of the results of studies performed on the organisms. The mechanism which provides the reference function for the classification is the assignment of names, an activity which can be called the practise of nomenclature. It is the ideal situation that each taxon have a distinctive name, and *only* one name which is used by all biologists. Modern nomenclature, for all the attention given to it, exists only as a labeling system for the units of classification.

Binomial Names While many folk taxonomies, particularly among some Amerindian tribal groups, make use of binomial or two part names, it is Linnaeus who is considered to have formalized and regularized the naming procedures to this form. As a result of his work, all names given to organisms are in two parts, hence each name is referred to as a *binomen*. To some extent the structure of the naming system reflects the basic classification criteria employed by Linnaeus. The first word of the name is always capitalized, and is referred to as the "Genus Name", or simply the *genus*. The second word of the name is never capitalized, and is referred to as the

"species name", or simply the *species*. These names are by tradition and convention, always underlined or printed in italicized type.

Binomial names, again by convention, are treated as though they were in a form of "Neo-Latin". Many names are in fact proper Latin words, many are Greek terms transcribed into Latin, but names may also be of non-classical origin such as *Alouatta* and *Ekgmowechashala* derived from native American languages, or even, quite frankly invented, as *Montypythonoides* (an Australian snake) seems to have been. It is quite common for names to commemorate an individual; researchers, taxonomists, palaeontologists, expedition sponsors, fieldwork aides, and many others have all been honoured in this fashion. A favourite derives from the 1924 Gobi desert expedition in China: *Andrewsarchus edwardsii*, an early creodont carnivorous mammal, manages to commemorate both the discoverer, 'Edwards', and the expedition sponsor, 'Andrews'. While most of the names applied during the eighteenth and nineteenth centuries were descriptive to some greater or lesser extent, such as *Homo sapiens* meaning "man, the wise", this has ceased to be very useful. The supply of appropriate Latin descriptive words is limited, Simpson (1961) even regarded it as exhausted. In modern nomenclature, while it is still possible to apply descriptive names, it is a practise which is becoming more difficult.

Naming Procedures The naming procedures employed for the Kingdom Animalia are under the control of the International Code of Zoological Nomenclature. This codex is periodically revised (every 20 to 30 years), with the most recent revision having the publication date of 1985. The Code of Zoological Nomenclature now occupies a modest book unto itself, unlike the situation in 1969 when Mayr was able to reprint the code in just thirty-two pages.

Taxonomic Evidence and Interpretation in Evolutionary Systematics

It is necessary to consider what evidence is acceptable in making classificatory judgements and how that evidence is to be used. In 1961 Simpson said: "in modern taxonomy, the concepts and definitions of categories and taxa are reached mainly by evolutionary considerations, but the evidence that validates them and demonstrates that definitions have been met is largely based on similarity data" and the situation thirty years later has not appreciably changed in this regard. The major revision of taxonomic theory which Simpson had seen begin in the 1930's when Neo-Darwinian evolutionary models were achieving a significant impact on biology with the resultant development of the "New Systematics" had not changed the use of similarity data from the patterns of employment first established by the empirical taxonomists. It was, however, expanded and given greater credence through the application of multivariate analysis techniques.

Evidence Since evolutionary systematics was rooted in evolution and based on phylogeny, the evidence required to meet taxonomic principles and to show that the classification reflects phylogeny has to be distinct from the definitions of taxonomic entities. While taxonomic categories below the generic level are defined in evolutionary and phylogenetic terms, the evidence used in classification is almost entirely nonphylogenetic when taken as individual observations. The case of "identical twins" serves as an example in this regard. Identical twins can be defined to be two individuals derived from a single zygote. Upon examination of the individuals, the investigator recognizes that the definition has been met by evidence of similarities sufficient to sustain the inference. These may be the presence of a single placenta at their birth, or the presence of sufficient correspondence in characteristics, such as commonality of hair, skin, eye, colours and morphology, or just the 90% correspondence of finger-prints which is usual for identical twins. As a result it can be seen that individuals do not belong to the same taxon because they are similar, but they are similar because they belong to the same taxon.

The matter of most importance to phylogenetic considerations in evolutionary systematics is the process of deciding on the propinquity of descent. This matter is viewed as crucial, but it is judged on the basis of "similarities" between forms. The problem is that there are different patterns which similarity can take.

Similarity Problems The problem of similarity is widespread through taxonomy. What constitutes similarity? Is it a mild, medium, or strong resemblance? What degree of structural, physiological, or behavioural similarity is useful or required by the taxonomist? Beyond this, similarity is a major problem in that there are different types of resemblance arising from distinctively different sources. It can be noted that these different sources yield only two major kinds of similarity: HOMOLOGY and HOMOPLASY.

These two terms are used to differentiate similarities which exist between two taxa because they have been inherited from a common ancestor, i.e. are homologous, or are not inherited from a common ancestor, hence are homoplastic. Homoplasy is a larger and more diverse category of similarity than homology. It can be the result of several distinct mechanisms which produce similarities which are not due to common inheritance. The major problem arises in distinguishing homology from convergence, the former of course indicates a closeness of descent, the latter does not, but may result in the achievement of a remarkably similar structure. It may be necessary in some cases to resort to a very careful embryological studies to make a distinction. An outstanding example of this is the convergence in the structure of the auditory bulla of primates and of tree shrews. It was only through the careful examination of the embryology of the auditory regions of both groups that it became clear that the bulla of the tree shrews is not produced as an outgrowth of the petrosal plate as it is in all primates (Macphee 1981). Thus there was sufficient justification after more than 50 years of controversy to remove the tree shrews from the Order Primates and install them as a separate Order within the Superorder Archonta.

Evidence Related to Similarity Evaluation?

The evidence utilized for similarity testing has been, until recently, primarily anatomical and morphological. But it has often been derived from a limited set of areas in the organism's structure. Since it is populations of organisms that are classified, then optimally, the entire structure and range of variations of the organisms should be used or at least considered for use as evidence. Unfortunately, this ideal is not normally possible, even for such a thoroughly studied species as the modern representatives of *Homo sapiens*. In the last two decades, these morphological forms of data have been joined by genetic, chromosomal, and molecular data, which has in many instances shown that some populations represent distinct species in spite of structural similarity, while others display apparent genetic identity with substantial structural variation.

It is one of Simpson's operant axioms that the variety of data should be pushed as far as possible towards the limits of practicability. The object of classification in Simpson's ideal should be the population of "Holomorphs", composed of all of the characteristics of the individual members of the population throughout their lifespans. The data derived from embryology is a significant portion of these holomorphs. The old saw "ontogeny recapitulates phylogeny" is often quoted and just as frequently misused in this regard. The more appropriate perspective is that the "ontogeny of embryos recapitulates the phylogeny of embryonic structures" and according to Gould (1977) these may be subjected to substantial changes in rate of development (see the discussion of Paedomorphosis in the Evolution Section). The suite of data derived from physiology, biochemistry, molecular genetics, and serology, plays important roles in this holomorph.

Other sources of data now considered to be useful include the ecological approach. In the examination of the relationship of organisms to their environments, it has been found that this type of data is most useful in lower taxa but can be useful in higher taxa as well. This type of data can also bear importantly on convergence problems. A good example of such utility is the matter of host and parasite specificity, where a close relationship can be indicated by the inability of a particular parasite to survive in any alternate host. Simpson feels that experimental breeding data is useful for distinguishing reproductive boundaries and establishing the form of RIMs, but it is not always practical to make use of it. Behavioural data can also be used, especially if elemental forms of behaviours such as "fixed action pattern" units can be utilized, and thus the basic concepts and methods of ethology can prove useful in classification. Konrad Lorenz (1903–1989) was able to produce an evolutionary sequencing of the fixed action units in the courtship behaviour of puddle ducks which also provided a classification perfectly coincident with that derived from morphological analyses (Eibbl-Eibbesfeldt, 1975).

Homology

Homology is straightforwardly a matter of resemblance due to inheritance from a common ancestry. It is important to note that homology is not always readily distinguishable from homoplasy. The problem lies in the fact that data on the time dimension may be lacking in many cases and very difficult to obtain in most others. Palaeontology suffers this fate to an extreme, and as a result most data used in classification of living organisms are derived from neontology, with relatively little input from palaeontology.

Homoplasy

The list of recognized homoplasies includes the patterns of Parallelism, Convergence, Analogy, Mimicry, and Chance. Homoplasy is resemblance which is NOT due to any relevant common ancestry.

Parallelism Parallelism is the development of similar characteristics separately in two or more lineages which do have a relatively recent common ancestry. The similarity is developed on the base of, or channeled by, characteristics of that ancestry. In other terms, the similarity itself is not inherited, but derived or evolved characteristics which are based on a common inheritance independently achieve a similar appearance. Thus the hooves of horses and cattle can be viewed as parallelisms, both inherited toenails from a common ancestor, and both proceeded to evolve hooves from them.

Convergence Convergence is the development of similar characters separately in two or more lines without common ancestry pertinent to the similarity but involving adaptation to similar ecological status. Thus the similarity is a truly independent development which results in similar form as a result of functional necessities. The overall similarity of body configuration between Mesozoic Ichthyosauria and modern Cetacea is an example of convergence due to adaptation for rapid locomotion in the fluid environment of the ocean.

Analogy Analogy is functional similarity without a common ancestry. (Convergence characters are analogous as far as similarity is related to function—this is the most common situation.) And consequently the Ichthyosauran-Cetacean example is both convergent and analogous.

Mimicry Mimicry is similarity which is adaptive as such and hence is not related to common descent in any fashion. Simpson (1961) notes: "It occurs when one group of organisms resembles another of different descent within the same community and when the resemblance is adaptively advantageous to the mimicking organism for any of several reasons. . . . The mimicking organism is the mimic and that mimicked is its model." Into this fall the multitude of crypticly coloured, patterned, or shaped insects, reptiles, etc., which mimic vegetation, flowers, leaves, thorns, or other organisms etc. Mimicry is primarily recorded in organisms which either make use of cryptic colours or patterns to avoid detection, or which copy the "advertising" of toxic or venomous forms.

Chance Chance similarity is resemblance in characteristics by independent causes and without causal relationships or common ancestry involving the similarity. In short, it really is just accidental resemblance, often of the form which in a rock formation presents a pictorial resemblance to a human head.

References Cited:

Conroy, G. C.
1990 Primate Evolution. W. W. Norton, New York.

Eibbl-Eibbesfeldt, I.
1975 Ethology. Holt, Rinehart, Winston. New York.

Gould, S. J.
1977 Ontogeny and Phylogeny. Belknap Press, Harvard University Press.

Groves, C. P.
1989 A Theory of Human and Primate Evolution. Oxford University Press.

Hershkovitz, P.
1977 New World Monkeys (Playtrrhini), Vol. 1. University of Chicago Press.

1983 Two new species of Night Monkeys, genus Aotus: a preliminary report on Aotus taxonomy. American Journal of Primatology, 4:209–243.

1987 The taxonomy of South American sakis, genus Pithecia (Cebidae, Platyrrhini): A preliminary report and critical review with the description of a new species and a new subspecies. Amer. Jour. of Primatology 12:387–468.

Linnaeus, C.
1758 De Systema Naturae. Upsala.

Macphee, R. D.
1981 Auditory regions of primates and Eutherian insectivores. Contributions to Primatology. Vol 18. Karger, Basel.

Mayr, E.

1969 Principles of Systematic Zoology. McGraw Hill, New York.

McKenna, M. C.

1975 Toward a phylogenetic classification of the Mammalia. In Luckett, W. P., and Szalay, F. S. (eds) Phylogeny of the Primates, a multidisciplinary approach. Plenum, New York p. 21–46.

Patterson, C., and Rosen, D. E.

1977 Review of ichthyodectiform and other Mesozoic teleost fishes and the theory and practice of classifying fossils. Bull. Amer. Mus. Nat. Hist. 158: 81–172.

Raup, D. M., and Stanley, S. M.

1971 Principles of Palaeontology. W. H. Freeman, San Francisco.

Simpson, G. G.

1961 Principles of Animal Taxonomy Columbia University Press. New York.

Simpson, G. G.

1945 The principles of classification and a classification of mammals. Bull. Amer. Mus. Nat. Hist. 85.

A Classification of Primate Locomotor Behaviour

J. R. Napier

Smithsonian Institution

It might appear from the classification of locomotor patterns (Table 5–1) that primates fall into a number of discrete behavioural categories such as Vertical Clinging. Brachiation and so on, and that field or captivity observations of a particular species would serve to pinpoint their precise category. This is far from the truth. Locomotor differences between groups of primates are quantitative rather than qualitative. The differences lie principally in the degree to which the forelimbs and the hindlimbs are used to jump, swing, climb or run, and the frequency with which each type of behaviour is employed by a particular species in different ecological situations within a single biome.

Any classification within a relatively homogeneous group showing continuous variation, inevitably leads to an over-simplification as a result of the need to compromise. Classifications however are necessary to provide a perspective, a basis for discussion and a framework on which further investigations can be built.

BIOMECHANICAL CLASSIFICATIONS

Primates are a fairly uniform group in respect of the anatomy of the limb skeleton, particularly of the hindlimb. The similarity of hindlimb structure is apparent both osteologically and osteometrically. A series of femora from a wide variety of species show, apart from allometric considerations, a remarkable similarity of form. Measurements of lower limb proportions (the Crural Index for example) show very little variation between taxa or between functional locomotor groups and are therefore of extremely limited value as diagnostic indices. The hindlimbs of primates are primarily supporting structures and their anatomy is in accordance with biomechanical requirements for resisting the compression forces exerted by the ground during walking and running. All primates walk, and therefore they all possess the same basic structural characters. Variation in these characters will depend on how often and under what circumstances they use their hindlimbs for walking and how often for other purposes. For example

Table 5–1. Locomotor Categories

Category	Subtype	Activity	Primate Genera
1. Vertical clinging and leaping		Leaping in trees and hopping on the ground.	Avahi, Galago, Hapalemur, Lepilemur, Propithecus, Tarsius, Indri.
2. Quadrupedalism	(i) Slow climbing type	Cautious climbing—no leaping or branch running.	Arctocebus, Loris, Nyctice-bus, Perodicticus.
	(ii) Branch running and walking type	Climbing, springing, branch running and jumping.	Aotus, Cacajao, Callicebus, Callimico, Callithrix, Ce-buella, Cebus, Cercopithecus, Cheirogaleus, Chiropotes, Lemur, Leontideus, Phaner, Pithecia, Saguinus, Saimiri, Tupaia.
	(iii) Ground running and walking type.	Climbing, ground running.	Macaca, Mandrillus, Papio, Theropithecus Erythrocebus.
	(iv) New World semibrachiation type	Arm-swinging with use of prehensile tail; little leaping.	Alouatta, Ateles, Brachyteles. Lagothrix
	(v) Old World semibrachiation type	Arm-swinging and leaping	Colobus, Nasalis, Presbytis, Pygathrix, Rhinopithecus, Simias.
3. Brachiation	(i) True brachiation	Gibbon type of brachiation	Hylobates, Symphalangus, Gorilla, Pan, Pongo
	(ii) Modified brachiation	Chimpanzee and orang-utan type of brachiation	
4. Bipedalism		Human type of walking (Heel-toe striding)	Homo

the hindlimbs of chimpanzees and orangs are adapted for suspension, having a notably free range of movement, particularly at the hip, ankle, mid-tarsal and toe joints. These special prehensile adaptations of the feet permit them to scramble and climb among the slender branches of trees supporting the body weight at very bizarre angles. Chimpanzees and orangs very often use their hindlimbs alone to suspend the body. On the ground however chimpanzees walk quadrupedally and even bipedally, their legs in this situation supporting the body from below. Other primates such as the quadrupedal howlers, spider monkeys and woolly monkeys of South America, also occasionally use their hindlimbs for suspension; so also do galagos and pottos. In fact, it would be true to say that the majority of primates can, and sometimes do, suspend themselves by their feet. Since all primates support themselves on the hindlimbs and many suspend themselves in this manner, a classification of locomotion simply in terms of the supporting and suspending functions of the hindlimbs is unlikely to be very satisfactory.

The situation with regard to the forelimbs is very similar. The limbs are used for both support and suspension, and are therefore subject to both compression and tensile forces. All primates, except the gibbons and man, walk quadrupedally using their forelimbs as props. Equally all primates, with again few exceptions, use the arms to suspend the body from above. The most striking examples of arm-swinging primates are of the gibbons and the siamangs; in certain ecological situations these primates use arm-suspension exclusively. The New World spider and woolly monkeys and some of the African and Asian Colobinae frequently employ arm suspension as a means of locomotion. Other primates such as the guenons and the macaques only occasionally use this method of locomotion. Arm-suspension in the primates therefore, comprises a *spectrum* of activity from the habitual to the occasional and can not be used very meaningfully, as it stands, as a means of classifying locomotion. However it is possible, using the same criteria of suspension and support, to grade the *degree* of these activities as demonstrated by different groups of primates; this involves an arbitrary segmentation of a continuous spectrum of activity as shown in Table 5–2. Such a method can help to differentiate limb function in certain groups but it contributes little to classification or primate locomotion as a whole.

Table 5–2. Analysis of Limb Function in Anthropoidea

	Forelimb		Hindlimb	
	Suspension	Support	Suspension	Support
Brachiators	+++	+(+)	++	+++
Semibrachiators New World	++	++	+	+++
Semibrachiators Old World	+(+)	+++	−	+++
Quadrupeds	(+)	+++	−	+++

Analysis of limb function in Anthropoidea. The plus signs indicate the relative extent to which the limbs are used for suspension and support.

A much more meaningful method of quantification of supporting and suspensory activities has been developed by Ashton and Oxnard (1963, 1964a, 1965, and Oxnard, 1963). They have undertaken extensive studies into the stress patterns of primate forelimbs in terms of both muscular and osteological form and proportions, and have subjected their results to appropriate statistical techniques. Theirs is essentially a metrical method and the results provide a quantitative assessment of the whereabouts in the spectrum of forelimb use (from suspension to support) of any particular species, living or fossil.

BEHAVIOURAL CLASSIFICATION

A classification by means of total locomotor pattern (Table 5–1) involves the consideration of both fore- and hindlimbs together; it is in fact concerned with locomotor behaviour of living animals rather than simply with their biomechanical adaptations. In adopting this method of classification, the basic problem—the segmentation of a continuous phenomenon into discrete categories—is by no means solved, but the available categories are wider; such factors as speed of movement, use of tail, body and limb postures and ecological situation can be woven into classification. The principal categories (Table 5–1) can be defined as follows:

1. Vertical clinging and leaping: A type of arboreal locomotor behaviour in which the body is held vertically at rest and pressed to the trunk or main branch of a tree; movement from place to place is effected by a leap or jump from one vertical support to another. The forelimbs take no part in propelling the body during leaping. Vertical clinging and leaping primates usually hop bipedally when moving rapidly on the ground, but assume a quadrupedal gait when moving slowly.

2. Quadrupedalism: A type of locomotion which can take place on the ground or in the trees; its principal component is four-legged walking or running. In an arboreal situation the hands and feet may be used, in a prehensile fashion, to provide stability. The movements of springing, jumping and leaping are associated with this mode of locomotion. Quadrupedalism also involves the vertical movement of climbing, using all four extremities. Movement may be rapid as in galloping on the ground or it may be cautious and slow. Quadrupedal primates in certain situations show a variable amount of arm-swinging with or without the additional use of a prehensile tail.

Subtypes of Quadrupedalism Category
i. *Slow climbing.* A type of quadrupedal locomotion in which either three or four of the extremities are applied to the branch at any given moment.

Movement is always slow and cautious. The limbs may act to suspend the body or to support it.

ii. *Branch running and walking.* Generalised quadrupedal locomotion in which running or walking in trees usually involves prehensile grasp with forelimbs or hindlimbs or both. The hand is usually plantigrade. Climbing, jumping or leaping in a dog-like fashion is also seen.

iii. *Ground running and walking.* Running and walking. Generalised quadrupedal locomotion in which running or walking on the ground does not usually involve prehensile grasp of limbs. The hands usually digitigrade in posture. Branch walking, frequently with a digitigrade hand posture, is seen, and also climbing and dog-like leaping.

iv. *New World semibrachiation.* A type of arboreal locomotion in which the forelimbs are used extended above the head to suspend the body or to propel it through space. The forelimbs may be used alone or in association with the hindlimbs and the prehensile tail. Quadrupedal walking and running constitute a major part of the habit. Leaping is uncommon.

v. *Old World semibrachiation.* Differing from the New World type mainly in the extent to which leaping is employed. During leaping the arms reach out ahead of the body to grasp a handhold or to check momentum. Hand over hand progression is seldom seen.

3. Brachiation. A form of locomotion in which the typical component is arm-swinging by which means the body suspended from above, is propelled through space. The hindlimbs are used to support the body in trees or on the ground either in the erect or in the quadrupedal position. In some brachiating primates the hindlimbs may be used to suspend the body.

Subtypes of Brachiation Category

i. *True Brachiation.* A form of arboreal locomotion in which the forelimbs alone are used fully extended above the head to suspend or to propel the body through space by means of hand over hand progress. Arm-swinging may be used to provide momentum to cross considerably wide gaps between forest trees. Bipedal walking on branches and bipedal walking on ground constitute part of the total pattern.

ii. *Modified Brachiation.* A form of arboreal locomotion in which the forelimbs extended above the head play a major role in suspending the body or propelling it through space. The hindlimbs contribute to the pattern to a greater lesser extent, being used to provide partial support for the body from below. Hindlimbs may also be used to suspend the body from above. On the ground quadrupedal walking, the weight of the forebody being taken on the knuckles or bunched fists, is commonly seen; bipedalism is also seen.

4. Bipedalism. A form of locomotion in which the body is habitually supported on the hindlimbs which move alternately to propel it through space. The quintessence of the movement is a striding, heel-toe gait. The forelimbs are only occasionally used to suspend the body. Quadrupedalism in bipedal primates is seldom employed except in infancy.

All four locomotor categories are serially linked by some facet of locomotor pattern common to each successive pair. Vertical clingers when moving slowly on the ground are quadrupedal. Quadrupeds may suspend themselves by the arms alone, in the manner of brachiating primates. Brachiating primates when on the ground and in the trees adopt bipedalism for short distances. Thus, the sequence Vertical Clinging-Quadrupedalism-Brachiation-Bipedalism forms a continuum of locomotor activity which only arbitrarily can be segmented into discrete categories. In terms of living primates a number of transitional forms are found which it is difficult to assign to a particular group. *Lemur catta* for instance is generally regarded as quadrupedal but field and captivity studies (Napier and Walker, 1967*a* and 1967*b*) indicate that a considerable element of vertical clinging and leaping behaviour figures in its repertoire. Spider and woolly monkeys though quadrupedal frequently swing by their arms for considerable distances as Erikson (1963) has pointed out. Ashton *et al.* (1965) have shown that, in the morphological characters of the shoulder girdle, *Ateles* occupies an equivocal New World position intermediate between Brachiation and Semibrachiation. Among the brachiating primates, the gibbons adopt a bipedal gait when on the ground. There are many other examples of primates which are intermediate in their locomotor patterns between one category and another. The significance of this state of affairs however is more easily understood if the sequence Vertical Clinging to Brachiation noted above is looked upon as a phylogenetic succession.

One would need to suppose that Vertical Clinging constituted the principal locomotor pattern of the Eocene primate stock from which the lemurs, monkeys and apes evolved. A somewhat generalised vertical clinger having the characteristic short arms and long legs but possibly lacking the extreme specialisation of *Tarsius* then evolved into a quadrupedal form simply by a relative increase in the length of the forelimb and a relative decrease in the length of the hindlimb. These changes would give rise to an animal something like the modern genus *Lemur* whose forelimbs are still rather short and hindlimbs rather long relative to trunk length. Further adaptive change in relative limb length would produce a more generalised quadrupedal morphology such as is seen in the Asian langurs and the African *Colobus* monkeys. These Old World monkeys are termed semibrachiators, a subtype of the Quadrupedalism category; their locomotion involves a major element of leaping and a minor element of arm-swinging. As has been suggested elsewhere (Napier and Davis, 1959; Napier, 1963), modern semibrachiators may represent a stage in primate locomotor phylogeny when brachiation in its fullest expression was evolving. In the palaentological record it has been suggested (Napier and Davis, 1959) that *Proconsul africanus* was the representative of this stage.

The derivation of bipedalism is somewhat equivocal. There appear to be two possibilities. Firstly that bipedalism evolved from quadrupedalism: and secondly that it evolved out of an early stage of brachiation. Most authorities now agree that human bipedal gait could not have been derived from fully evolved brachiation as Keith (1923) and many others at one time believed. The two alternatives noted above are not really alternatives at all. As has been already mentioned, quadrupedalism and brachiation are not wholly discrete categories. The quadrupedalism sub-type—semibrachiation—contains elements of both categories. Washburn (1950) stated "Spider monkeys brachiate [sic] . . . They also move in a quadrupedal fashion. . . . The combination of brachiation and quadrupedal locomotion . . . shows how the ape-type of locomotion may have arisen . . ." Straus (1949) stated that man's catarrhine ancestors "probably indulged in some swinging by the arms and in that sense might be regarded as primitive brachiators."

Whether in fact bipedalism evolved out of specialized quadrupedalism or unspecialised brachiation is entirely unimportant inasmuch as these two locomotor categories constitute a continuum of morphological and behavioural variation.

Locomotion among living primates must be viewed in the light of phylogeny in order to understand the significance of its continuous nature. Bridging forms that do not comfortably sit in one category or another are the modern descendants of ancestral primates whose locomotor evolution came to a halt at a point best suited to their ecological needs; it is not surprising that this halt should often lie *between* major categories.

Field studies of primates in their natural habitats very often reveal the variety of their locomotor habits. Langurs for instance are known to run, walk, leap, jump, hop and even swing by their arms (Ripley 1967). Baboons run, walk, jump and climb. Chimpanzees run and walk bipedally, climb, hop and brachiate. In the face of such a plethora of activities, all of which are adaptive for their particular way of life, it is difficult purely on behavioural grounds to place them in a single, meaningful category. It is important to assess their behaviour as far as it is possible in the light of their past evolution, a procedure which naturally involves a consideration of such morphology. The question that needs to be asked is what element within the broad range of the locomotor potentialities of any one species has been of major significance in their past history as reflected in the palaeontology of the group and in the present morphology of the species? In other words, on what particular aspect of their locomotion has natural selection operated?

While locomotor categories are expressed here in behavioural terms, their basis is essentially morphological. In order to recognize the brachiating affinities of the gorilla amid its secondary specialisations for ground life, for instance, recourse to morphology must be made as there is little in its behaviour which would support such a classification.

REFERENCES

Ashton, E. H., and C. E. Oxnard, 1963. The musculature of the primate shoulder. *Trans. zool. Soc. Lond.* **29**:553–650.

_____, and _____, 1964*a.* Functional adaptations in the primate shoulder. *Proc. zool. Soc. Lond.* **142**:49–66.

_____, and _____, 1964*b* Locomotor patterns in primates. *Proc. zool. Soc. Lond.* **142**:1–28.

Erikson, G. E., 1963, Brachiation in New World monkeys and in anthropoid apes. *Symp. zool. Soc. Lond.* **10**:135–164.

Hill, W. C. Osman, 1956, Behaviour and adaptations of the Primates. *Proc. R. Soc. Edinb.* B **66**:94–110.

Napier, J. R., 1963, Brachiation and orachiators. *Symp. zool. Soc. Lond.* **10**:183–195.

_____, and P. R. Davis, 1959, The fore-limb skeleton and associated remains of *Proconsul africanus.* London, *British Museum (Natural History) Fossil Mammals of Africa, No. 16.*

_____, and A. C. Walker, 1967*a.* Vertical clinging and leaping, a newly recognised category of locomotor behaviour among primates. *Folia Primat.* **6**:180–203.

_____, and _____, 1967*b,* Vertical clinging and leaping in living and fossil primates. In *Progress in Primatology.* Ed. D. Starck, R. Schneider, H. J. Kuhn. (Gustav Fischer Verlag, Stuttgart).

Oxnard, C. E., 1963, Locomotor adaptations in the primate fore-limb. *Symp. zool. Soc. Lond.* **10**:165–182.

Priemel, G., 1937, Die platyrrhinen Affen als Bewegungstypen unter besonderer Berücksichtigung de Extremformem *Callicebus* und *Ateles. Z. Morph. Ökol. Tiere.* **33**:1–52.

Reynolds, Vernon, and Frances Reynolds, 1965, Chimpanzees of the Budongo Forest. In *Primate Behaviour,* Ed. I. De Vore. (Holt, Rinehart and Winston, Inc., New York).

Ripley, S., 1967, The leaping of langurs. *Am. J. Phys. Anthrop.* **26**:149–170.

Straus, W. L., 1949, Riddle of man's ancestry. *Q. Rev. Biol.* **24**:200–223.

Washburn, S. L., 1950, Thoracic viscera of the gorilla. In *Anatomy of the Gorilla.* Ed. W. K. Gregory. (Columbia University Press, New York).

Are Flying-Foxes (Chiroptera: Pteropodidae) Really Primates?

J. D. Pettigrew
B. G. M. Jamieson
University of Queensland

Recent studies on the brains of bats have placed a spotlight on the evolution of these fascinating flying mammals (Pettigrew 1986, Martin 1986, Pettigrew and Cooper 1986). These studies have led to some startling conclusions which many bat scholars are reluctant to accept, as yet, but which have so far withstood vigorous debate. We are now convinced, as a result of this work, that mammals evolved flapping, powered flight on TWO separate occasions, not ONE, as is most commonly believed.

The first occasion was most likely in the Cretaceous era (evidence for the timing is only circumstantial at present), when a very small insectivore somehow successfully converted to full-flight from acrobatic leaps and somersaults in pursuit of flying insects. The legacy of that event is the highly successful group we know as the microchiropteran bats or microbats.

The second occasion was much later, during the Tertiary era, when one of the early primates improved its foraging in search of fruits by becoming a glider. The descendents of these primate gliders are living today, either as gliders (the two species of colugo or gliding lemurs in the genus *Cynocephalus*), or as the much-more-successful megachiropterans, or megabats (over 200 living species).

We shall now attempt to back up these bold, opening assertions. We shall proceed more or less historically, following the same path that we followed to reach these conclusions. The crucial landmarks along that path were the following findings: (1) megachiropterans have primate visual pathways, (2) microchiropterans have more primitive, non-primate visual pathways, (3) the only set of features which can be used to link mega- and microchiropterans is associated with the hand-wing, (4) the hand-wings of mega- and microchiropterans have evolved in opposite directions and cannot be used as a basis to argue that these two groups of flying mammals have a common origin, (5) megachiropterans have primate motor pathways, (6) biochemical studies on the haemoglobin sequences of bats reveal different patterns in micro- and megachiropterans, with the latter group closer to the primate pattern.

Reprinted from "Are Flying Foxes Really Primates?" by J. D. Pettigrew and B. G. M. Jamieson, *Australian Mammalogy* 10: 111–124 (1987).

VISUAL PATHWAYS

There are a half-dozen features in the primate visual pathway which are not found in any other of the many mammalian orders which have now been studied. These features are quantitative and reliably distinguish primates from non-primates. Even the tree-shrews, which were thought for a long time to be primates and are often billed as such in textbooks (Le Gros Clark 1959), are clearly excluded from the Order by their failure to show any of these features.

No one is sure what any of these primate visual brain features means for behaviour at the moment, although they are probably related to the primates' increased reliance on binocular vision. The feature which is best characterised is in the pathway from the eye to the midbrain. This pathway is drastically reduced in primates for which another visual pathway, the enormously enlarged geniculostriate system, is a much more important source of visual information. As well as being reduced in primates, this eye-midbrain pathway represents only a fraction of one retina instead of the complete retina which is represented in the midbrain of non-primates. The functional significance of this particular arrangement of the pathway in primates is quite obscure because it has become so reduced in primates as to be atrophic. (Indeed, until recently there was some doubt whether primates had this pathway at all.) Nevertheless these features in the visual system provided a unique signature enabling us to recognise a primate brain after a set of tests which involve labelling the pathways going from eye to brain (Allman 1977, Cooper and Pettigrew 1986, Pettigrew and Cooper 1986).

Imagine our surprise when we found these features in the brain of the flying-fox, *Pteropus poliocephalus*, during the course of routine investigation! Later work has confirmed that this is true for a number of species of megachiropterans in a variety of genera covering much of the range of variation in this group (*e.g. Rousettus, Pteropus, Syconycteris*). Recently, working with Dr. Howard Cooper of the INSERM Laboratorie de Neuropsychologie in Lyon, we have extended the comparison to include more visual nuclei, more species of megachiropteran and more prosimian primates. Under the microscope, the affinities between a megachiropteran brain and a lemur brain are so striking that it is quite difficult to tell them apart! In other words, so far as one can tell from intricate details of the wiring of thousands of nerve cells, primate and megachiropterans shared a common ancestor not shared by any other group of mammals.

The next priority was to test some microchiropterans. Bats had been placed in the Order Primates by Linnaeus (1767) in his original classification scheme, because of the pendulous penis and armpit location of the breasts, so we were interested to know whether microchiropterans would be primate-like in their visual pathway too. The answer was clearly negative. Microchiropterans have visual pathways like non-primates and have none of the features we found to be shared by megachiropterans and primates (Pettigrew 1986). The great technical difficulties of performing the necessary retinal whole mounts from the small eyes of microchiropterans have slowed down our survey somewhat, but the following species from three different families all show the primitive, non-primate, pattern of visual connections: *Macroderma gigas* (Megadermatidae), *Taphozous georgianus* (Emballonuridae) and *Nyctophilus gouldi* (Vespertilionidae).

These findings came as a shock, since they ran directly counter to prevailing opinion about bat taxonomy. Which data were to be trusted? Our new data linking primates and megachiropterans to the exclusion of the microchiropterans? Or the extensive data sets of the taxonomists linking the two bat groups? The resolution of this dilemma requires a little excursion into bat taxonomy and evolution.

SHARED CHARACTERS?

After extensive reading of the taxonomic literature on bats, we found little basis for the union of micro- and megachiropterans into a single order. Every detailed investigation we could find showed clear, often dramatic, differences between these groups. The list of differences between them is too long to detail here (see Pettigrew *et al.* 1987) but includes such things as diet, dentition, chromosomes, world geographic distribution, sperm, biochemistry, parasitology and numerous features of behaviour.

The only strong link between the two groups of flying mammals was the presence in both of a forelimb modification where four of the five digits have elongated to support a flight membrane. The dilemma then became focussed into the following question: which is more likely? That two groups of mammals independently 'discovered' how to modify their forelimbs into a handwing? Or that the megachiropterans, independently of primates, 'discovered' the exact details of wiring in each of five baroque sets of nerve tracts involving tens of thousands of nerve cells?

Our own biases about the unlikely nature of the second possibility are evident in both the phraseology and preamble. The case against it would be stronger if one could find some evidence for the first possibility that mammalian wings had evolved twice. Such evidence exists.

One can make a case that the hand-wings of the two groups have evolved separately. The problem most people have with this idea stems from the great similarity of the hand-wings in the two groups of bats. The hand-wing of both bat groups are so similar to each other, and so different from the 'ring-finger wing' of a pterosaur or the 'wrist-wing' of a bird (Padian 1983), that it is hard to see how the two hand-wings could have originated independently. The key insight here is the fact that the different wing designs of pterosaurs and birds were made possible only because each of these groups had unique structural elements to maintain the aerofoil of the wing membrane against the deforming forces of flapping flight. Birds have feathers (Rayner 1981) and pterosaurs had actinofibrillae (Welnhofer 1975)—these two kinds of structural elements acting to stiffen the wing membrane and to prevent loss of the necessary aerodynamic profile during flapping. Failing the invention of a new kind of stiffening member such as a feather or an actinofibrilla to stabilise the wing shape, flying mammals may have used the easiest structural elements which came to hand (so to speak)—the boney metacarpals and phalanges of the digits. If this is the case, one should look closely at the details of these bones of the digits rather than placing too much emphasis on the fact that all digits are incorporated into the membrane of both kinds of bat wing instead of single digits like the avian and pterosaurian arrangements.

Quantitative analyses can be used to show that the wings of mega- and microchiropterans are probably quite separate evolutionary 'inventions', despite their apparent similarity. These analyses, involving measurements of wings in over 500 species, enable one to separate the wings of all megachiropterans from the wings of all microchropterans on the basis of the relative sizes of the metacarpals and the first phalanx of the third and fourth digits (Pettigrew *et al.* 1987). These analyses suggest that the microbat wing evolved from an antecedent which was small (around 40 mm forearm length or shorter) and had very long metacarpals in relation to the proximal phalanges. In contrast, the megachiropteran wing evolved from an antecedent which was moderately large (around 100 mm forearm length) and had metacarpals more closely similar in length to the proximal phalanges, as in the living primates and gliding lemurs.

PRIMATE FEATURES OF MEGACHIROPTERANS

Prompted by a letter from Randolph Nudo, whose Ph.D. thesis defined a further set of criteria for distinguishing primates from all other mammals (Nudo 1985, Nudo and Masterton 1986), we began an investigation of the cortico-spinal motor pathways of bats. This work is being undertaken in our laboratory by Warren Kennedy (Kennedy 1986). We find that megachiropterans have a third cortico-spinal motor area (Area C) like primates, but unlike all other mammalian orders which have been studied (including microbats, tree-shrews, lagomorphs, elephant shrews, rodents, carnivores, ungulates, edentates and insectivores). The precise similarity between the details of motor pathway organisation in megachiropterans and primates are difficult to explain unless these two groups shared a common ancestor.

Taken together with the visual pathway similarities, these motor traits can be used to construct a phylogenetic tree according to the principles of Hennig (1963). Such a tree is shown in Fig. 1 where it can be seen that the flying-foxes (*Rousettus* and *Pteropus* spp.) group with primates and the dermopteran colugo or gliding lemur, *Cynocephalus*, while the microchiropteran, *Macroderma gigas* (which is the only one for which all the relevant investigations have so far been carried out) is well separated, branching off before all the other mammalian groups except the primitive pangolin.

Much biochemical work is in progress at present, stimulated to some degree by our radical suggestion of two separate origins for flying mammals. Some sequences have been published from bat haemoglobins, however, which tend to confirm the thesis that flying-foxes are closer to primates than to any other living group of mammals. For example, a full amino acid sequence is available for both chains of the haemoglobin molecule of *Rousettus aegyptiacus*, an African megachiropteran (Kleinschmidt and Braunitzer 1982). According to these molecular data, flying-foxes are much closer to higher primates than the treeshrews (Kleinschmidt, Czelusniak, Goodman and Braunitzer 1986) which are still thought by many to be primates. Microchiropteran haemoglobin, on the other hand, seems to be very distinct from that of all other mammals (Kleinschmidt, Koop and Braunitzer 1986), suggesting that this group had an ancient origin and that they may not have any close living relatives.

More molecular sequences will be necessary before a clear phylogeny emerges because of the enormous diversity amongst living microchiropterans, whose families may show more biochemical differences when compared with each other than any one family does when compared with other mammalian families (*e.g.* Cronin and Sarich 1960). For the present it can be said that there is support on molecular grounds for both of our radical suggestions—that mammalian flight evolved twice and that an early branch of the primates gave rise to the flying-foxes.

ORIGINS OF FLYING-FOXES

One of the predictions of the scenario for the evolution of megachiropterans which we have sketched in the introduction is that the gliding lemurs will prove to be *bona fide* primates too, even though they are presently placed off in their own order, Dermoptera. Preliminary work on their brain (Pettigrew and Cooper 1986), in addition to morphological and serological studies already published (Cronin and Sarich 1960), amount to a fulfillment of this prediction. We have yet to carry out all of the visual tests and the motor pathway studies, but the eye-midbrain connections of one gliding lemur we studied were clearly primatelike (Pettigrew and Cooper 1986).

One of the implications of our work is a little difficult for many primatologists to accept, even those with experience of the endearing personalities of megachiropterans. This is the implication that this branch of the flying mammals can really be accepted as a *bona fide* member of the Order Primates. I would like to conclude by discussing this question in the light of our current understanding of what constitutes a primate.

According to Alison Jolly (1985), a distinguished modern primatologist, primates are difficult to define by a single feature, but can be recognised by two sets of traits, one morphological and the other behavioural. The morphological traits were first set out by Le Gros Clark (1959) and have been extended by modern neurobiological techniques. 'Conventional primates' (*i.e.* both haplorhine and strepsirhine primates) and megachiropterans share all of these morphological traits. By these same criteria, microchiropterans are like other, non-primate, mammals.

The behavioural traits listed by Jolly include the following:

1. free and precise movement of the hands and forelimbs
2. a shift from reliance on smell to reliance on vision
3. detailed spatial patterning of the world
4. prolonged care of dependent young allowing time for learning the resources of the environment and the manners of the tribe.

She (1985: 230) suggests that 'if there is an essence of being a primate, it is the progressive evolution of intelligence as a way of life', a feature which would apply to flying-foxes in the opinion of the many people we know who have worked closely with them over an extended period.

Another primatologist has recently laid down a set of criteria for 'primates of modern aspect' which are much harder for flying-foxes to meet (Martin 1986). Nevertheless, of Martin's 30-odd features demarcating primates from other living mammals, only a few are clearly absent from flying-foxes (*e.g.* flat nails on the digits rather than claws, a tri-radiate calcarine fissure and a well-developed divergent hallux). Others will need more work to be clarified, such as the auditory bulla which is unossified in flying-foxes and therefore not readily assigned in conventional skull material to a particular element such as the petrosal which characterises the bulla of primates. Over 20 of Martin's 30 features are clearly present in flying-foxes, not to mention all the new features we have defined in the brain.

From our point of view, recognition of the phylogenetic affinity between primates and flying-foxes is more important than the more semantic question of where one should draw the line between primates and the nearest non-primate sister group (Fig. 1). Perhaps the question of whether megachiropterans and dermopterans should be included in the Order Primates should be deferred until there is both more agreement about how old a branch must be before it signifies ordinal ranking and there are better estimates of the time of the major branch point leading to primates, megachiropterans and dermopterans (Fig. 1). In the meantime, further close examination of the more than 200 living species of 'flying primates' may help in our understanding of the other 183 primate species, whose complex brain organisation is one of the more important and difficult puzzles facing contemporary students of behaviour.

This work was supported by grants to J.D.P. and B.G.M.J. from the Australian Research Grants Scheme and the National Health and Medical Research Council. Rita Collins provided excellent technical assistance with Mike Calford helped with many experiments. Warren Kennedy kindly allowed us to refer to unpublished data.

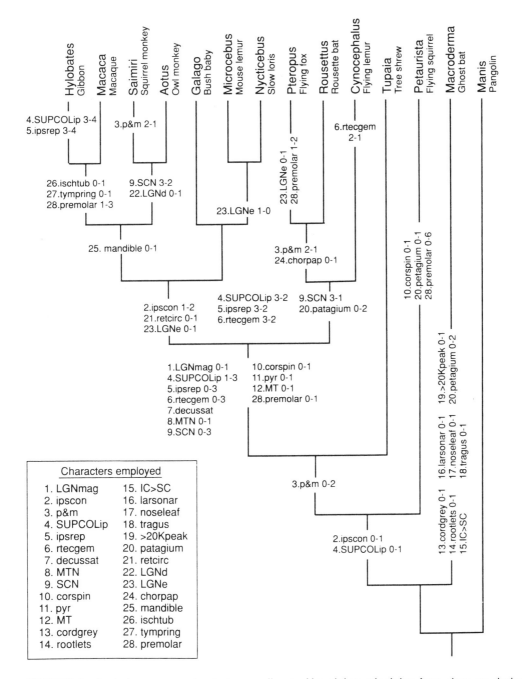

FIGURE 1. A cladogram constructed according to Hennigian principles from data on derived brain traits and morphological features of 14 mammal species. Note that there is a cluster of branches comprising primates (gibbon, macaque, squirrel monkey, owl monkey, bush baby, mouse lemur), megachiropterans (flying-fox, *Rousettus*) and the dermopteran, which is separated sharply from all other mammals by the acquisition of the derived characters 1, 4, 5, 6, 7, 8, 9, 10, 11 and 12 (which are all found in the visual and motor pathways and described in the text). The cladogram was chosen as one of the most parsimonious trees by using the PAUP program of David Swofford (1984). A branch and bound maximum parsimony consensus tree showed no change in the relative positions of the Mega-and Microchiroptera.

REFERENCES

Allman, J. M., 1977. Evolution of the visual system in the early primates. *Progr. Physiol. Psychol.* **7**:1–53.

Cooper, M. L. and Pettigrew, J. D., 1979. The decussation of the retinothalamic pathway in the cat. *J. Comp. Neurol.* **187**: 285–312.

Cronin, J. E. and Sarich, V. M., 1980. Tupaiid and archontan phylogeny: the macromolecular evidence. Pp. 293–312 *in* 'Comparative biology and evolutionary relationships of the tree-shrews.' by W. P. Luckett. Plenum Press: New York.

Hennig, W., 1966. 'Phylogenetic systematics'. University of Illinois Press: Urbana.

Jolly, A., 1985. The evolution of primate behaviour. *American Scientist* **73**: 230–239.

Kennedy, W. 'Comparative neuroanatomy of the spinal cord and corticospinal tract of microchiroptera and megachiroptera'. B.Sc. (Hons) Thesis: Department of Physiology and Pharmacology, University of Queensland, St. Lucia.

Kleinschmidt, T. and Braunitzer, G., 1982. Die primarstructure des haemoglobins vom agyptischen flughund (*Rousettus aegyptiacus*, Chiroptera). *Hoppe-Seyler's Biol. Chem.* **363**: 1209–1215.

Kleinschmidt, T., Czelusniak, J., Goodman, M., and Braunitzer, G., 1986. Paenungulata: a comparison of the haemoglobin sequences from elephant, hyrax and manatee. *Mol. Biol. Evol.* **3**(5): 427–435.

Kleinschmidt, T., Koop, B., and Braunitzer, G., 1986. The primary structure of a mouse-eared bat (*Myotis velifer*, Chiroptera) haemoglobin. *Hoppe-Seyler's Biol. Chem.* **367**: 1243–1250.

Le Gros Clark, W. E., 1959. 'The antecedents of Man'. (First Edition) Edinburgh University Press: Edinburgh.

Linnaeus, K., 1767. 'Systema natura,' 13th ed. J. T. Trattner: Vienna.

Martin, R. D., 1986. Are fruit bats primates? *Nature* **320**: 482–483.

Martin, R. D., 1986. Primates: a definition. Pp. 1–31 *in* 'Major topics in primate and human evolution' ed by B. Wood, L. Martin and P. Andrews. Cambridge University Press: Cambridge.

Nudo, R. J., 1985., 'A comparative study of cells originating in the cortico-spinal tract: comparative morphology in the anthropoid ancestral lineage.' Ph.D. Thesis: Florida State University, Tallahassee.

Nudo, R. J., and Masterton, R. B., 1986. Corticospinal tract: Qualitative and quantitative changes in the anthropoid ancestral lineage. *Soc. Neurosci. Abstr.* **12**: 262.

Padian, K., 1983. A functional analysis of flying and walking in pterosaurs. *Paleobiology* **9**(3): 218–239.

Pettigrew, J. D., 1986. Flying primates? Megabats have the advanced pathway from eye to midbrain. *Science* **231**: 1304–1306.

Pettigrew, J. D. and Cooper, H. M., 1986. Aerial primates: advanced visual pathways in megabats and gliding lemurs. *Soc. Neurosci. Abstr.* **12**: 1035.

Pettigrew, J. D., Robson, S. K., Hall, L. S. and McNally, K. I., 1987. A phylogenetic analysis of flying mammals. (submitted).

Rayner, J. M. V., 1981. Flight adaptations in vertebrates. Pp. 137–171 *in* 'Vertebrate locomotion' ed by M. H. Day, Academic Press: London.

Swofford, D. L., 1984. 'Phylogenetic analysis using parsimony'. Version 2.2 User's manual. D. L. Swofford, Illinois Natural History Survey: 607 East Peabody Drive, Champaign, Ill. 61820.

Welnhofer, P., 1975. Palaecology and phylogeny of *Ramphorhynchus* (in German). *Palaeontographica A band* **149**: 1–30.

Palaeontology and Primate Evolutionary History

James D. Paterson

The purpose of this section is to present an extremely brief overview of some of the data and major theoretical arguments associated with the evolutionary history of the primates. In the interests of such brevity, no effort has been made to provide a detailed or complete coverage of any of the fossil specimens upon which the validation of the theories are founded.

Dentition is the single most important source of data pertaining to the evolutionary history of any mammalian lineage, and thus a substantial portion of these notes are concerned with teeth and their evolution. This is not intended to exclude other body structures, but to emphasize that teeth constitute the overwhelming majority of all of the data sources in palaeontology. The second section of these notes provides brief coverage of major evolutionary events and developmental patterns within the major primate lineages.

BASIC EVIDENCES IN PRIMATE FOSSIL PHYLOGENY

The basic evidences for the phylogeny of the primates must obviously come from two sources—neontology and palaeontology. The neontological data about the relationships of modern primates is based upon both comparative anatomy, the examination of structure within them and on their embryology. These sources provide the soft tissue indications of relatedness, however they cannot directly substantiate evolutionary relationships. Palaeontology, the study of the fossilized remains of members of the order, provides the direct evidences. It is from primarily two regions of the skull that diagnostic evidence of primate association and evolution are derived for the earliest forms. The first and most consistently useful evidence is based on the dentition, the second is related to the morphology of the basicranium. The bony structure of the base to the skull, along with the associated circulatory system inferences derived from the neontology of living mammals is one of the most important aspects in determining primate status for the earliest forms.

BASIC DENTAL MORPHOLOGY AND EMBRYOLOGY

Morphology

Teeth are the hardest structures in any primate body, hence are the most likely components to survive a long period of interment, and provide a wealth of data relating to the genetic structure, diet, and adaptation, as well as the ecological niche or role of the animal bearing those teeth.

Teeth are composed of four major components—Enamel, dentine, cementum, and the pulp cavity (see Figure 1). Enamel is the most resistant to decomposition, and if soil conditions are appropriate can persist for many millions of years.

Enamel is ectodermal in embryological origin, and is the most highly calcified material in the teeth. It is variable in thickness according to the species, and the location on the tooth structure itself. Enamel is thickest over incisive edges

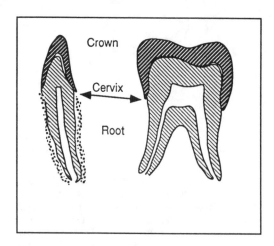

Figure 1: Tooth Construction:—enamel, dentine, pulp cavity, and cementum.

and the cusps of teeth, and thinnest at the cervical margin of the tooth. Likewise the density and hardness of the enamel varies. The density increases from the external surface towards the dentine, and from the incisive edge or cusp towards the cervical margin. Hardness is greatest at the surface, decreases slightly and remains constant until it nears the dentine, where it falls rapidly. Enamel as a material is 96 to 97% inorganic, 0.4 to 0.8% organic matter, and the remainder is water. The actual structure of enamel is composed of rods or prisms cemented together by the interprismatic substance (organic material and water). The prisms are oriented perpendicular to the underlying dentine, and under high magnification the ground surface of enamel shows a "fish scale" appearance. Enamel prisms have been examined with Scanning Electron Microscopes, and the variations in form have served as important taxonomic data within the primates.

Dentine forms the bulk of the tooth structure, it is yellowish in colour, less hard than enamel, but much harder than either bone or cementum. It is composed of an inorganic component of approximately 75% of the mass, and the remaining 25% is organic and water. Dentine is produced by the cells called "odontoblasts". The odontoblasts function very similarly to the osteoblasts of bone, except that they begin their lives attached to the inside of the enamel cap, and then secrete the intercellular matrix only on one side, that nearest to the enamel, while still actively maintaining an attachment to the enamel. Thus each odontoblast cell body resides on the inner surface of the dentine and maintains a protoplasmic extrusion to the enamel. These structures are referred to as the dentine tubules.

Pulp Cavity is the term given to the non dentinal volume inside the tooth. This contains the nerve, artery, and veins which supply the odontoblast cell bodies, plus some loose connective tissue elements around them. It has not been conclusively shown, but there is a possibility of nerve end organs or nerve tip endings being resident in the dentine.

Cementum is a bone like, hard yet flexible material which covers the entire root of the tooth as a thin layer. It is considered to be intermediate in many ways between bone and dentine. It acts primarily as a bonding agent between the root of the tooth and the alveolar bone.

Secondary Dentine is the development of a newer and perceptibly different dentine layer inside the tooth pulp cavity. This may be developed in response to stress applied to the tooth, as a result of trauma, or simply through age. In rooted teeth, if the production of secondary dentine proceeds far enough it can result in the compression and extinction of the nerve, artery and vein supply to the tooth, although secondary invasion of blood vessels is likely to occur. Where rootless teeth exist, the development of secondary dentine may promote and increase functional life-span.

MORPHOLOGICAL CONVENTIONS

The pointed structures of the surface of teeth are called either cusps or cones, and the lines depressed into the enamel between cusps are termed fissures. Cusps or cones are named and described according to their position on the surface of the tooth, their size and form, and their evolutionary significance.

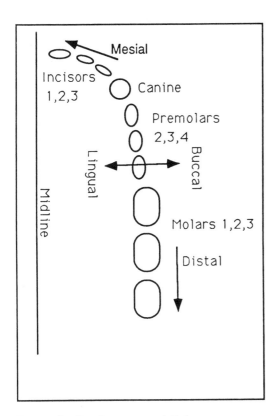

Figure 2: Tooth types and Reference Directions

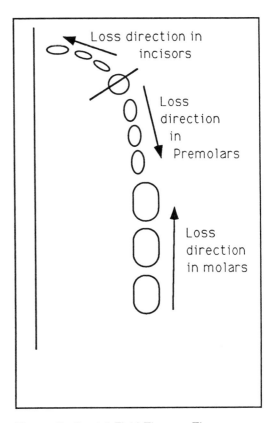

Figure 3: Dental Field Theory—The directions of tooth loss over evolutionary time.

A standard reference system is used (see Figure 2):

- **Buccal** the cheek side of the tooth, or when used as a direction (ie, buccally) it is towards the cheek side.

- **Lingual** the tongue side of the tooth, and similarly—towards the tongue side.

- **Mesial** the side towards the midline of the tooth row, or the incisor side, similarly for directionality—towards the centre of the tooth row (it may be better to conceptualize the tooth row as being straightened out from the curve to a straight line.)

- **Distal** the side away from the midline of the tooth row, that is towards the outer ends of the line.

- **Crown** the portion above the cervix of the tooth, and usually the enamelled portion of the structure.

- **Root(s)** the portion below the cervix of the tooth, usually covered by cementum, but without enamel.

- **Cervix** the "neck" band of the tooth, and generally can be considered to be the location at which the enamel and the cementum meet.

TOOTH TYPES

There are basically four types of teeth in primates, although for some species of fossils, a fifth type may be recognized.

Incisors are anterior teeth which tend to be simple in nearly all cases. The incisors of primates usually are broad spatulate teeth, the uppers have a cingulum or small bump on the lingual surface near the base or cervix, and this may be accompanied by a pit as well.

Canines are usually large sharp pointed conical teeth. The uppers may also have a cingulum and pit structure. Primates are among the few lines which have in some families developed the mechanisms of "honing" the teeth to apparently increase the sharpness of the canine edges.

Premolars are generally two cusped teeth with the inner, lingual cusp being an evolutionary enlargement of the cingulum structure. Again the inner or lingual cusp is larger in the upper dental arcade than in the lower. The "sectorial lower pre-molar" is a specialized feature found in cercopithecoids and apes which is designed for honing the rear of the upper canine, and also for acting as a shear with the canine. It may also be noted that unlike the anterior teeth, premolars usually have two roots.

Molars are teeth with 3 roots in the upper arcade and 2 roots in the lower set. These are the teeth which show the greatest amount of evolutionary variation.

The "Fifth" type? In some species of Palaeocene and Eocene Palaeoprimates, there appears to exist a highly specialized variation of either a premolar or a molar into a large bladelike shearing tooth which functionally parallels the "carnassial" tooth of carnivores but apparently, from microwear analyses, was used to process tough vegetative material.

DENTAL FIELD THEORY

The commonly utilized dental field theory describes three "fields" within the dental arcade, both in the upper and the lower sets, and proposes that the reduction of the number of teeth, from the primitive insectivore number of 44, is related to loss of tooth buds evolutionarily from each of these fields (Figure 3).

The incisor field is from the midline (ie—most mesial) surface to the canine, the premolar field is from the canine towards the molars, and the molar field is distal to that. The dental field theory treats each of these fields as independent evolutionary entities. The sequence of tooth bud loss is from the distal end of the incisor field towards the mesial direction—ie—if there were originally 4 incisors, then numbers 4 and then 3 have been lost in most modern primates. In the premolar field, the loss is from the mesial (canine) end towards the distal end. Thus the original insectivore condition with 4 premolars leads to the loss of PM1 and PM2 and the retention of PM3 and PM4 as the "first and second bicuspids/premolars" of catarrhini. The molar field works in the same direction as the incisor field, that is from distal towards the mesial, hence if the original mammal had 4 molars, the one lost is M4.

THE COPE-OSBORNE THEORY OF MOLAR DEVELOPMENT

The Cope-Osborne theory of molar development (Figure 4) had its beginnings in April 1883 when Cope published his discovery of a triagonal type of upper molar from some Eocene formations in Wyoming. Prior to this time, Cope had conceived of the dental sequence as one in which more complex teeth were derived from simple single cone teeth by repetition and fusion of tooth buds.

In December 1883 he revised his model to favour the tritubercular or triangular tooth as the basic form of mam-

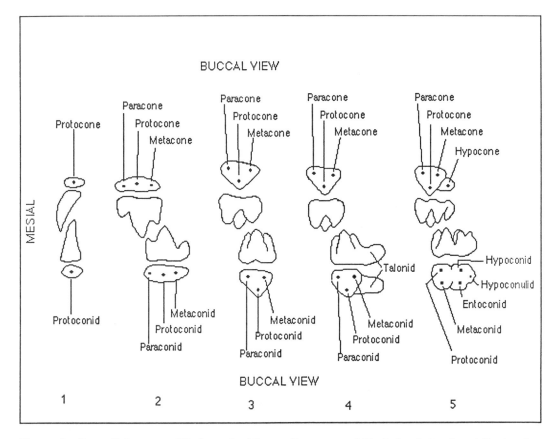

Figure 4: Cope-Osborne or Tritubercular Theory Sequence of Evolution Lateral and Occlusal views of 5 stages in Molar Evolution.

malian dentition. By 1884 he conceived that the simple single cone tooth was the basis and that all other types of teeth could be derived from this through the triangular form. He even set out two mechanisms for this to happen. 1) The cone is compressed to cause a horizontal hill to form. 2) The addition of lateral cusps to the simple cone takes place.

Cope finished with his involvement with the theory in 1885, but it was taken up and worked on by H. F. Osborn. Osborn replaced a great deal of the nomenclature that Cope had favoured, and gave us the current set of names for the four main cusps of the tribosphenic molar. These four cusps are now called the paracone, metacone, protocone, and hypocone. Osborn added the pattern of "id" ending for the lower set of cusps in order to distinguish them from the uppers.

The Cope-Osborne theory, or the tritubercular theory as it came to be known after 1907 when Osborn published his book on the theory, can be divided into two major parts, the first part dealing with the origin of the tritubercular pattern, and the second being a historical generalization that this pattern is the origin of more complex ones in later mammals.

In the tritubercular theory, the starting point for development is the dentition of reptiles, a single cone shaped tooth, without any embellishments. It may be wise to remember that even in modern primates this type of tooth remains in relatively conservative form as the canine, but many prosimians have incisors of this shape as well.

The second stage of development involves the mesial-distal expansion of the cone and when the small side cusps become apparent the tooth is referred to as being of the "protodont" form. As the anterior and posterior cusps increase in size, eventually reaching sufficiently obvious stature to be labelled, the tooth is called "triconodont". In the triconodont state, the mesial cusp is the paracone, the middle is the protocone, and the distal is the metacone.

SPECIALIZED VARIATIONS IN THE ANTHROPOIDEA

Within the anthropoidea, there have developed a number of variations based on the original Cope-Osborne forms, as appropriate to the evolution of the generally larger, more vegetarian forms of the suborder. There are two major developments within the suborder, these are specifically the development of larger size, both in terms of allometric scaled increases, but also in terms of shape modifications; and secondly the drift towards omnivory and increasingly a vegetarian input. The results of these changes are quite obviously displayed in the dental changes.

Of particular note are the development of the "sectorial premolar" and the appearance of quadrate molars with either 4 or 5 cusps arranged in what is known as a "bilophodont" pattern. This latter involves the development of a "loph" or continuous ridge between the paracone and protocone, on the mesial end of the molar, and a loph between the metacone and hypocone at the distal end. On the lower molar, the "lophids" develop between the protoconid-metaconid, and between the hypoconid-entoconid. This type of molar structure has come to be called bilophodont, and can be considered as a relatively efficient form of "chopping/mashing" of vegetative food materials. It should also be obvious that these teeth are very much lower in profile, the crown is relatively high, but the cusps and lophs are very much lower. This results in a tooth which is capable of some degree of forward-backward, and a little bit of side to side movement, without the risk of "dental lock" or breaking cusps.

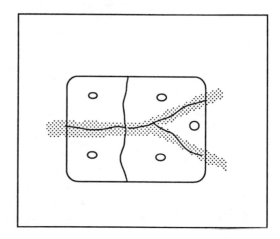

Figure 5: The Y—5 or Drypithecine Pattern Molar.

The larger members of the Hominoidea have taken this development even further. These forms, especially *Gorilla*, and *Pongo* have moved to 5 and 6 cusped molars, but retained relatively distinct cusps. The evolutionary purposes of this development appear to be adaptation to the crushing or pulping of vegetative material. The characteristic development in the line is the so-called "Y—5" or "Dryopithecine" molar marked by the presence of five cusps and a fissure pattern which forms a "y" shape across the tooth (see Figure 5).

THE AUDITORY REGION OF PRIMATES

A structure which distinguishes primates from all other mammals is the pattern of construction in the ear region. Mammalian ear structures are composed of three basic regions, the inner, middle and outer areas. The structure of the inner ear is encased within the petrosal or petrous portion of the temporal bone of the skull. This structure consists of the delicate system of nerve endings in the cochlea which constitute the auditory component, and the similar semicircular canals of the proprioceptive balancing systems. The outer ear is a cartilaginous tube and fan structure mounted externally to the skull, and serving to channel sound waves into the tube where they may reach the eardrum. The middle ear is a variably constructed air filled cavity connected to the throat via the eustachian tubes. The middle ear contains the tympanic membrane or eardrum, and the chain of small bones—malleus, stapes, and incus (hammer, stirrup, and anvil)—which conduct the sound waves to the cochlea.

In primitive mammals the middle ear was encapsulated in a cartilaginous capsule, but in most of the living mammals it has been transformed into a bony structure called the "auditory bulla". The formation of this bulla is through a different embryological origin, and hence distinct bone sources in the different lineages of the mammals. In most mammals it is formed from two bones, the tympanic which forms a mounting ring for the eardrum, and the entotympanic— a separate ossification which forms the bulla. In the primates, there is no entotympanic, the auditory bulla is produced by an outgrowth of the petrosal. This is consistent and conservative throughout the primates, and hence serves as a major defining criterion for referral of specimens to the order.

PALAEOPRIMATES AND THE ORIGIN OF THE PRIMATES

The collection of organisms which can be regarded as the "palaeoprimates", and thus the stem of closest approximation in time to the basal stock from which the later and "true primates" arose is now commonly given the subordinal classification of Plesiadapiformes. The Plesiadapiformes includes the archaic prosimians from the latest Cretaceous through to the late Eocene of North America and in Europe from the middle Palaeocene through the early Eocene. The superfamilies included are the Paromomyoidea and the Plesiadapoidea. The former contains the families Paromomyidae and Picrodontidae, while the Plesiadapidae, Saxonelli-

dae, and Carpolestidae compose the latter.

Since true primates are most frequently defined by the minimum hard tissue features of a closed post-orbital bar connecting the zygomatic to the frontal bones of the skull, and the possession of at least one pair of nails (as opposed to claws) on the digits, the Plesiadapiformes cannot be labelled within the order Primates. Like the members of the tree shrew group they are relatively closely related to primates and can be placed within the SuperOrder Archonta. Further details concerning the origin of the true primates and the ecological circumstances relating to that evolution are presented in the Cartmill article.

An important factor in the evolution of the primates has been the pattern of movement of the earth's crustal plates. This tectonic movement, the familiar continental drift, has strongly influenced the direction and locality of evolutionary development. Drift has also had major influence on the patterns of spread of species and populations over time. Routes between continents constantly change and the reconstruction of these is an important clue to understanding the relationships between the lineages. Just as important to this understanding is the information as palaeoclimate. The changes of climatic conditions over the past sixty-five million years have influenced primate evolution, exterminated populations, and changed migration pathways.

PROSIMIANS/ STREPSIRHINES— EARLIEST EUPRIMATES

Cartmill makes the case that the true beginnings of the order Primates is during the Eocene time period with the appearance of what Simons labelled the "first primates of modern aspect". There is a wealth of material from this epoch, and all of the known skulls from the three major families show enlarged braincases, closely approximated orbits with a postorbital bar, and grasping hind feet equipped with true nails.

Cartmill looks to the possibility of relationship between the plesiadapoids and the Eocene families, and concludes that the answer must be a resounding "NO". He sees virtually no possibility of any plesiadapid other than the very earliest—*Purgatorius*—as being a possible candidate for ancestry of the Eocene lemurs and tarsiers. It is thus his perspective that "if typical primates developed from plesiadapoids, they must have split off almost immediately after the first plesiadapoids came on the scene."

THE SUBORDER STREPSIRHINI AND INFRAORDER ADAPIFORMES

The concept of the Strepsirhini as put forward by Szalay and Delson (1979) is one which includes the living tooth-combed primates, the Lemuriformes, and the early tertiary primates which have been grouped under the Adapiformes. There are a large number of specialized traits seen in this suborder, and some substantial variations from the primate norm are somewhat glossed over. The diagnosis of the suborder seems to be primarily on basi-cranial continuity. They note that it is better to define the ancestral strepsirhine assemblage (Adapiformes) as a group with a distinct common ancestor distinguished from the antecedent plesiadapiforms in carrying advanced characteristics—enlargement of the stapedial artery, a postorbital bar, a grasping hallux and pollex, and a number of postcranial osteological features of the ilium and humerus. Mostly they are known by molar characteristics. They perceive this transition to the "lemur" grade to have been related to the development of superior arboreal adaptations necessitated by a particular feeding pattern.

A characteristic which is common to all lemuriforms is the "tooth comb". Martin (1972) suggests that this term should be replaced by "tooth scraper", since he points out that although all living strepsirhines utilize this structure for grooming, that this is a secondary function. Based upon his observations of the use of the tooth scraper in gathering gums and exudates, as well as prying off bark, Martin concludes that gum and resin scraping was the original function of the comb.

THE SUBORDER HAPLORHINI OR THE ANTHROPOIDS—LATER EUPRIMATES

The evolutionary development of the primates takes a substantial step upwards in the terminal phases of the Eocene, and completes that movement by the middle of the Oligocene—about 30 million years ago. This evolution is representative of a quantum leap from the strepsirhine primate forms to the haplorhine, with separate branches developing in slightly different directions. The results of this elaboration are the infraorders of the Haplorhini, the Tarsiiformes, Platyrhini, and Catarrhini, respectively, the tarsiers, new world monkeys, and the old world monkeys, apes, and hominids. This evolution is difficult to accurately document since there are relatively few fossil localities reflecting terrestrial environments of the late Eocene, and throughout the Oligocene. The primary Oligocene primate bearing locality is the El Fayum locality on the side of the block fault depression known as the Quatara Depression in western Egypt.

THE SUBORDER HAPLORHINI

The conception of the haplorhine primates takes the position that the tarsiers, who have always been a problem in that they display a set of highly advanced characteristics combined with a substantial number of conservative traits, are to be placed with the more advanced group. This marks the sole distinction between the concepts of the Haplorhini and the Anthropoidea, in the former the tarsiers are included, in the latter they are excluded. In part the use of Haplorhini represents a statement that the tarsiers, like Eocene and Oligocene primates, represent the most logical group from which to derive later forms.

Infraorder Tarsiiformes

The primary features which recommend inclusion of the tarsiers within the Haplorhini are soft tissue features associated with the eye—the presence of a fovea centralis even though there are no cone receptors, the external nose—which structurally resembles the rhinarium of strepsirhines but does not carry an external mucosal membrane, and fetal membranes which are typified as a haemochorial placentation pattern. Since these features are unavailable for study in fossil forms, the similarities of skull and dentition have been used to extend the relationships of modern tarsiers back to include the Omomyidae group. These specimens represent a very large range of forms which generally show some degree of similarity to tarsiers in some significant features, but in general would not be considered as "good" ancestors for later primates.

Some of the structural features of the tarsiers can be considered to be specialized adaptations to predatory behaviour. Among these would be the elongated bones of the ankle (the tarsus), the trumpet shaped ears, large eyes with extreme frontal rotation, and sharp cone patterns on their molar and premolar teeth.

New World Monkeys, Infraorder Platyrhini

The new world monkeys, set here to infraordinal rank, may be grouped with the Catarrhini as the "Section Simiiformes" as Groves (1989) and Hoffstetter (1982)

suggest. The infraorder Platyrhini is typified by the wide structure of the nasal region, the nares being oriented somewhat laterally with a wide septum between, and by the presence of three premolars in the dentition.

One critical problem associated with the new world monkeys is their evolutionary root. The South American continental mass is one of the offshoots of the ancient landmass of Gondwanaland, and was separated from the northern mass, Laurasia, since before the evolution of placental mammals. The major mammal evolution of South America was the Marsupial line until the continent drifted into contact with Central and North America at the beginning of the Pleistocene, three million years ago. Primates, and a group of rodents derived from the Hystricomorphs of Africa (Porcupines), were the only placental forms to invade before that event. Indeed, the palaeontological evidence indicates their arrival in the early Oligocene when the oceanic gap to Africa was at least 1200 kilometres, and that to North America was at least 700. The problem then is how these forms managed to cross such a gap, and which gap it was. In the modern world no gap of more than 500 kilometres has ever been spanned by an organism larger than a spider. The evidence available in the palaeontological arena is very inconclusive, suggesting possible affinities with African Parapithecidae and also with North American Omomyidae, but the neontological data, especially from molecular biology, suggests African relationships. This latter is especially significant for it indicates a common origin for both Old and New World primates which is separate from all living prosimian forms. There are an abundance of hypotheses about the mechanism of transfer between the old and new world areas, and the evolutionary mechanisms leading to parallel development of monkeys in both regions, but no adequate solutions have yet appeared.

The fossil history of new world monkeys has been very sparse until recently, but now a number of new specimens have begun to fill in some of the major gaps. Still the evolutionary picture of the new world marmosets and cebid monkeys is far less clear than that found in the old world. What we can say is that the recognized evolutionary lineages of *Aotus, Saimiri,* the pitheciine, alouattine, and marmoset groups all go back at least to the Miocene (Delson and Rosenberger, 1980; Setoguchi and Rosenberger, 1985).

Old World Monkeys and Apes, Infraorder Catarrhini

The other branch of the Simiiformes, the infraorder Catarrhini or "narrow nosed primates" is a much larger aggregation of forms, and has a significantly better, but far from clear history. Part of the problem derives from the vital importance of the Oligocene time period to understanding the evolution of the catarrhines, and the incredible lack of continental Oligocene age deposits. There is only one Oligocene deposit area in the old world, the El Fayum deposits along the western face of the Quatara Depression in western Egypt. The deposits were first worked in the 1890's by a German collector, Richard Markgraf, but have been under nearly continuous seasonal excavation since 1960 by teams from Yale and Harvard universities.

The deposits at El Fayum have yielded most of what we know about the initial evolution of catarrhines, and there would appear to be reasonable ancestral forms of monkeys and apes present between 34 and 28 million years ago. Some forms, in particular the Parapithecidae show significant similarities to later old world monkeys, but retain a second premolar, already specialized into the sectorial form. Thus they have substantial similarity to platyrhines, but there remains the transportation problem, unless we assume that like Thor Heyrdahl, they constructed papyrus boats and sailed to the new world. Some authorities consider the parapithecids to be an offshoot branch without issue since there are some dental characteristics in common between living platyrhines and catarrhines which parapithecids lack. It may also be worth noting that the earliest specimens of the family show substantial similarity to the ancestral strepsirhine pattern, and thus may represent transitional forms.

Basic Ape Forms— Dental Apes?

The second major set of fossils from the El Fayum Oligocene turn out not to be monkey grade forms but are instead ape-like in conformation. These forms include the set of propliopithecids, which incorporates the famous *Aegyptopithecus zeuxis* which holds the status of the "first ape" or member of the Hominoidea superfamily. These forms are very clearly transitional in configuration. There is sufficient skeletal material to describe *Aegytopithecus* in overall form as being the size of a housecat, or miniature poodle, having a tail, a brain organized along the ape pattern, ape teeth, and a skull which resembles a prosimian in structure. It may be certain that the Propliopithecidae did not directly give rise to the later catarrhines, but they are surely close to the line that did. One significant aspect of their dentition is the presence of the earliest version of the "Y-5" pattern but only on the lower molars of *Aegyptopithecus.*

Hominoid Fluorescence During the Miocene

The Miocene fossil record is very much better than the Oligocene, and there are literally hundreds of specimens of hominoid species from these deposits. Strangely enough monkeys are very poorly represented throughout the 20 million year period.

Family level distinctions have been made among the multitude of Miocene apes with Proconsulidae, Oreopithecidae, Pongidae, and Pliopithecidae forming the major groups. The taxonomic picture of the Miocene apes has fluctuated widely over the last century. Large numbers of fossil apes have been found in India, Africa, Europe, and most recently in China, and been individually labelled at species and generic levels. This situation was so out of hand that in the 1960's Elwyn Simons and David Pilbeam undertook a complete re-examination of all of the fossils, eventually allocating them to three subgenera under Dryopithecus, and only seven species. However in the late 1970's new fossil ape localities were discovered and throughout the 1980's a flood of new specimens and names was produced. As a result the current picture of hominoid evolution is far less clear than it was in 1970.

The mass of forms can, however, be reduced, as Conroy (1990) has done, to three categories: Dryomorphs who are primitive early and middle Miocene forms found in East Africa and Eurasia, typified by thin enamel on their molar teeth; Ramamorphs who are middle Miocene forms of Eurasia and East Africa carrying thick enamel on their molars; and Pliomorphs who are early and middle Miocene forms of Eurasia with many shared primitive catarrhine features. These morphs are not taxonomic categories but are akin to grades of apes. All three morphs cut across taxa boundaries. The Dryomorph forms include the genera *Proconsul*, *Rangwapithecus*, *Limnopithecus*, *Dendropithecus*, *Micropithecus*, and *Dryopithecus*. The Ramamorphs include *Sivapithecus*, *Ramapithecus*, and *Gigantopithecus*, while the Pliomorph genera are *Pliopithecus* and *Laccopithecus*. The temporal replacement in Eastern Africa of the Dryomorphs by the Ramamorphs appears to coincide with the developing desiccation of the environment. Due in part to the tectonic movements and the elevation of the Kenyan and Ethiopian highlands, and thus a dryer habitat, the vegetational community changed from tropical forests towards tree savannas and grasslands. In consequent the apes either had to withdraw with the forests or adapt to harder, dryer fruits and seeds— a pattern which the Ramamorphs apparently took up.

At the present time, the Dryomorphs seem to be terminal in the Miocene, though there is some possibility of one or more forms being related to evolution of the lesser apes. The Ramamorphs however are quite clearly related to the evolution of the orangutan forms, and somewhere in this cluster is likely to be the ancestral form for the great apes and hominids, although the evolutionary data indicates a clear separation of the *Sivapithecus* through *Pongo* lineage well before the development of the *Pan—Gorilla—Homo* clade.

Cercopithecoidea Submerged in Miocene

The superfamily Cercopithecoidea is very poorly represented during the Miocene time period, but is represented by two family level groups. The Victoriapithecidae represented by two genera, *Victoriapithecus* and *Prohylobates* (which in spite of a name that attributes it to ancestry of the gibbons, is a true monkey) and the modern Cercopithecidae, represented by *Macaca*, the longest surviving genus of modern primates. The Victoriapithecines are conservative forms which display cercopithecine dentition and colobine facial construction. They are also unspecialized as to locomotor functions, neither arboreal nor terrestrial in pattern. This would tend towards confirmation of Kingdon's thesis that modern arboreal cercopithecines are very lately evolved and from a form that was at least partially terrestrial. Victoriapithecines fit the requirements of the hypothesis quite adequately. If this structural adaptation is related to a forest edge and tree savanna environment, the reason for the relative scarcity of monkeys in the miocene can be attributed to a lack of suitable habitat in areas where fossilization was occurring. This would have been changing towards the latter half of the Miocene, but the monkeys would have been in competition with the Ramamorph apes in attempting to move into the new open environments.

The appearance of *Macaca* at the late Miocene stage in the open habitats of north Africa represents the transform of a true cercopithecine lineage out of the victoriapithecines or their unknown relatives. Macaques are conservative in structure and ecological role, and have managed to maintain stability for at least eight million years while developing in the Mediterranean basin and then spreading across the temperate zone as far as Japan. They are also undoubtedly the stock from which the larger and more terrestrial African baboons have developed. The case for this close relationship is founded upon the biomolecular similarities of the two, as well as the experimental cases of hybridization between rhesus macaques and savanna baboons.

Pliocene Decline in Hominoids and Upsurge of Cercopithecoids

The Pliocene epoch is a rather short and frankly transitional period between the end of the Miocene at five million years ago, and the beginning of the Pleistocene about two million years ago. The major characteristics associated with the Pliocene is a continuance of the desiccation marking the late Miocene, and the progressive lowering of temperature as the planet moved into the current series of glaciations. These environmental transformations made most of the old world unsuitable for the apes, and they became extinct in Europe and most of Asia, while remaining viable only in the reduced forest refuges of Africa and southeast Asia. At the same time conditions were improving for the monkeys and they underwent a substantial expansion both in population numbers and in species diversity. This explosion yielded ten genera of Cercopithecinae, of which five are currently surviving, and the significant development of the subfamily Colobinae which spawned a further ten genera, with three surviving to modern times. In spite of their association today with forest conditions, the majority of the extinct larger forms in both subfamilies were terrestrial in habitat. Since the terrestrial habitat is also one of the most dangerous, due to the high density of predators attracted by vast numbers of antelope and other ungulates which feed upon grasses, it must be assumed that they monkeys had well developed social groups and effective anti-predator defenses.

Gigantism as the Rule:

One of the consistent patterns found throughout the mammal lineages during the Pliocene—Pleistocene is a general increase in size. This has lead to the occasional label of this period as a time of gigantism. This was certainly evident in the cercopithecoid lineages, where several lines in Africa and Eurasia threw up forms that were considerably larger than any modern related species. Baboon forms the size of female gorillas and terrestrial colobines twice the size of modern baboons have been recognized. The causes for this pattern of gigantism is unknown, but there are two possible contributing forces, anti-predator response, and thermoregulation. The pattern for anti-predator response is a straightforward one of larger size meaning fewer predators preying upon the species, especially if the males become enhanced with much larger canines as part of the system. But in terms of thermoregulation, a larger size means a larger mass to store heat energy in, and a relatively smaller surface area to loose heat through. Thus a larger sized animal displays an increased efficiency in thermoregulation, albeit at the cost of larger food requirements, larger home ranges, and longer day travels. But these factors may be of sufficient importance under cooling conditions that selection for increased size is enhanced.

PLEISTOCENE AND HOLOCENE

The last two million years have been dominated by the wide oscillations of climate aggregated under the label of the 'Ice Age'. While these oscillations are most dramatic in the subarctic and temperate zones, they did produce significant climatic changes throughout the tropical world. In consequence forest blocks responded by expanding when temperatures and rainfall went up, and by contracting when both factors fell. There is no good correlation between glaciations and tropical fluctuations, indeed, the latter have not been precisely dated, but we do know that they did occur and have had significant impacts on the evolutionary history of the order.

Naturally, from an anthropocentric perspective, the most interesting aspect of the Pleistocene is the evolution of the genus *Homo*, with all of its cultural baggage. These topics will be covered in the papers by Pilbeam, Shreeve, and Steele later in this section. However, here we wish to look at the other primates.

The fossil records for non-human primates during the past two million years is rather sparse, and there are really few major developments of new species, certainly no new genera. The Pleistocene appears to have served primarily as a series of evolutionary filters which have significantly reduced the overall variability of the order. The gigantism which evolved prior to the full onset of the Pleistocene disappeared rather quickly as these large terrestrial primates, even though they probably functioned in social groups, were no match for weapon bearing hominids. In many other lineages, the same patterns of recurrent extinctions during the Pleistocene may be associated with the appearance of new hominids or their migration into new areas. If we accept the perspective of Martin (1966), then all of the Pleistocene extinctions may have been due to the activities of Man the Hunter.

The one area in which evolutionary novelty does seem to have arisen during the Pleistocene is in the arboreal forest dwelling species. The recurrent waves of expansion and contraction of forest habitats, both in Africa and the Americas has been theorized to be responsible for the generation of the large numbers of species—all similar and related, but functioning as separate populations—among the guenons of Africa, and among the marmosets of South Africa.

The most recent developments, associated with the Holocene, the time since humans developed agriculture, have been a continuation of the extinctions of primates and other organisms. This process has speeded up since the Industrial Revolution, and the development of preventive medicine has lead to the rapid expansion of the world-wide human population. At the current rates of forest cutting, and the concomitant destruction of the primate populations, the middle to late twenty first century will see the extinction of all members of the order except *Homo sapiens sapiens*.

References Cited:

Conroy, G. C.
1990 Primate Evolution. W. W. Norton, New York

Delson, E., and Rosenberger, A.
1980 Phyletic perspectives of Platyrrhine origins and anthropoid relationships. In Chiochon, R. and Chiarelli, B. (eds) Evolutionary biology of New World Monkeys and continental drift. Plenum, New York. p. 405–458.

Groves, C. P.
1989 A Theory of Human and Primate Evolution. Oxford University Press.

Hoffstetter, R.
1982 Les Primates Simiiformes (= Anthropoidea) (compréhension, phylogénie, histoire biogéographique). Annales de Paléontologie (Vertébrés-Invertébrés), 68:241–290.

Martin, P.
1966 Africa and Pleistocene overkill. Nature 212(5060): 339–342.

Martin, R. D.
1972 Adaptive radiation and behaviour of the Malagasy Lemurs. Phil. Trans. Royal Society, London, Ser B, Biol. Sci. 264: 295–352.

Setoguchi, T., and Rosenberger, A.
1985 Miocene marmosets: first fossil evidence. International Journal of Primatology, 6: 615–625.

Szalay, F. S., and Delson, E.
1979 Evolutionary History of the Primates. Academic Press, New York

Rethinking Primate Origins

Matt Cartmill

The characteristic primate traits cannot be explained simply as adaptations to arboreal life.

If you asked a student of human evolution to explain why human beings, unlike other mammals, walk around on only two legs, you would be baffled and unhappy if he answered, "Because in man's ancestral lineage, individuals who could not run away from predators left fewer offspring." You would be justified in retorting that the same remarks apply equally to thousands of other species of mammals, yet none of these have developed upright bipedal locomotion. The purported explanation, you would properly conclude, may be a true proposition, but is worthless as an explanation.

An explanation is a hypothesis of a complex sort. Ordinarily, to explain one fact in terms of another requires that there be an a posteriori rule which allows us to deduce the first from the second, and which warrants testable expectations other than the one in question (1). We reject the foregoing "explanation" of human bipedality because we sense that its explanatory force depends on the lawlike generalization, "Natural selection favors bipedal locomotion in any mammal species that has predators," and that this generalization is false. Yet some evolutionary biologists and philosophers of science (2) have argued that evolutionary explanations do not involve any such generalizations, and hence are not subject to refutation by counterexamples. In this view, we have no grounds for dismissing the "explanation" with which I began; the objection that the same remarks apply to species which have remained quadrupedal is beside the point.

I have suggested elsewhere (3) that this and similar objections are very much to the point; that, when valid, they demonstrate the inadequacy of the explanation in question; and that such objections must be raised systematically if we wish to arrive at adequate explanations of historical processes. These assumptions underlie the following reassessment of what has been called the arboreal theory of primate evolution.

THE ARBOREAL THEORY AND ITS BACKGROUND

The Linnean concept of the order Primates, which included the bats and colugos, was still current as late as 1870 (4). In 1873, Darwin's antagonist Mivart proposed ordinal boundaries which excluded these animals, but which (unlike the taxonomies then advocated by Milne-Edwards, Grandidier, and Gervais) included the prosimians as a suborder of Primates (5). Mivart also proposed a list of traits that distinguished prosimians and anthropoids from other placental mammals. These traits included a complete bony ring around the eye, a well-developed occipital lobe of the cerebral cortex, and a grasping hind foot with an opposable, clawless first toe.

In the second decade of the 20th century, G. E. Smith and his pupil, F. W. Jones, put forth the first systematic attempts at explaining these and other characteristic primate traits in terms of natural selection. Smith, a comparative neuroanatomist, was principally concerned with explaining the distinctive features of primate brains. He proposed (6) that the remote ancestors of the primates were shrewlike terrestrial creatures that entered upon an arboreal way of life. In the complex networks of tree branches through which these early primates moved and foraged, the olfactory and tactile receptors in the snout did not provide adequate guidance; snuffling blindly along in hopes of scenting something edible, as most living insectivores do, was no longer a viable foraging pattern. Accordingly, vision gradually replaced olfaction as the dominant sense. In correlation with this, the hand assumed the tactile and grasping functions primitively served by the mouth and lips; eye-hand coordination replaced nose-mouth coordination. Arboreal life also required more precise and rapid motor responses. Thus, Smith was able to account for the primates' reduced olfactory centers and elaborated visual, tactile, motor, and association cortex in terms of the selection pressures exerted by the arboreal environment.

Jones's reinterpretation of these ideas (7) reflects his professional interest in the anatomy of the hand and foot. Jones proposed that the arboreal habit led to a functional differentiation of the limbs. While the foot remained a relatively passive organ of support and propulsion, the hand, used by the primate ancestors for reaching out and grasping new supports when climbing about in trees, became specialized for prehension—and therefore preadapted to take over the mouth's functions of manipulation and food-gathering. As the snout lost importance as a sensory and manipulative organ, it dwindled in size; and the eyes were perforce drawn together toward the middle of the flattening face. The progressive specialization of the hind limb for support and propulsion led to a more upright posture, with correlated changes in the axial skeleton, gut, and reproductive organs. For Jones, most of the things that distinguish human beings from typical quadrupedal mammals were originally adaptations to living in trees.

The arboreal theory was open to the obvious objection that most arboreal mammals—opossums, trees shrews, palm civets, squirrels, and so on—lack the short face, close-set eyes, reduced olfactory apparatus, and large brains that arboreal life supposedly favored. Jones tried to account for these counter-examples.

Accepting Matthew's thesis (8) that primitive mammals had been arboreal creatures with opposable thumbs and first toes, Jones proposed that the absence of primate-like traits in other arboreal lineages resulted from a period of adaptation in each lineage to terrestrial locomotion. During this period, the thumb and first toe became reduced, the primitive reptilian flexibility of the forelimb was lost, and the primitive flat nails were replaced by claws. These changes blocked the specialization of the forelimbs for prehension. Accordingly, in nonprimate mammals that had reentered the trees, the primate evolutionary trends did not materialize.

Stated thus baldly, Jones's thesis is obviously inconsistent. His treatment of the evolution of the brain, which he borrows from Smith, presupposes that primitive mammals were small-eyed terrestrial beasts that nosed their way through the world, guided by specialized olfactory and tactile receptors in the snout; but when the evolution of the limbs is in question, he assumes that arboreality is primitive and that early mammals were neither terrestrial nor typically quadrupedal.

The late W. E. Le Gros Clark's reformulation of the arboreal theory, which more skillfully conceals this inconsistency, has been almost universally accepted by other students of primate evolution. Much of Le Gros Clark's primatological work centered around the now-discredited (9) proposition that the tree shrews (Tupaiidae) are persistently primitive lemuroids that have somehow failed to develop the perfected adaptations to arboreal life seen in the other extant primates. Le Gros Clark believed that primitive Insectivora were tree-climbing beasts with clawed, nonprehensile hands and feet, small eyes and brains, and elaborate olfactory apparatus. The unspecialized, squirrel-like climbing habit of tree shrews (and ancestral primates) is invoked by Le Gros Clark to explain their incipiently primate-like morphology; tree shrews have a complete bony ring around the orbit, a relatively extensive visual cortex, a highly differentiated retina, some simplification of the olfactory apparatus, and a few minor grasping adaptations of the joints and muscles of the hind foot. More perfect arboreal adaptations, of the sort seen in lemurs, involve the replacement of sharp claws by flattened nails overlying enlarged friction pads, the divergence and enlargement of the first toe and thumb to produce effective grasping organs, and the approximation of the two eyes toward the center of the face. This last change, in Le Gros Clark's view, had a positive selective advantage for acrobatic arboreal mammals; it produced a wide overlap of the two visual fields, allowing stereoscopic estimation of distance in jumping from branch to branch (10).

THE COMPARATIVE EVIDENCE

If progressive adaptation to living in trees transformed a treeshrew-like ancestor into a higher primate, than primate-like traits must be better adaptations to arboreal locomotion and foraging than are their antecedents. This expectation is not borne out by studies of arboreal nonprimates. The diurnal tree squirrels

(Sciurinae) provide the most striking counterexample. The eyes of squirrels face laterally, the two visual fields having only about a 60° arc of overlap (*11*); the olfactory apparatus is not reduced by comparison with terrestrial rodents (*12*); all the digits (except the diminutive thumb) bear claws, which are sharper and more recurved than those of terrestrial sciurids (*13*); and the marginal digits of the hand and foot are not opposable or even very divergent. Yet squirrels are highly successful arboreal mammals, and seem to have little difficulty in accomplishing the arboreal activities in which primates might be expected to excel. Despite their laterally directed eyes (and presumed lack of stereoscopy), squirrels of several genera may leap from 13 to 17 body lengths from tree to tree (*14*), which compares favorably with the 20 body lengths reported for the saltatory lemuroid *Propithecus verrauxi* (*15*). Although squirrel hands and feet are not adapted for grasping, squirrels easily walk atop or underneath narrow, sloping supports, and can forage for long periods in slender terminal branches hanging by their clawed hind feet. Clearly, successful arboreal existence is possible without primate-like adaptations.

A partisan of Le Gros Clark's form of the arboreal theory might still postulate that tree squirrels are under selection pressure which favors their developing primate-like morphology, but have not undergone a long enough period of adaptation to arboreal life for them to have converged markedly with primates. Accepting this, we would still expect that arboreal squirrels would differ in primate-like ways from terrestrial sciurids, at least to a slight extent. We would have similar expectations about arboreal members of other nonprimate families.

The facts do not bear out these expectations. Virtually the only features of the hands and feet which systematically distinguish arboreal from terrestrial squirrels are the longer fourth digits and generally larger carpal pads of the former; the arboreal genera show no tendency toward enlargement of the thumb, reduction of claws, or development of a wide or deep cleft between the first and second digits (*16*). Orbital convergence in all sciurids is slight, and is actually greater in the more terrestrial species (Fig. 1E), although the optic axes of ground squirrels' eyes are not more convergent than those of tree squirrels'.

Since small mammals have relatively large eyes, orbital-margin convergence in most mammals varies inversely with size, other things being equal (*3*). For a given skull length, this convergence is somewhat greater in higher primates than in lemurs (*17*). When convergence is plotted against skull length for several families of arboreal mammals and the lemuriform and haplorhine regressions are traced on the plot (Fig. 1), it is evident that arboreality (or saltatory arboreal locomotion, in wholly arboreal taxa) does not correlate with proximity to the primate regressions. The slow-moving lorises have, for their size, more convergent orbits than the saltatory galagos (Fig. 1A). Among feloid carnivores (Fig. 1B), the terrestrial *Felis bengalensis* approaches the primate regressions most closely. Both arboreal and terrestrial procyonids (Fig. 1D) fit a regression parallel to those of the primates, from which the semiarboreal coatimundi is widely displaced away from the primate lines.

Certain primate-like specializations of the visual pathways of the brain may perhaps represent adaptations to arboreal life per se. Diamond and his co-workers

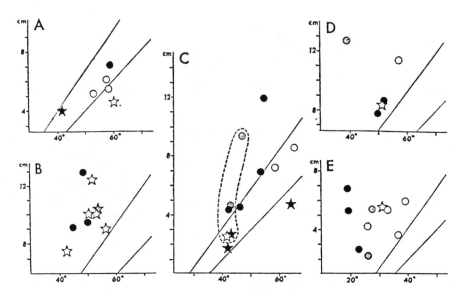

Figure 1: Five bivariate plots of species mean values of skull lengths (prosthion to inion, centimeters) and orbital convergence (dihedral angle between orbital and midsagittal planes, degrees): (A) lorisiform prosimians, (B) feloid carnivores, (C) didelphids (dashed line) and diprotodont marsupials, (D) procyonid carnivores and (E) sciurids. White symbols represent terrestrial animals (such as *Monodelphis*) or slow-moving arboreal forms (such as *Phalanger*); stippled symbols represent semiarboreal animals (such as *Didelphis*); stars represent predominantly carnivorous animals (such as *Monodelphis*). In each plot, the diagonal lines represent the least-squares regression of convergence on skull length for Madagascar lemurs (upper line) and haplorhine primates (tarsiers and anthropoids: lower line). [Data from (17)]

(18, 19) have found that the common tree shrew and the Carolina gray squirrel resemble *Galago senegalensis* in having little or no overlap between the projection from the retina to the occipital visual cortex (relayed via the lateral geniculate) and a significant visual projection to the temporal cortex from the superior colliculus (via the pulvinar). This is not the case in the cat, in which these areas overlap widely and the temporal cortex is given over to projections from the medial geniculate. Since arboreality is about the only thing that tree shrews, squirrels, and galagos have in common, the suggestion that this represents a specifically arboreal adaptation (18) may be correct. However, its adaptive significance is obscure. The expectation that "*any* mammalian line that relies heavily on visual cues" will develop a visual temporal lobe (19) is clearly unwarranted; cats rely heavily on visual cues, and in fact show several primate-like features of the visual system that are absent or unknown in squirrels and tree shrews—for example, parallel optic axes, substantial ipsilateral radiations of each optic nerve, and the presence of "binocular depth cells" in the striate cortex (20, 21). These features are all functionally related to stereoscopic depth perception. Since most of the projection from the retina to the lateral geniculate body seems to correspond to the binocular portion of the visual field (11, 22), the relative de-emphasis of the older tectopulvinar system in cats can even be described, from a different perspective (20), as a special similarity to higher primates.

The comparative evidence, then, does not support the idea that the selection pressures of arboreal life favor the replacement of tree shrew-like morphology by primate-like morphology. In many respects, the first sort of morphology is actually of superior adaptive value. Clawed fingers and toes are superior adaptations for locomotion on non-horizontal surfaces with large radii of curvature—including vertical walls as well as tree trunks (23). Like marmosets (24), squirrels tend to avoid very thin branches in normal arboreal locomotion, but can walk on them easily enough, relying on the largely passive grip of the proximal volar pads when the support is horizontal and (unlike marmosets) gripping with opposed hands and opposed feet when the support is sloping. Primate-like approximation of the orbits increases visual field overlap, but decreases parallax, reducing the distance over which visual field disparities can provide distance cues. In a leaping arboreal animal, selection should act against the extreme orbital approximation seen in tarsiers and higher primates. This expectation is borne out by a comparison of lorises with galagos; the slow-moving *Loris* and *Nycticebus* have more convergent and closely approximated orbits than the saltatory galagos (25), whose wider interorbital space allows stereoscopic ranging over greater distances.

Evidently, the close-set eyes and grasping extremities typical of extant primates are adaptations to some activity other than simply running about in the trees; arboreal life per se cannot be expected to transform a primitive tree shrew-like primate into a lemur. Le Gros Clark's version of the arboreal theory is not adequate.

WERE PRIMITIVE MAMMALS ARBOREAL?

Jones's version of the arboreal theory holds, not that the primate characteristics will be selected for in any arboreal mammal lineage, but that they all result from the primates' unique preservation of the grasping hands and mobile forelimbs supposedly found in the arboreal ancestors of the Mammalia. This conception of what early mammals were like can be traced to several sources. Huxley (26) and Dollo (27) proposed that the last common ancestor of the living marsupials had a grasping hind foot, but they thought this represented an arboreal specialization and that early mammals were terrestrial. Matthew (8), following Cope (28), reinterpreted this trait as a primitive retention, and suggested that Eocene and Paleocene placental mammals (and early ungulates in particular) also showed features indicating derivation from an arboreal ancestor.

Most of the supposedly arboreal features identified or inferred for the ancestral mammals by Matthew and his inheritors (8, 29, 30) can be shown (17, 31) to be either chimerical or irrelevant to arboreality. Others represent specializations fixed at various points along the reptilian lineage leading to mammals (such as the loss of all but two phalanges in the thumb and first toe, the "anomalous" arrangement of the thumb's extrinsic muscles, and the appearance

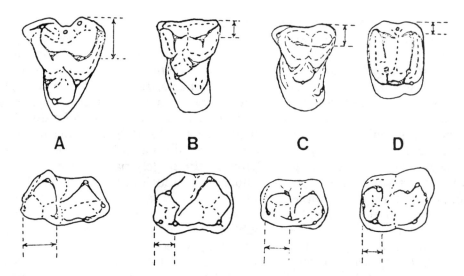

Figure 2: Upper left (above) and lower right (below) molar teeth of (A) the Cretaceous opossum *Alphadon wilsoni,* (B) the mid-Paleocene plesiadapoid *Palenochtha* minor, (C) the Late Cretaceous ungulate *Protungulatum donnae,* and (D) the early rodent *Paramys copei.* In the latter three, the stylar shelf (vertical arrows, above) and trigonid (horizontal arrows, below) are reduced by comparison with the more primitive condition seen in *Alphadon.*

of a tuber calcanei). Some are mere amphibian retentions (for example, persistence of the clavicle) that were lost in later mammalian lineages that developed cursorial specializations. Most of those who have believed that primitive mammals were lemur-like arboreal animals have also thought that terrestrial habits select for cursorial locomotion and thus for simplification and stabilization of the limbs; that "the final stage of this process is exemplified in the horse" (7); and that primates could therefore not be descended from ancestors that had long been terrestrial. However, the fact that placental ancestors could not have been very much like horses does not imply that they were very much like lemurs. The same suite of primitive retentions seen in the primates is also seen in many terrestrial Insectivora. Most extant insectivores manifest no ungulate-like trends toward simplifying the limb skeleton—apart from a general but not universal tendency toward distal tibiofibular fusion, which can also occur in arboreal primates (*Tarsius*) and marsupials (*Marmosa*) (32). Cursorial specializations are adaptations for rapid visually directed pursuit of prey or rapid and prolonged flight from predators, and are best developed in large mammals inhabiting open country. They would have had little or no selective advantage for the small, shrewlike mammals of the Mesozoic, and their absence does not imply arboreality.

In support of Matthew's hypothesis, Lewis (33) points out that in reptiles the peroneal muscles arising from the fibula insert on the fifth metatarsal, but in mammals part of this musculature forms a peroneus longus muscle, whose tendon runs across the sole to insert on the first metatarsal. Lewis suggests that peroneus longus originally acted to adduct a divergent first toe in arboreal grasping. However, in extant mammals with rudimentary first toes, the peroneus longus typically persists, shifting its attachment one toe over to the base of the second metatarsal. This demonstrates that it has some important function unrelated to adduction of the first toe. An alternative explanation of its original adaptive value is that it acted to evert the foot against resistance. If the earliest mammals walked with their feet pointing somewhat sideways, as echidnas do (34), eversion would have added propulsive thrust at the end of the stance phase, and would have worked more efficiently if part of the everting musculature exerted its force through an attachment at the anterior (preaxial) edge of the foot. Intermediate stages in the shift of this attachment across the sole would yield progressively more efficient eversion, whereas, if its original function had been to adduct the first toe, selectively advantageous intermediate stages would not be possible.

In short, there is no reason to believe that the Triassic ancestors of the Mammalia had clawless, grasping extremities, as Jones's version of the arboreal theory requires. The point may be settled by forthcoming studies of the virtually complete skeleton of the Triassic mammal *Megazostrodon* (35). There is in any event ample evidence to show that late cynodont reptiles and their mammalian descendants progressively developed a more elaborate olfactory apparatus than is found in other reptilian lineages (36), and that the earliest mammals had relatively small and degenerate eyes, in which the sauropsidan mechanisms of accommodation and nictitation had been lost (37). These facts suggest that the earliest mammals were shrewlike terrestrial creatures, guided largely by olfactory and tactile stimuli. This does not mean that early mammals were incapable of climbing branches that presented themselves as supports or obstacles; as Jenkins (38) points out, any small mammal needs this ability in a forest community.

THE VISUAL PREDATION HYPOTHESIS

If primate traits cannot be interpreted either as the products of a primitive arboreality retained only in primates, or as specializations necessarily selected for in any lineage of arboreal mammals, then neither form of the arboreal theory can explain why primates differ from squirrels or opossums, and an alternative set of explanations is needed. One recently proposed alternative (3, 23) has been induced from a survey of the distribution of primate-like traits in other taxa.

Grasping hind feet with a divergent first toe are characteristic of marsupials, chameleons, and certain arboreal mice and rats. Their adaptive significance varies. In at least some climbing mice, the grasping hallux is an adaptation to locomotion on the large siliceous stems of bamboos (39), on which claw grip is useless. In chameleons, grasping extremities represent a predatory adaptation, permitting prolonged and stealthy locomotion on slender terminal branches in pursuit of insects, which these specialized lizards stalk in the dense marginal undergrowth and lower canopy of tropical forests (40).

The notion that ancestral marsupials had a grasping hallux remains generally accepted. In the smaller South American opossums like *Marmosa robinsoni,*

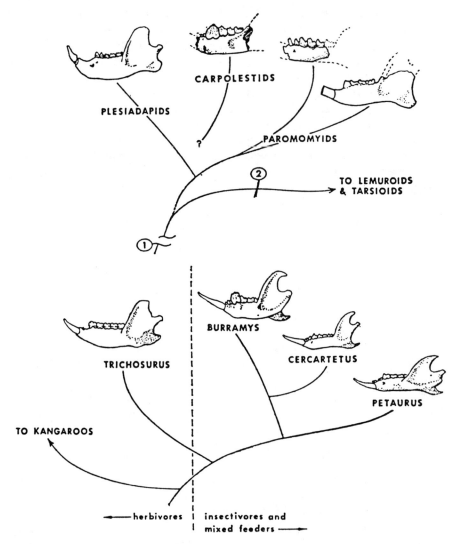

Figure 3: (Above) Representatives of the plesiadapoid radiation (left to right: *Plesiadapis tricuspidens, Carpodaptes aulacodon, Palaechthon alticuspis, Phenacolemur jepseni*). (Below) Possibly comparable extant representatives of the phalangeroid marsupial radiation: phylogenetic relationships after Kirsch (*58*). The morphological shift at ①, which established the dental traits shown in Fig. 3B, is usually taken as the boundary of the order Primates. The inferred shift at ②, here considered to be a shift toward visually directed predation, could (if monophyletic) serve as the boundary of a more coherent primate order.

this trait correlates with a chameleon-like way of life involving visually directed predation on insects "in the intricate interlacing of vine and branch that characterizes the second growth which abounds around the edges of clearings" (41). Insects, which these small didelphids require for adequate nutrition (42), are seized either in the hands or the mouth, bitten, and eaten held in one or both hands (41, 43, 44). The occasional use of the hands by didelphids in seizing prey becomes the most frequent pattern in small bush-frequenting Australian marsupials, including diprotodonts like *Cercartetus* as well as polyprotodonts like *Antechinus* (43, 45). *Cercartetus* and related small insect-eating diprotodonts like *Burramys* differ from other arboreal marsupials and resemble primates in having much-reduced claws (46). When allowance is made for allometry, insectivorous diprotodonts also have more convergent orbits than other marsupials (see Fig. 1C).

These comparisons suggest that the close-set eyes, grasping extremities, and reduced claws characteristic of most post-Paleocene primates may originally have been adaptations to a way of life like that of *Cercartetus* or *Burramys*, which forage for fruit and insects in the shrub layer of Australian forests and heaths. By this interpretation, visual convergence and correlated neurological specializations are predatory adaptations, comparable to the similar specializations seen in cats and owls, and allowing the predator in each case to gauge its victim's distance accurately without having to move its head. The grasping feet characteristic of primates allow insectivorous prosimians like the smaller cheirogaleines and lorisiforms to move cautiously up to insect prey and hold securely onto narrow supports when using both hands to catch the prey. Although claws are advantageous in most arboreal locomotor situations, they are actually a hindrance for a bush-dwelling animal that grasps slender twigs by opposition of preaxial and postaxial digits, and has little occasion to climb on larger supports (23).

Olfactory regression has not been characteristic of most arboreal mammals. The slight simplification of the olfactory apparatus seen in strepsirhine prosimians, and the marked regression found in haplorhines (tarsiers and higher primates), are necessary results of the approximation of the medial walls of the two orbits; since the optic nerve leaves the base of the skull and the orbital openings lie in the dermal bones of the skull roof, the olfactory connections between braincase and snout must necessarily be constricted if the orbital cones draw closer together. This effect is evident in a comparison of small felids with canids: in the former, the interorbital space is generally narrower, and the olfactory bulbs are correspondingly smaller and have constricted connections with the olfactory fossa (47). In *Tarsius*, the close approximation of the huge eyeballs reduces the interorbital volume (filled, in typical mammals, by olfactory scrolls of the ethmoid) to a single plate of compact bone, the interorbital septum, over the top of which a few olfactory fibers arch to reach a much-reduced nasal fossa (3, 48, 49). Small ceboids and cercopithecoids resemble *Tarsius* in these respects. Other lineages of visually directed predators have achieved comparable degrees of visual field overlap without pronounced olfactory constriction; in marsupials, optic convergence is produced by the co-existence of a low frontal region with a broad and high zygomatic arch (3), while in lorises the eyeballs come together around and outside the olfactory connections, which reach the nasal fossa between the optic nerves (3, 49). The unique arrangement seen in the smaller extant haplorhine primates probably reflects derivation from a big-eyed Eocene prosimian like *Pseudoloris* (which appears to have had a *Tarsius*-like interorbital septum); it does not represent perfected adaptation to arboreal life. Marsupial lineages which have evidently been arboreal since the Cretaceous have undergone no olfactory regression; arboreal life per se does not encourage loss of olfactory acuity.

Most of the distinctive primate characteristics can thus be explained as convergences with chameleons and small bush-dwelling marsupials (in the hands and feet) or with cats (in the visual apparatus). This implies that the last common ancestor of the extant primates, like many extant prosimians (for example, *Tarsius, Microcebus, Loris, Arctocebus,* and the smaller galagines), subsisted to an important extent on insects and other prey, which were visually located and manually captured in the insect-rich canopy and undergrowth of tropical forests.

THE FOSSIL RECORD

Like any other evolutionary explanation, the visual-predation theory must be tested against the relevant paleontological data. Here it encounters difficulties. However we choose to define the order Primates, its early representatives differ from the earliest placentals in several features of the molar teeth, including reduction of the stylar shelf and associated cristae and decrease in the size and height of the trigonid. Since similar changes are seen in the earliest rodents and ungulates (Fig. 2), Szalay (50, 51) has proposed that the differentiation of the Primates from the Insectivora involved an adaptive shift from an insectivorous diet to a predominantly herbivorous one. If true, this vitiates the visual-predation hypothesis.

Szalay's thesis has recently been challenged by Simons (52), who suggests that, in at least four of the six families of early Tertiary mammals usually assigned to the order Primates, the earliest representatives have molars functionally similar to those of the carnivorous prosimian *Tarsius*. Although it has been said that the carnivorous diet of *Tarsius* could not be inferred from the morphology of its dentition (51), my colleague R. F. Kay has recently developed a multivariate biometric statistic which is over 90 percent accurate in "predicting" the dietary habits of the extant primates, including *Tarsius*. Despite the reduction of the stylar shelf in extant prosimians, at least some of them have recognizable dental adaptations for masticating prey; other shearing mechanisms have replaced the primitive shear of trigonid against paracrista and metacrista (53). The application of Kay's procedure to early primate dentitions will permit us to test certain aspects of the visual-predation theory.

The plesiadapoids of the Paleocene (Plesiadapidae, Paromomyidae, Carpolestidae) are assigned by paleontologists to the order Primates, although they show none of the diagnostic primate traits listed by Mivart (5). Where known, plesiadapoid orbits are small and widely set, there is no postorbital bar, the braincase is small relative to the facial skeleton, and there is no apparent reduction of the olfactory apparatus; *Plesiadapis*, at least, also had clawed digits resembling those of a squirrel or dermopteran (*50, 54*). The plesiadapoids are assigned to the primates on the basis of minutely detailed resemblances between their molars and those of later undoubted primates; where known, the ear region of plesiadapoids also shows certain diagnostic primate features (*50, 55*).

There is little doubt that the plesiadapoids are close collateral relatives of the Eocene prosimians. There is also little doubt that the known plesiadapoids are not directly ancestral to the Eocene prosimian, since at least one genus in two of the three Eocene families (Adapidae, Anaptomorphidae, and Tarsiidae) retained teeth that had been lost in known plesiadapoids (*56*). Plesiadapoid lineages that can be traced through time did not converge with the early lemurs and tarsiers of the Eocene, but developed progressively more specialized dentitions displaying loss of canines and anterior premolars, hypertrophy of the fourth lower premolar, enlargement and complication of the anterior incisors, and other peculiarities. The fossil evidence suggests that the (unknown) lineages leading to the Eocene "primates of modern aspect" (*57*) must have branched off from the plesiadapoid lineages at least by the Torrejonian (mid-Paleocene).

The radiation of the phalangeroid diprotodont marsupials in Australia provides suggestive parallels with the plesiadapoid radiation. Plesiadapoid-like dental specializations, including reduction of the stylar shelf and hypertrophy of the lower central incisors, must have characterized the last common ancestor of the diprotodonts. Of the three extant diprotodont superfamilies (*58*), the phalangeroids have been the most successful. The ancestral phalangeroids were probably small arboreal mixed feeders; from these are derived not only the kangaroos, but also a complex radiation of arboreal marsupials. These include many forms with plesiadapoid counterparts (Fig. 3). The larger and more herbivorous phalangeroids like *Trichosurus* and *Pseudocheirus* have strong claws and post-incisor diastema, and are roughly comparable to the plesiadapids. Smaller phalangeroids have retained varying amounts of insect prey in their diets, and generally more complete dental formulas; they can be compared to the early paromomyids. From such an ancestry there have arisen the gliding omnivore *Petaurus*, likened by Gingerich (*59*) to the specialized paromomyid *Phenacolemur*, and the mountain pygmy possum *Burramys*, whose enlarged, serrated third lower premolars, used in cutting open seeds and hard insect cuticles (*60*), find a parallel in the carpolestid plesiadapoids. Unspecialized paromomyids like *Palaechthon* (Fig. 3) may prove to be plesiadapoid counterparts of *Cercartetus*.

As shown above, the adaptations of *Cercartetus* for visually directed predation among fine branches represent plausible structural antecedents for the traits that distinguish the extant primates. However, *Cercartetus* is considerably more primitive in these respects than superficially similar prosimians like *Microcebus murinus*. This is equally true of *Palaechthon*, which resembles *Plesiadapis* and differs from typical Eocene prosimians in having widely separated orbits, an unossified postorbital ligament, and a relatively small braincase (*54*).

Since early plesiadapoids had not acquired the traits (considered here to be adaptations to visually directed predation in forest undergrowth) that distinguish primate families from the Eocene on, and since later plesiadapoids did not converge with the true prosimians of the Eocene, it has been suggested (3) that the order Primates would be more coherent if the plesiadapoids were relegated to the Insectivora, and the postorbital bar and clawless, divergent hallux were taken as diagnostic primate traits, as Mivart considered them 100 years ago. It has been objected that "this diagnostic simplification certainly would not justify the resulting loss of phylogenetic information" (61). Similar objections could be made to the exclusion of the therapsid reptiles from the Mammalia, or of the rhipidistian fishes from the Amphibia. Taxonomic boundaries must reflect more than mere phylogenetic affinity; they must also mark important adaptive shifts that underlie the evolutionary trends characteristic of a radiating higher taxon.

SUMMARY

Clawed digits, nonopposable thumbs and first toes, and wide-set eyes are primitive mammalian traits. For an arboreal mammal, the adaptive value of these traits is equal or superior to that of primate-like grasping extremities and closely apposed eyes. The loss of the primitive traits in the order Primates therefore cannot be explained by merely invoking the putative selection pressures imposed by arboreal locomotion per se. Visually directed predation on insects in the lower canopy and marginal growth of tropical forests is characteristic of many living prosimians, and also of small marsupials and chameleons. Primate-like specializations of the visual apparatus and extremities occur in all these groups. This suggests that grasping extremities were evolved because they facilitate cautious well-controlled movements in pursuit of prey on slender supports; and that optic convergence and stereoscopy in primates originally had the same adaptive significance they have in cats. The arboreal theory of primate differentiation, proposed in two incompatible forms by G. E. Smith and F. W. Jones, can be shown to be inadequate by counterexamples drawn from other lineages of arboreal mammals. Although some evolutionary biologists and philosophers regard such counterexamples as irrelevant, their relevance must be admitted if we want to work toward genuinely explanatory accounts of historical processes.

REFERENCES AND NOTES

1. J. Hospers, in *Essays in Conceptual Analysis*, A. Flew, Ed. (Macmillan, London, 1966), pp. 94–119.
2. See, for example, M. Scriven, *Science* **130**, 477 (1959); G. G. Simpson, *This View of Life* (Harcourt, Brace & World, New York, 1964), p. 121; R. C. Lewontin, *J. Hist. Biol.* **2**, 35 (1969); A. Feduccia, *Evolution* **27**, 166 (1973).
3. M. Cartmill, in *The Functional and Evolutionary Biology of Primates*, R. Tuttle, Ed. (Aldine-Atherton, Chicago, 1972), pp. 97–122.
4. J. E. Gray, *Catalogue of Monkeys, Lemurs, and Fruit-eating Bats* (British Museum, London, 1870).

5. St. G. Mivart, *Proc. Zool. Soc. Lond.* (1873), p. 484.
6. G. E. Smith, *Smithson Inst. Annu. Rep.* (1912), p. 553.
7. F. W. Jones, *Arboreal Man* (Edward Arnold, London, 1916).
8. W. D. Matthew, *Am. Nat.* **38**, 811 (1904).
9. L. Van Valen, *Evolution* **19**, 137 (1965); C. B. G. Campbell, *ibid.* **20**, 276 (1966); R. D. Martin, *Science* **152**, 1402 (1966); W. P. Luckett, *J. Reprod. Fertil.* (Suppl. 6), 419 (1969).
10. W. E. Le Gros Clark, *History of the Primates* [British Museum (Natural History), London, 1970], p. 30. This idea seems to have originated with T. Collins, *Trans. Ophthalmol. Soc. U.K.* **41**, 10 (1921).
11. J. H. Kaas, R. W. Guillery, J. M. Allman, *Brain Behav. Evol.* **6**, 253 (1972).
12. W. E. Le Gros Clark, *Proc. Zool. Soc. Lond.* (1925), p. 559.
13. H. E. Peterka, *Trans. Kans. Acad. Sci.* **39**, 313 (1937).
14. F. D'Souza, in *Prosimian Biology*, G. A. Doyle, R. D. Martin, A. C. Walker, Eds. (Duckworth, London, in press); W. C. O. Hill, *Zoo Life* **4**, 98 (1949); J. L. Harrison, *Malay. Nat. J.* **5**, 134 (1951); R. T. Hatt, *Bull. N.Y. State Coll. For. (Syracuse)* **2** (No. 1-B), 1 (1929); M. Shorten, *Squirrels* (Collins, London, 1954).
15. A. Jolly, *Lemur Behavior* (Univ. of Chicago Press, Chicago, 1966). Leaps of 12 to 24 body lengths are reported for *Lemur macaco* by J. Buettner-Janusch [*Physical Anthropology: A Perspective* (Wiley, New York, 1973), p. 302]; *Galago senegalensis* is reported to leap more than 36 body lengths by J. M. Watson [*Uganda J.* **15**, 193 (1971)].
16. R. I. Pocock, *Proc. Zool. Soc. Lond.* (No. 2), (1922), p. 1171.
17. M. Cartmill, thesis, University of Chicago (1970). The data points yielding these regressions are pictured in *Nature (Lond.)* **232**, 566 (1971).
18. I. T. Diamond and W. C. Hall, *Science* **164**, 251 (1969).
19. J. K. Harting, K. K. Glendenning, I. T. Diamond, W. C. Hall, *Am. J. Phys. Anthropol.* **38**, 383 (1973).
20. S. Polyak, *The Vertebrate Visual System* (Univ. of Chicago Press, Chicago, 1957), pp. 308–322.
21. G. L. Johnson, *Phil. Trans. R. Soc. Lond.* **194**, 1 (1901); D. H. Hubel and T. N. Wiesel, *Nature (Lond.)* **225**, 41 (1970).
22. M. Glickstein, *Science* **164**, 917 (1969).
23. M. Cartmill, in *Primate Locomotion*, F. A. Jenkins, Jr., Ed. (Academic Press, New York, 1974), pp. 45–83.
24. H. Rothe, *Z. Morphol. Anthropol.* **64**, 90 (1972).
25. This is true for the three Asian lorisine species; but *Perodicticus potto* and (judging from one specimen) *Arctocebus calabarensis* have galago-like interorbital breadths. Character divergence from the sympatric galagines has resulted in a specialized dependence on olfaction in *Perodicticus* and *Arctocebus;* their retention of a broad interorbital space probably reflects this, rather than any need to maximize parallax. See P. Charles-Dominique, *Biol. Gabonica* **7**, 121 (1971); A. Bishop, in *Evolutionary and Genetic Biology of Primates*, J. Buettner-Janusch, Ed. (Academic Press, New York, 1964), vol. 2, p. 181.
26. T. H. Huxley, *Proc. Zool. Soc. Lond.* (1880), p. 649.
27. L. Dollo, *Miscellanés Biologiques* (Station Zoologique de Wimereux, Paris, 1899), pp. 188–203; *Bull. Sci. Fr. Belg.* (1900), p. 275.
28. E. D. Cope, *Am. Nat.* **19**, 457 (1885).
29. H. Klaatsch, *The Evolution and Progress of Mankind* (Unwin, London, 1923), p. 68; D. J. Morton, *The Human Foot* (Columbia Univ. Press, New York, 1935), p. 23.
30. R. D. Martin, *Man J. R. Anthropol. Inst.* **3**, 377 (1968).
31. J. W. Gidley, *J. Wash. Acad. Sci.* **9**, 273 (1919); R. W. Haines, *Q. Rev. Biol.* **33**, 1 (1958); A. S. Romer, *Osteology of the Reptiles* (Univ. of Chicago Press, Chicago, 1955).
32. C. H. Barnett and J. R. Napier, *J. Anat.* **87**, 207 (1953).

33. O. J. Lewis, *Int. Rev. Gen. Exp. Zool.* **1,** 165 (1964).
34. F. A. Jenkins, Jr., *Science* **168,** 1473 (1970).
35. A. W. Crompton and F. A. Jenkins, Jr., *Biol. Rev. (Camb.)* **43,** 427 (1968); P. Wood, L. Vaczek, D. J. Hamblin, J. N. Leonard, *Life Before Man* (Time-Life Books, New York, 1972), p. 58.
36. G. G. Simpson, *A Catalogue of the Mesozoic Mammalia* [British Museum (Natural History), London, 1928], p. 87; J. A. Hopson, *Ann. N.Y. Acad. Sci.* **167,** 199 (1969).
37. E. P. Stibbe, *J. Anat.* **62,** 159 (1928); G. L. Walls, *The Vertebrate Eye and Its Adaptive Radiation* (Hafner, New York, reprint, 1965).
38. F. A. Jenkins, Jr., in *Primate Locomotion,* F. A. Jenkins, Jr., Ed. (Academic Press, New York, 1974), pp. 85–115.
39. L. Medway, *Malay. Nat. J.* **18,** 104 (1964); G. G. Musser, *Am. Mus. Nov.* No. 2503 (1972).
40. K. P. Schmidt, *Bull. Am. Mus. Nat. Hist.* **39,** 385 (1919).
41. R. K. Enders, *Bull. Mus. Comp. Zool.* **78,** 383 (1935).
42. G. E. Hudson, *J. Mammal.* **13,** 159 (1932).
43. J. F. Eisenberg and P. Leyhausen, *Z. Tierpsychol.* **30,** 59 (1972).
44. P. Murray, personal communication. Eisenberg and Leyhausen (*43*) report that the hands are never used to seize prey; but the observations of Enders and Murray contradict this.
45. V. V. Hickman and J. L. Hickman, *Proc. Zool. Soc. Lond.* **135,** 365 (1960).
46. F. W. Jones, *The Mammals of South Australia* (British Science Guild, Adelaide, 1924), part 2; R. M. Warneke, *Aust. Mammal Soc. Bull.* **2,** 94 (1967).
47. L. B. Radinsky, *Ann. N.Y. Acad. Sci.* **167,** 277 (1969).
48. A. J. E. Cave, *Am. J. Phys. Anthropol.* **26,** 277 (1967).
49. W. B. Spatz, *Folia Primatol.* **9,** 22 (1968); *Acta Anat.* **75,** 489 (1970). Chameleons have a tarsier-like rostral configuration.
50. F. S. Szalay, *Bull. Am. Mus. Nat. Hist.* **140,** 193 (1969).
51. _____, in *The Functional and Evolutionary Biology of Primates,* R. Tuttle, Ed. (Aldine-Atherton, Chicago, 1972), pp. 3–35.
52. E. L. Simons, in *Prosimian Biology,* G. A. Doyle, R. D. Martin, A. C. Walker, Eds. (Duckworth, London, in press).
53. R. F. Kay, thesis, Yale University (1973).
54. D. Russell, *Mém. Mus. Natl. Hist. Nat. Ser. C. Sci. Terre* **13,** 1 (1964); R. W. Wilson and F. S. Szalay, *Am. Mus. Nov.* No. 2499 (1972).
55. F. S. Szalay, *Am. J. Phys. Anthropol.* **36,** 59 (1972).
56. Four upper and four lower premolars on each side are still present in the adapid dentition, and (in Simons' interpretation) in the dentition of the probable anaptomorphid *Teilhardina.* The lower dental formula of Eocene tarsiids may be 0.1.4.3, but this is debated (*57*).
57. E. L. Simons, *Primate Evolution* (Macmillan, New York, 1972).
58. J. A. W. Kirsch, *Nature (Lond.)* **217,** 418 (1968).
59. P. D. Gingerich, *J. Dent. Res.,* in press.
60. H. Dimpel and J. H. Calaby, *Victorian Nat.* **89,** 101 (1972).
61. P. D. Gingerich, *Nature (Lond.)* **244,** 517 (1973).
62. I thank K. Brown, P. D. Gingerich, W. C. Hall, W. L. Hylander, F. A. Jenkins, Jr., R. F. Kay, and V. T. Lukas for their help. Several of the drawings of early Tertiary mammals are redrawn after materials furnished by Dr. Kay. Portions of the research underlying this paper were supported by grants-in-aid from the Society of the Sigma Xi and the Wenner-Gren Foundation for Anthropological Research, Inc.

A New Ancient Ape

Kevin McKean

The most important fossil to come out of Africa in recent years was dug not from a dusty hillside but from the National Museum of Kenya in Nairobi. Two scientists sorted through 10,000 fossil fragments in the museum's vast collection to assemble the most complete skeleton ever of what may well be a distant ancestor of apes and men. The bones of this slender, monkey-like creature may clarify the evolutionary steps leading to modern apes and their close relatives, human beings. They should also help resolve a 30-year controversy over the place in evolution of the small tree-dwelling ape named *Proconsul africanus*, the genus and species to which the skeleton belongs.

Anatomist Alan Walker and geologist Martin Pickford, who assembled the skeleton, have yet to publish their work. But Walker described it at an anthropologists' meeting this April in Detroit. Elwyn Simons, director of Duke University's primate center and a prominent student of human origins, calls it flatly "one of the most important fossils ever found." John Fleagle, of the State University of New York at Stony Brook, finds the discovery "very exciting" because so much of the skeleton was found. Most ancient fossils consist of teeth or fragments of jaws, the tough, inedible parts that are likely to survive. But the *Proconsul* skeleton, which belonged to a young female that lived more than 17 million years ago, is from half to three-quarters complete. This makes it possible for scientists to measure the relative lengths of the limbs and draw conclusions about how the animal moved. For comparison, the famous Lucy, a 3.7-million-year-old female *Australopithecus* found by Don Johanson in Ethiopia in 1974, is about 40 per cent complete.

Scientists are particularly intrigued with *Proconsul* because the Miocene, the period from 24 million to 6 million years ago during which it lived, was a time of radical change in the earth's climate and in its animals. Average temperatures in the middle latitudes dropped as much as 10 degrees Fahrenheit. Dry savannahs replaced many of the tropical and subtropical forests that had once stretched as far north as southern England and Canada.

In Africa, some groups of primates ventured out of their trees and onto the ground, a shift that may have begun the evolutionary changes that ultimately led to man. There is not enough evidence yet to say whether *Proconsul africanus* belongs directly on this pre-ape and pre-human line or only near it. But, says

Simons, "even if it's not the direct ancestor, it's a good approximation of what the common ancestor might have looked like."

The relationship of *Proconsul africanus* to modern apes and men has been a matter of debate ever since the species was named in 1933. Arthur Hopwood of the British Museum thought the jaw and tooth fragments he was studying looked remarkably like a chimpanzee's. With a touch of whimsy, he coined the name *Proconsul*—"forerunner of Consul"—because Consul was then a popular name for performing chimps.

The eminent anthropologist Louis Leakey later insisted that *Proconsul africanus* was not related to apes. Always eager to push back the time when apes and human beings branched out from a common ancestor, he proclaimed *Proconsul* the earliest direct ancestor of man. Leakey based his opinion on a *Proconsul* skull found by his wife, Mary, on Rusinga Island in Lake Victoria in 1948. The skull, about the size of a present-day gibbon's, was one of the most complete fossil primate skulls then known. It lacked the bony ridges over the eyes that are characteristic of apes. Moreover, it had no trace of the so-called simian shelf, a flat inner lip of bone where the two halves of an ape jaw meet. Leakey took this to mean that the split between men and apes had already occurred by *Proconsul's* time. Scientists today think it was more recent, somewhere between 5 million to 15 million years ago.

In 1951 the British geologist Thomas Whitworth, while surveying Rusinga Island, stumbled on evidence that was to unseat *Proconsul* from the human line. Whitworth found a rock formation that he thought had resulted from limestone sediments filling a pothole in an ancient river. It was chock full of fossils.

Once the limestone was broken up and sent to the Nairobi museum, scientists identified a virtual Noah's ark. There were fossils from four pigs, twelve rodents, one lizard, two snakes, one flamingo-like bird, two ruminants, two carnivores—and some limb bones from an immature *Proconsul africanus*.

The new fossils joined others gathered earlier on Rusinga by the British-Kenya Miocene Expedition. There were so many fossils—a New York *Times* article of 1953 placed the number in the millions—that it took several years for them to be sorted and sent to scholars for study. Thus it was not until 1959 that the classic monograph of the limb bones was published. This paper, by the British anatomists John Napier and Peter Davis, concluded that the animal was far different from what any sort of human ancestor ought to be. Its limb bones, they said, made it resemble a primitive monkey-like ape.

In the mid-1960s Simons and David Pilbeam tried to do away with the genus *Proconsul* altogether by lumping it under *Dryopithecus*, another genus of Miocene ape.

By this time the creature's status had become quite confusing. Some scholars were certain that it had scrambled along branches like a cebid monkey; others had it swinging by its arms like a gibbon; still others thought it walked on its knuckles like a chimpanzee. Says the University of Michigan's Philip Gingerich, "I like to use *Proconsul* as a teaching example of how every anthropologist has studied the thing and come to a different conclusion."

94

The Napier-Davis paper on which much of this more recent scholarship was based dealt only with bones from the left arm, the right foot, the jaw, and portions of the skull of *Proconsul*. In the mid-1970s, says Alan Walker, the first hint appeared that more parts of the skeleton might have been excavated and lost.

"I was in Nairobi doing work on the hominids," Walker recalls, "when one day somebody said that Martin Pickford had noticed a primate foot in some collections of fossil pigs." Walker, an anatomist at the Johns Hopkins School of Medicine in Baltimore, had done his Ph.D. thesis under Napier and was familiar with the Rusinga fossils and the kind of rock in which they had been found. When he saw the yellow primate bones protruding from the coarse limestone matrix, he exclaimed, "I know where that comes from. That's from Rusinga Island." A check of the records showed that, sure enough, the specimen was from Whitworth's pothole. That, plus the fact that the bones (like the ones studied by Napier and Davis) were those of an immature *africanus*, made it almost certain that they were from the same individual. (The mix-up apparently occurred because fossils are hard to identify while still encased in stone; museum workers did not recognize them as belonging to primates.)

Walker and Pickford had known each other since 1966. Both had been born in Britain and were friends of Louis Leakey and his son Richard, the museum's director (see Reviews). Yet they did not know each other well. Walker, 42, had settled in the United States, while Pickford, 38, a geologist at the museum, had lived in Kenya since childhood. Also, Pickford was studying fossils from the Miocene period while Walker worked in the more recent Pleistocene. "You could say we were several million years apart," Pickford jokes.

Now the two men realized they had stumbled on an important find. If the foot of *Proconsul africanus* had been misidentified as a pig's, they wondered, how much more of the skeleton might be lying around the museum under the wrong label?

They did not act on their suspicion immediately. But in 1979 Pickford visited Rusinga Island and came back with a new primate foot—that of *Proconsul nyanzae*, a contemporary, slightly larger relative of *africanus*. These were the most complete bones known for *nyanzae*. But they were missing a crucial bone known as the cuboid, which serves as a pivot for the foot and provides clues to its flexibility.

To search for this bone, and to examine the sites where *africanus* and *nyanzae* had been found, Pickford returned to Rusinga last February with Walker. The island today is covered with dry grasses and occasional fig trees that serve as nesting places for a local species of wading bird. But during the Miocene it was covered with tropical rain forest. The age of its fossils can be fixed quite accurately (they are between 17 million and 18.5 million years old) by radioactive dating of its volcanic sediments. The sediments are rich in calcium carbonate, or limestone, which is almost ideal for preserving fossils. Says Walker, "You'd get a limestone mud that would encase like cement any little bugs, insects, or whatever." Even soft body tissue was sometimes preserved; one fossil lizard was found with its tongue hanging out.

95

After collecting some promising blocks of rock that later proved to contain the missing *nyanzae* cuboid, the two men walked to the area of Whitworth's pothole.

"Whitworth recorded that it was two hundred and eighty yards west, thirty degrees north of the summit of the hill," says Walker. "So I stood on the summit with a compass and Martin paced off two hundred and eighty yards. Soon he stopped and turned around, and there were all these bones lying on the surface." The two men knew they were close to the pothole, but they could not see it. Then a local tribesman came up and said, "Are you looking for where they dug a long time ago? You are standing on it." Pickford and Walker gathered the fossil-bearing rocks into a pile to be collected on a future trip.

"When we came back from Rusinga, having seen all the bones at the site, we said, 'Hey, let's see if there are more bones in the museum,' " Walker recalls. The two scientists appropriated a large museum table and began to lay out every unidentified or dubiously identified specimen that had been collected from the Rusinga pothole in earlier years. Says Walker, "We got parts that were labeled as pigs, parts that were labeled as birds, and parts that were indeterminate. Then we started going through the pieces we had, looking on each block for other bones to see if we could find ends that glued on." Soon bits of the fossil began to emerge. The bones clearly belonged to the same skeleton studied by Napier and Davis; some of the new bones fit perfectly on the old ones.

The result was a skeleton that represents nearly every bone in *africanus's* hand, forelimb, hind limb, and feet. All told, the recovered bones make up about 50 per cent of a full skeleton. But if they are "mirror-imaged"—that is, if missing bones on one side can be considered identical to known bones on the other—the skeleton is 75 per cent full.

Besides limb bones, the skeleton includes most of the right shoulder blade, several vertebrae and ribs, and, of course, the jaw and skull fragments found earlier. Spreading casts of some of the fossils on a table in his Baltimore lab in June, Walker totted up the bones that have been recovered. "We don't have the pelvis yet, but we're pretty sure it will come. It may still be on the site. I think I saw the piece that goes just here on this ulna [a lower arm bone], but we didn't bring it back." The fossils themselves reside in a foam-lined plywood box at the museum in Nairobi.

Scientists know that this *Proconsul* was female because its canine teeth were small; the males had prominent canines. It was seven or eight years old, the equivalent of the late teens in a human being, and weighed about 25 pounds. In normal stance on all fours, *Proconsul africanus* was a towering 18 inches high. It probably lived almost entirely in trees, scrambling to the ends of branches to get fruit, the food of modern apes.

Ever since Napier and Davis's paper, conventional wisdom has regarded *Proconsul* as apelike in its teeth and monkey-like in its limbs. But the new fossil skeleton may upset that. For one thing, Napier and Davis concluded that the animal had monkey-like limbs in part because its radius (one of the two lower-arm bones) was short relative to its humerus (the upper-arm bone). They based this conclusion on the fact that the radius tends to be shorter in animals that get around on four legs and elongated in modern animals that swing from branch to branch, a form of locomotion called brachiation. But Napier and Davis had only a fragment of the left humerus from which to estimate its total length. Walker can use the right humerus to show that the Napier-Davis estimate was too large. The real radius-to-humerus ratio, he says, is in the range of that of a modern chimpanzee.

The implications of this and other features is that *Proconsul africanus* may be a more advanced creature than has been thought; it may be more firmly headed down the evolutionary path that led to modern apes and men. It seems unlikely that *africanus* spent much time on the ground. But *Proconsul nyanzae*, judging from its foot bones, may have used the ground to get from tree to tree much as modern chimps do.

The question now is whether one of the *Proconsul* species was an ancestor of a creature known as *Ramapithecus*, which appeared in Africa in the mid-Miocene, then spread across India and Asia. Only a few limb bones thought to be from *Ramapithecus* have been found. But some scholars argue on the basis of jaws and teeth that the animal may have walked upright. If so, it would explain why Lucy and her contemporaries 3.7 million years ago already had a well developed, erect, human-like posture. Scientists theorize that the roots of this upright posture may lie in either the tendency of some apes to swing from branch to branch or the tendency of others to spend more time on the ground. *Proconsul africanus's* wrist and hand bones show some ability for overarm swinging. Such swinging forces the pelvis and thigh into an upright posture. *Proconsul nyanzae*, at least from a preliminary analysis of its foot, may have been partly a ground-dweller. Thus these ancient apes may have been taking the first faltering steps toward an upright stride.

The Descent of Hominoids and Hominids

David Pilbeam

Findings over the past five years have made it possible to trace with greater assurance the divergence of the apes from the Old World monkeys and the later divergence of humans from apes.

Human understanding of human evolution has advanced greatly in the past generation and even in the past five years. Since the 1960's, for example, paleoanthropology has ceased being a discipline of concern only to physical anthropologists and a few interested paleontologists. It has evolved into a broad multidisciplinary pursuit that enlists the services of historical geologists, ecologists, molecular biologists, zoologists, students of animal behavior and even chemists and physicists.

In the Linnaean classification of living things human beings belong to the Order Primates, which also includes the apes, the monkeys and prosimians such as the lemurs. Within that order is the superfamily Hominoidea, including only humans and the apes. Within that superfamily, in turn, is the family Hominidae, including only humans and their extinct relatives closer than the apes.

Let me briefly review how the evolution of hominoids and hominids was understood some five years ago by a leading physical anthropologist, Sherwood L. Washburn of the University of California at Berkeley, and contrast that summary of the consensus then with the consensus now [see "The Evolution of Man," by Sherwood L. Washburn; SCIENTIFIC AMERICAN, September, 1978]. At that time revolutionary advances in geology and molecular biology had already challenged earlier ideas about the geography and timing of hominid evolution and the biological relations between humans and the other higher primates. For example, data from molecular biology made the reconstruction of primate descent a simpler task. Many physical anthropologists were skeptical, however, of the molecular biologists' suggestion that African apes (chimpanzees and gorillas) were closely related to humans but Asian apes (orangutans and gibbons) were not. The biggest surprise was the molecular biologists' proposal that humans had diverged from the African line of apes much less than 10 million years ago.

Washburn's summary also suggested the *Ramapithecus*, a Miocene hominoid widely distributed in the Old World, could have been the hominoid ancestral to all living great apes and to human kind. Further, the discovery in Ethiopia of *Australopithecus afarensis* (widely known from the partial skeleton called "Lucy") and in Tanzania of the famous Laetoli footprints showed that by more than 3.5 million years ago there had evolved in Africa primitive hominids: small-brained, ground-dwelling primates that walked on two legs and had canine teeth that were relatively small and did not project. The discoveries in Ethiopia and Tanzania showed bipedalism was the first and most basic of hominid evolutionary adaptations. By analogy with chimpanzees, these early hominids probably used wood and other naturally occurring materials as tools. Indeed, the contrast between the hominids' small canines and the projecting canines of the chimpanzee suggested that among the hominids the offensive role of canines had already been taken over by tools.

By the time another million years had passed, in Washburn's summary of the consensus, hominids with larger brains had evolved in Africa. They made stone tools and lived alongside a robust (that is, relatively heavy-boned and large-toothed) species of *Australopithecus* that became extinct in about another million years. Even before then, say by 1.5 million years ago, a more advanced hominid had appeared: *Homo erectus*. The association of its stone tools with animal bones was accepted as clear evidence that hunting behavior had become a hominid attribute long before the hominid brain expanded to its modern size.

Brain size and tool complexity increased only slowly between then and about 100,00 years ago, when a still more advanced hominid arose: *Homo sapiens*. These increases, however, are indirect evidence for the reorganization of the hominid brain. With the arrival of *H. sapiens* the rate of change in stone-tool types began to accelerate. The anatomical evolutionary changes are seen mainly in the skull. Then, about 40,000 years ago, anatomically modern humans appeared and spread rapidly throughout the Old World. At the same time the rate of behavioral change, as attested by changes in stone tools and other human artifacts, approached what we now expect from "normal" human cultural behavior. Washburn closed his discussion with the suggestion that fully modern human language, which possibly did not exist before the appearance of anatomically modern man, catalyzed this behavioral advance, although no direct anatomical evidence bears on the point.

In the five years since Washburn's summary important new fossil discoveries have been made, not all of them in the field. Fuller descriptions of earlier fossils have been published. Paleoanthropologists have become better able to interpret their data through the work of behavioral scientists, and they have become increasingly aware of relevant developments in the other natural sciences. These trends have shifted the discipline toward a greater integration with the rest of the biological community.

At the same time there is increasing doubt about the degree to which narratives of human evolution can be "brought to life." Just how detailed and reliable can such accounts be? Hard problems arise when the hominids of the past are interpreted in terms of the hominids of the present. The early hominids were, after all, markedly different from any living today. In many instances, however, these differences have been ignored and early hominids have been made to seem too much like modern human beings. Let me review some of these problems, starting at the beginning with the evolution of hominoids, the group from which the hominids sprang.

HOMINOID EVOLUTION

The earlier debate between physical anthropologists and molecular biologists over the pattern and timing of hominoid evolution is now basically settled. Most paleontologists (and comparative anatomists) agree the molecular patterns showing the African apes are genetically very little different from humans and the Asian apes are about twice as different reflect the fact that the common ancestor hominids share with the chimpanzee and the gorilla was in existence only about half as long ago as the last common ancestor of all the larger hominoids.

Detailed comparative anatomy shows that the patterns of morphological resemblance among living hominoids confirm the molecular findings. The great apes and the hominids do not form what is called a monophyletic group, that is, they did not share a last common ancestor after the lineage leading to humans diverged. Instead African apes and humans are monophyletic with respect to the Asian apes. (That had in fact been proposed by certain earlier anatomists.)

This means features common to all apes, such as the absence of a tail, must either have been retained from the last ancestor of all large hominoids or have evolved separately in the different apes. As a consequence of the molecular findings morphologists are reexamining hominoid anatomical characteristics and similarities and looking more closely at the processes of embryonic development and their genetic controls.

These "new" molecular branching patterns are not incompatible with the hominoid fossil record. The time is past when many paleontologists placed the origin of the hominids in the middle Miocene, 16 or 15 million years ago, or when some molecular biologists held that the entire hominoid radiation took place within the past 10 million years, with the hominids diverging only a brief four million years ago. A tentative consensus would now place the radiation of all the great apes from an ancestral stock in the middle Miocene, with the hominids splitting from an African ape lineage in the late Miocene, perhaps eight or seven million years ago.

Why was the hominoid fossil record misinterpreted, at least by dimmer paleontologists such as me? There are a number of reasons. First, far too much attention was being paid to the fossil record as a source of information about evolutionary branching sequences. It is now clear that the molecular record can tell more about hominoid branching patterns than the fossil record does. (The fossil record remains, however, the only source of direct knowledge of past evolutionary states.) Misinterpretation also resulted from the fact that the hominoid fossil record going back before the last four million years of hominid evolution has until recently been both fragmentary and poorly dated. It consisted almost entirely of teeth and small pieces of jaw, which are parts of the body that are

100

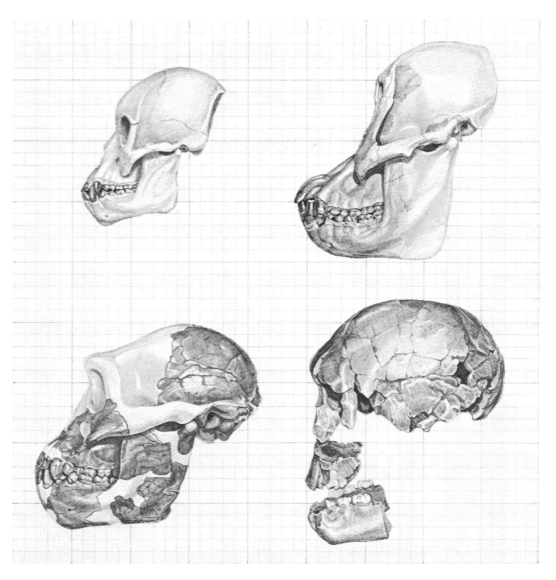

FOUR FOSSIL SKULLS, shown in profile in this painting, exemplify key stages in the branching off of hominoids from ancestral Old World monkey stock and the later branching off of hominids from ancestal hominoid stock. At the top left is the best-known of the early Miocene apes, *Proconsul africanus*, a baboon-size primate that is perhaps similar to the common ancestor of all apes and humans. At the top right is the substantially larger late Miocene ape. *Sivapithecus*, first known from fossil teeth and jaw fragments found in foothills of the Himalayas in the 1900's. It may have been ancestral to the only living large hominoid of Asia, the orangutan. At the bottom left is the earliest-known African Pliocene hominid, *Australopithecus afarensis*, a species that walked erect in the period between four and two million years ago. At the bottom right is the much larger-brained hominid *Homo habilis*, which was first found in Kenya in 1972. Members of the species ranged southern and eastern Africa for a few hundred thousand years beginning about two million years ago.

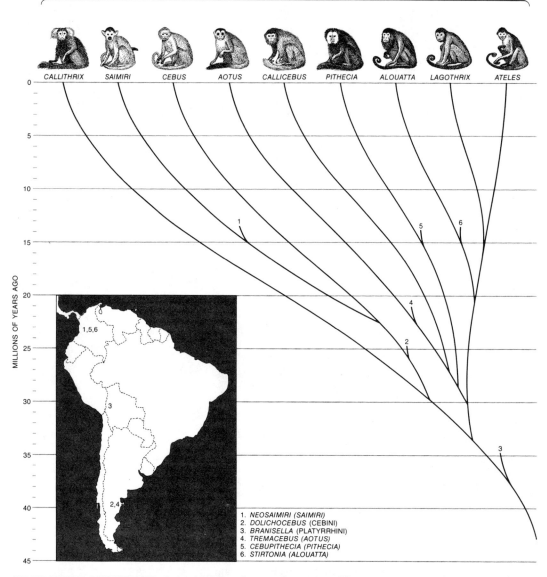

PLATYRRHINI

CALLITHRIX SAIMIRI CEBUS AOTUS CALLICEBUS PITHECIA ALOUATTA LAGOTHRIX ATELES

MILLIONS OF YEARS AGO

1. NEOSAIMIRI (SAIMIRI)
2. DOLICHOCEBUS (CEBINI)
3. BRANISELLA (PLATYRRHINI)
4. TREMACEBUS (AOTUS)
5. CEBUPITHECIA (PITHECIA)
6. STIRTONIA (ALOUATTA)

BRANCHING SEQUENCE of the higher primates from 45 million years ago to the present is shown under two major headings, the Platyrrhini, or the New World monkeys, at the left and the Catarrhini, or the Old World monkeys, at the right. The hominoid and hominid branches are at the far right. The sequences are based on such biochemical data as small differences in the amino acid sequence of the same protein in different living species. The specific dating of the branches is based on the age of fossils and on other kinds of geochronological data. The maps at left and right indicate where the earliest fossil representative of the genus was found. The name to the right of each fossil genus indicates its relation to living forms. Thus *Sivapithecus* pairs with *Pongo* but *Proconsul* pairs with all hominoids.

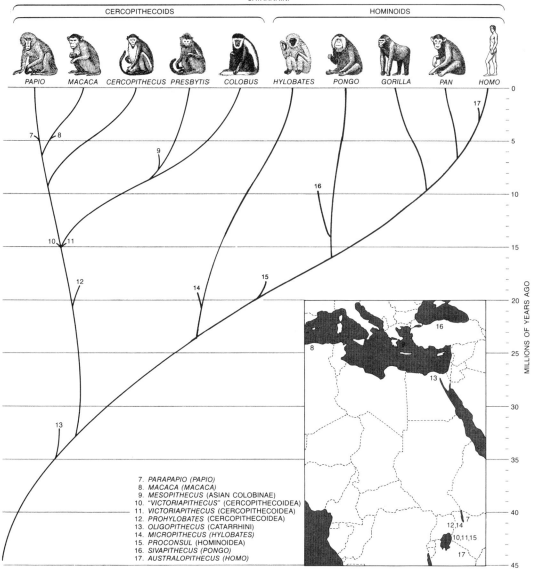

CATARRHINI

CERCOPITHECOIDS | HOMINOIDS

PAPIO   MACACA   CERCOPITHECUS   PRESBYTIS   COLOBUS   HYLOBATES   PONGO   GORILLA   PAN   HOMO

MILLIONS OF YEARS AGO

7. *PARAPAPIO (PAPIO)*
8. *MACACA (MACACA)*
9. *MESOPITHECUS (ASIAN COLOBINAE)*
10. *"VICTORIAPITHECUS" (CERCOPITHECOIDEA)*
11. *VICTORIAPITHECUS (CERCOPITHECOIDEA)*
12. *PROHYLOBATES (CERCOPITHECOIDEA)*
13. *OLIGOPITHECUS (CATARRHINI)*
14. *MICROPITHECUS (HYLOBATES)*
15. *PROCONSUL (HOMINOIDEA)*
16. *SIVAPITHECUS (PONGO)*
17. *AUSTRALOPITHECUS (HOMO)*

seldom very informative on questions of taxonomy. For example, the equivalent parts of the body in living mammals are generally not of much help in sorting individuals into species or clustering species into higher taxonomic groups.

A third cause of misinterpretation is the very diversity of middle and late Miocene hominoids. The living large hominoids are not notably diverse: only five genera have survived. When all the fossil evidence of past hominoids is taken into account, what emerges is a group that is quite heterogeneous; each hominoid species is in many respects unique. These factors have made it hard to reconstruct by means of fossils the branching sequences of living hominoids. It is even harder to link particular fossil species to particular living ones.

103

PARTS OF PROCONSUL found at the time of its initial discovery by Tom Whitworth in 1951 are shown in dark gray in this restoration of the four-footed hominoid. The additional parts of the skeleton shown in light gray are those recently found in museum collections by Alan Walker and Martin Pickford, who prepared this restoration. The parts shown in outline only, such as the pelvis, most of the spine and parts of the skull and jaw, have not been found.

Significant new Miocene hominoid fossils, however, have changed the earlier state of affairs. Skeletal parts—faces, brain cases and limbs—that were misidentified or have only now been uncovered are yielding a clearer and often surprising picture of both evolutionary relations and the nature of the early hominoids. One can even catch glimpses of how they may have lived and what their ecological relations were.

At the same time newer molecular analyses are clarifying and expanding ideas about the pattern and timing of hominoid evolution; an example is the work of Charles G. Sibley and Jon Ahlquist of Yale University, in which DNA's from different primate species are hybridized to establish the differences and similarities of their sequences of nucleotides. Slowly paleoanthropology is moving from the time when the fossil record contributed nothing to an understanding of phylogenetic patterns to a time when it is one component of a synthesis that renders data of all kinds compatible: fossil, anatomical, molecular and developmental.

THE HOMINOID RADIATION

An account of the radiation of the hominoids that represents a consensus of current opinion can be summarized as follows. First, it is not clear when the great apes diverged from their relatives, the Old World monkeys. (The New World monkeys played no part in hominoid evolution.) It seems almost certain, however, that the divergence came after middle Oligocene times (some 30 million years ago) and before early Miocene times (some 20 million years ago). However that may be, the radiation of the hominoids was under way in the early or middle Miocene (20 to 15 million years ago) and certain lineages of this moderately successful group did not become extinct until the late Miocene (eight to six million years ago).

It is similarly not clear when the small hominoids, the gibbons of Asia, diverged from the larger ones. The split is possibly documented by some of the earlier Miocene primate fossils, although it is a controversial point. There is better documentation, however, for the divergence of the large apes into Asian and African species by middle Miocene times, say 16 million years ago. The orangutan is the odd and sole survivor of a group of middle and later Miocene Asian apes that were previously more diverse and widespread.

Sadly, for most of the Miocene the African hominoid branch is virtually without fossil representation. From the molecular record, however, one can infer a late Miocene splitting of first gorillas, then chimpanzees and hominids (between 10 and six million years ago), and it is known that bipedal hominids were present in eastern Africa by at least four to 3.5 million years ago. Until there is a better African fossil record (particularly a fossil record for the African apes) one can only guess about the timing and precise branching sequence of these lineages and about the nature of their early members, including the very earliest hominids.

If one goes back to Oligocene times, the African fossil primate record is comparatively rich. Elwyn L. Simons of Duke University has been hunting successfully for primate fossils in the Fayum of Egypt on and off since 1961. Since 1977 he and his collaborators John G. Fleagle of the State University of New York at Stony Brook and Richard F. Kay of Duke have uncovered some truly remarkable material. Substantial parts of the skeleton of *Aegyptopithecus*, a species hitherto known only from a skull found earlier by Simons, and *Apidium* are now in hand. Even the very sparsely represented *Parapithecus* and *Propliopithecus* are now relatively well characterized.

These fossils represent a diverse group of unspecialized tree-living primates that had attained the biological status of monkeys at least as early as middle Oligocene times, 30 million years ago. They were not, however, primitive primates like the lemurs but bore a general resemblance to the living New World monkeys. They are nonetheless too primitive and too different from the living higher primates of the Old World for one to know whether they are representative of a time before the divergence of the hominoids from the Old World monkeys or a time after the divergence.

The early Miocene of eastern Africa is a happy exception to the fossil-poor record for Africa as a whole. Collecting over the past 50 years in Kenya and Uganda has yielded some 1,000 fossils of higher primates that are between 17 and 22 million years old and that almost certainly represent hominoid lineages of a period after their divergence from the Old World monkeys. Mainly through the work of Peter Andrews of the British Museum (Natural History) the paleoecology of the period is now well known. The landscape was a mixture of forest, open woodland and grassland, with the forest predominating. The forest and woodland were inhabited by at least six hominoid species. One of them, *Proconsul africanus*, has for some time been the best-known Miocene ape, and it has now become even better known.

A small animal the size of a baboon, *Proconsul* has played a central role in thinking about hominoid evolution. The species had been represented until recently only by an almost complete forelimb, a jaw, skull fragments and a few foot bones, all of one individual, an almost complete skull of another individual and other limb fragments, teeth and jaws. Then Alan C. Walker of Johns Hopkins University and Martin Pickford of the National Museums of Kenya discovered—in museum and laboratory collections—many more pieces of the "forelimb" individual, so that it is now represented by much of its skeleton.

Until now *Proconsul* had been interpreted in several contradictory ways. At one extreme was the view held by some that its form was too specialized for it to be the ancestor of any living hominid and that it was possibly not even a hominoid. Others saw it as an unspecialized early hominoid and still others accepted it as being ancestral to the chimpanzee. The addition of the new material clarifies the issue to some extent. *Proconsul*, the consensus now holds, is a hominoid, albeit a very unspecialized and primitive one. It was a tree-dwelling, fruit-eating "formative ape" in which the sexes were distinctly different in size. In its total pattern it was unlike any living higher primate. Its elbow and shoulder joints and feet are like a chimpanzee's, its wrist is like a monkey's and its lumbar vertebrae are like a gibbon's. Many of its other features are unique, as is its total configuration. *Proconsul* provides a salutary lesson for students of evolution: the relations inferred for the animal have depended on what part of the body was being studied. When a fossil animal is found in fragments and over a period of time, the very order of discovery of its various parts will affect the phylogenetic interpretations, particularly in the case of a "mosaic" species such as *Proconsul.*

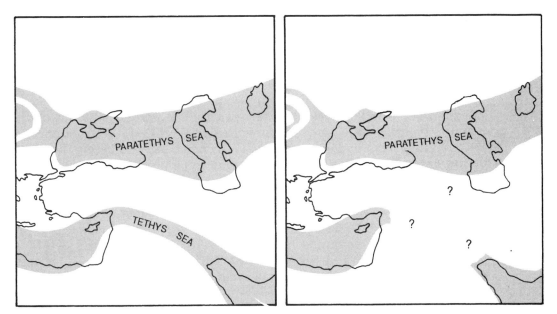

JOINING OF AFRICA AND EURASIA followed the time 20 million years ago when the Tethys Sea separated the two landmasses, as is shown at the left. In early Miocene times, some 17 million years ago, the sea shrank, as is shown at the right, leaving a land bridge that allowed animals to migrate between Africa and Eurasia. Among migrants to Eurasia were some of the African hominoids.

DRYOMORPHS AND RAMAMORPHS

The end of the early Miocene, some 17 million years ago, was marked by a highly significant geologic event: continental drift linked Africa and Arabia with mainland Eurasia, thereby allowing the migration of African hominoids (and other mammals) into the rest of the Old World. The linkup initiated major mountain building: the Alps rose in Europe, the Taurus Mountains in Turkey and the Zagros Mountains in Iran. The Tethys Sea disappeared and oceanic and atmospheric circulation patterns shifted, bringing about large-scale changes in climate and habitats.

The Eurasian climate was seasonal in the middle and late Miocene, from 17 to five million years ago. The winters were milder, however, than they are today. Much of what is now grassland and even desert was then woodland, and the forests were more widespread. The mammalian fauna reflected these conditions: grassland grazers were scarce but woodland and forest browsers abundant.

The hominoid fossil record for this period in Eurasia consists mainly of jaws and teeth, so that the phylogenetic relations are still not clear. As an approximate summary, however, the hominoids can be divided into two broad groups. One group can informally be called the dryomorphs, after the various European species of the genus *Dryopithecus*, a primate with many primitive hominoid characteristics. The other can be called the ramamorphs, after

107

Ramapithecus and similar genera. The ramamorphs were mainly Asian in distribution; they differ from other Miocene hominoids in certain characteristics that resemble those of later hominoids.

Edward Lewis, a Yale graduate student who was later with the U.S. Geological Survey, gave the name *Ramapithecus* to a fossilized fragment of a primate upper jaw from India he had found in 1932. The fossil is now known to be a little more than seven million years old. By the 1960's more primate jaws and teeth from India, Pakistan and other parts of the Old World had been found and assigned to the same genus. The animal was seen as being different from its supposedly more apelike contemporaries, *Dryopithecus* and another Indian fossil find, *Sivapithecus*. Its various remains showed that its jaws were robust and its cheek teeth large, with thick enamel caps. These features and a few others resemble those of the later African hominids of the genus *Australopithecus*. The resemblances led many, including me, to argue that *Ramapithecus* was in fact an early hominid, that the hominids had diverged from the hominoids of Africa at least 15 million years ago and therefore that the divergence data of four million years ago, based on the molecular data, was wildly incorrect.

In 1973 I began a collaborative research project with the Geological Survey of Pakistan aimed at finding additional *Ramapithecus* fossils. The fossil-rich formations where we are still at work are the product of the erosion of the rising Himalayas; they are called the Siwalik series. They vary in age from one million to 17 million years and form a thick wedge that runs along the southern flank of the great mountain range from Afghanistan to Burma. In the section of the Siwalik formation in Pakistan we have been fortunate in finding many new hominoid fossils, including specimens of both *Ramapithecus* and its relative *Sivapithecus*, and thousands of other mammalian fossils.

Our large interdisciplinary team has now built up a dated sequence of faunal changes over the 16 million years of deposition in the region and has made considerable progress in reconstructing its animal communities of the past. It is clear from the new primate material that *Ramapithecus* and *Sivapithecus* are much more alike than I had thought; they may even belong to the same genus.

In any event the new *Sivapithecus* fossils, which include a partial skull and isolated limb bones, show a number of features, particularly of the face and palate, that resemble those of the sole surviving Asian great ape, the orangutan (*Pongo pygmaeus*). They do not, as expected, resemble features of *Australopithecus*. The jaw and tooth resemblances to *Australopithecus* remain but their phylogenetic significance can be dismissed; they are probably either instances of parallel evolution or features retained from the last common ancestor of all living hominoids. At least this is my opinion and that of my colleague Steven Ward of Kent State University. Some of the hominoid fossils from Pakistan that are at least 12 million years old show similar features. If our interpretation is correct, the split between African and Asian hominoids is certainly that old and probably even older. Perhaps the split coincided approximately with the continental-drift linkup of Africa and Asia and the consequent mixing of faunas 17 or 16 million years ago. Tentatively I now place the split at about 16 million years ago.

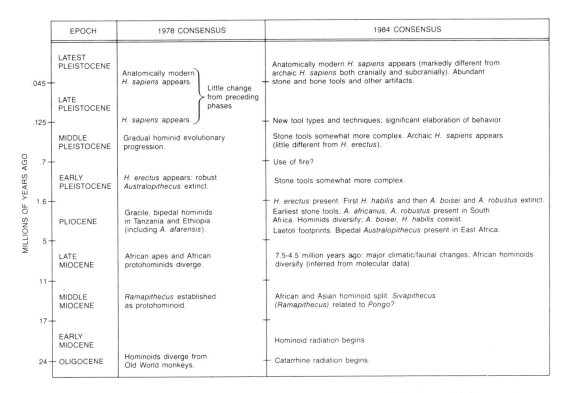

MILLIONS OF YEARS AGO	EPOCH	1978 CONSENSUS	1984 CONSENSUS
	LATEST PLEISTOCENE	Anatomically modern *H. sapiens* appears.	Anatomically modern *H. sapiens* appears (markedly different from archaic *H. sapiens* both cranially and subcranially). Abundant stone and bone tools and other artifacts.
.045	LATE PLEISTOCENE	Little change from preceding phases	
.125		*H. sapiens* appears.	New tool types and techniques; significant elaboration of behavior.
	MIDDLE PLEISTOCENE	Gradual hominid evolutionary progression.	Stone tools somewhat more complex. Archaic *H. sapiens* appears (little different from *H. erectus*).
.7			Use of fire?
	EARLY PLEISTOCENE	*H. erectus* appears: robust *Australopithecus* extinct.	Stone tools somewhat more complex.
1.6			*H. erectus* present. First *H. habilis* and then *A. boisei* and *A. robustus* extinct. Earliest stone tools; *A. africanus, A. robustus* present in South Africa. Hominids diversify; *A. boisei, H. habilis* coexist.
	PLIOCENE	Gracile, bipedal hominids in Tanzania and Ethiopia (including *A. afarensis*).	Laetoli footprints. Bipedal *Australopithecus* present in East Africa.
5	LATE MIOCENE	African apes and African protohominids diverge.	7.5-4.5 million years ago: major climatic/faunal changes; African hominids diversify (inferred from molecular data).
11	MIDDLE MIOCENE	*Ramapithecus* established as protohominoid.	African and Asian hominoid split. *Sivapithecus (Ramapithecus)* related to *Pongo*?
17	EARLY MIOCENE		Hominoid radiation begins.
24	OLIGOCENE	Hominoids diverge from Old World monkeys.	Catarrhine radiation begins.

CHANGING VIEWS on hominoid and hominid evolution appear on this chart, which extends from Oligocene times at the bottom to the most recent Pleistocene at the top. Numerals between the geologic subdivisions give the terminal dates of each subdivision in millions of years or fractions thereof before the present. The 1978 consensus of scholarly opinion on the subject is given at the left in the chart, together with items of fossil or archaeological evidence in support of such opinion. Today's consensus of opinion is given at the right.

EARLY HOMINIDS

The first undoubted hominids appear from perhaps four million to 3.75 million years ago in Tanzania and Ethiopia. Hominid evolution before then is obscure. Changes in fauna and habitat between 7.5 and 4.5 million years ago reflect a number of climatic and geographic events, the most spectacular one being the drying up of the Mediterranean on several occasions about 5.5 million years ago. The connection between these events and the evolution of the hominoids of Africa is not clear. Nevertheless, the footprint evidence of hominids that walked on two legs, uncovered by Mary Leakey and her colleagues at Laetoli in Tanzania, is firmly dated at 3.75 million years ago. Moreover, the almost half-complete skeleton of "Lucy" and other specimens of *Australopithecus afarensis* found by Donald Johanson and his colleagues at Hadar in Ethiopia are dated, somewhat less certainly, at between four and three million years ago. There is some tax-onomic dispute about Lucy and the associated hominid remains from Hadar. Do they represent a new single species, *Australopithecus afarensis*? Two or more species? Tiptoeing past these questions, I shall give only one version, acknowledging that the situation is not clear-cut.

A. afarensis is primitive in most of its features. The adult males were probably from 50 to 100 percent larger than the females. Individuals weighed from 25 to 50 kilograms or more. Their brain was the size of an African great ape's, but with such a wide range of adult weights it is not clear whether the brain size with respect to body weight was larger or smaller. In some features of the face and palate these early hominids resembled chimpanzees. Overall, however, the skull as it has been reconstructed looks more like a female gorilla's: *A. afarensis* has larger teeth and is more robust than a chimpanzee.

The dentition includes a few plausibly primitive features, although the canine teeth of both sexes have a low crown and have lost their apelike forward projection. The cheek teeth are relatively large and are capped with a thick enamel, probably an adaptation to chewing large quantities of fruits, seeds, pods, roots and tubers, some of which may have been quite tough.

It is impossible to prove that the footprints in Tanzania were made by hominids like those represented by the Hadar fossils, but the morphology of the hip, knee and ankle joints of Lucy and her companions shows that the Hadar population was clearly bipedal. The foot bones show the same adaptation to bipedalism and an intriguing additional feature: the toe bones and metatarsals are long and curved. Compared with members of the genus *Homo* the arms of *A. afarensis* were long and the legs were short. Its hands were capable of powerful grasping. Judging by the proportions of the hand bones and the morphology of their joints, its manipulations were probably more precise than those of living chimpanzees.

The Hadar hominids lived in an area of woodland and savanna, away from the Pliocene forests, as part of a community of mammals that was structurally quite like the later communities of the Pleistocene. Such communities began to develop in eastern Africa in the later Miocene, and it is possible that they included hominids still unknown to us. By analogy with living mammals it is unlikely that the Hadar hominids were monogamous.

No stones that have been altered as tools have been found associated with the Hadar hominids. This may not, however, be entirely relevant. Suppose *A. afarensis* used the same kind of tools living chimpanzees do: stems, leaves, wood and stone casually adapted to food gathering, food processing and display behavior. Suppose, moreover, they did so more often than chimpanzees do today. Such tools would be impossible to recognize four million years later even if some near-miracle had preserved them.

Tool use of this kind, if it may be postulated, might have been an important component of those behaviors that stimulated walking on two legs and the reduction of the canine teeth. Concepts such as these are much debated. Were the Hadar hominids protohunters and killers, opportunistic scavengers or gentle vegetarians? Did monogamy evolve along with bipedalism? Did pair-bonded males bring food to their female partner at a home base? Was gathered food, animal or plant, shared or did the Hadar and Laetoli hominids forage on an individual basis? Each of these viewpoints, to say nothing of others, has its

resent, however, any picture of what these early hominids
breathing animals must be deferred until there is more
ture of their basic adaptations. Above all, we must resist
them as modern humans merely some distance removed

CLOSING IN ON *HOMO*

en 2.5 and two million years ago African hominids under-
ive radiation. By the later date at least two, probably three
ore species of hominids were present, although in any one
s no evidence for more than three. In eastern Africa a spe-
us, *A. boisei*, robust and with very large teeth, lived at the
r-brained hominid whose type-fossil cranium is catalogued
in Kenya as E.R.–1470. The species is now most commonly known as *Homo
habilis*, a name that was coined in 1964 by L. S. B. Leakey, Philip V. Tobias and
John R. Napier, and was applied to E.R.–1470 by its discoverers, Richard
Leakey and his colleagues. There was probably a third hominid species, small-
toothed and small-brained, living in eastern Africa at the same time. Moreover,
in southern Africa there was another species of *Australopithecus*, *A. robustus*,
and possibly *H. habilis* as well. By about 1.75 million years ago, however, *H.
habilis* disappeared from Africa and was replaced by an even larger-brained
hominid: *Homo erectus*. A clearer picture of what kinds of animals these were is
slowly emerging. The picture cannot ever, of course, be genuinely sharp, and
one must avoid peering at it too closely lest, like a newspaper halftone, it dissolve into meaningless dots.

Consider *A. boisei*. A larger species than either *A. afarensis* or the *Australopithecus* species of southern Africa, it was small-brained and the male was
markedly larger than the female. The species appeared more than two million
years ago and survived, apparently with little morphological change, for a million years. *A. boisei* may have dug with sticks and hammered with stones, but
there is no evidence that it used tools intensively.

Although *A. boisei* was larger than other species of *Australopithecus*, it may
have behaved much like them. Studies of the chewing surfaces of the teeth of
various *Australopithecus* species by Alan Walker and by Frederick Grine of the
State University of New York at Stony Brook suggest that all of them were basically rather apelike vegetarians, eating broadly similar diets that called for much
repetitive chewing. Possibly their diet included more roots and tubers and less
fruit than the diet of forest-dwelling apes.

Why did *A. boisei* evolve, and from what did it evolve? Was its evolution the
result of a change in climate and habitat, perhaps a change in the availability of
certain kinds of plant foods? Why did *A. boisei* become extinct after a million
years of apparent stability? None of these questions can yet be answered. The

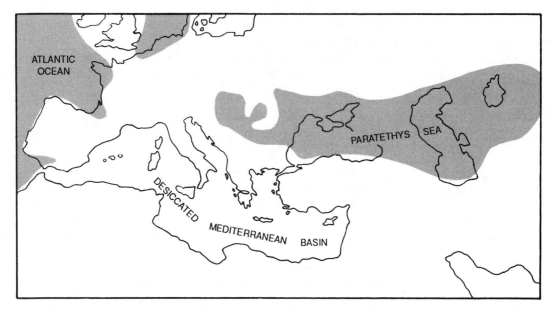

LATE MIOCENE EPISODE, the drying up of the Mediterranean basin after it was sealed off from the Atlantic by mountain building, must have had catastrophic effects on the climate and ecology of Africa. The episode took place about 5.5 million years ago. Its effects on the mammalian fauna, hominoids included, are not clear, but it was perhaps a million and a half years later that hominids appeared.

fossil hunt in eastern Africa is intense, however, and one may hope *A. boisei*, its ancestor and the transition between them will eventually be better understood.

Understanding the transition to *Homo habilis* from its ancestor (which might also be the ancestor of *A. boisei*) is another matter. The various species of *Australopithecus* are difficult animals to "imagine"—to reconstruct as though they still lived—because nothing like them lives today. Still, they can be perceived dimly as an odd kind of ape. *H. habilis* is even more difficult to imagine. It is rather like *Australopithecus* in a number of ways, for example in its face and teeth, but it has a significantly larger brain, averaging about 700 cubic centimeters. There are no clear associations between the skulls of *H. habilis* and the other bones of the species, but the limb bones that are assumed to represent it, unlike those of *Australopithecus*, resemble those of later species of the genus *Homo* (with the exception of modern *H. sapiens*). It has been suggested that the resemblance reflects changes in the mode of locomotion and in the dimensions of the female pelvis demanded by the size of the newborn infant.

At about the same time that *A. boisei* and *H. habilis* appear in Africa so do the first archaeological sites: concentrations of used or altered stone, often brought from some distance away, together with animal remains. The consensus is that the sites document a shift in diet to include more animal food; *H. habilis* rather than *A. boisei* is generally implicated. The dietary change and the increase in brain size are also linked causally. Thereafter the consensus breaks down. Was *H. habilis* a hunter-gatherer who transported food to home bases to

112

be shared and who practiced a division of labor that left hunting to the males and gathering to the females? This is to ask: Was *H. habilis* behaviorally "modern" or was it still basically vegetarian, perhaps adding some meat to its diet mainly by scavenging?

The archaeological record is itself ambiguous. The same scattering of tools and bones could be produced by opportunistic scavenging for individual consumption, with little or no food transport and sharing, or could represent home bases as sites of intense social interaction. In short, the picture of *H. habilis* remains blurred. More fossil material and more archaeological sites are needed, and even then the transition from *Australopithecus* to *Homo* is likely to be obscure. Both animals are too different from any known today. What happened to *H. habilis*? It survived for a few hundred thousand years only to be replaced by a much more durable species, *H. erectus*. Was *H. habilis* the ancestor of *H. erectus*? Although it is widely assumed to be the case, it may not be so.

GETTING AROUND

Homo erectus is the first widely distributed hominid species. It appeared earliest in Africa, as far as is known, and it may indeed have originated there some 1.6 million years ago. Whether or not that is so, by one million years ago the species was present in southeastern and eastern Asia and survived in that area at least until 300,000 years ago. In that span of time, well over a million years, the physical record of *H. erectus* is one of prolonged morphological stability.

H. erectus resembled later species of *Homo* (modern *H. sapiens* excepted) in both body size and robustness. Larger-brained than *H. habilis* (more than 800 cubic centimeters), it had front teeth as big as those of earlier hominids, but its cheek teeth and its face were smaller. The archaeological record suggests that some *H. erectus* populations were makers of larger, symmetrically flaked stone tools: bifaces, or "hand axes." Moreover, some *H. erectus* populations may have used fire. Some later *H. erectus* populations may have commanded more sophisticated techniques of producing and modifying stone tools, but the overall impression is one of prolonged stability, in behavior as well as in morphology. Arthur Jelinek of the University of Arizona has proposed that "paleocultural" is the appropriate term for such behavior, so different is it from the rapid changes we associate with "cultural" behavior in modern humans.

Paleoanthropologists shift gears, often without realizing it, when they talk about human evolution over the past 1.5 million years. The problems in hominoid and hominid evolution I have presented up to this point concern macroevolutionary questions: issues of broad adaptations, evolutionary trends and speciation. The hominids labeled *H. erectus*, "archaic" *H. sapiens* (including the Neanderthals) and "modern" *H. sapiens* probably represent a continuum, and the patterns of change within these lineages represent in contrast microevolution. Nevertheless, some of the most interesting paleoanthropological work concerns the last great step in human evolution: the shift, about 45,000 or 40,000 years ago, from archaic *H. sapiens* to modern *H. sapiens*.

Erik Trinkaus of the University of New Mexico has shown that the Neanderthals (and probably their contemporaries in other parts of the Old World) were probably as unlike us behaviorally as they were physically. The Neanderthals' skeletons were much more robust and the muscle attachments on the bones indicate that they were much stronger than we are. Their teeth were larger and are heavily worn, probably (by analogy with living Eskimos) from being used for a variety of nonfeeding activities (such as the chewing of animal hides to soften them). The transition to modern *H. sapiens* was marked by a loss of the Neanderthal robustness in skeleton, face and dentition. There were also changes in the morphology of the female pelvis. These perhaps suggest that formerly easy births had become harder or even that the time of gestation was being reduced to our present nine months from perhaps 11 months (a period in line with predictions based on general mammalian relations among maternal body size, fetal size and length of gestation).

Important behavioral changes are also evident in the archaeological record. They include a proliferation of superior stone and bone tools, shifts in hunting patterns, in the use and control of fire, in the use of clothing, in settlement patterns, in population size, in ecological range, in art and other evidences of ritual activity. All of this points to the emergence of a species possessing modern behavioral capabilities (and potential) from an ancestral species lacking, at least by modern standards, in some significantly human characteristics.

No brief summary such as this one can do justice to the richness and complexity of the information available regarding this most recent, even if microevolutionary, transition. Yet it remains the best-documented and potentially the most understandable of all the transitions of the past 30 million years. As an outsider, working in a time span that may contain no relevant fossils at all in any particular 100,000-year period, I am ruefully envious of those who work with this most recent period. Viewed at long range it is, in a very real sense, the icing on the cake. Yet one must remember that it is only the icing. The cake itself—the many earlier stages of human evolution—remains for now much harder to digest.

Argument Over a Woman

James Shreeve

Her name was Eve, and she was trouble right from the start. Sure, the public loved her; she was brash, sexy, and surprising, with a body of data you could reach out and grasp and implications that just wouldn't quit. She made the cover of Newsweek. She even got a mention from Johnny Carson. Not too shabby for a human-origins hypothesis born in a biochemist's beaker. But for paleoanthropologists, the hard-boiled types who earn a living make dead men talk, Eve spelled poison forward and backward. She was an interloper, a biochemical bauble, a dolled-up set of assumptions masquerading as a breakthrough. To them, the only good Eve was a refuted Eve.

Three years ago a team of biochemists announced that they had discovered the genetic mother of us all. Every person on Earth today, they said, could trace his or her ancestry back to a single woman—quickly dubbed Eve—who lived in Africa just 200,000 years ago. Their methods and their stubborn insistence on a shockingly recent date for the origin of modern humans infuriated a powerful group of anthropologists, who felt their professional authority had been maligned. Since then they've been looking for ways to reclaim their turf.

The story of Eve actually starts in the 1960s, before she was given the name. Back then, if you wanted to find out something about human origins, you went out to the field and dug for it. If you got lucky, you brought home some hard evidence, like a skull or some ancient tools. Then two Berkeley biochemists named Vincent Sarich and Allan Wilson got it into their head to look for clues to the past not out on the African savanna but inside the body, among proteins and cells.

Sarich and Wilson were trying to answer the basic questions, When did the human line first branch off from our relatives the apes? They were looking at proteins because they knew that, like beaks, skulls, and other anatomical parts, proteins evolve by accumulating mutations. And like beaks and skulls, the same protein in related species is slightly different because of mutations that occur after the species split off from a common ancestor.

Nothing too controversial so far. But then Sarich and Wilson added a twist. The mutations, they said, occur across the millennia at a steady rate, like dependable ticks of a molecular clock. And because of this, proteins could serve to date the separation of species. Species that today have the most diverse proteins have been separated for the longest time; those with more kindred proteins split apart more recently.

"The proteins show that the primates most distantly related to humans are lemurs," Sarich says, "and the closest are chimps and gorillas." So similar are the proteins of humans, chimps, and gorillas, in fact, that according to the biochemists' calculations the species must have diverged a scant 5 million years ago.

This date grossly disagreed with that put forth by most anthropologists, who believed that the first hominids—the group of nonape primates that eventually evolved into humans—appeared not 5 million but 15 million years ago. And the anthropologists thought they had hard evidence on their side, in the form of fossils from that period. To say the least, then, these researchers were not pleased with two Berkeley upstarts who, without even a glance at a scrap of bone, were telling them they were dead wrong.

"We were rubbing a lot of nerves raw," Sarich says. "We were saying, 'Look guys, without even looking at the fossils, we know you're making a mistake.' Plus, we were doing it in a lab." The bone experts countered that the molecular clock was an unproven phenomenon, and they pressed their case pretty hard. After all, if Sarich and Wilson were right, then the paleoanthropological approach was about as scientifically relevant as medieval attempts to turn base metal into gold.

"I'd have to paraphrase what they told us to do," Sarich recalls. "It was something like we should go away somewhere in particular."

Sarich and Wilson, however, turned out to be right. And ironically, the anthropologists were done in by the very bone evidence they had championed. New fossil discoveries in the late 1970s showed that the 15-million-year-old fossils probably belonged to direct ancestors of the orangutan, not to forebears of human beings. The road to humankind, bone experts grudgingly began to admit, started about 5 to 7 million years ago.

In victory Sarich and Wilson showed little charity to their detractors, and the passing years have not mellowed their views. "Paleoanthropologists would like to forget that fifteen-million-year date now," says Sarich. "No one talks about that mistake. Physicians bury their mistakes; paleoanthropologists rename theirs."

"The rules have changed since the 1950s, and the old perspectives have been overthrown," Wilson says. "Anthropologists are no longer the authorities. They are socially isolated from modern biology and have trouble understanding what is going on conceptually."

Those are academic fighting words, to be sure. This dispute, however, would turn out to be only a preliminary skirmish; the big battle between bones and genes was yet to come.

By the late 1970s Wilson and his associates had begun to use a molecular timepiece to date the origin of the one hominid species still living: *Homo sapiens*. The prevailing view among anthropologists then was that all modern human populations could trace their beginnings back to one million years ago, when our hominid ancestor *Homo erectus* first left Africa and traveled to Asia,

Europe, and Indonesia. In each place, according to traditional fossil interpretations, *H. erectus* gradually became fully modern *H. sapiens*. In that time people also developed the regional differences that provide the variety of our species: Asians became characteristically Asian, Europeans European, and so on.

The Wilson team thought the one-million-year divergence date offered them a good opportunity to test a new molecular clock based on a kind of genetic material called mitochondrial DNA. Mitochondria are rodlike structures in the cell, outside the nucleus, that are responsible for supplying the energy that drives the cell's various activities. They are also home to a form of DNA that differs in at least one significant way from the familiar DNA that's lodged inside the cell's nucleus.

Nuclear DNA is the combined genetic material from both a mother and a father, and so it changes in every generation. Mitochondrial DNA, however, is inherited solely from one's mother. Thus the only differences between the mitochondrial DNA of a child and that of its mother—or grandmother or great-great-great-grandmother—are the result of random mutations. Moreover, Wilson's studies indicated that human mitochondrial DNA mutates at a steady rate of 2 to 4 percent every million years.

Like the earlier work with proteins, the new mitochondrial DNA clock focused on the diversity caused by these mutations. But this time, instead of looking at differences between species, the biochemists were examining differences between separate populations of one species. They were trying to determine how mitochondrial DNA in Asians, say, differed from its counterpart in Europeans and Africans. If, as they believed, mitochondrial DNA changed at a constant rate, they could calculate the amount of time needed to amass these differences and thus find the date when all human populations diverged from a single female ancestor.

In the mid-1980s, working under Wilson's direction, Rebecca Cann and Mark Stoneking (now at the University of Hawaii and Penn State, respectively) took samples of mitochondrial DNA from women representing five geographic areas: Europe, Asia, Africa, New Guinea, and Australia. In 1987 the researchers announced their results. Most of the mitochondrial DNA samples were extremely similar, showing that the groups had diverged only recently. But the mitochondrial DNA of one group, the African lineages, showed twice as much diversity as the rest. The simplest explanation was that African mitochondrial DNA had been around twice as long as the others.

Nobody argued with that, even the anthropologists—after all, the oldest hominid fossils have been found only in Africa. The harmony between the genes and the bones ended, however, when Cann and her colleagues ran their clock backward and placed a date on human divergence. It wasn't one million years ago, they said; it was 800,000 years later.

Simply put, their hypothesis suggested that all living humans share as their last common ancestor an African woman—"mitochondrial Eve"—who lived only 200,000 years ago. From that not-so-modest proposal the implications went scurrying out in several directions, and more often than not they wriggled right up the pants legs of a group of anthropologists who had already had quite enough of Wilson and his biochemistry ten years earlier.

For starters, if the genetic evidence was correct, then a lot of fossil ancestors that had been hanging around museum shelves weren't really our ancestors at all. These far-flung descendants of the *H. erectus* migration a million years ago all became extinct, their territories taken over by Eve's children after a much more recent invasion. Neanderthals in Europe, Peking man in Asia, Java man in Australia and Indonesia—all gone. Mind you, these were not demiapes stumbling half-wittedly around the landscape: they were highly successful human populations who conquered harsh environments, used fire, and fashioned fairly sophisticated stone tools. The Neanderthals had particularly elaborate tool kits, probably buried their dead, and most certainly possessed brains every bit as large as those of people today. Yet all were swept aside by the advance of the African arrivistes.

And not just shoved around, but completely eliminated. The Eve hypothesis holds that current humans—*all* humans, everywhere—harbor no non-African genes predating the lady in question. In other words, there was no consorting with the locals when the Africans hit town—or at least none that left a lasting genetic legacy. Any offspring produced by interbreeding between the groups died off without leaving any heirs.

Respected human ancestors weren't the only ones being pushed out by newcomers. Anthropologists themselves, who had spent decades painstakingly tracing the connections between ancient *H. erectus* and modern humans in several corners of the world, were closer than ever to being run off the field of prehistory by the biologists. For example, if the progeny of someone who lived in Java 750,000 years ago were totally replaced by our ancestors who came out of Africa over half a million years later, that doesn't reflect too kindly on the researcher who devoted a career to showing how the Java skull evolved into our own.

To make matters worse, Eve became a rallying point for a number of anthropologists who believed the bones themselves told of a relatively recent wave of Africans. "I've been arguing for nearly sixteen years that—based on fossils—modern humans replaced Neanderthals," says paleoanthropologist Christopher Stringer of the Natural History Museum in London. "And I was quite confident six years ago that fossil evidence supported an out-of-Africa replacement. Modern humans did not arise in Europe." But analyzing bones is a subtle and subjective discipline, and the same fossil is often viewed differently by two equally qualified experts. When Eve showed up, promising to cut through bony ambiguities and deliver the hard molecular facts, Stringer's view got a real boost.

So the battle lines were drawn. On one side, supporting Eve and a recent replacement scenario, were the biologists, along with a few anthropologists like Stringer. On the other side was most of the American anthropological community, contending that fossils show continuity, and that current human lineages run deep into the past in each region, stretching back to the original *H. erectus* migration a million years ago. The anthropologists were also trying to prove, of course, that they knew what they were doing.

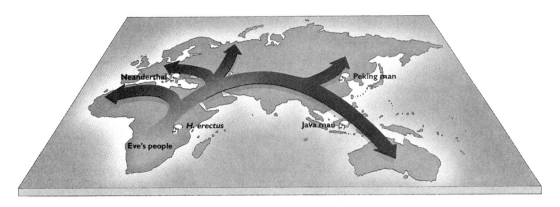

The arrows indicate the migration of Eve's people, a group of modern humans who arose in southern Africa 200,000 years ago and moved out into the world. They swept across Europe, India, Asia, and Australia, wiping out and replacing all previously existing human groups, shown by skulls at the sites of specific fossil finds.

Since Eve has turned up, things have started to get a little nasty. She makes things personal. Feelings get hurt. Professional pride gets trampled. Because, let's face it, if she means what the gene people say, then a lot of honest fossils—and the people who study them—are gonna be shoved out on a limb forever. There are people around who aren't about to let that happen.

Continuity advocates know that Eve has a weakness. They realize that if they can prove, by bones or by any other means, that a modern human lineage runs deeper than 200,000 years in just one region outside Africa—any region— then the whole genetic argument, for all its high-tech appeal, collapses like a pinpricked cell. And the guy who thinks he has the pin is University of Michigan anthropologist Milford Wolpoff.

Wolpoff is a man of ursine proportions famous for the vigor of his opinions, if not his tact in expressing them. At a recent conference in Zagreb, Yugoslavia, for example, Wolpoff was scheduled to speak after Stringer. When the British scientist finished his arguments, Wolpoff took the podium and asked for the first slide. It was of a *National Enquirer* headline breaking the news that Adam and Eve were actually aliens. His second slide was of Piltdown man, the infamous human fossil find that duped the English anthropological establishment for 40 years, until 1953, when it was finally proved to be a fraud.

"The British Museum has a long history of contributions to paleoanthropology," said Wolpoff, his voice heavy with sarcasm. "Next slide, please."

Wolpoff insists, however, that such ad hominid criticism should be taken in the context of an escalating professional dispute more often characterized by mutual respect. Later in the same conference, Stringer, a lightly built cockney, was threatened with bodily harm by a Greek anthropologist enraged by Stringer's devastating criticism of his dating of an important specimen. As the man moved toward the podium, yelling, a bearlike figure intercepted him, blocking his path. It was Wolpoff.

119

"I guess you could say that Zagreb represented the two extremes of my relationship with Chris," Wolpoff says.

In February of this year Wolpoff tried to publicly bury Eve under the weight of fossil evidence against her. He organized a session at the annual meeting of the American Association for the Advancement of Science in New Orleans, bringing together a panel of experts on modern human origins in various regions, all continuity advocates. Their task was clear: to demonstrate that fossils found outside Africa, fossils *older* than Eve, have features that link them to populations living in the same region today. If these regional features survived the alleged recent African invasion, then either the residents interbred with invaders, or there was never any invasion in the first place. In either case, so long Eve.

Take Australia, for instance. As Alan Thorne of the Australian National University pointed out, a whole suite of features—including thick cranial bones, a low, sloping forehead, a large, projecting face, and very large teeth—link modern Australian aborigines through a chain of regional ancestors right back to Java man, 750,000 years ago. Equally important, this same combination of features distinguishes the aborigines from *H. sapiens* living in other regions today.

"If these reputed Africans came into Australia and Asia and replaced the people who were there, they would have had to reevolve these same characteristics from scratch," Thorne explains. "I find that extremely difficult to believe."

It's the same story in other regions. According to Geoffrey Pope of the University of Illinois, Peking man and other early Chinese fossils bear features that are distinctly Asian by modern standards, including some cheekbone anatomy that Pope claims is seldom found outside East Asia. There is also fossil evidence for continuity in western Europe, according to David Frayer of the University of Kansas. But, he says, it rarely gets a fair hearing. He believes that Neanderthals are unfairly dismissed as the forebears of modern Europeans because of an ingrained historical bias against them.

"If I call you a Neanderthal, you know right away I'm not paying you a compliment," he says. It's easy to view western European Neanderthals, with their massive skeletons, heavy brow ridges, and huge projecting noses and faces as distinct from modern humans anywhere. But Frayer points to a collection of Neanderthal traits in the jaw and back of the skull that do indeed seem to carry through into modern Europeans. A more convincing case for the survival of Neanderthal genes comes from central Europe. There a series of 40,000-year-old fragmentary remains show patterns of facial reduction and brow ridge shape that could mark the transition from Neanderthals to modern humans.

Stringer was in New Orleans also, as were some members of Wilson's lab. They had heard these arguments for continuity before, but never so boldly laid out. "Wolpoff's seminar was like a sales pitch for a time-share condo," commented one geneticist. "They brought one guy in after another to hammer at you until you wanted to sign on the dotted line out of sheer exhaustion."

"It was meant to be a sales pitch," Wolpoff says bluntly. "We planned the whole thing, rehearsed it, worked over the exact phrasing. We felt that we had to do this, because we were becoming the victims of the complexity of our own ideas. Our hypothesis of regional continuity with gene flow may not be as sensational as this idea of killer Africans sweeping out across Europe and Asia, overrunning everybody. But we think the fossils absolutely support our position."

The term *gene flow* is crucial to Wolpoff's hypothesis. In this model human populations of the past are separated enough to allow regional traits to persist, but they are still united by a flow of genes—in other words, by some interbreeding—carrying the advantageous traits of full modernity from one area to another. This genetic commerce was reinforced by the exchange of technology, language, subsistence strategies, and other aspects of culture. As a result, people in all regions of the world evolved characteristics typical of all *H. sapiens*: increased brain size, lighter skeleton, and less powerful chewing apparatus.

If the bones mean anything at all, Wolpoff and crew have an impressive arsenal of evidence to use against Eve. But bones can be unwieldy weapons, and Stringer insists that the same fossil record can be used to answer most of the multiregionalists' arguments. Some supposedly "regional" characteristics, he points out, also appear on fossils found outside the region. Stringer maintains, for example, that the purportedly "Asian" cheekbone traits outlined by Pope can also be found on early modern fossils in North Africa, Europe, and Australia. "So how essentially Asian could they be?" he asks. Furthermore, he says, other so-called regional traits may indeed have reevolved, despite Thorne's skepticism, because different populations coming into an area at different times had to adapt to similar environments, such as the harsh climate of the Australian desert.

And there are the fossils in Africa itself, where the evidence records a transition from *H. erectus* to modern *H. sapiens* more clearly than anywhere else. The earliest known modern human fossils come from sites in southern Africa, Ethiopia, and—if some revolutionary new dating techniques prove accurate—the nearby Middle East. All are believed to be between 130,000 and 80,000 years old, at least 40,000 years older than any modern humans found in Europe or East Asia.

This line of reasoning doesn't sit well with Wolpoff at all. If these African Adams and Eves subsequently left their home continent to repopulate the planet, he says, the earliest *H. sapiens* everywhere should look like Africans. And they don't. "If there are African features in the early moderns of Europe and Asia, I wish Chris would show them to me," says Wolpoff. "Where are they? Where's the beef?"

"That's ridiculous, and Milford knows it," Stringer retorts. He says that Wolpoff is looking for *current* African anatomy in these fossils, and it's just not there. "The *Homo sapiens* that stayed in Africa have had a hundred thousand years to evolve the traits that distinguish them today, just like other populations. We have to get away from the *Newsweek* syndrome, picturing the common ancestor looking like a contemporary African."

Instead, Stringer says, one can see more generalized features in the earliest modern humans both within and outside Africa, a sort of *H. sapiens* blank slate—including a light skeleton, a high cranium, reduced brow ridges, a small jaw, and small teeth—that only recently took on regional characteristics.

Wolpoff counters that traces of these generalized features show up in non-African fossils that were around long before Eve's supposed birth. And Thorne adds that traces of Stringer's "blank slate" can't be found at all in some current *H. sapiens.* "According to Stringer's own definition, forty thousand Australian aborigines don't qualify as human beings," he says.

Wolpoff and company find fault not only with Stringer's interpretation of the fossil evidence; they save some of their harshest comments for the likelihood of the replacement scenario itself, which they say is a particularly bloodthirsty one. "There is no way one human population could replace everybody else and wipe out their genes except through violence," says Wolpoff. "The people advocating replacement have to come to terms with what they are saying. I'm just glad it's them and not me."

"Wolpoff constantly represents the replacement scenario as a Pleistocene holocaust," Stringer says. "It simply isn't true. There are plenty of ways for a population to become extinct without being murdered by another population." The newcomers, perhaps with better technology or better able to act as a group than other inhabitants, could take over the best land, such as the lowlands in Europe. They would squeeze the older group into less-productive highlands; once there, a series of adverse climate changes could wipe out the older group.

Left to their own devices, most of the fossil experts puzzling over modern human origins would probably opt for a scenario somewhere between complete replacement and total continuity. For example, perhaps modern humans from the south did drive the Neanderthals in western Europe to extinction—but only after they had first interbred with other Neanderthals in central Europe. A few more discoveries, some improvements in dating techniques, and who knows, maybe the fossils would sort themselves out.

But what about Eve?

Everybody knows fossils are fickle; bones will sing any song you want to hear. But Eve was different. She promised so much, made things seem so simple. Wolpoff and his people had to keep their sights on her, and on the mitochondrial malcontents looking for truth in the bottom of a test tube. They weren't going to be satisfied until Eve was brought down on her own turf, once and for all.

"Our real quarrel is not with Chris Stringer," says Wolpoff. "Our public enemy number one is Allan Wilson, and the people in his lab. In the broad scientific context, our dispute is with the geneticists."

The weak link in the genetic chain of evidence, according to Wolpoff, is the molecular clock itself. For the clock to work, the only factor contributing to the variation among mitochondrial gene types today must be the random mutations that accumulated over generations. But Wolpoff sees at least two wrenches in the clockworks, both of which reduce the amount of variation among mitochondrial genes and result in a common human ancestor who appears much younger than she really is.

The first clock-stopper is natural selection, which will favor some mutations while eliminating others. Environmental pressures, for example, might have got rid of certain disadvantageous mutations that arose at various times and reduced the amount of genetic variation now seen among modern human populations. Less variation, of course, has the effect of making Eve look younger. But the geneticists claim that the mitochondrial DNA mutations they're looking at occur only in places that are "neutral" for selection; they aren't within sequences that code for any proteins, so any changes won't affect how an individual adapts to his or her environment.

The other wrench Wolpoff thinks is interfering with the clock's regular ticking is the phenomenon known as random loss. In each generation some women will have only male children or no children at all. Whenever this happens a mitochondrial type will be lost to history, just as family names are lost each time a generation passes without a son. So while mutations are continually increasing the amount of variation within a population, random loss is constantly destroying it.

"If you take these factors into consideration," Wolpoff says, "it looks more and more like the common ancestor is closer to a million years old, rather than two hundred thousand. That suits me just fine. If the mitochondrial clock has any validity at all, it is simply measuring the original migration of *Homo erectus* out of Africa. The Eve hypothesis is refuted. Case closed."

"That's bull," says Wilson. He point out that, despite the wrenches in the timing mechanism cited by Wolpoff, the clock just plain works. The molecular dates of species separation agree with fossil dates in many cases, such as the split between apes and humans 5 million years ago, as well as the split between New World and Old World monkeys 35 million years ago. "There is a clock," he says. "Finding out there is one is quite a different endeavor from explaining why it's there."

Stoneking also thinks the clock keeps ticking despite Wolpoff's kicking. In his view, random loss of lineages might influence the number of mitochondrial types around at any point in time, but the ones that survive will have the same degree of variation among them. So the clock still runs as well as it ever did.

"Based on the work now going on in Wilson's lab, I'm more confident of a two-hundred-thousand-year date for Eve, not less," Stoneking says. Indeed, aided by the powerful new technique of polymerase chain reaction, or PCR, the Berkeley geneticists have garnered new evidence that both supports their original study and greatly expands its scope. PCR allows researchers to isolate a targeted length of DNA and make millions of copies of it for analysis. Instead of comparing patterns of DNA fragments cut by enzymes, as was done by Cann in the original Eve study, PCR produces samples that can be compared base pair by base pair along any chosen stretch of DNA. This has given the Wilson lab a burst of new ammunition with which to answer their critics.

One of the most intriguing uses of PCR is a recent study by Linda Vigilant, one of Wilson's graduate students. Vigilant compared samples of mitochondrial DNA extracted from single hairs plucked from almost 100 people, including a group of Africans. With the precision of PCR, Vigilant could look at changes along a section of mitochondrial DNA called the control region, which mutates at a faster rate than other sections.

As was true in Cann's study, the African lineages were the oldest. But Vigilant went one step further. She compared the amount of diversity among the different African mitochondrial DNAs with the diversity between African mitochondrial DNA and the mitochondrial DNA of a chimpanzee. Chimpanzees, everyone now seems to agree, split off from the human line 5 million years ago. Vigilant demonstrated that the chimp and human mitochondrial DNA diverged by 42 percent during those 5 million years, or 8.4 percent per million years. Among African types, however, the degree of divergence was just 2 percent—in molecular clock terms, that's less than 250,000 years ago, very close to Cann's original date for the mitochondrial mother of us all.

This is not, however, the confirmation that everyone is looking for. "The truth is," says Stoneking, "that neither we nor the anthropologists are looking at what we'd really like to be seeing, which is the underlying genetic basis for the transformation to modern humans. They look at bone morphology, which may or may not be significant. We look at mitochondria, which are at best indirect markers for what was really going on."

The real answer is locked up inside our nuclear DNA. Some of these genes, researchers have recently learned, are passed down intact from parent to child without recombining with the DNA of the other parent, which makes them potential candidates for a nuclear DNA clock. But these genes are extremely long sequences, consisting of hundreds of thousands of base pairs. This is much more extensive than mitochondrial DNA, and thus mapping any changes is a slow, tedious process. However, the pace of this research promises to pick up with the advent of the multibillion-dollar human genome project, the endeavor to map every piece of DNA we have. As the information about various nuclear genes accumulates, we may catch a glimpse of the true face—and age—of Eve.

What can you say about her in the end? Only that she's still out there somewhere, not accepted, not denied, waiting for someone to end the uncertainty. And while she waits, the bone men will keep digging for answers, and the biologists will fine-tune their genetic clocks. Everyone's hoping for the clue that will break the case wide open, and no one's sure just when and if that clue will come.

"I don't like to make predictions, because I might be wrong," says Stoneking. "But I bet we'll have an answer within ten years. Maybe less."

"They've had ten years on this already," Wolpoff retorts, "and what have they given us? A hypothesis that doesn't hold water. And there's good reason to think it'll never work."

Hominid Evolution and
Primate Social Cognition

————————————— *James Steele* —————————————

Selection for corticalization and complex language in later hominid evolution (genes *Homo*) indicates an adaptive context favouring increased capacity for mental-model representation (implicated in intentional action), and for social exchange and modification of such representations. Two current hypotheses for non-human primate encephalization are reviewed. Non-human primate grouping patterns and social systems are determined by three major factors: dietary characteristics, predation risk, and social competition. If social systems are determined by grouping patterns, and the latter by factors other than those of optimal foraging, then these two hypotheses for primate encephalization (foraging complexity and social cognition) refer to two distinct sources of selection pressures.

Application of these hypotheses to the hominid case entails discriminating between the three possible determinants of hominid grouping patterns. Evidence for scavenging and for increased predation risk for early genus *Homo* groups suggests that optimal foraging models are not sufficient to predict later hominid social strategies. Increased social competition resulting from larger grouping patterns, the latter a response to predation risk, is hypothesized to have presented the dominant selection pressure for human social cognitive and socially manipulated group-living skills, and thus for hominid brain and language evolution.

Keywords: hominid selection pressures, corticalization, language, primate socioecology, grouping patterns, predation, social cognition.

Journal of Human Evolution (1989) **18**, 421–432.

INTRODUCTION

The purpose of this paper is to review the points of similarity in two human and non-human primate traits (brain and speech), to review the two major current hypotheses of their evolution in non-human primates (feeding-niche complexity and social cognition), and thereby to derive and to test hypotheses of the relative importance of these two factors in the selection environments of the hominids.

Reprinted from "Hominid Evolution and Primate Social Cognition" by James Steele, *Journal of Human Evolution* (1989) 18, 421–432.

Human Neuroanatomy: Primate Perspectives

Mammals show constant, predictable relationships in brain-to-body-size ratios across taxa (Armstrong, 1983; Riska & Atchley, 1985). *Relative brain size* is an index of residual variation in brain-size after body-size related variation has been controlled for. Primates taken as a whole are a relative brain-size "grade" higher than other mammals (cf. Martin, 1982: 45). Within the primate order, in Martin's study (1984: 85), a *Homo sapiens sapiens* sample had 3–6 times the brain-size expected for a "normal" Old World simian primate of our body-size. The great apes, our closest living relatives, are also quite highly encephalized compared to this Old World simian norm, although much less so than *Homo sapiens*.

Cranial volume (as measured by "brain-size") correlates very well with overall neural tissue mass, while among the human brain's substructures Deacon (1988b) claims to have detected a pattern of proportional relationships which vary among primates (at the species level) with *relative brain size*, but in an apparently orderly and predictable way. Thus humans have a relatively high percentage of neocortical neural tissue (which is basically uniform in structure [Rockel *et al.*,, 1980], such that more neocortex implies an additive effect in terms of adaptive function), but this is predictable. More encephalized primates may have proportionally more neocortex (and cortical neural tissue in general as opposed to subcortical nuclear tissue, in all brain substructures) than less encephalized primates. It is a pattern of orderly, relative brain-size related variation in proportions of different substructures, which may therefore derive from some high-level genetic regulatory mechanism controlling primate brain development.

Evidence from bird song-learning nuclei supports the parcellation theory, of a correlation of relative proportions among adaptively significant brain substructures with relevant aspects of behavioural repertoires (Nottebohm *et al.*, 1981). Psychological studies suggest that primate corticalization (relative expansion of cortical neural tissues), a pattern marked most notably by relative expansion of neocortex, and more specifically of prefrontal association cortex, enables cognitive operations involving associative learning across broad spatio-temporal distributions of stimuli (Passingham, 1985; cf. Bechtel, 1985), mental representations (Goldman-Rakić, 1987, 1988; cf. Phillips *et al.*, 1984; Kaplan, 1987), and co-ordinated goal-directed behaviour involving the development of inhibition (Diamond, 1988). Human language does not appear to be fundamentally involved in human cognitive operations, which are not propositional but analogical in structure: language is dependent on the blueprint supplied by these (analogically-structured) mental representations (Bisiach, 1988). Common chimpanzees (*Pan troglodytes*) show evidence of abstract representations and cognitive manipulations without language (Premack 1988): "displacement", mental representations of the world as a means of dealing with times and places different to the here-and-now, is *not* linguistic, but a more basic central nervous system attribute (Premack 1984). Comparative evidence from other higher vertebrates suggests the existence of "beliefs" and purposive "rational" skills in non-speaking animals that require a "non-linguistic mode of representation" (Weiskrantz, 1988); ecologically, we would expect what laboratory evidence now demonstrates, the widespread existence in higher vertebrates of stimulus-generalization to object-classes (Pearce, 1988), and of cognitive maps of spatial environments, which as environmental representations can be updated and reorganized through exploratory behaviour (Thinus-Blanc, 1988). Dickinson (1980) distinguishes primitive procedural representation ("if X is perceived, do Y") from declarative (model-based) representation, and notes the increasing focus on the latter in animal cognitive learning theory, as applicable to species without speech.

Human Language: Primate Perspectives

Mental representation is a prerequisite of symbolic communication: the dependence of verbal language on a more fundamental core of cognitive conceptual structures shared with the visual system, a dependence explicitly incorporated into recent cognitive science formalisms (Jackendoff, 1987; Talmy, 1988), indicates a basis for mental-model representations in non-linguistic cognitive processes. Deacon (1988b) speculates that the highly encephalized human brain is a product of selection for expanded prefrontal cortex, which is implicated in language production and comprehension, and has demonstrated (Deacon, 1988a) that the prefrontal cortical areas known to be involved in human auditory processing and in speech production have homologues in non-human primates, as indicated by his own experimental work on macaque monkeys; thus the basic neural circuitry of human language capabilities represents no major species-specific structural innovation (refuting both Chomsky's invocation of a human "language organ" and some palaeoanthropologists' invocations of hominid neuroanatomical reorganization). Cerebral cortex functions symmetrically for basic somatosensory and motor functions, but the "extra capacity" is used asymmetrically in the two hemispheres, apparently as an adaptation for "effective use of neural space" (Levy, 1988: 157) for functionally-differentiated neural programmes. Thus in humans, the left hemisphere is involved in "speech, phonetics, grammar, and its coordinated specialization for regulating serially ordered oral and manual movements" (ibid.: 160), while the right hemisphere is hugely more efficient in "a variety of highly complex visuospatial skills" (loc. cit.), and related aspects of language use such as interpreting emotional intonations, "appreciating humour, verbal emotional descriptions, metaphor, and the general schemata and global structure of stories" (ibid.: 161).

Functional lateralization is not unique to humans: findings in macaque monkeys indicate left hemisphere dominance for processing of species-specific vocalizations, right hemisphere dominance for con-specific facial recognition, and different handedness preferences for different tasks (Falk, 1987). Phonological evidence shows that monkeys use acoustic patterns in vocal communication which are common to human language phonology (frequency modulation, changes in power spectrum, amplitude modulation and call duration) (Maurus et al., 1988). At the semantic level, primate social communication in the vocal-auditory modality has been discovered in the past decade to be frequently far more complex than had previously been supposed, with widespread representational vocal signalling, structured in some instances by simple syntax (with meanings encoded in the order of elements within a phrase) (Steklis, 1985). The semantic content of such signals can convey social information about the sender's sex, group-membership, and social relationships, while the example of vervet monkey alarm calls (with different signals for at least three different types of predator) demonstrates communication of categorial information about the non-social environment (Seyfarth, 1986).

Lieberman (1984, 1988) suggests that the human supralaryngeal tract and associated cognitive speech-perception abilities differ from those of all other living species in features enabling introduction of greater complexity into the acoustic energy output which constitutes a speech signal, at the cost of greater maladaptedness for respiration, swallowing, and chewing (1988: 149); he argues that:

> "Comparative and fossil studies indicate that the evolution of human supralaryngeal vocal tract may have started in hominid populations like that of the *Homo habilis* KNM-ER 3733 fossil. More recent hominid lineages differ with respect to the presence of a modern supralaryngeal airway. Hominids like classic Neanderthal retained the non-human supralaryngeal vocal tract; other hominids contemporary with Neanderthal had human supralaryngeal airways" (1988: 150).

and thus the capacity "to achieve a maximum phonetic output" (*ibid.*: 151). Studies of human *narrative comprehension* (the way in which serially-ordered propositional information is transferred and reorganized into non-propositional mental-model representations in memory [Stenning, 1986]), emphasize the "bottleneck" of short-term memory as a buffer and limiting factor in discourse comprehension. It is *phonological* processing limits which constrain the amount of information which can be held in short-term memory while a more durable mental-model representation of propositional meaning is constructed (Baddeley & Wilson, 1988; Fletcher & Bloom, 1988). The expansion of cortical tissues and the modification of the supralaryngeal airways in human evolution therefore imply selection for increased capacity for, for social exchange of, and for interactive modification of the mental-model representations involved in intentional (goal-directed) behaviour.

FEEDING-NICHE COMPLEXITY OR SOCIAL COGNITION?—NON-HUMAN PRIMATES

Of the two main selection-pressure arguments for the evolution of non-human primate intelligence and of inter-specific variation in relative brain-size, one explains such variation by covariation in feeding-niche complexity, and the other explains it by the complex cognitive demands of negotiating social relationships in groups.

Feeding-Niche Complexity

The evidence for and the problems with feeding-niche complexity explanations are discussed in Martin (1984). There *are* significant correlations between relative brain-size and dietary category in primates, as in other mammalian groups; however, correlation is not therefore causal explanation, since dietary categories also co-vary with levels of basal metabolism: frugivores are "high-energy", folivores are "low-energy". According to Martin (*op. cit.*), variation in relative brain-size may thus be in part a side-effect of selection for differing energy-strategies in differing niches, as mediated by maternal metabolic investment in foetal brain development; selection for brain-size itself could operate on variation in reproductive parameters, such as gestation period and investment in postnatal development. However, Harvey (1988: 208–209) has pointed out some difficulties in squaring fresh data and analyses with Martin's "metabolic constraints" hypothesis as applied to mammals and birds in general (Martin, 1981), noting that it fails "to specify the costs and benefits of having small or large brains at particular times in an animal's life, or the nature of the constraints acting on brain development". Pagel & Harvey (1988) argue now that there is no empirical support for a linkage of neonate brain size with maternal metabolic rate in mammals, and that variation in the former trait correlates rather with life-history tactics (gestation length and litter-size).

Milton (1988: 287–288) has recently restated the case for seeing primate intelligence as an evolved adaptation to patchy but high-quality plant-foraging in a tropical rainforest:

> "It seems maladaptive in general, given the dynamic nature of tropical forests, to try and code a great variety of dietary information genetically. Rather, what appears to be required is a great deal of behavioural flexibility—flexibility to respond to continually changing forest conditions. Increasing mental complexity with a strong emphasis on learning and retention is one direction selection could take."

Cohesive group-living thus enables social transmission of learned information about the characteristics of a particular ranging area. Milton supports this argument with a specific comparison of two large Neotropical primates, howler monkeys (*Alouatta palliata*) and spider monkeys (*Ateles geoffroyi*), which share many basic characteristics (similar average adult body-weight, arboreality, solely plant-based diet, relatively unspecialized digestive tracts, and relatively closed mixed groups with a high degree of interrelatedness [*op. cit.*: 288]). The two species *differ* in relative brain-size and in dietary focus: howlers are smaller-brained and more folivorous, while spider monkeys are relatively larger-brained and more frugivorous. Milton's field data show that howler monkeys have smaller, highly delineated home ranges, with highly routinized food-search patterns: the social group is thus the unit of information transmission. Spider monkeys, on the other hand, forage in sub-groups or individually for their patchier principal food-resource, ripe fruit, with the larger group dispersed among individual trees, individuals visiting other sub-groups to assess the best feeding. There is markedly longer maternal dependence, associated with individ-

129

ual learning of foraging routes. Social behaviours are, in general, more complex. Thus for spider monkeys, the individual is the unit of information acquisition; their relatively larger brains are an adaptation for foraging in a more complex, patchily distributed resource-space, entailing individual representation of resource distributions, and the generation of daily foraging strategies from there.

At a proximal level, such evidence and arguments appear persuasive. Howler monkeys *are* the only predominantly folivorous cebid monkeys, and they *do* have relatively small brains (Clutton-Brock & Harvey, 1980). However, the howlers' relatively small brains can be explained by the proportion of their cranium which is occupied by their massive vocal apparatus (hence "howler" monkeys):

> "The spatial requirements of the tremendously enlarged vocal apparatus have resulted in extreme alterations in the topography of both viscerocranium and neurocranium (Biegert, 1957). The changes in the neurocranium include an extreme backward relocation of foramen magnum and occipital condyles, and a complete extension of the cranial base. Because the cranial base in the howler monkey is even more extended than in, for example, the treeshrew with its tiny and primitive brain (Biegert, 1963), the exceptionally small brain of the howler monkey may be best explained in this context." (Leutenegger 1982: 91).

Howler monkeys are polygynous, and Sekulić, who studied the function of howling in red howler monkeys in the field, suggests that it serves in males "to repel solitary males and subordinate males in neighbouring troops who may attempt to replace them [and thus to gain and maintain access to breeding females]" (Sekulić, 1982: 52). Thus if howlers *are* exploiting a low-complexity niche, this may be because of a small relative brain-size *which was the side effect of* earlier, more rigorous sexual selection for a greater vocal apparatus (Crockett, 1987: 120). An additional effect from predator-pressure may be implicated in howler monkey group-size: adult howlers are known to be preyed on by Harpy eagles (*Harpia harpyja*), while there have been no observations of predation upon members of the spider monkey genus (*Ateles*) (Terborgh & Janson, 1986: 120).

Social Cognition

The principal alternative hypothesis for the evolution of primate intelligence is focussed not on spatio-temporal complexity of resource distributions, but on social complexity and the cognitive demands of primate sociality. This hypothesis can be traced back to proposals made independently by Chance & Mead (1953), Jolly (1966), Kummer (1967) and Humphrey (1976). As restated by Whiten & Byrne (1988a), this "Machiavellian hypothesis" accounts for primate cognitive abilities primarily as adaptations to complex sociality, and thus to situations in which an animal's predictions of future states on the basis of past experience cannot simply be generated from accumulated (foraging) knowledge, but instead entail constant reassessment of data which is changeable and contingent upon the animal's own actions (social-interactive cognition). They outline a two- or three-stage account of the evolution of primate cognitive abilities: a first stage of sociality entailing some social learning, but little capacity for inferring the probable future outcomes of *novel* conjunctions of events (Humphrey, 1976); a second stage entailing "Machiavellian" cognitive operations (the capacity to continuously modify behaviour in response to the changing behaviours of other con-social animals, including the ability to switch tactics as this becomes advantageous); and a possible third stage, in which such a cognitive capacity for "Machiavellian" social skills is generalized to cognitive operations directed at the behavioural interface with a physical environment (including feeding resources)—technical, or object intelligence. Whiten & Byrne (1988b) discuss primate cognitive operations of differing orders of complexity, *discovery behaviours* (curiosity and exploration of physical objects, and "social play" for gathering information about social relationships); *innovation or tactical flexibility* as responses to novel associations of events (spatio-temporal fluctuations in food availability, or in social interactions the abstraction of "conditional social rules" as a basis for social actions, in relation to specific actions by other con-sociates whose past social-interactive patterns can be stored in short-term and long-term memory); *cognitive representations of the intentionality and attentional states of others,* perhaps involving attribution of several levels of intentions ("X thinks Y knows that X wants Y to do such-and-such", or in more complex tripartite interactions "X thinks Y knows that Z wants Y to do such-and-such", etc.); and (perhaps only in humans) *self-reflective monitoring* as a means of abstracting an explanatory model of human action.

They note that these operations are not found distributed equally among primate species: primates appear to show more general curiosity than other mammals, while "tactical flexibility" through transference of strategies from one type of problem to another type with common underlying principles has been seen experimentally in both monkeys and great apes. However, great apes appear to be more skilled in complex social-cognitive operations, chimpanzees exhibiting triadic play in 25% of their social play, as opposed to 3–5% in baboons, while imitative learning or true copying (as opposed to observational learning from another animal's behaviour through stimulus enhancement, where attention is thereby focussed on a particular aspect of the environment without copying of the animal's actual behaviour sequence) appears to be found only in great apes (chimpanzees), due to the complex cognitive operations of translating perceived behaviour of others into motor actions, decomposing it into sub-routines and then recombining them into a motor action sequence which "will from this new point of view look quite different to the model behaviour originally observed in others" (Whiten & Byrne, 1988b: 65).

EVALUATING THE ALTERNATIVE MODELS

Distinguishing between these two hypotheses entails not simply distinguishing between two aspects of a single source of selection-pressures, but rather between two possibly *divergent* selection-pressures. This distinction becomes significant if the factors determining group size, and dependent aspects of social systems, cannot be deduced purely from optimal foraging models.

Comparisons of living non-human primate species suggest that group size and social system are functionally related, but the processes involved are not obvious; if internal social factors (e.g., co-operation, mate competition, kin selection) are independent sources of inter-species variation, then group size is a dependent variable, while if group size is determined by external factors (predation, diet characteristics, etc.) then social system is a dependent variable (Terborgh & Janson, 1986). Most recent models for the evolution of primate social systems favour the determinacy of environmental factors acting to optimize group size. An important instance is predator pressure. Terrestrial primates experience greater predation than arboreal primates, from mammals as well as from birds: one would therefore expect terrestrial primate groups to be larger, on average, and this appears to be the case (*ibid.*: 121). A possibly conflicting pressure will come from feeding-competition, with which mean group size should vary inversely: "if group size is adjusted to the available food supply, then greater intragroup competition should be associated with higher rates of death and emigration or with decreased birth rates" (*ibid.*: 123), while in absolute terms larger groups will almost always need to range more widely to meet their food requirements. Wrangham (1986b: 284) argues that primate social systems are influenced by ecological variables which affect specifically female grouping strategies (defensibility of resources, patch distribution, and predator pressure), since male behaviour "is generally adapted to maximize mating success, which depends on the distribution and behaviour of females", while female behaviour "often appears to be adapted more directly to ecological pressures because female fitness tends to be limited by environmental pressures such as food availability". He has also suggested (Wrangham, 1980) that in patchy environments, larger group size enhances intraspecific competitive ability *vis-à-vis* other groups. In the case of the great apes (very large-bodied species with fewer predators), Wrangham (1986a: 378) argues that social competition is the dominant factor determining grouping patterns (and thus dependent social behaviours): "vulnerability to conspecifics is the principal source of social bonds, and defensive groups are therefore formed when foraging constraints permit" (*ibid.*: 378).

HOMINID EVOLUTION: SELECTION PRESSURES

Deriving testable hypotheses from these models concerning the dominant selective factors in human brain and language evolution will entail, in part, discerning empirically the relative importance of feeding-niche structure, predation, and social competition in determining hominid group size and grouping patterns. The last two of these factors may be partially interconnected, inasmuch as social competition will intensify when group size is set at levels above those optimal for foraging, due to predation pressure.

Feeding-Niche Complexity

Feeding-niche complexity oriented accounts of later hominid evolution (genus *Homo*) tend to follow two patterns: either downplaying selection for encephalization and complex language in favour of some other "central" trait or trait complex, such as body-size and body-size related adaptions (e.g., Foley, 1987), or invoking a qualitatively new hominid feeding niche with characteristics demanding them (e.g., Tooby & DeVore, 1987). The first of these strategies, in downplaying the most distinctive derived human morphological traits, violates the selectionist axiom that it is precisely such traits which will have been subject to strongest selection pressure. The trend to larger body-size in earlier hominid evolution, a trend generally related to gaining social dominance over other competing species in an ecological community, may indeed demonstrate interspecific competition; however, the intraspecific competitive advantages of larger body-size in monopolizing resources will have provided the main selection pressure for this trait at the inter-individual level (Brown & Maurer, 1986). Evidence suggesting the co-existence of hominid species (genus *Homo*) (Lieberman *et al.*, 1988) is also consistent with models of sympatric speciation as a product of intraspecific resource competition through assortative mating (with regard to some unambiguous phenotypic trait) (cf. Seger, 1985).

However, the invocation of a major, qualitatively new hominid feeding niche, "the hunting hypothesis", is unsupported by any unambiguous evidence from the archaeological record for hunting by *H. habilis* or by *H. erectus*, the taxa whose members demonstrate the most significant shift toward a more encephalised morphology (Tobias, 1987): on the contrary, the available evidence supports a "scavenging hypothesis" at least as well (Binford & Stone, 1986; Binford *et al.*, 1988). Lithic assemblages from the Koobi Fora sites (1·9–1·4 Myr BP) may reflect complex organizational strategies involving more planning and foresight than is seen in living non-human primates, with curation and transport of flaked stone artefacts (Oldowan and early Acheulian traditions) over distances of several kilometres from geological source (Toth, 1987): this may represent a well-developed, habitual strategy from *H. habilis* times (Schick, 1987). The dual-patterning in site and lithic assemblage variability seen with *H. erectus* and the Acheulian tradition, with large "multi-context", repeated-occupation sites and "transitory, single-activity assemblages" (Clark, 1987: 822), may reflect a more developed territorial strategy involving several core-areas of closed vegetation, limited extent and with permanent water sources nearby, with more arid open savannah areas "regularly exploited and patrolled by small groups" (*ibid.*: 809). However, it remains unclear whether or not this reflects a strategy of exploitation of secondarily-scavenged carcasses. Modern human gut morphology, compared to that of the great apes, is characterized overall by a relatively small gut, and within the gut by a relatively small colon and an enlarged small intestine. Variation in primate gut morphology is correlated with dietary preference, these human traits indicating a common ancestor with a relatively high-quality diet, relatively nutrient-dense and rapidly absorbed (Milton, 1988; cf. Martin *et al.*, 1985). This pattern may derive from new dietary patterns in *H. erectus*, for which palaeopathological (Kennedy, 1985) and dental and masticatory evidence (Lucas *et al.*, 1985) indicate a shift to greater use of higher grade plant foods, and to seasonally-varying, heavy consumption of meat. However, as Milton (1988) points out, this need not imply a causal relationship of new dietary strategy demanding greater cognitive capacity, but could equally well indicate (conversely) new dietary patterns answering the nutritional and metabolic demands of maintenance of a more encephalised nervous system (cf. Harvey & Bennett, 1983), itself functionally adapted to some other suite of environmental problems.

In the context of this paper, it can be suggested that empirical testing of the "hunting" and "scavenging" hypotheses also constitutes a test of the feeding-niche complexity hypothesis for primate brain evolution, as applied to hominids. If it is with *H. habilis* and *H. erectus* that corticalization and respiratory-tract specialization for speech become subject to strong selection pressure, then the "scavenging hypothesis" demands recourse to an alternative adaptive explanation of these traits. Social cognition, as an adaptive response to grouping patterns determined by predation and social competition, is the principle alternative model.

Social Cognition

Given the nature of the data, it is difficult to devise tests which could discriminate between the effects of predation and those of hostile intergroup social competition on the grouping patterns of *H. habilis* or *H. erectus*. Wrangham's emphasis on social competition in the great apes is based largely on observations of gorillas and woodland chimpanzees (Gombe and Mahale); hostile intergroup relations have not yet been seen in bonobos or forest chimpanzees (Reynolds, 1988). There *is* clear evidence for carnivore predation on Australopithecines (Brain, 1981), and while there is no evidence that it was a major selective pressure in later hominid evolution (genus *Homo*), it is possible that the perceived risk of predation would have affected later hominid grouping patterns even if actual mortality levels remained below archaeologically detectable thresholds. A shift to a fully terrestrial strategy would have increased the risk of predation, in comparison with the risks faced by the arboreal great apes (Terborgh & Janson, 1986), and it is significant to note in this context that while early hominid locomotor adaptations (*A. afarensis* and *A. africanus*) may have been a persisting "compromise adaptation" retaining a significant amount of arboreal positional behaviour (Hill, 1987; Rose, 1984; McHenry, 1986), *H. erectus* morphology is characterized by enlarged hindlimb joints and elongated lower extremity, interpreted as an adaptive shift connected to longer distance travel and "prolonged repetitive loading of the hindlimb joints" (Jungers, 1988: 264). On the other hand, indications of extension of hominid ranging areas are inconsistent with observations of the conditions of hostile intergroup competition in non-human primates, which correlate this with small, defended ranges ("territories").

It would be purely speculative to argue that predation was the major determinant of later hominid grouping patterns in the absence of any supporting evidence. Certainly, however, an increase in body-size coupled with large social groups would demand greatly increased home range areas (Ripley, 1984: 40), and this appears to be confirmed by lithic transport over successively greater distances in the later hominid artefactual record (Toth, 1987). If predation risk promoted later hominid grouping patterns entailing larger group sizes than were optimal simply for *foraging*, then increased levels of intragroup competition and decreased group stability would have occurred. In such contexts the capacity for social cognition, and that for complex language as "a delicate instrument for establishing and modulating ever more intricate relationships between human beings" (Burling, 1986: 14–15; cf. Bruner, 1984), would have come under strong selection pressure as a mechanism for learning, communicating and manipulating shared mental-model representations of the contexts of and constraints on action. In contrast, while social representation entails great operational complexity in response to the unpredictability of human social interactions, lithic technology may not have demanded such sophisticated abilities: everyday tool manufacture and use entails only rote-learning of sequences of actions (Wynn, 1988), while technology is innovated and transmitted primarily through visual representation and visual sharing. Tool use in non-human primates is relatively rare, although "primatologists repeatedly emphasize the ability of the subjects to use other individuals as 'social tools' to achieve particular results" (Cheney *et al.*, 1986: 1365).

An increased emphasis on selection for social cognition and language in human evolution, as a product of grouping patterns *not predictable from optimal foraging theory alone*, could account not just for patterns of simultaneous scavenging, encephalization and respiratory tract evolution in the later hominid fossil record (*H. habilis* and *H. erectus*), but also (less directly) for some challenging aspects of the archaeological record of anatomically-modern human societies: thus the archaeological evidence for the Neanderthal replacement in Europe indicates that what distinguishes the social behaviour of *H. sapiens sapiens* was not "planning depth" (Roebroeks *et al.*, 1988), but an increased elaboration in social markers and status attributes, as shown by their material culture (Chase & Dibble, 1987).

Human brain and language characteristics indicate selection for increased capacity for mental-model representation (implicated in intentional behaviour), and for social exchange and social manipulation of such representations. By analogy with non-human primates, two hypotheses of the selective advantages of these hominid traits have been considered: adaptation to foraging complexity, and adaptation to predation and social competition (with grouping patterns and social systems dependent variables in both cases). Evidence for hominid scavenging (early genus *Homo*) fails to support the first of these hypotheses, while predicted increased predation risk for early *Homo* groups would have favoured larger grouping patterns than were optimal for foraging: this prediction may be supported by evidence of increased body-size and ranging area at this time. In such a context, intensified social competition would have occurred, and thus selection for social cognitive and socially manipulative group-living skills.

ACKNOWLEDGEMENTS

I am very grateful to Clive Gamble, Stephen Shennan, Peter Andrews, and three anonymous referees for their criticisms of earlier drafts.

REFERENCES

Armstrong, E. (1983). Metabolism and relative brain size. *Science* **20**, 1302–1304.

Baddeley, A. & Wilson, B. (1988). Comprehension and working memory: a single case neuropsychological study. *Journal of Memory & Language* **27**, 479–498.

Bechtel, W. (1985). Contemporary connectionism: are the new parallel distributed processing models cognitive or associationist? *Behaviorism* **13**, 53–61.

Biegert, J. (1957). Der Formwandel das Primatenschädels und seine Beziehungen zur ontogenetischen Entwicklung und den phylogenetischen Spezialisationen der Kopforgane. *Morph. Jb.* **98**, 79–199.

Biegert, J. (1963). The evaluation of characteristics of the skull, hands, and feet for primate taxonomy. In (Washburn, S. L., Ed.) *Classification and Human Evolution*, pp. 116–145. Chicago: Aldine.

Binford, L. R., Mills, M. G. L. & Stone, N. M. (1988). Hyena scavenging behavior and its implications for the interpretation of faunal assemblages from FLK 22 (the Zinj floor) at Olduvai Gorge. *J. Anthrop. Archeol.* **7**, 99–135.

Binford, L. R. & Stone, N. M. (1986). Zhoukoudian: a closer look. *Curr. Anthrop.* **27**, 453–475.

Bisiach, E. (1988). Language without thought. In (Weiskrantz, L., Ed.) *Thought without Language*, pp. 464–484. Oxford: Clarendon Press.

Brain, C. K. (1981). *The Hunters or the Hunted?* Chicago: University of Chicago Press.

Brown, J. H. & Maurer, B. A. (1986). Body size, ecological dominance and Cope's rule. *Nature* **324**, 248–250.

Bruner, J. S. (1984). Pragmatics of language and language of pragmatics. *Soc. Res.* **51**, 969–984.

Burling, R. (1986). The selective advantage of complex language. *Ethology and Sociobiology* **7**, 1–16.

Chance, M. R. A. & Mead, A. P. (1953). Social behaviour and primate evolution. *Symp. Soc. Exp. Biol.* **7**, 395–439.

Chase, P. G. & Dibble, H. L. (1987). Middle palaeolithic symbolism: a review of current evidence and interpretations. *J. Anthrop. Archeol.* **6**, 263–296.

Cheney, D., Seyfarth, R. & Smuts, B. (1986). Social relationships and social cognition in nonhuman primates. *Science* **234**, 1361–1366.

Clark, J. D. (1987). Transitions: *Homo erectus* and the Acheulian: the Ethiopian sites of Gadeb and the Middle Awash. *J. hum. Evol.* **16**, 809–826.

Clutton-Brock, T. H. & Harvey, P. H. (1980). Primates, brains and ecology. *J. Zool. Lond.* **190**, 309–323.

Crockett, C. M. (1987). Diet, dimorphism, and demography: perspectives from howlers to hominids. In (Kinzey, W. G., Ed.) *The Evolution of Human Behavior: Primate Models*, pp. 115–135. New York: SUNY Press.

Deacon, T. W. (1988a). Human brain evolution: I. Evolution of language circuits. In (Jerison, H. J. & Jerison, I., Eds) *Intelligence and Evolutionary Biology*, pp. 363–382. Berlin: Springer Verlag.

Deacon, T. W. (1988b). Human brain evolution: II. Embryology and brain allometry. In (Jerison, H. J. & Jerison, I., Eds) *Intelligence and Evolutionary Biology*, pp. 383–416. Berlin: Springer Verlag.

Diamond, A. (1988). Differences between adult and infant cognition: is the crucial variable presence or absence of language? In (Weiskrantz, L., Ed.) *Thought without Language*, pp. 337–370. Oxford: Clarendon Press.

Dickinson, A. (1980). *Contemporary Animal Learning Theory.* Cambridge: Cambridge University Press.

Falk, D. (1987). Brain lateralization in primates and its evolution in hominids. *Yearb. phys. Anthrop.* **30,** 107–125.

Fletcher, C. R. & Bloom, C. P. (1988). Causal reasoning in the comprehension of simple narrative texts. *Journal of Memory and Language* **27,** 235–244.

Foley, R. (1987). *Another Unique Species.* London: Longmans.

Goldman-Rakić, P. S. (1987). Circuitry of the prefrontal cortex and the regulation of behavior by representational memory. In (Plum, F., Ed.) *Handbook of Physiology* Section 1, Volume 5, pp. 373–417. USA: Oxford University Press.

Goldman-Rakić, P. S. (1988). Topography of cognition: parallel distributed networks in primate association cortex. *Ann. Rev. Neurosci.* **11,** 137–156.

Harvey, P. H. (1988). Allometric analysis and brain size. In (Jerison, H. J. & Jerison, I., Eds) *Intelligence and Evolutionary Biology,* pp. 199–210. Berlin: Springer Verlag.

Harvey, P. H. & Bennett, P. M. (1983). Brain size, energetics, ecology and life history patterns. *Nature* **306,** 314–315.

Hill, A. (1987). Causes of perceived faunal change in the later Neogene of East Africa. *J. hum. Evol.* **16,** 583–596.

Humphrey, N. K. (1976). The social function of intellect. In (Bateson, P. P. G. & Hinde, R. A., Eds) *Growing Points in Ethology,* pp. 303–317, Cambridge: Cambridge University Press.

Jackendoff, R. (1987). On Beyond Zebra: The relation of linguistic and visual information. *Cognition* **26,** 89–114.

Jolly, A. (1966). Lemur social behaviour and primate intelligence. *Science* **153,** 501–506.

Jungers, W. L. (1988). Relative joint size and hominid locomotor adaptations with implications for the evolution of hominid bipedalism. *J. hum. Evol.* **17,** 247–265.

Kaplan, S. (1987). Associative learning and the cognitive map: differences in intelligence as expression of a common learning mechanism. *Behavioral and Brain Sciences* **10,** 672–673.

Kennedy, G. E. (1985). Bone thickness in *Homo erectus. J. hum. Evol.* **14,** 699–708.

Kummer, H. (1967). Tripartite relations in hamadryas baboons. In (Altmann, S. A., Ed.) *Social Communication among Primates.* Chicago: University of Chicago Press.

Leiner, H. C., Leiner, A. L. & Dow, R. S. (1986). Does the cerebellum contribute to mental skills? *Behav. Neurosci.* **100,** 443–454.

Leutenegger, W. (1982). Encephalization and obstetrics in primates with particular reference to human evolution. In (Armstrong, E. & Falk, D., Eds) *Primate Brain Evolution,* pp. 85–95. New York: Plenum Press.

Levy, J. (1988). The evolution of human cerebral asymmetry. In (Jerison, H. J. & Jerison, I., Eds) *Intelligence and Evolutionary Biology,* pp. 157–174. Berlin: Springer Verlag.

Lieberman, D. E., Pilbeam, D. R. & Wood, B. A. (1988). A probabilistic approach to the problem of sexual dimorphism in *Homo habilis:* a comparison of KNM-ER 1470 and KNM-ER 1813. *J. hum. Evol.* **17,** 503–511.

Lieberman, P. (1984). *The Biology and Evolution of Language.* Cambridge, Mass.: Harvard University Press.

Lieberman, P. (1988). Language, intelligence, and rule-governed behavior. In (Jerison, H. J. & Jerison, I., Eds) *Intelligence and Evolutionary Biology*, pp. 143–156. Berlin: Springer Verlag.

Lucas, P. W., Corlett, R. T. & Luke, D. A. (1985). Plio-Pleistocene hominid diets: an approach combining masticatory and ecological analysis. *J. hum. Evol.* **14**, 187—202.

Martin, R. D. (1981). Relative brain size and basal metabolic rate in terrestrial vertebrates. *Nature* **293**, 57–60.

Martin, R. D. (1982). Allometric approaches to the evolution of the primate nervous system. In (Armstrong, E. & Falk, D., Eds) *Primate Brain Evolution*, pp. 39–56. New York: Plenum Press.

Martin, R. D. (1984). Body size, brain size and feeding strategies. In (Chivers, D. J., Wood, B. A. & Bilsborough, A., Eds) *Food Acquisition and Processing in Primates*, pp. 73–104. New York: Plenum Press.

Martin, R. D., Chivers, D. J., MacLarnon, A. M. & Hladik, C. M. (1985). Gastrointestinal allometry in primates and other mammals. In (Jungers, W. L., Ed.) *Size and Scaling in Primate Biology*, pp. 61–90. New York: Plenum Press.

Maurus, M., Barclay, D. & Streit, K.-M. (1988). Acoustic patterns common to human communication and communication between monkeys. *Language and Communication* **8**, 87–94.

McHenry, H. M. (1986). The first bipeds: a comparison of the *A. afarensis* and *A. africanus* postcranium and implications for the evolution of bipedalism. *J. hum. Evol.* **15**, 177–191.

Milton, K. (1988). Foraging behaviour and the evolution of primate intelligence. In (Byrne, R. W. & Whiten, A., Eds) *Machiavellian Intelligence*, pp. 285–305. Oxford: Clarendon Press.

Nottebohm, F., Kasparian, S. & Pandazis, C. (1981). Brain space for a learned task. *Brain Research* **213**, 99–109.

Pagel, M. D. & Harvey, P. H. (1988). How mammals produce large-brained offspring. *Evolution* **42**, 948–957.

Passingham, R. E. (1985). Cortical mechanisms and cues for action. *Phil. Trans. R. Soc. London.* **B 308**, 101–111.

Pearce, J. M. (1988). Stimulus generalization and the acquisition of categories by pigeons. In (Weiskrantz, L., Ed.) *Thought without Language*, pp. 132–155. Oxford: Clarendon Press.

Phillips, C. G., Zeki, S. & Barlow, H. B. (1984). Localization of function in the cerebral cortex: past, present and future. *Brain* **107**, 327–361.

Premack, D. (1984). Comparing mental representation in human and nonhuman animals. *Soc. Res.* **51**, 985–999.

Premack, D. (1988). Minds with and without language. In (Weiskrantz, L., Ed.) *Thought without Language*, pp. 25–45. Oxford: Clarendon Press.

Reynolds, V. (1988). *Man* N.S. **23**, 381.

Ripley, S. (1984). Environmental grain, niche diversification and feeding behaviour in primates. In (Chivers, D. J., Wood, B. A. & Bilsborough, A., Eds) *Food Acquisition and Processing in Primates*, pp. 33–72. New York: Plenum Press.

Riska, B. & Atchley, W. R. (1985). Genetics of growth predict patterns of brain-size evolution. *Science* **229**, 668–671.

Rockel, A. J., Hiorns, R. W. & Powell, T. P. S. (1980). The basic uniformity in structure of the neocortex. *Brain* **103**, 221–244.

Roebroeks, W., Kolen, J. & Rensink, E. (1988). Planning depth, anticipation and the organization of Middle Palaeolithic technology: the "archaic natives" meet Eve's descendants. *Helinium* **28,** 17–34.

Rose, M. D. (1984). Food acquisition and the evolution of positional behaviour: the case of bipedalism. In (Chivers, D. J., Wood, B. A. & Bilsborough, A., Eds) *Food Acquisition and Processing in Primates,* pp. 509–524. New York: Plenum Press.

Schick, K. D. (1987). Modeling the formation of Early Stone Age artifact concentrations. *J. hum. Evol.* **16,** 789–807.

Seger, J. (1985). Intraspecific resource competition as a cause of sympatric speciation. In (Greenwood, P. J., Harvey, P. H. & Slatkin, M., Eds) *Evolution. Essays in Honour of John Maynard Smith,* pp. 45–53. Cambridge: Cambridge University Press.

Sekulić, R. (1982). The function of howling in red howler monkeys (*Alouatta seniculus*). *Behaviour* **81,** 38–54.

Seyfarth, R. (1986). Vocal communication and its relation to language. In (Smuts, B. B. *et al.,* Eds) *Primate Societies,* pp. 440–451. Chicago: University of Chicago Press.

Steklis, H. D. (1985). Primate communication, comparative neurology, and the origin of language re-examined. *J. hum. Evol.* **14,** 157–173.

Stenning, K. (1986). On making models: a study of constructive memory. In (Myers, T., Brown, K. & McGonigle, B., Eds) *Reasoning and Discourse Processes,* pp. 165–185. London: Academic Press.

Talmy, L. (1988). Force dynamics in language and cognition. *Cognitive Science* **12,** 49–100.

Terborgh, J. & Janson, C. H. (1986). The socioecology of primate groups. *Ann. Rev. Ecol. & Syst.* **17,** 111–135.

Thinus-Blanc, C. (1988). Animal spatial cognition. In (Weiskrantz, L., Ed.) *Thought without Language,* pp. 371–395. Oxford: Clarendon Press.

Tobias, P. V. (1987). The brain of *Homo habilis:* a new level of organization in cerebral evolution. *J. hum. Evol.* **16,** 741–761.

Tooby, J. & DeVore, I. (1987). The reconstruction of hominid behavioral evolution through strategic modeling. In (Kinzey, W. G., Ed.) *The Evolution of Human Behavior: Primate Models,* pp. 183–237. New York: SUNY Press.

Toth, N. (1987). Behavioral inferences from Early Stone Age artifact assemblages: an experimental model. *J. hum. Evol.* **16,** 763–787.

Weiskrantz, L. (Ed.) (1988). *Thought without Language.* Oxford: Clarendon Press.

Whiten, A. & Byrne, R. W. (1988a). The Machiavellian intelligence hypotheses: editorial. In (Byrne, R. W. & Whiten, A., Eds) *Machiavellian Intelligence,* pp. 1–9. Oxford: Clarendon Press.

Whiten, A. & Byrne, R. W. (1988b). Taking (Machiavellian) intelligence apart: editorial. In (Byrne, R. W. & Whiten, A., Eds) *Machiavellian Intelligence,* pp. 50–65. Oxford: Clarendon Press.

Wrangham, R. W. (1980). An ecological model of female-bonded primate groups. *Behaviour* **75,** 262–300.

Wrangham, R. W. (1986a). Ecology and social relationships in two species of chimpanzee. In (Rubenstein, D. I. & Wrangham, R. W., Eds) *Ecological Aspects of Social Evolution,* pp. 352–378. Princeton: Princeton University Press.

Wrangham, R. W. (1986b). Evolution of social structure. In (Smuts, B. B. *et al.,* Eds) *Primate Societies,* pp. 282–296. Chicago: University of Chicago Press.

Wynn, T. (1988). Tools and the evolution of human intelligence. In (Byrne, R. W. & Whiten, A., Eds) *Machiavellian Intelligence,* pp. 271–284. Oxford: Clarendon Press.

PART 2

Prosimians/Strepsirhini and the New World Primates

Ecology, Socioecology and Behavioural Biology

M. E. Stephens

Strepsirhines receive less attention than deserved in this book. The wonderfully varied lemurs of Madagascar are completely ignored simply because space and economic budgets did not allow inclusion, not from a lack of interest. The wet-nosed strepsirhines with their less-efficient gestation systems are represented only by five nocturnal species of lorisids from Gabon. The article also introduces the law of competitive exclusion and explains how five species which subsist on identical diets in laboratories manage to avoid competition and live sympatrically in the wild.

Tarsiers, the major classification problem among living primates, are also missing from this section. These prosimian/haplorhines are mentioned in the overview and general primate model sections.

Primates often seem at first glance to be exceptions to generalizations about animal behaviour and ecology. As many of the articles in this section indicate, they are frequently "the exceptions which prove the rule".

New world monkeys are useful as examples of extreme or exceptional primate adaptations. All new world monkeys are arboreal. All have a different dental formula from other anthropoids. Some, four species only, have prehensile tails, a characteristic unlike any other primates. A few species, belonging to the family Callitrichidae, regularly give birth to twins. Many new world monkeys have intensive male care of infants which is an unusual trait for primates. And, finally, the only nocturnal anthropoid is a new world monkey, *Aotus trivirgatus*.

Many of the articles in this section detail the complex interplay of an animal's morphology, physiology, subsistence strategy, reproduction, social organization, and relationships with other organisms in a rain forest environment. The seeming exception to rules of ecology make sense when examined in this context.

These papers look at animals with extreme adaptations. Thus papers include small animals with high metabolic costs, animals with expensive offspring, and large primates who barely manage an arboreal existence.

Ecology and Feeding Behaviour of Five Sympatric Lorisids in Gabon

P. Charles-Dominique

INTRODUCTION

This study was carried out in Makokou (Gabon) in the period 1965–1969, on the basis of four study visits of 7, 8, 14 and 3 months' duration, respectively. Field-work was carried out from the CNRS Laboratory in Gabon (originally known as the Mission Biologique au Gabon, under the direction of Professor P. P. Grassé), which is now referred to as the Laboratoire de Primatologie et d'Écologie Equatoriale (Director: A. Brosset).

The study region is located in the heart of the Congolese block of rain-forest (Ogoue-Ivindo basin). It lies 550 km. from the Atlantic coast and 0.4° latitude north of the equator. Along the access routes (roads, certain water-courses, etc.), the forest has been degraded for cultivation which has been subsequently abandoned at various times, thus giving rise to areas of secondary forest at different stages of reconstitution. Primary forest is found a few km. away from these inhabited zones.

Five prosimian species live sympatrically in Gabon; two lorisines:

1. *Perodicticus potto edwardsi* (Bouvier, 1879). Body-weight 1100 gm. Head + body length 327 mm.; tail-length 52 mm.
2. *Arctocebus calabarensis aureus* (De Winton, 1902). Body-weight 200 gm. Head + body length 244 mm.; tail-length 15 mm.

and three galagines:

1. *Galago demidovii* (Fischer, 1808). Body-weight 61 gm. Head + body length 123 mm.; tail-length 172 mm.
2. *Galago alleni* (Waterhouse, 1837). Body-weight 260 gm. Head + body length 200 mm.; tail-length 255 mm.
3. *Euoticus elegantulus elegantulus* (Le Conte, 1857). Body-weight 300 gm. Head + body length 200 mm.; tail-length 290 mm.

(These figures represent averages based on 33, 30, 66, 17 and 39 specimens respectively.)

The Lorisinae and the Galaginae represent two quite distinct subfamilies: the former are exclusively slow climbers which never leap and always move around slowly and cautiously, whilst the latter are rapid and vigorous leapers.* These behavioural differences are paralleled by numerous anatomical adaptations, primarily affecting the limbs and the tail. In particular, the tarsus is extremely developed in the Galaginae, whilst the tail is very reduced in Lorisinae. By contrast, the skull, the dentition, the digestive tract and the reproductive organs exhibit only very slight differences which would not, in themselves, justify a separation into two subfamilies.

The leaping specialisation of the bushbabies is generally regarded as providing a means of rapid escape, at the same time permitting exploitation of an extensive home-range. On the other hand, the slow and deliberate gait of the lorises has been given different interpretations by different authors: ". . . high-grade specialisations for an arboreal existence" (Hill); ". . . [1] directly related to catching prey such as insects and roosting birds" (Walker).[2] Some authors have, in fact, expressed astonishment that these animals, which are apparently so vulnerable, have not been decimated by predators. From the author's observations in the forest,[3] it seems very likely that some kind of cryptic mechanism is involved, though this would of course operate only in the natural habitat of these species. (The eye, particularly that of raptors, is more sensitive to rapid movement than to slow progression, and many nocturnal arboreal predators are guided primarily by the auditory sense in localising their prey.) A cryptic mechanism would not, in any case, be the sole means of defence. As a last resort, when an encounter occurs, the lorises utilise active defence mechanisms which vary from species to species. The behaviour of the potto and the angwantibo towards predators has already been described, along with the morphological adaptations involved.[3]

In sum, the two lorisid groups have developed two radically different methods of escaping from predators. Whereas the bushbabies flee rapidly once detected by a predator, the lorises avoid detection by means of an elaborate pattern of slow locomotion. It will be shown that such adaptation has been associated with extensive modification of the feeding behaviour and the diet of the lorisines.

ECOLOGY

The lorisids represent a tiny fraction of the forest mammalian fauna; there are 5 species among 120 mammal species living sympatrically at Makokou. Over and above this, these lorisid species live at relatively low population densities. Sys-

---

*Many authors have exaggerated the locomotor performance of the bushbabies. Sanderson,[5] in particular, writes of a leap of over 10 m. made by *E. elegantulus*, with the animal purportedly gaining in height! We have measured leaps of 2 m. for *G. demidovii*, and of 2.5 m. for *G. alleni* and *E. elegantulus*, with take-off and landing at the same level. The present record is a leap of 5.5 m. (orthogonal projection of horizontal displacement) made by *E. elegantulus*, with a loss in height of 3.1 m.

tematic counting along pathways and the results of trapping[3] indicate the following average densities per square km.:

- *Perodicticus potto*   8 per square km.
- *Arctocebus calabarensis*   2 per square km.
- *Galago demidovii*   50 per square km.
- *Galago alleni*   15 per square km.
- *Euoticus elegantulus*   15 per square km.

Using the same techniques, we have calculated far higher densities for lemurs in Madagascar, where the prosimians represent the bulk of the mammalian fauna.[4] However, one must take allowance for heterogeneous distribution of populations, which occur as "nuclei" ("noyaux") which can be separated to varying degrees. The extreme case seems to be that of the angwantibo, which is abundant in certain parts of the forest (7 per square km.) and virtually lacking over large areas. Nevertheless, we have observed the sympatric occurrence of three, four and even five of these prosimian species in some areas. In fact, numerous interspecific encounters were observed in the forest, without any sign of attack or escape behaviour. In general, any two lorisids of different species which encounter one another exhibit a brief bout of mutual observation and then continue on their way. Thus, any hypothesis of direct interspecific competition based on aggression must be discarded.

The lorisids are all nocturnal. Certain authors, on the basis of observations made in captivity, have suggested that they are partially diurnal or crepuscular.[5,6,7] Such observations must arise from artefacts of captivity, since all of the individuals followed in the forest showed themselves to be strictly nocturnal. In fact, although the lorises only move around during the night, the bushbabies exhibit some initial activity in twilight. But night falls so rapidly at the equator that the bushbabies are only moving around for ten minutes or so before the twilight has faded. The following values for the luminosity of the sky were measured at the times when activity began:

- *Euoticus elegantulus*   300 to 100 lux
- *Galago demidovii*   150 to 20 lux
- *Galago alleni*   50 to 20 ux

even then, it must be remembered that the light penetrating into the undergrowth of primary forest represents only one hundredth of the values measured above the canopy.

Quite erroneously—again as a result of observations in captivity—numerous authors have reached the conclusion that all lorisids use tree-holes as retreats. Of course, when placed in cages deprived of foliage, the animals do actually retreat into the only boxes placed at their disposition. However, of the five species studied, *Galago alleni* is the only one which sleeps in tree-holes under natural conditions. Usually, such tree cavities are in split hollow trunks, which can be entered from above. The bushbaby can spend the whole day clinging to the internal face of such a "chimney." Sometimes a rudimentary nest is built at the base with a few collected leaves. Interspecific competition for daytime retreats can be excluded; the observer has to examine a large number before finding one which is occupied. In addition, *Galago alleni* seems to be quite tolerant of other mammal species. We observed one individual sleeping a few metres away from an arboreal rodent (*Anomalurus erythronotus*) and a group of five bats in a hollow trunk of *Scyphocephalium ochocoa*. The two other bushbaby species sleep singly or in small groups on a small, leafy branch or in a tangle of lianes. *Galago demidovii* will also sleep in spherical nests constructed with green leaves.[3,8,9] The two lorisine species sleep singly on branches or lianes, protected by foliage.

The modern concept of the "ecological niche" involves a large number of factors. Here, we will only examine the spatial localisation of the animals and their respective diets. These two factors cannot be dissociated, since food-seeking occupies the major part of the activity period of these lorisid species.

SPATIAL LOCALISATION

In order to define in an objective manner the localisation and nature of the supports utilised, we considered the following criteria:

- height relative to the ground
- orientation of the support
- diameter of the support
- nature of the support (ground, small trunk, liane base, large trunk, large branch, foliage, foliage mixed with lianes, lianes)

Every time a lorisid was encountered in the forest, we noted the various characteristics of the support on which the animal was *first* seen. (The presence of the observer could modify the selection of any subsequent pathway taken by the animal.) A large number of such observations (642 sightings of the five species) permitted statistical consideration of the data, which are discussed in detail in a previous publication.[3] All that will be given here is a brief description of the forest biotopes most frequently visited by each lorisid species (see Fig. 1):

1. Perodicticus potto

The potto inhabits the canopy (10–30 m. in primary forest; 5–15 m. in secondary forest). It is an exclusive climber, using supports with a wide range of sizes (1–30 cm. diameter). This permits the potto to pass from tree to tree by successively utilising large forks (20%) and small branches which interlock from one branch to another (21%). Lianes which permit short-cuts are also utilised (20%). The support orientations are: horizontals 39%, obliques 35%, verticals 26%. In exceptional cases, the potto descends to the ground (escape from a conspecific, crossing a deforested area, etc.). When this occurs, the potto is extremely cautious and heads directly for the nearest tree.

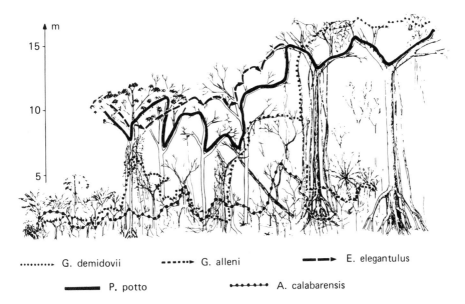

.... ▸ G. demidovii   ------▸ G. alleni   ━ ━ ▸ E. elegantulus

━━━▸ P. potto   ◆◆◆◆◆◆▸ A. calabarensis

Figure 1a: Schematic illustration of the paths taken by the five prosimian species in young secondary forest, established secondary forest and flooded forest (passing from left to right).

2. Arctocebus calabarensis

The angwantibo lives at 0–5 m., both in primary forest and in secondary forest, though it may rarely flee up to 10–12 m. when greatly alarmed. When progressing, this slow climber generally utilises small lianes passing between the small bushes in the undergrowth (43%). Quite frequently, the angwantibo is sighted in the foliage of these small bushes (43%), where it hunts for insects. This species will descend quite readily to the ground to eat fallen fruits or to follow the tracks made by terrestrial mammals (4%). 40% of the supports utilised have a diameter of less than 1 cm.; 52% are between 1 and 10 cm. in diameter. Orientations of supports are: horizontals 20%, obliques 30%, verticals 50%.

3. Galago demidovii

This bushbaby lives primarily in dense vegetation invaded by small lianes (35%) and in foliage (25%). Accordingly, it is found at a great height in primary forest (10–30 m.) and low down in secondary forest (0–10 m.); the vertical distribution follows the distribution of the biotopes utilised. 64% of the supports used are less than 1 cm. in diameter; 25% are between 1 and 5 cm. in diameter. The support orientations are: horizontals 22%, obliques 30%, verticals 48%.

4. Galago alleni

This bushbaby species is more or less restricted to primary forest, living at a height of 0–2 m. It hunts for animal prey at ground-level, at the same time

Figure 1b. Similar illustration of the characteristic pathways taken by the five prosimian species in primary forest.

collecting fallen fruits; but locomotion consists primarily of leaping from one vertical support to another (small tree-trunks; bases of large lianes). The supports utilised have the following diameters: 9% less than 1 cm., 60% between 1 and 5 cm., 19% between 5 and 10 cm. The support orientations are: horizontals 6%, obliques 13%, verticals 81%.

5. Euoticus elegantulus

This bushbaby, which scarcely ever descends to the ground, lives in the canopy up to 50 m. However, it may descend to a height of 3–4 m. on certain large lianes which provide droplets of gum. Much progression is along large branches (62%) or large lianes (30%), and along the larger tree-trunks. The special structure of the nails, which terminate in small "claws," permits movement head-downwards or head-upwards along large, smooth trunks where no other lorisid species would be able to maintain a grasp. It will be seen that this adaptation is related to the diet. The support orientations are: horizontals 22%, obliques 51%, verticals 27%.

To summarise the above information, it can be said that within each sub-family the closest species are ecologically separated by the height of the forest stratum exploited. In the Lorisinae, the potto exploits the canopy and the ang-wantibo lives in the undergrowth. Among the Galaginae, *Euoticus elegantulus* principally exploits the canopy, whilst *Galago alleni* inhabits the undergrowth. *Galago demidovii* provides a special case: this species depends upon dense vege-

148

tation, in which it can move easily thanks to its small size, and it follows the distribution of such vegetation (high up in primary forest and low down in secondary forest).

This latter example provides a good illustration of the fact that the height of the stratum exploited is not due to a "height preference" exerted by each animal. It is an indirect consequence of choice of particular vegetation zones in each case. We were able to observe that the same applies to *Galago alleni*. After hand-rearing two young animals captured at the age of 1 week (at which stage they can only move a few centimetres), we found that, from the age of 1 month onwards, they sought out all supports with a vertical orientation (especially chair and table legs). Such selection, which has an apparent hereditary basis, is accompanied by a specific leaping "style" which is adapted to this kind of support.[3] In addition, *Galago alleni* captured as adults and placed in secondary forest (where they scarcely ever occur naturally) moved around at heights of 10–15 m. They utilised vertical or oblique branches at this height when progressing, whereas the average height utilised in primary forest is 1–2 m. With *Galago alleni*, it seems very likely that the vertical orientation of supports of a certain size contributes greatly to the localisation of this species in the undergrowth zone of primary forest.

It will be seen that spatial localisation of these lorisid species is no more than the bare framework of ecological separation permitting closely related species to avoid dietary competition. In parallel with such spatial localisation, there has been dietary specialisation, which has particularly affected feeding behaviour.

DIET

Direct observation of lorisids under natural conditions is difficult. When they are surprised by the light-beam of a headlamp they remain immobile for a few seconds and then disappear rapidly into the vegetation. Under these conditions, analysis of the diet could only be carried out through examination of stomach contents. In Gabon, the prosimians are virtually untouched by hunters, and it was therefore possible to collect a large number of specimens without endangering the local prosimian populations. The animals were collected with the aid of a rifle, samples being taken at different times of the night and in all months of the year. This permitted us to study alimentary rhythms during the night as well as annual rhythms (examination of 174 digestive tracts for the 5 species). The food is quite finely chewed before swallowing; but it is still quite easy to separate the different constituents, which are mixed only to a slight extent in the stomach. We were thus able to separate animal prey from fruit and gums and to obtain fresh weights for these constituent fractions for each stomach examined. The fruits can be identified when the kernels are ingested, but it is often impossible to obtain a precise identification for animal prey. The analysis was therefore restricted to the level of large taxonomic groups: Coleoptera, Lepidoptera (both caterpillars and moths), Orthoptera, Hymenoptera (ants), Isoptera (termites), Myriapoda (centipedes and millipedes), Arachnida, Gasteropoda (slugs), Batracia.

After calculating for each species the percentage of the three principal dietary categories, we obtained the following results (Table 1):

Table 1. Stomach Contents

	Animal Prey	Fruits	Gums
Perodicticus potto	10%	65% (+ some leaves and fungi)	21%
Arctocebus			
calabarensis	85%	14% (+ some wood fibre)	—
Galago demidovii	70%	19% (+ some leaves and buds)	10%
Galago alleni	25%	73% (+ some leaves, buds and wood fibre)	— (small amounts only)
Euoticus elegantulus	20%	5% (+ some buds)	75%

If this first result were taken at face value, one might conclude that the bushbabies include one insectivore, one frugivore, and one gummivore, whilst the lorises represent one frugivore and one insectivore. Since the most closely related animals are separated by stratification of the vegetational zones utilised, it would seem that there can be no dietary competition. However, the problem is in reality more complex than this. The percentage figures do not take into account differences in body size of the five prosimian species concerned—that is, they do not reflect the real weight of food ingested. By calculating the average weight of each of the three dietary categories per stomach, the following results are obtained (Table 2).

Table 2. Weights of Dietary Components

	Animal prey	Fruits	Gums
Perodicticus potto	3.4 gm.	21 gm.	7 gm.
Arctocebus			
calabarensis	2.0 gm.	0.3 gm.	0 gm.
Galago demidovii	1.16 gm.	0.3 gm.	0.15 gm.
Galago alleni	2.2 gm.	9.2 gm.	(negligible)
Euoticus elegantulus	1.18 gm.	0.25 gm.	4.8 gm.

Although the differences for fruits and gums are very clear, this is not the case with animal prey, which are consumed in virtually equal quantities by all five species. Insects (which represent the bulk of the animal prey) are dispersed in the vegetation, and a hunting animal must explore large areas in order to capture large numbers of prey. A small bushbaby and a large bushbaby cover approximately the same distance in the course of the night, and thus each has approximately the same number of opportunities to encounter insects. The same applies to the potto and the angwantibo.

This mechanism has already been described by Hladik and Hladik[10] for the platyrrhines of Panama, which consume roughly the same absolute quantities of insects regardless of their own body-size. The smaller platyrrhines obtain almost all of their food by hunting animal prey, whilst the larger species have to supplement their diet with plant food.

Among the bushbabies, *Galago demidovii* (60 gm.) relies almost entirely on hunting, whereas the two larger species supplement their diets with fruits (*G. alleni*, 260 gm.) or with gums (*E. elegantulus*, 300 gm.). Among the lorises, the angwantibo (200 gm.) derives most of its food by hunting, whilst the potto (1100 gm.) augments its diet of insects with fruits and gums.

In captivity, lorisids are often seen to "ignore" fruits when they have a large quantity of insects available. The same applies in the forest, where pottos which begin the night with a "good hunting session" do not go on to eat fruits afterwards. All the individual pottos dissected which had 8–15 gm. of insect matter in the stomach had failed to eat fruits or gums. On the other hand, all individuals with less than 1 gm. of insect matter in the stomach had eaten 20–60 gm. of fruits and/or gums. In *Galago demidovii* the diet is observed to be slightly less insectivorous in the early part of the night, when the animals are still hungry, than in the second half of the night (35% fruits and gums devoured before midnight, and 20% thereafter). Accordingly, in the dry season (when insects are rarer) this species consumes 50% fruits and gums, as against 30% during the rest of the year.

Thus it seems probable that the availability of animal food is the major factor influencing the diet of these lorisid species. Naturally, secondary specialisations affect the feeding behaviour of the "large" species oriented towards gums or fruits.

1. Animal Food

In this analysis, we have considered the lorisines and the galagines separately. However, it is conceivable that the members of the two subfamilies may compete with one another in hunting insects. An examination of the categories of prey taken by each species shows that this is not the case. Table 3 shows, in order of importance, the different prey categories found in the stomach contents. The most common categories are followed by percentage figures based on the relative weights of animal food types in the stomachs.

Among the galagines, 78% of the prey are beetles, nocturnal moths and grasshoppers, whereas in the lorisines caterpillars and ants represent 70% of the prey. Pottos particularly prey upon ants (*Crematogaster* sp.) which release large quantities of formic acid, on centipedes (*Spirostreptus* sp.) which release large quantities of iodine, and on "criquets puants" (malodorous orthopterans), which also emit repellent substances. The angwantibo feeds primarily on caterpillars, most of which are covered with stinging hairs. (The caterpillars eaten by the bushbabies never bear such hairs.) Thus, it would seem that the two lorisine species are specialised to tolerate "noxious" prey left untouched by the galagines.

This special tolerance of the lorisines for "noxious" prey permits the capture of a sufficient quantity with a minimum of movement from place to place. In fact, these efficiently protected "noxious" organisms almost always display certain forms, colours or (especially) odours, which normally signal their "unpalatable quality" to potential predators. They are easily found, and their immobility permits easy capture. (In the case of ants of the genus *Crematogaster*, the potto follows moving columns, licking them up.) Over and above this, these prey organisms—which are ignored by many other predators—are abundant.

Table 3 Animal prey in order of preference

	1	2	3	4	5
Perodicticus potto[a] (N = 41)	ants (65%)	large beetles (10%)	slugs (10%)	caterpillars (10%)	orthopterans (malodorous), centipedes, spiders, termites
Arctocebus calabarenis (N = 14)	caterpillars (65%)	beetles (25%)	orthopterans	—	dipterans, ants
Galago demidovii (N = 55)	small beetles (45%)	small nocturnal moths	caterpillars (10%)	hemipterans	orthopterans, millipedes, homopterans, pupae
Galago alleni (N = 12)	medium-sized beetles (25%)	slugs	nocturnal moths	frogs (8%) ants (8%)	grasshoppers, termites millipedes, pupae, caterpillars
Euoticus elegantulus[b] (N = 52)	grasshoppers (40%)	medium-sized beetles (25%)	caterpillars (20%)	nocturnal moths (12%)	ants homopterans

[a]Examination of 41 stomachs from pottos did not reveal one case of vertebrate remains. However, whilst following a population of tame animals in the forest we were able to observe a female attempting to capture weaver-birds in a tree carrying a large number of nests. On another occasion, we surprised a female devouring a young frugivorous bat (*Epomops franqueth*). Capture of such prey must be relatively rare.

[b]No vertebrate remains were found in 52 E. *elegantulus* which were dissected; but we did once come across a tame individual eating a bird (*Camaroptera brevicauda*) in secondary forest.

In this case, the lorisines are actually exhibiting a *tolerance* rather than a preference. If, in captivity, pottos or angwantibos are presented with their habitual prey alongside grasshoppers or moths normally eaten by galagos, they will eat the latter insects. In actual fact, angwantibos exhibit a particular form of behaviour prior to eating caterpillars. These animals are gripped by the head in the angwantibo's teeth, and the two hands "massage" the prey for 10–20 seconds, with the result that many of the hairs are removed. Nevertheless, once it has eaten the caterpillar, the angwantibo spends some time wiping its snout and hands by rubbing them on a branch.

Despite their slow locomotion, which serves to protect them from predators, the lorisines succeed in capturing a sufficient quantity of animal prey to ensure a balanced diet. Proteins necessary for physiological equilibrium are found principally in animal prey or in the green parts of plants (leaves and buds). The primates are, in fact, either insectivorous/frugivorous (usually the more rapid species) or folivorous/frugivorous (usually the slower forms, with a few intermediate types).[10] Among the Lorisidae (insectivore-frugivores), the lorises exhibit an exceptional adaptation. These slow-moving animals have conserved the typical diet of the family Lorisidae by obtaining their proteins from a category of animal prey generally left untouched by insectivorous species.

One can therefore discount the idea of any competition between lorisines and galagines in predation on insects. A second contributory factor is important in this context: whereas the lorises capture resting, slow-moving prey, the bushbabies frequently capture rapid-moving prey, quite often when the latter are on the wing. In order to do this, the bushbaby projects its body forward with great rapidity, whilst maintaining a grasp on the branch with its hind-feet. The insect is trapped in flight with both hands, and the bushbaby returns to its starting position (immediately in the case of *Galago demidovii*, which returns like a spring, and only after a short time-lapse in the case of *Euoticus elegantulus*, which ends up suspended head-downwards after the capture).

On the other hand, the potto and the angwantibo—already separated by their height in the vegetational strata—hunt animal prey which are malodorous (potto) and irritating (angwantibo). On the other, the two large bushbaby species are separated by the heights at which they are active. *Galago demidovii* and *Euoticus elegantulus*, which both exploit the canopy in primary forest, are unlikely to compete with one another. The first species preys primarily upon small animals (beetles, moths), and the second feeds upon larger prey (grasshoppers, larger beetles).

2. Fruits

The dietary tables given above show that only the potto and Allen's bushbaby can be regarded as frugivorous. In fact, the other three species consume absolute quantities of fruits amounting to only 1/30th of that eaten by *Galago alleni* and 1/70th of that consumed by the potto. In general, all of the lorisids primarily select soft, sweet fruits (*Uapaca* sp., *Musanga cercopioides*, *Ricinodendron africanus*). However, the potto can attack certain fruits with a hard exterior, and on two occasions we saw *Galago demidovii* profiting from the passage of a potto to eat the remains of a large fruit which the latter had opened. As far as *P. potto* and *G. alleni* are concerned, the former eats fruits in the canopy, whilst the second collects them on the ground. This excludes any competition between the two species. These field observations have been confirmed experimentally in captivity. In a cage containing a tree, the pottos preferred to eat fruits placed in the branches, whilst *G. alleni* preferentially ate those placed on the ground.

Trees which are in fruit not only attract animals which are seeking the fruit—they also attract predators. Frugivores are presented with an abundant source of food; but the more time they spend there, the more they expose themselves to predation. Thus, the optimal solution for them is to collect *rapidly* and *in large numbers* fruits which can be eaten in some protected place. These two necessities are met in different ways in different zoological groups: by the crop in birds, by the cheek-pouches in monkeys and rodents, by the rumen in ruminants, etc. The potto and Allen's bushbaby have particularly distensible stomachs which can contain up to 1/13th of the body-weight. With the other three species, by contrast, we have never found any individuals with more than 1/30th of their body-weights in the stomach. Whereas the species which are not specialised for a frugivorous diet primarily utilise their tooth-scraper for slow removal of small fruit morsels, the potto and Allen's bushbaby can swallow rapidly large pieces of fruit, often including the kernels. In 30–60 seconds, a potto can eat an entire banana, and Allen's bushbaby swallows cherry-sized pieces of fruit by pushing them into the mouth with both hands and keeping the head up. It is actually quite rare to find these two species in immediate proximity of trees in fruit. In general, they are found 30–50 m. away, digesting under cover.

In the forest, the sites of fruit production are diverse and continually fluctuating. Through systematic counts, we established that large trees with high productivity are roughly 50 times less numerous than small trees or lianes with medium or low productivity. This is of capital importance for the distribution of small territorial mammals with permanent, restricted home-ranges (in particular, murids and prosimians). When a large tree comes into fruit from time to time in such a home-range, it is exploited straight away; but for the rest of the year food is obtained from trees with low productivity. The latter suffice for mammals of small body-size, but they must be abundant enough to provide a permanent supply of ripe fruits in the existing home-ranges. At night, trees with high fruit productivity are rarely visited. Using traps, we never captured more than 2–3 individuals of any given mammal species in such a tree (i.e. just as many as around trees with low productivity). Conversely, trees with low fruit productivity are little exploited during the daytime—approximately ten times less, according to our counts. This is doubtless associated with the fact that diurnal animals detect fruits by sight (at long range, when large fruiting trees are involved), whereas most nocturnal mammals detect by smell fruit which is isolated and hidden in the vegetation.

In order to study the social life of the prosimians, we have conducted a great deal of trapping with banana as bait. The animals were marked and released, which permitted us—among other things—to investigate their natural feeding behaviour. A basket of lianes containing 10 bananas is discovered in 1–5 days by *Galago alleni* and in 1–10 days by *Perodicticus potto*. On subsequent nights, if the bananas are replenished as necessary, the animals will return regularly by direct routes, often immediately after waking. They spend a few hours close to the bait and then move on to other fruiting areas. If several baskets of bananas are placed in the home-range of one individual, they will all be discovered and 2–3 may be visited during one night. By dissecting numerous pottos and Allen's bushbabies which were collected at the end of the night, we were able to observe that they can eat 2–3 different types of fruit in one night, which must oblige them to visit several fruiting points every night.

From all of these observations, it would seem that frugivorous prosimians (and murids) exploit simultaneously several fruiting trees, and that they never cease to explore their home-ranges in search of new trees in fruit. This mechanism, which is based on memory and exploration, permits them to feed themselves even if habitually visited fruiting trees cease production, or if they have been visited and depleted by another animal. Through continuous exploration of the home-range, they can locate trees at the start of fructification which will replace those which are ceasing to bear fruit.

3. Gums

The tables show that the potto and the needle-clawed bushbaby (*E. elegantulus*) are the principal feeders on gums. (*G. demidovii* consumes only 1/50th of the quantity of gums eaten by *E. elegantulus*, whilst *G. alleni* and *Arctocebus calabarensis* scarcely eat gums at all.) Both the potto and *E. elegantulus* inhabit the canopy, so it might be expected that they compete for gums.

Gums form principally along trunks and large branches at the site of old wounds and holes made by the mouth-parts of homopterans, (Examination of stomach contents revealed the presence of certain Auchaenorhynch homopterans—Fulgorids, Membracids, Tibinicids, etc.—which were no doubt swallowed involuntarily along with the exudations of resins which they provoked.) In contrast to fruits, gums appear regularly at the same places throughout the year. However, their production—which is dependent upon the metabolism of the trees—may be diminished during the main dry season.

In equatorial West Africa, the main dry season (15 June–15 September) is characterised by almost complete absence of rain, continuous cloud cover during the daytime, and a reduction of 3–4° C in mean temperatures. During this period, we were able to identify a marked decrease in the biomass of insects and a reduction in fructification. In parallel, we have observed that the prosimians lose 1/10th to 1/14th of their body-weights during this critical period. The weight-loss is directly dependent upon food availability. For example, *G. demidovii* consumes an average of 0.65 gm. of insects per night during the main dry season, as against 1.28 gm. per night during the rest of the year (stomach contents taken between 20.00 hrs. and midnight). Under the same conditions, we found smaller quantities of insects and gums in the stomachs of *E. elegantulus* examined during the dry season than in those collected at other times of the year. Thus, any competition would be exaggerated during this critical period.

When the dietary habits of the lorisids are examined in greater detail, it emerges that the potto eats only fruits and insects during the dry season, whereas fruits, gums and insects are taken at other times of the year. Conversely, *E. elegantulus* examined during the dry season had not eaten any fruits, although they eat small quantities during the rest of the year. Throughout the critical period, apart from the animal prey consumed, the potto is thus strictly frugivorous and *E. elegantulus* is strictly gummivorous.

Observation of the feeding behaviour of these two species renders the mechanism of such competition easily comprehensible. Whereas the activity of the potto is primarily oriented towards searching for and visiting trees which are in fruit. *E. elegantulus* spend most of their time visiting trees which are gum-producers. Needle-clawed bushbabies have an excellent memory for gum-production sites, and they follow veritable "rounds" which permit them to collect (with the aid of the tooth-scraper) tiny droplets of gum formed after their last visit. Visits are made almost every night, even though each animal must visit a very large number of production-sites (about 300) in order to collect sufficient quantities of gums. *E elegantulus* rapidly covers its "rounds" thanks to its powerful leaps, stopping only for a few minutes at each gum-exuding site. In addition, the "claws" at the ends of the nails permit access to sites which are inaccessible to the other prosimian species, right along the largest trunks. During the dry season, when the gums accumulate more slowly, *Euoticus* must visit a larger number of production-sites, whereas smaller "rounds" suffice at other times of the year. Under these latter conditions, larger aggregations of gums collect on trees which are not often visited, and it is such gums which are eaten by the pottos. Indeed, the gums found in the stomachs of pottos are often harder and darker in colour than those found in stomachs of *E. elegantulus*, and they occur as large lumps.

Thus, one cannot really talk in terms of real competition for gums between these two species, since the gums eaten by the potto are those left untouched by *E. elegantulus*. Dietary specialisations are most evident during the critical period of the year, and it is doubtless during this time that natural selection for adaptive characters is most active.

CONCLUSIONS

In both the Lorisinae and the Galaginae, the different sympatric species are morphologically relatively similar, and their dietary requirements are quite comparable: insects, with a supplement of fruits and gums in the larger species. In captivity, the five lorisid species can be maintained easily without any provision of foods (e.g. gums, fruits or certain insects) of the kinds eaten under natural conditions. In our present captive colony, all five species have become perfectly adapted to the same diet: milk, banana, apple, pear and crickets. In the forest, it is primarily through exploitation of different vegetation strata that the various species avoid dietary competition. Their ecological delimitations (in particular, their stratification) follow from "preferences" which orient each species towards a particular type of support. This orientation is complemented by certain behavioural and anatomical specialisations associated with utilisation of supports. These anatomical adaptations are relatively minor; it is primarily behavioural differences which permit the separation of ecological niches.

ACKNOWLEDGMENTS

My thanks go to Professor P. P. Grassé and A. Brosset for their generous provision of facilities and assistance at the CNRS field laboratory in Makokou, Gabon, throughout this study. The photographs were taken by A. R. Devez.

I should also like to make a special note of thanks to my friend and colleague, R. D. Martin, who offered to translate the manuscript for this article, despite his heavy commitments with the organisation of the Research Seminar. Our discussions, which have been numerous and very rewarding, have permitted me to extract a number of valuable conclusions.

NOTES

1 **Hill, W. C. O.** (1953), *Primates: Comparative Anatomy and Taxonomy*, 1.*Strepsirhini*, Edinburgh.
2 **Walker, A.** (1969), "The locomotion of the lorises with special reference to the potto," *E. Afr. Wild. J.* 7, 1–5.
3 **Charles-Dominique, P.** (1971), "Eco-éthologie des prosimiens du Gabon," *Biol. Gabon.* 7(2), 121–228.
4 **Charles-Dominique, P. and Hladik, C. M.** (1971), "Le *Lepilemur* du Sud de Madagascar: écologie, alimentation et vie sociale," *Terre et Vie* 25, 3–66.
5 **Sanderson, I. T.** (1940), "The mammals of the North Cameroons forest area," *Trans. Zool. Soc. Lond.* 24, 623–725.
6 **Napier, J. R. and Napier, P. H.** (1967), *A Handbook of Living Primates*, New York, 258.
7 **Jones, C.** (1969), "Notes on ecological relationship of four species of lorisids in Rio Muni, West Africa," *Folia primat.* 11, 255–67.
8 **Vincent, F.** (1969), "Contribution à l'étude des prosimiens africains: le Galago de Demidoff," Doctoral thesis, CNRS, AO 3575.
9 **Charles-Dominique, P.** (1971), "Ecologie et vie sociale de *Galago demidovii*," *Z. f. Tierpsychol.*, Suppl. 9,7–41.
10 **Hladik, A. and Hladik, C. M.** (1969), "Rapports trophiques entre végétation et Primates dans la forêt de Barro Colorado (Panama)," *Terre et Vie* 23, 25–117.

The Surreptitious Life of the Saddle-backed Tamarin

John Terborgh
Margaret Stern

Why are some species common and others rare? This is a question that has intrigued generations of biologists, and one that even today continues to elude facile generalization. To be sure, there are some rules that hold quite well for species that feed at different levels of the food chain. Predators, for example, are constrained by simple energetics to be less numerous than their prey, and species that feed directly on foliage tend to be more abundant than those which feed only on plant reproductive parts such as fruits and seeds. Other things being equal, species of small body size are generally more common than their larger counterparts. But among species that consume the same types of resources and pursue similar lifestyles, why some should be rare and others common remains a persistently elusive question.

Our attention was drawn to this issue by the paradox of a small South American monkey, the saddle-backed tamarin (Fig. 1). Members of the marmoset family, tamarins are among the most diminutive primates, weighing about 450 grams. Apart from their small size, tamarins and marmosets differ from other New and Old World monkeys in having two instead of three molar teeth and in possessing claws rather than nails on their feet. Anatomists are now of the opinion that the claws are secondarily derived from nails, rather than representing a primitive condition (Hershkovitz 1977). In any case, their claws give the tamarins and their relatives an unrivaled squirrel-like agility on tree trunks, where they are capable of rapid movement either straight up or straight down. Other monkeys are incapable of this feat.

Tamarins live in close-knit social units of three to ten individuals, typically containing three or more adults along with their offspring of various ages. Although tamarins have long been cited by primatologists as simian examples of monogamous fidelity, it has recently been shown that their social system is more accurately described as cooperative polyandry (Terborgh and Goldizen 1985). In this unusual social contract, two (or sometimes more) males cooperate amicably in helping to raise a female's twin offspring. While the males stand guard, baby-sit, and carry the young from place to place, the unencumbered

"The Surreptitious Life of the Saddle-Backed Tamarin," by John Terborgh and Margaret Stern, American Scientist 75:260–269, 1987. Reprinted by permission of American Scientist, journal of Sigma Xi, The Scientific Research Society.

female is free to feed. This is a matter of high priority, as during lactation the female's metabolic needs are almost double those of normal times. In larger families, the older offspring also help in the communal effort by taking turns at the carrying task and by allowing the ravenous infants to snatch away freshly caught katydids and lizards.

In exchange for their exertions on behalf of her litter, the female obliges both or all of her consorts during the annual mating period, while they uncomplainingly acquiesce in each other's privilege. In fact, the lack of strife in these groups is quite remarkable and stands in contrast to the constant assertions of dominance one typically sees among both the males and females of polygynous primate societies (Richard 1985).

Tamarins are interesting not only for the peculiarities of their social system but for their ecology as well. At our pristine research area at Cocha Cashu in Peru's Manu National Park (Figs. 2 and 3), there are two species of tamarins, the saddle-backed and the emperor (Fig. 4), among a total of ten species of monkeys (Table 1). In the context of the primate community in which they live, the tamarins are unusual in being small and relatively rare. Out of the ten species, the two tamarins rank eighth and ninth, respectively, in abundance. Only the pygmy marmoset, which is even smaller, is less abundant. The tamarins' scarcity cannot be dismissed as a consequence of their diet, because they feed on a mixture of fruit, nectar, and small prey such as katydids, lizards, and frogs, just as do several of their more numerous larger counterparts, including the capuchins, the squirrel monkey, and the night monkey. The diets of these species are very similar, though in detail there are differences, such as the relative proportions in which different fruits are harvested. It is hard to imagine that such subtle differences are crucial to understanding the rarity of tamarins.

To emphasize just how anomalously rare the tamarins are, we can compare them to the other omnivorous primates in the community. In terms of numbers of individuals per km^2, they rank well below the two capuchins, the squirrel monkey, and the night monkey. But in terms of biomass, or the weight of individuals supported by a unit area of habitat, each tamarin species is present at only one-twentieth the mass of brown capuchins or one-tenth that of squirrel monkeys.

To gain another perspective, we can consider the spatial requirements of tamarins. Tamarins are rigidly territorial, vigorously expelling any intruders that may stray within the sharply defined boundaries of their domains. Groups invest an appreciable part of their time and energy in patrolling their territorial boundaries, announcing their presence to their neighbors with shrill, sweeping cries. Such concerted territoriality is rather exceptional among primates, though the gibbons and siamangs of Asia show it, as do a few other New World species such as the titi and night monkeys.

What is most surprising about tamarin territories is their size. Titi monkeys routinely live within territories of 6 to 9 hectares, and night monkeys seldom defend more than 10 hectares (Wright 1985), but tamarin groups routinely occupy areas of 30 to 120 hectares. Contrast this with the 1 to 2 hectares needed by the common North American gray squirrel, a nonterritorial mammal of about the same size. A group of tamarins uses about as much space as a troop of brown capuchins, though the latter weighs 15 times as much. Tamarins are thus not only rare; they require an amount of space that seems completely out of proportion to their size. In what follows we will try to answer the questions posed by these enigmatic creatures.

THE TERRITORIAL SYSTEM

The saddle-backed tamarins at Cocha Cashu have been under study for a decade. Over this period, the picture of population dynamics that has emerged is one of surprising stability. The number of territories within our 5-km^2 study area has remained strikingly constant, though there have been relatively brief periods in which one or another territory was temporarily vacant. Since the outlines of the territories became known to us ten years ago, the locations of most boundaries have not changed more than a few meters. The pattern shown in Figure 2 has remained fixed. The territories have an existence which transcends that of their occupants. The original population of a decade ago has been completely replaced; new groups have formed, others have disappeared, and still others have moved intact from one territory to another. Yet the territories in all their features—size, shape, and location of boundaries—have remained virtually unchanged. To all appearances the territories are incompressible and fixed in space, as if possessed of special properties that could not be duplicated within different boundaries.

If, as seems to be the case at Cocha Cashu, there is no flexibility in the number of territories that can be carved out of the environment, then the size of the breeding population is effectively constrained. This is suggested also by dispersal behavior of young tamarins. Sexual maturity is attained at age two, and two-year-olds will readily move into breeding positions in adjacent groups upon the death of one of the established adults. If, however, appropriate breeding opportunities do not arise in a nearby group, young adults, especially males, will remain in their natal groups until age three or even four. The frequent presence in the population of such nonreproductive adults strongly suggests that the reproductive potential of the population is constrained by the number of territories rather than by the number of individuals.

Avian territorial systems generally lack such rigidity. The number of territories in a given area may increase or decrease in accordance with fluctuations in local population density (Robinson 1981). Among tamarins, stability is achieved through the apparent incompressibility of territorial boundaries and the presence in the population of nonreproductive adults that are available to fill any vacancies in the breeding class.

While it seems reasonable to conclude that the number of tamarins at Cocha Cashu is limited by the availability of a fixed set of incompressible territories, the level of understanding this provides is very superficial. The significance of territories lies in what they contain, and until we know something about that we shall be at a loss to explain why tamarin territories are so large.

FOOD RESOURCES

Tamarins engage in a distinctive type of feeding behavior, which in contemporary ecological jargon is referred to as traplining. This is a term used to describe species that gather small amounts of food at many places along a lengthy route. It was first coined to differentiate the behavior of certain subordinate hummingbird species from that of larger dominants that could aggressively monopolize a concentrated aggregation of flowers. Tamarins, being near the bottom of the primate pecking order, have assumed this feeding strategy of subordinate species.

As a mechanism for avoiding competition, traplining is quite effective. A larger species can easily assert its dominance over smaller ones and drive them away from rich food resources, but by being larger it requires more food. A small species, by virtue of its lesser metabolic need, can afford to travel farther for smaller rewards than can its larger competitor. Two species can even exploit the same resource without eliminating one another if, for example, the larger harvests the fruits of large trees and the other of small individual trees of the same plant species. The larger cannot eliminate the smaller because it does not have the energy to visit many small scattered groups of trees. In turn, the smaller cannot eliminate the larger because it is unable to gain access to the most productive trees. The outcome is a stable competitive balance in which the abundances of the two species reflect the relative amounts of resource that are available in small and large packets.

Tamarins are consigned to the role of trapliners by their avoidance of larger monkeys. Instead of feeding to satiation in a few large trees, as do the capuchins and spider monkeys with whom they share their territories, tamarin groups visit a succession of small trees, remaining only a few minutes in each one. They are so dedicated to their traplining habit that they frequently pass up opportunities to feed in large trees as they travel between smaller ones. At most seasons they exhibit an obsessive preference for one fruit species, all but ignoring others that are fruiting simultaneously. Just why they do this is still unclear. The behavior results in a diet that is much less diverse than that of other monkeys in the same environment (Terborgh 1983). The plant species that are selected for intensive exploitation, roughly six over the course of a year, are all exploited by larger monkeys, but not with the same intensity. Individual trees may be harvested as the troops chance upon them, but the visits can be regarded as incidental to travel between more substantial resources.

The plant species that are intensively exploited by tamarins share a definite set of characteristics: they are small and relatively common, and they have unusually long fruiting periods, with only a small fraction of the crop ripening at any time. The latter trait is particularly significant, for it minimizes the reward available at any visit, thus discouraging larger monkeys and encouraging many return visits over the fruiting season.

Through traplining, tamarins effectively husband their resources, because the interval between successive visits is adjusted to accommodate the ripening schedule of the species being exploited. During one of our standard ten-day observation periods, many plants will be harvested, but any one will receive only a small number of visits, normally just one or two. By staggering their returns to individual trees, tamarins achieve a controlled and systematic harvest of the resources within their territories. Their ability to do this, however, depends crucially on the integrity of their territories, for if other tamarin groups were visiting the same trees, the territory holders (as well as the trespassers) would no longer have control over the spacing of visits, and would consequently waste time and energy traveling to empty trees. Efficient harvesting of trees whose crops ripen on an extended schedule thus requires not only a certain form of management, but territories that are reliably free of trespassers. It is to this that we attribute the extraordinary vigor with which tamarins defend their territorial boundaries.

SCARCITY IN THE MIDST OF PLENTY

Tropical forests are the subject of many popular misconceptions. One of them is that the exuberant vegetation offers a cornucopia of edible fruits available for harvest at any time. The reality is quite different.

Recent research has shown that tropical forests all over the world are subject to major seasonal fluctuations in their production of food resources such as fruits, foliage, and insects (Leigh and Windsor 1982; Leighton and Leighton 1983; Terborgh 1986). Each year the forest at Cocha Cashu, for example, produces about two metric tones of fruit per hectare (Terborgh 1983). This would be more than enough to support the local frugivore community of birds, bats, primates, and other mammals such as kinkajous, opossums, and peccaries, provided it were uniformly available throughout the year. Actually, about 90% of the total is produced in the eight rainy season months from September through April, while only 10% ripens during the four-month dry season.

During the latter period there is not enough to eat, and members of the frugivore community adapt to this situation in various ways. Most species do not produce young during the dry season. Others (mostly birds) migrate out of the area. Many of those that stay are seen to forage longer and rest less often than at other seasons. And most remarkably, species that are strict frugivores during the seasons when fruit is plentiful switch to feeding on other kinds of resources such as foliage, pith, nuts, flowers, sap, and nectar (Terborgh 1983). Very often these foods of last resort are difficult of access, such as pith and nuts, are of poor nutritional quality (flowers, pith), or are available only in tiny quantities (sap, nectar). In spite of such drawbacks, it is important to realize

162

Table 1. The primate community of Cocha Cashu

Species	Adult weight (kg)	Population density (no. km^2)	Biomass (kg km^2)
Black spider monkey (*Ateles paniscus*)	7.0	25	175
Red howler monkey (*Alouatta seniculus*)	6.0	30	180
Brown capuchin (*Cebus apella*)	3.0	40	120
White-fronted capuchin (*Cebus albifrons*)	2.8	30	84
Squirrel monkey (*Saimiri sciureus*)	0.8	60	48
Night monkey (*Aotus trivirgatus*)	0.7	40	28
Dusky tit monkey (*Callicebus moloch*)	0.7	24	17
Emperor tamarin (*Saguinus imperator*)	0.5	10	5
Saddle-backed tamarin (*Saguinus fuscicollis*)	0.4	12	5
Pygmy marmoset (*Cebuella pygmaea*)	0.1	5	0.5

that these resources are of the utmost significance to the frugivore community, because they tide the animals over through an otherwise inimical time of year.

The dwindling of fruit supplies at the onset of the dry season is general, affecting the small, long-yielding species that tamarins use as well as the major species that sustain the larger monkeys. Much of the fruit that does ripen during the dry season takes the form of figs on trees of gigantic stature. When a crop of figs ripens, the tree immediately becomes an epicenter of activity. Monkey troops converge over a radius of more than a kilometer, and on occasion we have seen as many as 100 animals feeding simultaneously in a crown that shades an area a third the size of a football field.

Tamarins do not attempt to compete in these free-for-alls. Denied access to figs, they resort to what appears to be the only recourse available to them: harvesting the nectar of two species of plants. One of these, *Combretum assimile*, a robust canopy vine (Fig. 5), flowers in July, and the other, *Quararibea cordata*, a midcanopy tree, flowers in August. Together, these two plants account for more than three-quarters of the feeding time of tamarin groups over the two-month period, and for intervals of several days the tamarins may consume no other plant material at all.

Except for their small size, tamarins possess no physical characteristics that suit them for nectar feeding. To extract nectar they must insert their tongues into the floral cups and lap up what they can. The technique is undoubtedly inefficient compared to the deft maneuverings of professional nectarivores such as hummingbirds and bees. But in their clumsy nuzzling of flowers, the faces of tamarins become covered with pollen, which the tamarins then transfer to other plants as they trapline from one to the next. This behavior, as well as the heavy construction of *Combretum* and *Quararibea* flowers and their unusually dilute nectars, suggests that these plants may be among the few in the world that are regularly pollinated by primates (Janson et al. 1981). The relationship is of a one-sided kind, in which the plants show special adaptations for attracting mammalian pollinators, while the pollinators do not show corresponding adaptations for their role.

Combretum vines and *Quararibea* trees are plentiful within the territories of the tamarin groups we have studied, so that even if the nectar they provide is of low energy content, there does not seem to be any shortage of it. Nevertheless, from earlier observations we knew that both *Combretum* and *Quararibea* were heavily exploited by other monkeys, several nocturnal mammals, and many birds (Janson et al. 1981). Unlike the long-yielding fruit resources that tamarins depend on for most of the year, these nectar resources are avidly sought by other species. This, along with the finding that some of the tamarins lost as much as 15% of their body weight during the nectar season, suggested that they might be exposed to exceptional levels of competition just when they were being obliged to survive on food supply of low quality. We thus decided to undertake an intensive study of the exploitation of *Combretum* by tamarins and other species.

COMPETITION FOR NECTAR IN THE DRY SEASON

A casual human observer might imagine *Combretum* nectar to be an abundant resource, because the vines are large and their flowers showy. We suspected, however, that from the point of view of a tamarin the situation might appear quite different. To bridge the gap between appearance and reality, we needed to know about several things: the availability of the resource in the environment at large, the use of the resource by tamarins, the use by all other species, and the degree to which other species reduce the availability of the resource to tamarins.

Fortunately, *Combretum* has features that allow one to make all the necessary observations. The flowers are borne in showy spikes that rise conspicuously above the foliage of the supporting tree. Each spike carries an average of 90 flowers that open simultaneously and produce nectar for two days and nights. Conveniently, the flowers change color as they mature, opening greenish yellow, then turning yellow on the second day and orange on the third. Producing spikes are thus either greenish or yellow and are easily distinguished through binoculars from spikes that are no longer yielding nectar.

To monitor the availability of *Combretum* flowers through the season, we selected six vines that offered good visibility from stations on our trail system. Before the flowering season began, we determined that the total number of spikes visible from the viewing stations was approximately 3,475. Then, each day from 1 July through 13 August, we counted the number of green and yellow spikes visible at each of the stations. The total number of such spikes counted over the season was 7,010, double the number of visible spikes, indicating that each one had been counted twice in correspondence with the two-day production period. The number of producing spikes rose steadily from 1 July through the middle of the month, and then remained at a high level before declining precipitously at the end of the month (Fig. 6).

To monitor the use of nectar by tamarins, we followed two groups of saddle-backed tamarins for a total of 40 days covering the entire *Combretum* flowering season. The period during which the tamarins exploited *Combretum* corresponded quite closely to the availability of the resource in the environment. Between 9 July and 1 August, *Combretum* accounted for more than 80% of the feeding time of both groups, and during brief intervals it was virtually the only resource the animal used. *Combretum* nectar was thus of critical importance to both tamarin groups for about three weeks.

We mentioned above that *Combretum* nectar is sought by a wide variety of birds and nonflying mammals. Professional nectarivores, such as bats, hummingbirds, bees, and wasps, almost entirely ignore it, perhaps because, at only 8 to 10% sucrose, its energy content is too low. Birds and monkeys are the only diurnal users of consequence. This is fortunate, because the exploitation rates of these large vertebrates are easy to observe through binoculars, while those of invertebrates are not.

We made two kinds of observations to document the exploitation of *Combretum* nectar. First, we visited each of the viewing stations many times each day and scanned the producing spikes to determine how many and what kinds of exploiters were visiting the spikes at any given time. Second, with a stopwatch we recorded the number of flowers probed or licked per minute by each of the common visitors. Five species of monkeys and more than twelve species of birds were documented as exploiters in 1,274 scans covering the entire flowering period. Exploitation rates varied surprisingly little, averaging 15.4 flowers per minute for monkeys and 17.0 for birds.

A total of 611 birds and 90 primates were observed at flowers during the scans. Weighing these totals by the respective exploitation rates, we found that birds accounted for 88% of the overall consumption of the resource and primates for the remaining 12%. In spite of the overwhelming importance of *Combretum* to tamarins, both species combined accounted for only 2% of the aggregate consumption. Although the value of 2% sound small, it is hard to attach any significance to it without knowing whether the observed rates of exploitation by all species combined were adequate to exhaust the supply of the resource. This required measurements of the rate of production of nectar by *Combretum* flowers and of the frequency with which any given flower is emptied.

To measure production rates, we covered spikes with plastic screening to block the access of exploiters while allowing free passage of sun and air. Every three hours, day and night, we withdrew the contents of the flowers with a graduated syringe and hypodermic needle, keeping record of the number of producing flowers on each spike. At each collection a sample of the nectar was taken for determination of its refractive index. The latter measurements are convertible into equivalent percentages of sucrose—the concentration of a solution of pure sucrose having the same refractive index. We do not know that the predominant sugar in *Combretum* is sucrose, but sucrose is the major constituent of many nectars that have been analyzed (Baker 1975). The yield of nectar in each three-hour collection period typically ranged between 25 and 35 µl per flower, corresponding to a production rate of 10 µl/hr. It appears that any given flower is either producing at a more or less fixed rate or is shut down.

Now we are ready to consider how the intensity of exploitation of *Combretum* nectar varied with its availability over the season. The bars in Figure 6 represent specific use rates, that is, the average number of visitors at any instant divided by the number of producing spikes visible from the six monitoring stations. It is clear that the combined demand by birds and primates is greatest early and late in the season, when the number of producing spikes is relatively low. Specific exploitation rates for all species combined ranged between 0.9 and 2.4 visitors per 100 producing spikes. Exploitation by birds was heaviest early in the season and declined later to about a third of the initial rate, perhaps because alternative nectar sources were available in August but not in early July. Exploitation by all species of primates combined was low but steady through most of the season until the very end, when it jumped ahead of the avian rate. This rise is probably related to the decline in avian use, because, as pointed out above, primates can only remove nectar with their broad tongues while birds have the advantage of pointed bills. Birds are thus superior competitors for the resource.

A measure of the intensity of exploitation of *Combretum* can be derived from the specific use rates, provided an assumption is made about the pattern of visits. One could assume that flowers were visited randomly, but this would not jibe with the observation that both birds and monkeys were highly selective in their emptying of flowers. The nectar level in a flower is obvious at a glance, and it was clear that both types of visitors were visually orienting to particular flowers, often no more than two or three per spike. We shall thus assume that only the fullest flowers on a spike are emptied, while the rest are ignored.

Following this assumption, the reciprocal of the specific use rate can now be interpreted as the relative availability of the resource, which is expressed as the number of producing spikes per visitor (Table 2). One now needs to know how long it takes the average visitor to harvest that number of producing spikes.

The spikes we monitored for nectar production contained a mean of about 50 producing flowers over the first and second days of the flowering cycle. Given an average exploitation rate of 17 flowers per minute (the value for birds, because nearly 90% of visitors are birds), one can readily calculate the mean time between visits to a given flower. During the five subdivisions of the flowering season indicated in Figure 6, these times ranged between 2.0 and 5.4 hours, at most barely sufficient to allow a flower to fill to the brimming level.

With each producing flower being visited so frequently, few would be able to fill to the level needed for harvest by the inefficient tongues of monkeys. This inference is in good agreement with what we observed. Squirrel monkey and capuchin troops passed through the vines very quickly, remaining only a few

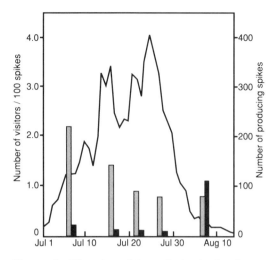

Figure 6. The size of tamarin territories is dependent on the availability during the dry season of a sufficient number of *Combretum* vines to supply nectar for a group after the competing needs of birds and other primates are met. The curve gives the number of nectar-producing spikes on six vines selected for daily monitoring during the period 1 July through 13 August 1981. The bars indicate the average number of visitors—birds (*light gray*) and primates (*dark gray*)—per 100 nectar-producing spikes at any instant during five subdivisions of the flowering period.

minutes. During these sessions, the animals hurried from spike to spike, seldom licking more than five to ten flowers on any one. Birds behaved in much the same manner, arriving in flocks and probing only a few flowers per spike. Neither the larger monkeys nor birds showed any inclination to be methodical in harvesting flowers.

Only among the tamarins did we observe a tendency to methodical rather than cursory harvesting of the flowers. Although the tamarins sometimes visited a few vines in rapid succession, on other occasions they remained several hours in the vicinity of a single *Combretum,* alternately feeding and resting. The extreme example of this occurred during a five-day period between 9 and 13 July, when a group of saddle-backed tamarins spent 626 out of a total 801 feeding minutes (78%) in a single interconnected pair of *Combretum* vines. About two dozen other vines were flowering within their territory, including some of the ones that we were monitoring, but the animals ignored them.

It did not seem reasonable that the tamarins should prefer to harvest the same vine repeatedly at more or less hourly intervals, when, with relatively little effort, they could have visited a succession of different vines that they had not exploited previously. What we believe to be the solution to this paradox emerged unexpectedly from the data on the six plants we monitored for general exploitation.

While doing scan samples day after day, we came to realize that one of the *Combretum* vines (no. 5) was not attracting its share of avian visitors. Over the whole season, fewer than 4% of the birds registered in the scans were found in vine no. 5, even though it contained 20% of the spikes visible at all 6 stations. All of the other monitored vines attracted birds at more than twice the rate of no. 5.

There was nothing superficially peculiar about this vine. It produced a conspicuous show of flowers in the crown of a tall tree located more or less midway between two other vines that did attract birds. Nevertheless, the flowers of vine no. 5 were being visited at the rate of only once in 17 hours, more than enough to allow the flowers to fill completely with nectar between harvests.

Table 2. Intensity of exploitation of Combretum

Subdivision of flowering period	Mean number producing spikes/day	Relative availability (spikes/visitor)	Calculated exploitation frequency (hours)
I	115	40	2.0
II	278	62	3.0
III	303	100	4.9
IV	297	111	5.4
V	43	53	2.6

Why did birds shun this particular vine? One can make at least two reasonable guesses: either it failed to produce a normal quantity of nectar, or the nectar was of inferior quality. If the vine had simply failed to produce nectar, it should have been no more attractive to primates than to birds. In fact, primates visited this vine at the expected rate. Thus one could infer that vine no. 5 produced a dilute nectar that was not attractive to birds but was acceptable to primates, which, being inefficient at extracting nectar, had reason to prefer quantity over quality. (Unfortunately this possibility can only be inferred, because the flowers were 40 meters up in a tree crown and inaccessible to us.)

There was undoubtedly something special about vine no. 5. Shunned by birds, it was a magnet for tamarins. We recorded tamarins 11 times in the scans, always in vine no. 5. The probability of obtaining this result, had the tamarins been choosing *Combretum* vines at random, is less than one in ten million. We thus surmise that the reason the tamarins preferred to stay all day at one vine rather than visit many is that they were selectively exploiting a few plants in the *Combretum* population that were relatively unattractive to birds. Hence, a mere count of the number of *Combretum* vines in a territory does not suffice to estimate the availability of the nectar to the tamarins. It appears that there must be many vines in a territory in order that there be even a few that are not continuously drained by birds.

Birds are not the only competitors that reduce the nectar supply available to tamarins; other monkeys do so as well. While birds compete through a superior ability to drain the flowers, other monkeys compete by interference. This is an ecological euphemism for aggression. Tamarins normally avoid other monkeys, and apart from the nectar season are rarely supplanted by them from trees. But in the present study, tamarins were supplanted 19 times in 33 days from *Combretum* vines in which they were feeding, and on two other occasions they were prevented from entering vines by the presence of other monkeys, always either capuchins or squirrel monkeys. At this rate they were being denied access to food twice every three days. Given the scarcity of vines that provided suitable feeding opportunities for tamarins, they could have been deprived of an appreciable quantity of food.

LIVING AT THE EDGE

The tamarins at Cocha Cashu live for most of the year in a way that puts them well out of the mainstream of the primate community. Fruit is generally abundant, and the particular fruits tamarins exploit most heavily are ones that are relatively little used by either larger monkeys or birds. When conditions are good, a tamarin need spend only 50 to 60 minutes a day feeding (Terborgh 1983). Another two or three hours are consumed traveling and foraging for prey. An individual's needs are thus satisfied in less than four hours, leaving the remainder of the day free for seeking refuge from the threat of predators in sheltered spots such as hollow limbs and canopy vine tangles.

This tranquil existence changes dramatically during the months of July and August, when the stocks of slow-yielding fruit have run out. Tamarins are then forced into a scramble of competition with a host of other species for limited access to a poor resource: *Combretum* nectar. The inferior quality of the resource can be judged from the fact that tamarins must feed for an average of 150 minutes a day when subsisting on nectar (vs. 50 minutes a day for fruit), and from our finding that many of the animals lose weight during the period. One can hardly doubt that the nectar season represents an annual bottleneck, a period that has a critical bearing on how tamarins perceive their territories.

We now return to the questions posed at the outset: why tamarins are relatively rare and why a group of them required as much space as a troop of capuchins weighing 15 times as much. We also wondered why tamarin territories have fixed boundaries that appear to be incompressible. We think that *Combretum* is the key that unlocks the answers to these questions.

Each of the five tamarin territories we have studied contains between 20 and 50 *Combretum* vines. Surrounding the contiguous area that contains these territories is a great expanse of mature and late successional habitat that is devoid of tamarins. The extent of this surrounding area (hundreds of hectares) precludes a systematic survey of *Combretum*, but many kilometers of trails pass through these forests, and we have verified that the density of *Combretum* in them is very low.

It appears to us that a tamarin territory must contain a minimum of 20 to 30 *Combretum* vines. If this is so, it can explain why tamarins occupy part of our study area and not the rest, and why there are so few territories. It does not explain why some of the territories are so large, and why the boundaries transcend the lifespans of the occupants.

For answers to these remaining questions, we must look at what the tamarins do during the rest of the year. We have said that they feed on a succession of gradually ripening fruit crops, concentrating on one species at a time for period of two to four months. When we have surveyed tamarin territories for these preferred food species, we have found that they often show distinct spatial distributions.

The habitat within the five tamarin territories is conspicuously variegated. Each territory contains at least three distinct vegetation types, such as mature forest, flood-disturbed forest, fig swamp, and canebreak. All of these vegetation types are used, but the emphasis given to each varies with the time of year in accordance with the distribution of the fruit crop currently being exploited. These observations, together with the fact that large uniform areas of mature forest are not occupied by tamarins, lead us to conclude that habitat diversity is another requisite of tamarin territories.

Finally, we ask whether there is anything distinctive about where territorial boundaries are fixed. Figure 2 provides the answer: territorial boundaries divide habitats in two. This practice guarantees that each territory contains a maximum diversity of habitats and assures the availability of a year-round supply of long-yielding fruit, in addition to the requisite quota of *Combretum* vines, which are especially abundant in flood-disturbed vegetation. The traditional boundaries of the five territories appear to achieve a near-optimal allocation of the available habitat diversity. One can presume that any compression would entail the loss of one or another element of the habitat mosaic.

The extraordinarily varied sizes of tamarin territories at Cocha Cashu—from 30 to 120 hectares—can now be understood as a result of the need for habitat diversity. The larger territories are not noticeably more heterogeneous than the smaller ones; they are distinguished by containing a large extension of one habitat that may be used quite sparingly at some times of year. Space per se thus appears to be of little consequence. Instead, the important criterion seems to be the inclusion of sufficient numbers of each of the several plant species that together provide a year-round food supply.

Perhaps because tamarins are such poor competitors, their requirements for fitting into the primate community at Cocha Cashu are especially complex. Much of the available habitat is of little value, while critically important resources such as *Combretum* are located in restricted patches. There are consequently only a few parcels of habitat within our area that simultaneously satisfy all the requirements of a tamarin territory. It is for this reason that tamarins, in spite of being so small, are so rare.

170

REFERENCES

Baker, H. G. 1975. Sugar concentrations in nectars from hummingbird flowers. *Biotropica* 7(1):37–41.

Hershkovitz, P. 1977. *Living New World Monkeys (Platyrrhini), With an Introduction to Primates,* vol. 1. Univ. Chicago Press.

Janson, C. H., J. Terborgh, and L. H. Emmons. 1981. Non-flying mammals as pollinating agents in the Amazonian forest. *Biotropica* 13(supp.):1–6.

Leigh, E. G., and D. M. Windsor. 1982. Forest production and regulation of primary consumers on Barro Colorado Island. In *The Ecology of a Tropical Forest: Seasonal Rhythms and Long-term Changes,* ed. E. G. Leigh, A. S. Rand, and D. M. Windsor, pp. 111–22. Smithsonian Inst. Press.

Leighton, M., and D. R. Leighton. 1983. Vertebrate responses to fruiting seasonality within a Bornean rain forest. In *Tropical Rain Forest: Ecology and Management,* ed. S. L. Sutton, T. C. Whitmore, and A. C. Chadwick, pp. 181–96. Blackwell Scientific.

Richard, A. J. 1985. *Primates in Nature.* Freeman.

Robinson, S. K. 1981. Ecological relations and social interactions of Philadelphia and Red-eyed vireos. *Condor* 83:16–26.

Terborgh, J. 1983. *Five New World Primates: A Study in Comparative Ecology.* Princeton Univ. Press.

_____. 1986. Community aspects of frugivory in tropical forests. In *Frugivores and Seed Dispersal,* ed. A. Estrada and T. H. Fleming, pp. 371–84. Dr. W. Junk.

Terborgh, J., and A. W. Goldizen. 1985. On the mating system of the cooperatively breeding saddle-back tamarin. *Beh. Ecol. Sociobiol.* 16:293–99.

Wright, P. C. 1985. The costs and benefits of nocturnality for *Aotus trivirgatus* (the night monkey). Ph.D. diss., City College of New York.

Sociosexual Development, Pair Bond Formation, and Mechanisms of Fertility Suppression in Female Cotton-top Tamarins (*Saguinus oedipus oedipus*)

Anne Savage, Toni E. Ziegler, and Charles T. Snowdon
——————————— *University of Wisconsin, Madison* ———————————

The effect of various social environments on sociosexual behavior was examined in six young female cotton-top tamarins (*Saguinus oedipus oedipus*) and in three established breeding females. Behavioral observations and hormonal samples were collected on young females while they were living with their families, when they were isolated from conspecifics, and after they were paired with an unrelated male. While living with the family, all females showed a suppression of fertility and low frequencies of sociosexual behavior. Following removal from the family, isolated females displayed an increase in rate of scent marking and an increase in hormonal levels. When young females were paired with males, they were exposed to scent secretions from their natal families, from an unfamilar family, and from a control for a total of 24 weeks. After pairing, hormonal levels increased dramatically, and ovarian cyclicity began. An increase in sociosexual behavior and elevated levels of scent marking accompanied this physiological change. Newly paired females had higher rates of affiliative behavior and scent marking than did established breeding females. However, both newly paired and established breeding males were more likely to initiate contact, grooming bouts, and social sniffing than were females. Time to first ovulation was later in females who were exposed to scent secretions from their natal families than it was in those females given a control for the first 8 weeks following pairing. No female conceived during exposure to scent secretions. However, once normal ovarian cycling had begun or a pregnancy was established, exposure to scent secretions had no effect. Thus, the social environment influences the fertility, sociosexual behavior, and pair bond formation of cotton-top tamarins. In addition, chemical stimuli found in the scent secretions produced by the natal family are most likely involved in reproductive suppression.

Key words: tamarin, fertility suppression, sociosexual behavior, scent marking

INTRODUCTION

Recent studies of the behavioral and reproductive biology of marmosets and tamarins have illustrated a clear distinction between Callitrichids and most other nonhuman primates. Some field studies and extensive laboratory research suggests that most callitrichids form relatively small social groups consisting of a breeding pair and their offspring [Dawson, 1978; Epple, 1975; French et al., 1984; Hampton & Hampton, 1966; Izawa, 1978; Kleiman, 1977; Neyman, 1978; Rothe, 1975; Ziegler et al., 1987b]. However, recent data on the saddle-back tamarin (*Saguinus fuscicollis*) [Terborgh and Wilson Goldizen, 1985], the moustached tamarin (*Saguinus mystax*) [Garber et al., 1984], and the golden-lion tamarin (*Leontopithecus rosalia*) [Dietz & Kleiman, 1986] have suggested an alternative strategy: a polyandrous or communal mating system.

While living in families, some common marmoset (*Callithrix jacchus*) and golden-lion tamarin daughters have ovulated in the presence of their mothers [Abbott, 1984; French & Stribley, 1987]. However, in most *Saguinus* species, there is only one reproductively active female, even when several adult daughters and sons are present [Epple & Katz, 1980, 1984; French et al., 1984; Ziegler et al., 1987b]. This appears to be true for some wild populations as well [Dawson, 1978; Izawa, 1978; Neyman, 1978]. In general, these studies have indicated that while a female tamarin lived with her family, she was reproductively suppressed; reproductive activity could be induced, however, by removing her from the family and pairing her with a male. Thus, evidence to date suggests that the mating system of marmosets and tamarins may be more flexible than previously described and that suppression of reproductive behavior and fertility is socially induced.

One of the mechanisms involved in the physiological suppression of fertility observed in some callitrichids is believed to result from the inhibitory influence exerted by the reproductively active female [Abbott, 1984; Abbott & Hearn, 1978; Abbott et al., 1981; French et al., 1984; Tardif, 1984]. Epple and Katz [1984] showed that exposure to chemical signals found in the scent secretions of the reproductively active female (*S. fuscicollis*) resulted in a partial reproductive inhibition in one newly paired female. In addition to direct suppression of ovarian cyclicity, the failure of suppressed females to reproduce may be affected by a variety of causes, such as the suppression of sexual behavior [Abbott, 1984], delay of onset of puberty [Kleiman, 1977; Tardif, 1984], or general stress effects.

The study reported here addressed the complex issues of sociosexual development, the influence of the social environment on fertility, the mechanisms of reproductive suppression, and pair bond formation in captive cotton-top tamarins (*Saguinus oedipus oedipus*). Detailed behavioral observations and hormonal data were collected from females while living with their families, while isolated from conspecifics, and after being paired with males, as well as from established breeding females. This longitudinal study examined females under varying social environments, and in addition provided new information on pair bond formation and maintenance in another species of callitrichid.

TABLE I. Group Composition and Order of Scent Transfer

Subject	Age (mo)	Twin	Mother	Age (yr: mo)	Family composition	Order of scent transfer
Lew	20	Kla	Mab	7:11	1 breeding pair 1 subadult male 2 subadult females	Control, natal, unfamiliar
Kla	20	Lew	Mab	7:11	3 juvenile females 1 infant female	Natal, control, unfamiliar
Hal	20	Male	Rox	6:9	1 breeding pair 1 subadult female 1 subadult male 2 juvenile females	Control, natal, unfamiliar
Pip	23	Male	Van	6:2	1 breeding pair 1 subadult female 1 juvenile male 2 infant males	Natal, control, unfamiliar
Yas[c]	25	Zie	Mab	8:3	1 breeding female[a] 2 subadult females 2 juvenile females	Control, natal, unfamiliar
Zie[c]	25	Yas	Mab	8:3	1 juvenile male 2 infant males[b]	Natal, control, unfamiliar

[a]Breeding male died.

[b]Twins born during the observation period.

[c]Isolated from conspecifics following removal from their family.

Since the suppression of fertility appears to be more pronounced in *Saguinus* species than in other callitrichids, the hypothesis that the reproductively active female suppresses ovarian activity in her daughters was examined. When females were removed from their families and paired with males, a scent transfer technique was employed to attempt to continue a physiological and behavioral suppression.

MATERIALS AND METHODS

Subjects and Social Environments

Comparison of females under varying social environments. To examine the suppression of reproductive behavior under varying social conditions, six female cotton-top tamarins (range 20–25 mo, $\bar{X}$ = 22.2 mo at the beginning of the study) were observed in their natal families for 8 weeks. These families consisted of two sets of twin females (Lew & Kla, Yas & Zie) and the females from two sets of male-female twins (Hal, Pip). All females were the eldest daughters present in a family at the time of the study. Natal families consisted of the adult breeding pair and three to seven siblings of varying ages and sexes (Table I).

Family cages were 1.8 m W × 3.0 m L × 2.3 m H and contained an elaborate trail system of branches and ropes. For additional colony information and husbandry techniques, see Snowdon et al. [1985].

Following the 8-week observation period, four of the six females were removed from their families and paired with males in a different colony room (pair cage: 0.85 m W × 1.5 m L × 2.3 m H) so that behavioral and hormonal changes could be observed and the pair bond established. Observation of newly paired animals continued for 24 weeks.

Two of the six females (Yas & Zie) were isolated from conspecifics (isolation cage: 0.64 m W × 0.64 m L × 2.44 m H) to determine if reproductive cycling would begin and scent marking would increase following removal from the suppressing effects of the family or in the absence of a new male. Females were isolated for 4 weeks from all olfactory and visual cues, and auditory cues were greatly attenuated. After this period of isolation, these two females were paired with males.

Scent transfer manipulation. While paired with a male, each female was exposed to three different scent transfer conditions (see Table I for order of presentation) in an attempt to 1) continue a physiological and behavioral suppression, 2) inhibit or disrupt normal cyclicity once cycling had begun, and 3) distinguish whether scent secretions from the natal family versus those from an unrelated family would have a similar effect on fertility. Each female was exposed to scent secretions from her natal family, to secretions from an unrelated but established breeding family, and to a control condition in which no scent was present.

Scent secretions were collected from the natal family or unfamiliar family by placing a wooden plank (38 cm × 4.5 cm with four wooden dowels 0.5 cm diameter × 0.7 H cm placed approximately 8 cm apart) in the cage for 24 hr. Scent secretions on the plank were deposited primarily by the adult breeding female. Each day the marked plank was removed from the family cage and placed in the newly paired female's cage for 24 hr. During the control condition, a new unmarked plank was placed in the newly paired female's cage. Planks were changed daily throughout the observation period and were discarded after use. Each female was exposed to every condition for 8 weeks.

Establishment and maintenance of the pair bond. To compare the behavior and pair bond maintenance of cotton-top tamarins, three established breeding females (Rox, Mab, Van) were observed for eight weeks. All of the established breeding females had reared at least two sets of offspring, were mothers of the daughters studied, and were pregnant throughout the observation period. One female (Mab) gave birth to twins during the sampling period. Frequency of social interactions, scent marking, and spatial relationships of newly paired individuals were compared to those of established pairs to examine the long-term changes and maintenance of the pair bond.

Hormonal Collection and Assays

First-morning void urine was collected almost daily (0800–0900 hr) from every female throughout this study. Urine was collected without restraint or handling by holding a polypropylene container underneath the female when she urinated. Following urine collection, females were given a food reward. This noninvasive technique did not interfere with behavior observations.

Urine samples were subjected to analysis by radioimmunological assays measuring estrone-conjugates (E_1C) and luteinizing hormone/chorionic gonadotropin (LH/CG). (For complete details of sample collection and analysis, see Ziegler et al. [1987a,b]).

Behavioral Observations

Established breeding females and females under the varying social conditions (family, isolation, paired) were observed for 30 min per day four to five times per week. Observations were made between 0800 and 1100 hr when the animals were most active. Mean interobserver reliability for all behavioral categories for the three observers was 89%.

A combined method of instantaneous and continuous sampling was used [Altmann, 1974]. This scoring system records a focal animal's behavior, object of interaction, and duration of each activity. Observations of established breeding females and young females housed with their families were recorded on standardized data sheets at 30-sec intervals. Observations of females in isolation or when paired with males were recorded using a Radio Shack TRS-80 Model 100 portable computer (Tandy Corp., Fort Worth, TX). The data entry system for the TRS–80 (Keybored, Dr. J. R. Baylis) was identical with the scoring system used with the standardized data sheets, with the exception that the duration measures were more precise.

Behavioral observations focused on the following.

Aggressive social interactions between family members as a possible mechanism to maintain suppression. These encounters ranged from overt aggression (fighting) to dominance interactions involving "face-offs" (two animals are on opposite ends of the cage and are pilo-erected, tongue-flicking, and vocalizing at one another) and "face-pressing" (an animal grabs the head of another and presses his/her open mouth to his/her opponent's open mouth). These displays were often accompanied by the following vocalizations: squeals, squawks, type A trills, and rapid whistles [Cleveland & Snowdon, 1982].

Contact-promoting behavior between family members and paired animals. This included the following measures: time spent in contact, grooming, huddling, and olfactory investigation (social sniff) of another animal.

176

Copulations observed in families and in paired animals. Sexual activity, including attempted mounts (no pelvic thrusting), full mounts (pelvic thrusting observed), and mounts with ejaculation (male grooms genitals after ejaculating) were monitored under the varying social conditions. Since sexual behavior was infrequently observed, all types of mounting were combined for data analysis.

Frequency of scent marking under the varying social conditions. Anogenital and suprapubic marking were observed and correlated with levels of estrogen excretion while females lived in the different social environments, and the rates were compared to scent-marking rates of established breeding females. In addition, measurements of the female's scent glands were taken while the female was housed in her family and approximately 4 weeks after pairing with a male. The size of the scent gland was estimated by measuring the length and width of the anogenital and suprapubic glands [French, 1982]. The length of the glandular fields was measured from the most anterior portion of the gland to the most posterior portion. Three measurements of the width were estimated by measuring the lateral extent of the gland at three different places (anterior, mid, and posterior) and computing a mean value. The area of the glands was estimated by multiplying the length of the glands by the mean width of the glands. Appearance of the scent glands was noted and categorized as follows: 1) darkly pigmented glands; 2) active secretory glands, as indicated by the appearance of sebum; and 3) extensive matting of the fur surrounding the perigenital region, which appeared to be sebum from the gland combined with urine.

Analysis

All data files were transferred to an Apple IIe, where frequencies and duration measures of each behavior could be extracted using programs developed by Drs. M. C. Cook and G. W. Kraemer. Raw data was analyzed for treatment effects using BMDP7V-ANOVA statistical package (BMDP Statistical Software Inc., Los Angeles). t-Tests for independent and dependent samples were all two-tailed tests.

RESULTS

Comparison of Female Under Varying Social Conditions

The social environment had a marked effect on a female's behavior. While females lived in families, they spent less time in contact ($t = 6.14$, $P < .01$), huddling ($t = 3.56$, $P < .01$), grooming ($t = 2.08$, $P < .05$), and sniffing ($t = 3.02$, $P < .05$) group members than when they were paired with males (Figs. 1, 2). In one family, infants were born during the observation period. These females exhibited an increase in huddling ($\overline{X} = 281.35/2$ wk ± 32.45 SEM) following the birth of

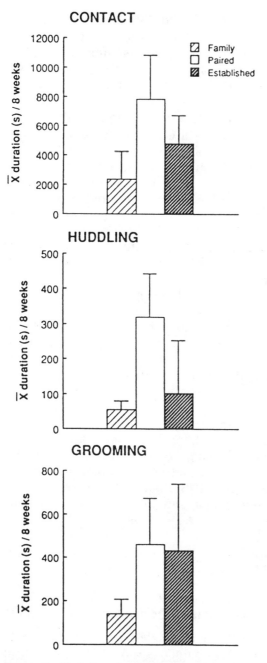

Figure 1. Variations in the amount of time spent in contact, huddling, and grooming under the various social conditions. While living with the family, the rates for these behaviors were low and showed a dramatic increase when females were removed from the family and paired with a male. Only the rates of huddling prior to the birth of infants were used in this analysis. Rates of established breeding females are shown for comparison.

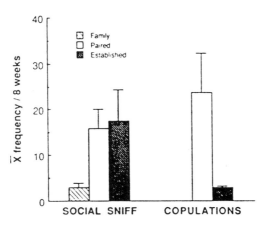

Figure 2. Variations in the frequency of
social sniffs and copulations under the
various social conditions. The frequency of
social sniffs was low, and no copulations
were observed while females lived in their
families. Following removal from the family
and pairing with a male, dramatic increases
in the rates of social sniffing and copulation
were observed. Data from established
breeding females are shown for comparison.

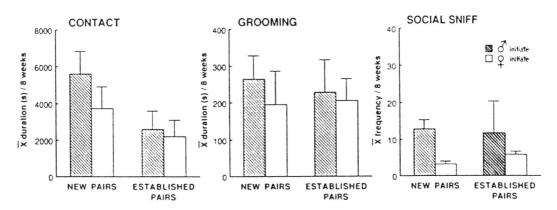

Figure 3. Variations in the time spent in contact and grooming and the frequency of social
sniffing by males and females. Newly paired males are significantly more likely to initiate
contact, grooming, or social sniffing of females than is the reverse. Established breeding males
show a similar trend, although the results were not significant.

the infants that was comparable to levels observed in paired animals ($\overline{X}$ = 319.34/8 wk ± 123.03 SEM).

After pairing, clear sex differences were observed. Paired males were more likely than females to initiate contact (t = 4.61, P < .01), to groom (t = 2.91, P < .01), and to sniff their mates (t = 3.44, P < .01) (Fig. 3).

Overt aggression was rarely observed while females lived in families or in pairs. However, face-offs and face-pressing bouts between same-sex twins were frequently observed ($\overline{X}$ = 21.25/8 wk ± 4.17 SEM). In females with a male twin (N = 2), face-offs and face-pressing were rarely observed ($\overline{X}$ = 10.0/8 wk ± 10.0 SEM).

Copulations were never observed while the female lived in her family (Fig. 2). Sexual behavior was restricted to the reproductively active pair in the family. When the female was removed from the family and paired with a male, copulations occurred throughout the entire ovarian cycle as well as during pregnancy. Females were not observed to solicit males or to exhibit any detectable behavioral changes that could signal their reproductive state to males. The first observed copulations occurred as early as 2 days after pairing to as late as 34 days after pairing. All newly paired females were pregnant by the end of the 24-wk observation period. All females had full-term pregnancies except one (Pip), who miscarried while being transferred to another colony.

Table II illustrates the dramatic change in the frequency of scent marking under the varying social conditions. While a female remained in her family, the frequency of scent marking was quite low. When the female was removed from her family and paired with a male, there was a significant increase in the rate of scent marking (t = 5.86, P < .01). Also, when the two females were removed from their family and placed in isolation, the frequency of scent marking increased. However, the greatest increase in scent marking activity occurred when these females were paired with males. While the family, same-sex twins scent marked less ($\overline{X}$/wk = 17.86 ± 12.26) than those females with a male twin ($\overline{X}$/wk = 200.89 ± 117.40).

The frequency of scent marking was not only influenced by the social environment but was positively correlated with estrogen activity (r^2 = .425, P < .01). Estrogen levels have been found to be low and acyclic while a female lives in her family, to increase slightly during isolation, and to occur normally when a female was paired with a male [Ziegler et al., 1987b]. This same pattern of increase was observed in the rates of scent marking by females, with rates occurring at a low level while the female was with the family, increasing slightly during isolation, and reaching the highest frequency when the female was paired with a male (Fig. 4).

Note the rates of scent marking by a female (Yas), one of a set of twin females (Yas & Zie) whose mother gave birth to twins during the observation period. Prior to the birth of infants, scent marking occurred infrequently; following the birth of infants, however, scent marking was *never* observed. This pattern was also reflected in their hormonal profiles. Prior to the birth of the new infants, hormonal levels were low and acyclic; following the birth, the hormonal

YAS

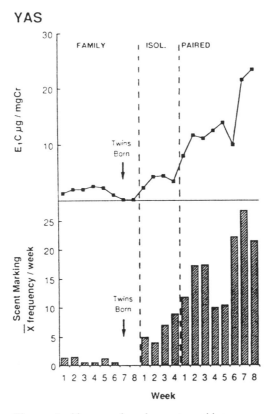

Figure 4. Hormonal and scent marking profile of a twin female (YAS). While living with her family, the levels of E_1C (estrone-conjugate) were low and acyclic, and scent marking was infrequently observed. Following the birth of twins, hormonal levels and rates of scent marking decreased dramatically. While in isolation, E_1C increased but cycling did not occur, and the frequency of scent marking increased slightly. When the female was paired with a male, hormonal cyclicity was apparent, and rates of scent marking increased dramatically. mgCrf = milligrams of creatinine.

Table 2. Variations in the Rates of Scent Marking and E_1C Levels

	Family (n = 6)	Paired (n = 6)	Established female (n = 3)
Scent marking ($\bar{X}$/wk)	$\bar{X}$ = 78.87, SEM = 90.32	$\bar{X}$ = 410.55, SEM = 74.63	$\bar{X}$ = 216.31, SEM = 82.01
E_1C, (µg/mg Cr)[a]	$\bar{X}$ = 1.22, SEM = 0.36	$\bar{X}$ = 11.62, SEM = 2.02	$\bar{X}$ = 11.52, SEM = 2.03
	Family	Isolated	Paired
Isolation phase (N = 2)			
Scent marking, ($\bar{X}$/wk)	$\bar{X}$ = 3.67, SEM = 1.85	$\bar{X}$ = 28.98, SEM = 11.23	$\bar{X}$ = 318.53, SEM = 52.61
E_1C, (µg/mg Cr)	$\bar{X}$ = 1.79, SEM = 0.08	$\bar{X}$ = 2.74, SEM = 1.38	$\bar{X}$ = 15.17, SEM = 4.55

[a]Cr = creatinine.

182

levels decreased sharply and remained so until the females were removed from the family.

Estimates of the total area of the scent glands showed no significant changes in the size of the scent glands under the varying social conditions (family: $X = 7.89$ cm$^2 \pm .45$ SEM, paired: $\overline{X} = 8.31$ cm$^2 \pm .69$ SEM). While a female lived in her family and had low hormonal levels and low frequencies of scent marking, her glands appeared moist and lightly pigmented, and the appearance of the fur surrounding the perigenital region was clean. However, when a female was removed from the family, concurrent with rising estrogen and increased scent marking activity, the scent glands appeared very oily and darkly pigmented and the surrounding fur was matted with sebum.

Scent Transfer Manipulation

Exposure to scent secretions did not inhibit hormonal cyclicity nor did it influence the behavior of the female. Using Duncan's multiple-range posthoc tests, no significant differences were found in contact, grooming, huddling, social sniffing, scent marking, or copulations across the three conditions. However, the rates of scent marking on the plank varied across conditions. Females scent marked the plank more frequently in the conditions of natal family scent transfer ($q = 15.406$, $P < .05$) and unfamilar family scent transfer ($q = 16.035$, $P < .05$) than in the control condition. There were no significant differences in the rates of scent marking on the plank between natal family or unfamilar family conditions.

Exposure to scent secretions for the first 8 weeks following pairing did, however, affect the time to first ovulation. Those females exposed to natal family scent secretions for the first 8 weeks following pairing took significantly longer to ovulate ($\overline{X} = 52.67 \pm 17.80$ days) than those females given the control condition first ($\overline{X} = 20.00 \pm 13.11$ days, $t = 2.80$, $P < .05$). No conceptions occurred in females who were exposed to natal family secretions for the first 8 weeks following pairing. All conceptions occurred during the control condition in this study. Once a pregnancy was established, it was not disrupted by exposure to scent secretions from the natal family or from the unfamilar family.

Establishment and Maintenance of the Pair Bond

Newly paired females spent more time in contact ($t = 83.32$, $P < .001$), grooming ($t = 2.46$, $P < .05$), huddling ($t = 26.91$, $P < .001$), and copulating ($t = 11.85$, $P < .001$) with their mates than did established breeding females (Figs. 1, 2). In addition, newly paired females in the control condition scent marked more frequently ($t = 20.99$, $P < .001$) than established breeding females. When observed initially, one established breeding female (Mab) had relatively high rates of scent marking ($\overline{X} = 188.72/8$ wk). However, when observed at a later date, after her mate had died, her rates of scent marking decreased dramatically ($\overline{X} = 43.0/8$ wk).

The rates of social sniffing were not significantly different between newly paired and established breeding animals. Newly paired males initiated contact, groomed, and sniffed females more frequently and for longer periods of time than females did males. Established breeding males showed a similar trend, although statistical differences were not found in male initiation of contact, grooming, or sniffing partner (Fig. 3).

DISCUSSION

Social environments have a pronounced effect on the behavioral and hormonal state of cotton-top tamarin females [French et al., 1984; Ziegler et al., 1987b]. This study found that grooming, huddling, contact, copulations, and social sniffing were much more frequent when the female was paired with a male than when she lived in the family. These results are in agreement with those that report infrequent bouts of affiliative behavior and copulations while female callitrichids lived in families [Box, 1975a,b; French et al., 1984].

It appears that family composition affected the social dynamics of the family. This study found that twin females scent marked less and engaged in face-offs and face-pressing more frequently than singleton females or those females with a male twin. Although our observations on this small sample suggest that one twin is likely to dominate the other, this phenomenon warrants further investigation.

Of interest, however, are the data from twin females who experienced the birth of infants while living in their families. While in the family, levels of scent marking and E_1C excretion were noted, but following the birth of infants these levels decreased dramatically. Why the birth of infants in a family would directly affect levels of scent marking and E_1C excretion is unknown and requires future investigation.

When a female was removed from her family and placed in isolation, the release from the suppressing effect of the family was apparent. Rates of scent marking began to increase, as did hormone levels. Although the levels of hormones increased while the female was in isolation, there was no hormonal cyclicity, and while the rates of scent marking increased relative to the levels observed while the female lived in her family, they were clearly lower than the rates of scent marking observed when the female was paired with a male. Our data also demonstrated that when an established breeding female was without a breeding male, rates of scent marking decreased. However, the rates of scent marking in this established female where still greater than those observed when young females were in isolation. Rates of scent marking increased further when the older female was paired with a new male.

Contrary to our findings, Evans and Hodges [1984] isolated three common marmoset females and noted the onset of urinary pregnanediol cyclicity as early as 18 days after females were removed from the family. However, no behavioral data were reported. The hormonal response to isolation was different in these callitrichids, suggesting possible species differences or differences in the type of experimental isolation conditions. Thus, unlike polygamous female primates

[Bernstein, 1970] and common marmosets [Evans & Hodges, 1984] that will exhibit normal reproductive functioning in isolation, our data suggest that removal from the family alone is not sufficient to induce reproductive activity.

Striking behavioral changes occurred across conditions in this study. Newly paired animals exhibited differences in behavior compared to established breeding pairs. Newly paired females engaged in sexual activity more frequently than did established breeding females. This finding also has been reported in newly paired golden lion tamarins and common marmosets [Evans, 1983; Evans & Poole, 1983, 1984; Kleiman, 1977, 1978]. Newly paired cotton-top tamarin females showed dramatic increases in rates of scent marking, rates much higher than those observed when females lived with their families [French et al., 1984] or in isolation. A positive correlation was found between the amount of estrogen activity and rates of scent marking. However, the greatest frequency of scent marking occurred when the female was paired with a male.

This increase in scent marking also parallels the similar change in the apparent amount of sebum produced by the scent glands. Although the total area of the scent gland did not change, it appeared to produce more sebum after the female was removed from her family or isolation and paired with a male. Thus, it appears that the sweat glands were fully developed in these females by the age of 20 months but required the stimulation of elevated levels of estrogen to produce sebum and a darkening of the pigment.

Established breeding pairs differed from newly paired animals in the frequency of contact-promoting behavior. Sociosexual behavior was much more frequent in newly paired cotton-top tamarins than in established pairs. This increase in affiliative behavior when the female was removed from the family and paired with a male appears to be important in establishing the pair bond in this species and others [Evans, 1983]. However, as the duration of the pair bond lengthened, compounded by the addition of offspring, established pairs spent less time in affiliative behavior with one another and directed more of their attention toward their offspring. Nonetheless, the pair bond appears to be strong in these animals as intruders are viciously attacked [French & Snowdon, 1981], and territorial displays between cages in the colony room are frequent.

According to Kleiman [1977], most marmosets and tamarins, in addition to other monogamous species, show little sexual dimorphism, and the behavior of the two sexes is similar. However, several consistent behavioral sex differences were detected in this study. Male cotton-top tamarins were much more likely than females to initiate contact, groom, and sniff their mates. This sex difference in the rate of social sniffing has been observed by French et al. [1984], and sex differences in grooming have been found in other species of callitrichids [Evans & Poole, 1984; Kleiman, 1977].

This study has provided insight into how suppression of fertility is maintained in the family. Aggressive encounters between mothers and daughters were infrequent, suggesting that overt aggression is unlikely to maintain fertility suppression. The lack of fertility that was observed in the family was not due to a delay in sexual maturation. As Ziegler et al. [1987b] noted, the process of sexual maturation is masked by the suppression of fertility that occurs while a daughter lives with her family. Puberty has occurred by age 24 mo in these animals [Ziegler et al., 1987b] and is likely to be completed by age 18 mo [Tardif, 1984; Ziegler et al., 1987b].

However, results from the scent transfer manipulation suggest that chemical signals influence a female's fertility. Scent secretions in marmosets and tamarins have been suggested to have strong inhibitory chemical properties [Epple, 1978; Epple & Katz, 1984]. Because of the importance of chemicals signals in dominance interactions [Epple & Katz, 1984] and the importance of the inhibiting influence of the reproductively active female on other females in a group [Abbott, 1984; Epple, 1975; French et al., 1984], it is quite likely that the scent marks from the reproductively active female contain chemical signals that inhibit reproductive activity in other females living in a group. Epple and Katz [1984] demonstrated the importance of chemical signals in dominance interactions by exposing one young female saddle-back tamarin to scent secretions from her family. Their results illustrated a partial reproductive inhibition as long as the family odor was present. When the family odor was no longer present, normal ovarian activity occurred.

Our study expands upon the findings of Epple & Katz [1984]. Cotton-top tamarin females given scent secretions from their family for the first 8 weeks after pairing took significantly longer to ovulate for the first time than those females given a control plank. All females exposed to the control plank for the first 8 weeks became pregnant during this period. However, all females given scent secretions from their families for the first 8 weeks after pairing did not become pregnant until they received the control plank (wks 9–16). Once normal cycling and/or a pregnancy was established, exposure to scent secretions from the natal family or an unfamiliar family had no effect.

The method of presentation of scent secretions may account for the fact that a complete suppression of fertility was not observed. Planks were placed in the female's cage daily, and females were able to scent mark on the plank. Females frequently marked the planks in the natal family and unfamilar scent transfer family conditions, and they were observed to mark the control plank much less. This increased scent marking of natal and unfamilar family planks may have masked the chemical signals, thereby decreasing the effect. Possibly, by using multiple presentations of the scent secretions and not allowing the females access to the planks, a more complete suppression may have been found. Regardless, evidence from this study and that of Epple and Katz [1984] suggest that scent secretions from the natal family can indeed affect the fertility of newly paired females.

On first thought, it may appear that suppression of fertility may be maladaptive for females. However, an alternative argument is possible. Cotton-top tamarins have a highly developed parental care system [Cleveland & Snowdon, 1984] in which all family members act as caretakers of infants. This early infant caretaking experience by older siblings is critical for the future reproductive success of an individual. Animals denied this early infant caretaking experience have a lower infant survival rate than those individuals who have had this critical social experience [Snowdon et al., 1985]. Thus, by assisting in raising her siblings, a female not only increases her inclusive fitness [Hamilton, 1964] but gains the necessary social skills to ensure her future reproductive success at a time when she is reproductively inactive.

Moreover, the migration of suppressed females between groups may be an adaptive strategy. Bernstein [1970] hypothesizes that the severity of aggression directed to strangers in primate groups may be proportional to the threat those individuals pose to a groups' social order. Thus, a reproductively active animal poses a direct threat to an established breeding pair, whereas a reproductively suppressed animal may present a less serious threat to the pair.

Studies have shown that both paired male and female callitrichids respond aggressively to intruding conspecifics [Anzenberger, 1985; Epple, 1981; Epple & Alvearno, 1985; Evans, 1983; French & Snowdon, 1981; Inglett & French, 1987; Sutcliffe & Poole, 1984]. However, Sutcliffe and Poole [1984] found that young common marmosets (7–16 mo) were more easily integrated into a social group than adults. Thus, it appears that young, nonreproductive animals are more easily integrated into a group, since they may pose little threat to the resident pair and will most likely aid in the rearing of their offspring.

Frequent intergroup transfers of wild cotton-top tamarins have been observed by Neyman [1978]. Most of these individuals were fully adult and appeared in general to be nulliparous. McGraw and McLuckie [1986] noted in a laboratory experiment that young female cotton-top tamarins were the individuals most likely to leave the family and explore a new "territory." If young females are the individuals most likely to leave a group, then it would remain advantageous for them to continue their reproductive suppression until they could be integrated into existing groups or find males and establish their own groups. Males without mates readily accept new females [Anzenberger, 1985; Epple & Alvearo, 1985; Evans, 1983], and as shown here and in other studies [French et al., 1984; Ziegler et al., 1987b] females become reproductively active in the presence of a male quite rapidly. The suppression of fertility that is observed while the female is with the family and when removed from the family but in the absence of a male is beneficial to the female and may be part of the reproductive strategy of the cotton-top tamarin.

CONCLUSIONS

1. Social environment influences the fertility, sociosexual behavior, and pair bond formation of cotton-top tamarins.
2. Following removal from the family, all females showed an increase in the rates of scent marking, sociosexual behavior, and affiliative behavior.
3. The frequency of scent marking was influenced by the social environment and was positively correlated with estrogen activity.
4. Exposing daughters to scent secretions from their mothers for the first 8 weeks after pairing with a male significantly lengthened the time to first

ovulation. Therefore, chemical stimuli found in these scent secretions are likely to be involved in reproductive suppression.

5. The suppression of fertility may be adaptive for young females since they gain the necessary social skills to ensure their future reproductive success at a time when they are reproductively inactive.

ACKNOWLEDGEMENTS

This study was supported by NIMH grant No. MH 35215 to C. T. Snowdon. We wish to thank M. Carr, C. Gerrish, S. Rubin, and J. Scott for their assistance in data collection and analysis. L. Dronzek provided helpful comments and criticisms on earlier versions of this manuscript.

REFERENCES

Abbott, D. H. Behavioral and physiological suppression of fertility in subordinate marmoset monkeys. AMERICAN JOURNAL OF PRIMATOLOGY 6:169–186, 1984.

Abbott, D. H.; McNeilly, A. S.; Lunn, S. F.; Hulme, M. J.; Burden, F. J.; Burden, F. J. Inhibition of ovarian function in subordinate female marmoset monkeys (*Callithrix jacchus jacchus*). JOURNAL OF REPRODUCTION AND FERTILITY 63:335–345, 1981.

Altmann, J. Observational study of behavior: Sampling methods. BEHAVIOUR 49:227–267, 1974.

Anzenberger, G. How stranger encounters of common marmosets (*Callithrix jacchus jacchus*) are influenced by family member: The quality of behavior. FOLIA PRIMATOLOGICA 45:204–224, 1985.

Bernstein, I. S. Primate status hierarchies. Pp 71–109 in PRIMATE BEHAVIOR: DEVELOPMENTS IN FIELD AND LABORATORY RESEARCH VOL 1. L.A. Rosenblum, ed. New York, Academic Press, 1970.

Box, H. O. The social developmental study of young monkeys (*Callithrix jacchus*) within a captive family group. PRIMATES 16:419–435, 1975a.

Box, H. O. Quantitative studies of behaviour within captive groups of marmoset monkeys (*Callithrix jacchus*). PRIMATES 16:155–174, 1975b.

Cleveland, J.; Snowdon, C. T. The complex vocal repertoire of the adult cotton-top tamarin (*Saguinus oedipus oedipus*). ZIETSCHRIFT FUR TIERPSYCHOLOGIE 58:213–270, 1982.

Cleveland, J.; Snowdon, C. T. Social development during the first twenty weeks in the cotton-top tamarin (*Saguinus o. oedipus*). ANIMAL BEHAVIOUR 32:432–444, 1984.

Dawson, G. A. Composition and stability of social groups of the tamarin (*Saguinus oedipus geoffroyi*) in Panama: Ecological and behavioral implications. Pp 23–38 in THE BIOLOGY AND CONSERVATION OF THE CALLITRICHIDAE. D. G. Kleiman, ed. Washington, DC, Smithsonian Press, 1978.

Dietz, J. M.; Kleiman, D. G. Reproductive parameters in groups of free-living golden lion tamarins. PRIMATE REPORT 14:77, 1986.

Epple, G. The behavior of marmoset monkeys (Callitrichidae). Pp 195–239, in PRIMATE BEHAVIOR. L. Rosenblum, ed. New York, Academic Press, 1975.

Epple, G. Studies on the nature of chemical signals in scent marks and urine of *Saguinus fuscicollis* (Callitrichidae, Primates). JOURNAL OF CHEMICAL ECOLOGY 4:383–394, 1978.

Epple, G. Effect of pair bonding with adults on the ontogenetic manifestation of aggressive behavior in a primate, *Saguinus fuscicollis*, (Callitrichidae, Primates). HORMONES AND BEHAVIOR 15:54–67, 1981.

Epple, G.; Alveario, M. C. Social facilitation of agnostic responses to strangers in pairs of saddle back tamarins (*Saguinus fuscicollis*). AMERICAN JOURNAL OF PRIMATOLOGY 9:207–218, 1985.

Epple, G.; Katz, Y. Social influences of first reproductive success and related behaviors in the saddle-back tamarin (*Saguinus fuscicollis*, Callitrichidae). INTERNATIONAL JOURNAL OF PRIMATOLOGY 1:171–184, 1980.

Epple, G.; Katz, Y. Social influences on estrogen excretion and ovarian cyclicity in saddle-back tamarins (*Saguinus fuscicollis*). AMERICAN JOURNAL OF PRIMATOLOGY 6:215–227, 1984.

Evans, S. The pair-bond of the common marmoset, *Callithrix jacchus jacchus:* An experimental investigation. ANIMAL BEHAVIOUR 31:651–658, 1983.

Evans, S.; Hodges, J. K. Reproductive status of adult daughters in family groups of common marmosets (*Callithrix jacchus jacchus*). FOLIA PRIMATOLOGICA 42:127–133, 1984.

Evans, S.; Poole, T. B. The pair-bond formation and breeding success in the common marmoset *Callithrix jacchus*. INTERNATIONAL JOURNAL OF PRIMATOLOGY 4:83–97, 1983.

Evans, S.; Poole, T. B. Long-term changes and maintenance of the pair-bond in common marmosets, *Callithrix jacchus*. FOLIA PRIMATOLOGICA 42:33–41, 1984.

French, J. A. The role of scent marking in social and sexual communication in tamarins (*Saguinus o. oedipus*). Ph.D. Thesis, University of Wisconsin, 1982.

French, J. A.; Abbott, D. H.; Snowdon, C. T. The effect of social environment on estrogen excretion, scent marking, and sociosexual behavior in tamarins. AMERICAN JOURNAL OF PRIMATOLOGY 6:155–167, 1984.

French, J. A.; Snowdon, C. T. Sexual dimophism in responses to unfamiliar intruders in the tamarin, *Saguinus oedipus*. ANIMAL BEHAVIOUR 29:822–829, 1981.

French, J. A.; Stribley, J. A. Synchronization of ovarian cycles within and between social groups in golden lion tamarins (*Leontopithecus rosalia*). AMERICAN JOURNAL OF PRIMATOLOGY 12:469–478, 1987.

Garber, P. A., Moya, L.; Malaga, C. A. A preliminary field study of the moustached tamarin monkey (*Saguinus mystax*) in northeastern Peru: Questions concerned with the evolution of a communal breeding system. FOLIA PRIMATOLOGICA 42:17–32, 1984.

Hamilton, W. D. The genetic theory of social behavior, I. and II. JOURNAL OF THEORETICAL BIOLOGY 7:1–52, 1964.

Hampton, J. K.; Hampton, S. H. Observations on a successful breeding colony of the marmoset, *Oedipodimas oedipus*. FOLIA PRIMATOLOGICA 4:265–287, 1966.

Inglett, B. J.; French, J. A. Sexually dimorphic aggressive responses to intruders in lion tamarins (*Leontopithecus rosalia*) AMERICAN JOURNAL OF PRIMATOLOGY 12:350, 1987.

Izawa, K. A field study of the ecology and behavior of the black-mantle tamarin (*Saguinus nigricollis*). PRIMATES 19:241–274, 1978.

Kleiman, D. G. Monogamy in mammals. QUARTERLY REVIEW OF BIOLOGY 52:39–69, 1977.

Kleiman, D. G. Characteristics of reproduction and sociosexual interaction in paris of lion tamarins (*Leontopithecus rosalia*) during the reproductive cycle. Pp 181–190 in THE BIOLOGY AND CONSERVATION OF THE CALLITRICHIDAE. D. G. Kleiman, ed. Washington, DC, Smithsonian Press, 1978.

McGrew, W. C.; McLuckie, E. C. Philopatry and dispersion in the cotton-top tamarin, *Saguinus o. oedipus:* An attempted laboratory simulation. INTERNATIONAL JOURNAL OF PRIMATOLOGY 7:401–422, 1986.

Neyman, P. E. Aspects of the ecology and social organization of free-ranging cotton-top tamarins (*Saguinus oedipus*) and the conservation status of the species. Pp 39–71 in THE BIOLOGY AND CONSERVATION OF THE CALLITRICHIDAE. D. G. Kleiman, ed. Washington, DC, Smithsonian Press, 1978.

Rothe, H. Some aspects of sexuality and reproduction on groups of captive marmosets (*Callithrix jacchus*). ZIETSCHRIFT FUR TIERPSYCHOLOGIE, 37:255–273, 1975.

Snowdon, C. T.; Savage, A.; McConnell, P. B. A breeding colony of cotton-top tamarins (*Saguinus oedipus oedipus*). LABORATORY ANIMAL SCIENCE 35:477–480, 1985.

Sutcliffe, A. G.; Poole, T. B. Intragroup agonistic behavior in captive groups of the common marmoset *Callithrix jacchus.* INTERNATIONAL JOURNAL OF PRIMATOLOGY 5:473–489, 1984.

Tardif, S. D. Social influences on sexual maturation of female *Saguinus oedipus oedipus.* AMERICAN JOURNAL OF PRIMATOLOGY 6:199–210, 1984.

Terborgh, J.; Wilson Goldizen, A. On the mating system of the cooperatively breeding saddle-backed tamarin (*Saguinus fuscicollis*). BEHAVIORAL ECOLOGY AND SOCIOBIOLOGY 16:293–299, 1985.

Ziegler, T. E.; Bridson, W. E.; Snowdon, C. T.: Eman, S. Urinary gonadotropin and estrogen excretion during the postpartum estrus, conception and pregnancy in the cotton-top tamarin (*Saguinus oedipus oedipus*). AMERICAN JOURNAL OF PRIMATOLOGY 12:127–140, 1987a.

Ziegler, T. E.; Savage, A.; Scheffler, G.; Snowdon, C. T. The endocrinology of puberty and reproductive functioning in female cotton-top tamarins (*Saguinus oedipus*) under varying social conditions. BIOLOGY OF REPRODUCTION 36:327–342, 1987b.

Biparental Care in
Aotus trivirgatus and *Callicebus moloch*

Patricia C. Wright
City University of New York

INTRODUCTION

Half the species of nonhuman primates in the New World exhibit an unusual division of labor in infant care taking. Soon after the infant is born, the mother is no longer primary care taker, and only suckles and occasionally cleans the infant. The father, often with the help of previously born juveniles, carries the infant on his back, shares food, and plays with and protects the infant. In Old World primates direct male parental care has been observed [Busse and Hamilton, 1981], but the mother is still the primary care taker, and males do not habitually carry infants (except in the siamang) [Chivers, 1974; Mitchell and Brandt, 1972; Redican, 1976]. It has been suggested that monogamous pairing and shared parental duties constitute a primitive trait within the New World primates as a whole, which is now expressed in *Aotus*, *Callicebus*, perhaps *Pithecia*, and the callitrichids [Eisenberg, 1981] (Table 1).

The New World biparental care system has been well documented in captivity for many species [Box, 1977; Dixson and Fleming, 1981; Epple, 1975, 1977; Fragaszy et al, 1982; Heltne et al, 1973; Hoage, 1977, 1982; Ingram, 1977; Pook, 1978]. But there is confusion regarding the adaptive significance of this system. Because most of the species studied are small (under 750 g) and most have multiple births, it has been suggested that there is a litter/maternal weight ratio above which the mother is no longer able to carry her offspring without aid [Kleiman, 1977]. Leutenegger [1980] argues that for these small primates monogamy and high male parental investment are best explained by the need for aid in carrying multiple offspring. This explanation for the father's role as primary infant care taker focuses on callitrichids and ignores two successful Neotropical genera who do not twin, but do have biparental care (*Aotus* and *Callicebus*), and the Old World genera such as galagos that twin, but are not monogamous, nor have any form of male parental care. A long-term field study of the Neotropical parental care system with the father as primary infant carrier should clarify the issues. My research focuses on two species of New World

TABLE I. Neotropical Genera With Biparental Care

Genus	Adult Weight (g)	Mean litter size
Aotus	961[a]	1
Callicebus	875[a]	1
Callimico	472[b]	1
Callithrix	241[b]	2
Cebuella	145[b]	2
Leontopithecus	745[b]	2
Pithecia (?)	1,046[b]	1
Saguinus	492[b]	2

[a]Weights from wild-shot specimens in Paraguay Museum of Natural History. *Aotus* weights from 5 females and 4 males. *Callicebus* weights from 1 female, 1 male.

[b]Weights from Eisenberg [1981].

primates that are monogamous, do not twin, and are not extremely small, *Aotus trivirgatus*, and *Callicebus moloch*.

DESCRIPTION OF STUDY SPECIES

Aotus trivirgatus (Night Monkey or Owl Monkey)

This small (1 kg), arboreal species, the only nocturnal monkey, exists in forests from western Panama south to northern Argentina, including much of the Amazon basin. *Aotus* live in a variety of habitats, including cloud forests, primary tropical moist forests, and subtropical dry forests in the chaco [Wright, 1981, 1978].

Callicebus moloch (Dusky Titi Monkey)

This small (1 kg), diurnal, arboreal monkey is one of three species of *Callicebus*, and is found in forested areas from Colombia throughout much of the Amazon basin to northern Paraguay [Kinzey, 1981]. Dusky titis prefer dense vegetation, vine tangles, and bamboo thickets along river edges or swamps.

Both *Aotus* and *Callicebus* live in small territories (4–12 ha), and eat fruits supplemented with insects, leaves, and flowers. Both genera live in monogamous groups composed of an adult pair and 1–3 sequential offspring. Only one infant is born a year, and juveniles do not disperse until 2–2 1/2 years of age. Both *Aotus* and *Callicebus* exhibit no sexual dimorphism and no distinctive coat color in infants.

TABLE II. Group—Composition of *Aotus* and *Callicebus* Focal Groups

Group	Year	Adult male	Adult female	1 year old	2 year old	0–11 months
Callicebus in Peru						
I	1980–81	X	X	Male	Male	Sept—male
I	1982	X	X	Male	Male	Sept—male
II	1980–81	X	X	Male	Male	0
II	1982	X	X	0	Male	Aug—male
Aotus in Peru						
I	1980–81	X	X	X	X	Feb
I	1982	X	X	X	X	Sept
Aotus in captivity						
I	1978–79	X	X	0	Male	Mar—female

STUDY SITES AND METHODS

The ecology and social behavior of *Callicebus moloch* and *Aotus trivirgatus* were studied for a total of 15 months at the Cocha Cashu Biological Station in the Manu National Park, Peru (71° 22' W, 11° 52' S). This isolated park in southeastern Peru includes 15,000 km^2 of undisturbed virgin forest. The research station is at 400 m elevation in "tropical moist forest" [Holdridge, 1967], with an annual rainfall of 2,000 mm. Cocha Cashu has diverse flora and fauna, including 13 sympatric species of monkey—one of the highest counts in any area of the Neotropics.

Information on the timing of births and dispersals was obtained by censuring six groups of *C moloch* and six groups of *A trivirgatus* at least once a month throughout the 15 months. Two focal groups of *C moloch* and one of *A trivirgatus* were each followed for five consecutive complete activity periods of 12 h each month. In *C moloch* focal animal sampling [Altmann, 1974] every 5 min on all group members documented general activities such as feeding, traveling, and resting. Opportunistic notes were kept on playing, grooming, copulating, weaning conflicts, father-offspring carrying conflicts, calling, fighting, insect foraging, nursing, and food sharing. Observations of infant and juvenile behavior were made in both groups (see Table II) throughout the 15 months, but to obtain the detailed parental care data needed for this study the infant born to group I became the focal animal for 3 consecutive days each week for 12-h days from age 3 weeks to 13 weeks. Infant carrying, suckling, sibling interactions, grooming, and food sharing were recorded. Positions of group members in progressions while foraging, traveling, and entering and exiting food trees were recorded. Because the visibility of all five group members was generally excellent, I was able to record feeding rates, insect foraging success, and activity of all group members throughout the day. Crown diameters of all fruits trees entered were recorded, and fruit availability in the forest was measured in 100 fruit traps distributed in 25-m intervals along trails (Janson, in preparation).

When studying *Aotus*, I recorded general group activity every 5 min throughout the night. (In both species most activities of group members are synchronous.) Activity categories were traveling, fruit feeding, resting, calling, and fighting. It was possible with the aid of an ITT pocket image intensifier and a Varo Noctron IV image intensifier to see the infant *Aotus* within a week of its birth, the position of the male carrying the infant in progressions, and to record play bouts, weaning conflicts, and father-offspring conflicts over carrying. The frequent vocalizations by the infant aided in data collection.

Infant development in *Aotus* was also studied at the City College Primate Research Laboratory in New York City. A group was housed in a large cage (4 × 2 × 3 m) and group members were an adult pair of *Aotus trivirgatus* born in northern Columbia, their 2-year-old son born in captivity, and a female infant also born in captivity (see Table II). Continual observations were conducted for 24-h periods 1 day each week for the first month after birth. The infant was observed in 12-h intervals each week from age 5 weeks until age 52 weeks. All pertinent behaviors, including infant carrying, suckling bouts, food sharing, playing, and sibling interactions were recorded.

RESULTS

Callicebus moloch

Males and females have clearly differentiated roles, not only in infant carrying, but also in playing, food sharing, grooming, leading, and of course suckling. There were also differences in insect foraging success between males and females. Both adult males and adult females participated in territorial calling and intergroup confrontations.

Carrying and babysitting. From the first weeks, the father was the primary carrier (Fig. I). Although the juveniles helped carry the infant (2% of the time) and the infant returned to the mother to suckle (6%), the father carried the infant 92% of the time by the third week. During the fourth week, the infant was first independent (19% of the time), but never strayed more than a few centimeters from the father. By the time the infant was 2 months old, the father carried it 57% of the time and the infant was independent 40% of the time. However, at this age the infant did not travel independently. For 1- or 2-h intervals the father sat in a vine tangle, while the infant moved from substrate to substrate, not straying more than a half meter from the father, returning to him after each excursion, as if tethered. At 12 weeks the infant was independent for 60% of the time and for the first time followed closely behind the father when

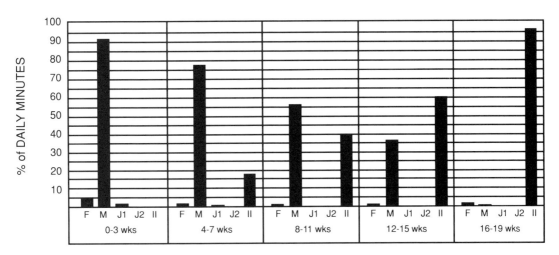

Figure 1. Percent of time each member of *Callicebus moloch* Group I in Peru carried infant and percent of time infant was independent aged 3–19 weeks. Group I was observed dawn to dusk for 3 days each week when infant was aged 3–12 weeks and 5 complete days when infant was aged 16 weeks (total 366 hours). F—adult female; M—adult male; J1—1-year-old juvenile; J2—2-year-old juvenile; II—infant independent (4 feet off carrier).

the group traveled. The father carried the 3-month-old infant (now nearly 40% of the male's weight) for 38% of the time. At this age the infant continued to leap onto the father's back at the least disturbance. At 4 months the infant rode on its father's back only 1% of the time, and father-offspring conflicts over carrying averaged four a day. The only time the father allowed the 4-month-old infant to ride was during chases by large monkeys *(Cebus apella).*

Suckling. After the infant was a week old, mother-infant contact was limited to suckling bouts. The mother nursed the infant four or five times a day (average bout length was 3 min) until the infant was 8 months old. During the first month, the female initiated these nursing bouts, by seeking out the father and pulling the infant gently from his back onto her breast. For the first 2 months, the mother licked and cleaned the genitalia of the infant during nursing bouts, a behavior never performed by the father. At bout end, the mother presented her back to the father, the infant transferred, and the mother moved 3–15 m away.

By the second month, the female often foraged 25–50 m ahead of the father, and called when she wanted to nurse. The male answered and the female found the father and infant. The infant independently transferred to the mother when she perched near the father. By the third month (12 weeks), the infant dismounted from the father and traveled independently a meter or two to meet the approaching mother. The average interval between suckling bouts for the first 6 months was 2 h 41 min. During the seventh and eight months weaning conflicts resulted in less frequent suckling bouts.

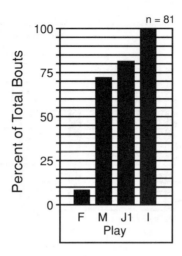

Figure 2. Play bouts in *Callicebus moloch* group I in Peru. Percentage of total bouts each member participates in when the infant is aged 4–9 months. F—adult female; M—adult male; J1—1½-year-old juvenile; 1—infant.

Food sharing. The mother rarely shared food with the infant. During the first 6 months, the infant did not approach the mother to beg for food. When the infant from group I was 7–11 months old, the infant approached the feeding female and tried to take her food on eight occasions. In five of the eight the female reluctantly shared. In contrast, the father willingly shared fruits and insects with the infant an average of five times a day from the second month until the offspring was over a year old.

Playing. The mother rarely played with the infant and juveniles (Fig. 2). The female participated in only 9% of the play bouts when the infant was 4–9 months old. At this time the father participated in 72%, the 1 1/2-year-old sibling in 82%, and the infant in 100%. When the infant was being carried (age 1–3 months old), no play behavior was observed except among the older juveniles who played together an average of four times a day.

Grooming. The mothers in both groups of *Callicebus* were ardent groomers. The mother in group I groomed in 53% of the bouts. As also observed in other species of *Callicebus* [Kinzey and Wright, 1982], the female keeps the male and offspring free of parasites.

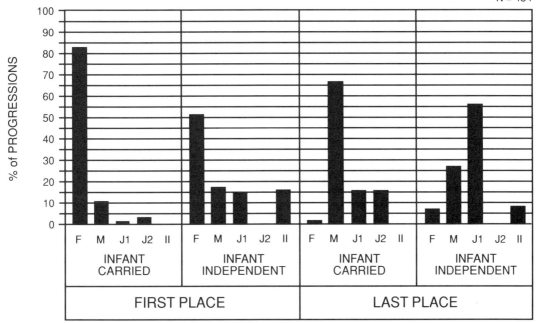

Figure 3. Progressions (into fruit trees, traveling and foraging) in *Callicebus moloch* group I in Peru. Individuals in first place and last place in each progression were scored. Time periods are divided into 1) infant ages 1–3 months (mother lactating and father carrying). and 2) infant aged 9–11 months (infant independent and mother gestating). F—adult female; M—adult male; J1—1- to 1½-year-old juvenile; J2—2- to 2½-year-old juvenile; II—independent infant.

Leader. Females led the groups more often than the males. The mother's role as leader was most dramatic when the infant was being carried and the female was lactating. At this time the mother led in foraging ventures and in progressions to fruit trees, 84% of the time in group I and 71% of the time in group II. The father (carrying the infant) was most often last (Fig. 3). However, when the infant was independent and no longer suckling, the consistent ordering of individuals in progressions was less marked.

Insect foraging. Lactating females spent more time insect foraging and had greater success than other group members (Fig. 4). They caught three times as many insects as the adult males and twice as many as the juveniles. A large 2–5 cm Orthopteran (grasshopper, etc) was caught by lactating mothers 0.6 times a day (once every other day), whereas these choice prey items were rarely caught by the fathers or juveniles. Insects are most abundant at this time of year (C.H. Janson and M. Brecht, personal communication), which partially accounts for female success. In addition, the females may have an insect-foraging advantage by being leaders, and the males may be handicapped in insect foraging by the active interference of infants. During the time of year when the mother is pregnant and the infant is independent, differences between group

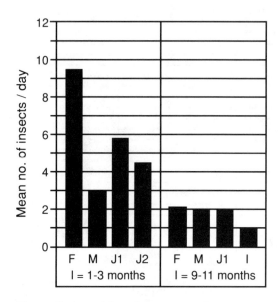

Figure 4. Insect foraging success in *Callicebus moloch* group I in Peru. The mean number of insects eaten per day for each group member when the infant was 1–3 months old (mother lactating and father carrying) is compared to mean number of insects eaten per day for each group member when the infant was 9–11 months old (mother gestating and infant independent). The latter time period was a period of insect scarcity. F—adult female; M—adult male; J1—1- to 1½-year-old juvenile; J2—2- to 2½-year-old juvenile; I—infant under 1 yr.

members in insect-foraging success are minimal. Insects are scarce at this time of year, which may account for their low rates of success. Time spent insect foraging doubles in October and November, when insects are abundant. (Each *Callicebus* spends an average of 35 min a day insect foraging in all months except November and October, when 75 min a day is the mean.)

Calling. Both adult male and adult female participate in ritualized duetting that serves the advertise their occupancy of the territory [Robinson, 1979, Mason, 1966]. In an average of 15 mornings a month (n-11), both males and females duetted for 5–7 min. Juveniles over 1 1/2 years old often joined in the territorial song.

Fighting. In 15 months I observed seven intergroup confrontations, and the adult females participated in only two out of seven. In both these battles, the female joined the male in actively chasing the neighboring group from a border

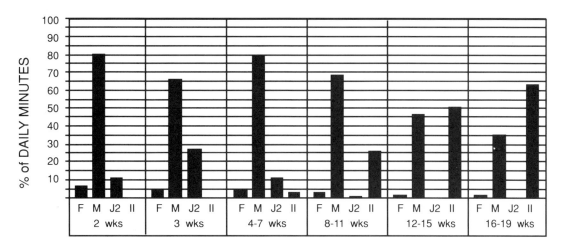

Figure 5. Percent of time each member of *Aotus trivirgatus* group I in captivity carried infant and percent of time infant was independent aged 2–19 weeks. Group I was observed for 24 consecutive hours each week when infant was aged 1–4 weeks, and 12 consecutive hours each week from week 5 to week 19 (total 276 hours). F—adult female; M—adult male; J—2-year-old juvenile; II—infant independent.

fruit tree. From these observations, it appears that the female plays a limited role in defending the territory.

Aotus trivirgatus

Both in the wild and in captivity, *Aotus* males and females have clearly differentiated behaviors. *Aotus* mothers, like *Callicebus* mothers, suckle infants and often lead in progressions, and *Aotus* fathers, like *Callicebus* fathers, carry, play with, and share food with infants. In contrast to *Callicebus*, *Aotus* pairs do not duet and both *Aotus* adults participate equally in intergroup confrontations.

Carrying and babysitting. In the group studied in captivity the father was primary infant carrier from the first day (Fig. 5). During the first week the mother carried the infant 33% of the time, and the father carried the infant 51% and the juvenile 15%. By the day 17 the sibling carried the infant 28% of the time, but as the infant became heavier this carrying dropped to 14% by the day 23 and to 13% by the day 30 and ceased by the fifth week. Independence began at 4 weeks, although the infant was carried by the father 81% of the time. From 8 to 11 weeks the infant was independent an average of 27% of the time, and carried by the father 69%. By 5 months of age the infant was totally independent. Father-offspring conflicts over carrying were observed in Peru at 4 months of age. With the aid of an image intensifier, I watched the father try to bite and push the infant off his back, while the infant squealed and held on tight. At 4 months the infant still rode on his father's back during tree gap jumps 3–4 m long, but by 5 months of age the *Aotus* made these jumps on his own.

199

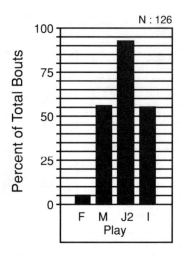

Figure 6. Play bouts in *Aotus trivirgatus* group I in activity. Percentage of total bouts each member participated in when infant is aged 3–9 months. F—adult female; M—adult male; J—2½-year-old juvenile; I—infant.

Suckling. After the first week, mother-infant contact was limited to suckling bouts. For the first month the infant nursed an average of 20 bouts per 24-h period. At the end of each bout the mother nipped the infant gently, the infant vocalized, and the father quickly approached for the infant to transfer. From the first to eighth month the infant nursed 4–5 times a day. I could not document suckling bouts in Peru.

Food sharing. In captivity the mother rarely shared food with the infant. When the infant was 3–5 months old, the mother shared food with it in only four out of 40 food-sharing incidents (10%). Most often when the infant approached the feeding mother, the mother turned her head away, or turned her back on the infant. In contrast, the father shared 27 times (68%) and the juvenile 9 (23%).

Playing. Mothers rarely played with infants, either in the field or in captivity (Fig. 6). Most play involved the father, juvenile, and infant. The infant first played at 6 weeks, when still on the father's back, by cuffing at the juvenile.

Grooming. *Aotus* rarely grooms. In captivity grooming was minimal, but grooming has been associated with copulation in other captive *Aotus* [Moynihan, 1964].

Leader. In the Peruvian *Aotus* groups the father carrying the infant was last in 77% (n = 35) of the progressions observed.

Calling. *Aotus* did not duet when giving the intergroup call. An adult (male) hooted along borders for 1–2 hours in the nearly full moon an average of once a month. Both males and females gave a resonant "war whoop" during battles with other groups.

Fighting. Both males and females participated in intergroup confrontations. In captivity individuals fight only with members of the same sex [Wright, 1981], but this was difficult to document in the field.

DISCUSSION

It is clear from these data that males and females in *Aotus* and *Callicebus* have different roles in parenting, but the adaptive advantage of these differences is unclear. To understand better the evolution of the biparental care system, the energetic costs of lactation and gestation are reviewed.

Costs to the Female

The cost of milk production is difficult to quantify because the nutritive quality during early weeks can differ from the quality of milk at weaning [Oftedal, 1978]. Also there is variability in protein, fat, and carbohydrate composition between species [Jenness, 1974], and, to my knowledge, the milk of *Aotus* and *Callicebus* has not been analyzed. However, marmoset milk has been analyzed and contains five times as much protein as human milk [Deinhardt, 1970]. It may be possible that *Callicebus* and *Aotus* also produce a milk high in protein and therefore expensive to produce.

In general among mammals, gestation is less expensive to the mother than lactation [Crampton and Lloyd, 1959; Millar, 1975, 1976; Randolph et al, 1977]. In primates the energy requirement for an adult female rhesus monkey is 100 kCal/kg, for a gestation female 125 kCal/kg, and for a lactating female 150 kCal/kg [Portman, 1970]. The reproductive energy costs of lactating humans increases 50% over nonlactating females [Blackburn and Calloway, 1976]. Again, laboratory data on *Callicebus* and *Aotus* are lacking, but we may assume that these strong trends probably apply to them.

A paired *Aotus* or *Callicebus* female is usually pregnant or lactating. How does the female meet these high energy costs of gestation and lactation? Differences in the female's feeding and activity patterns throughout the year seem to correlate the differences in the energy costs of gestation and lactation. During the first months after birth, the female is the first animal of the group to enter fruit trees. This guarantees her the choice of the best fruits for at least 10 min. Her feeding rate is also faster than the male's at this time of year. Often the male, last in progression when carrying offspring, enters a tree emptied of fruits, or he has to search longer for the fruits that are left. Although fruits provide ready energy, protein must be found in insects or new leaves. During the first 3 months after the infant's birth, the female avidly forages for insects and consumes three times as many insects as the male and twice as many as the juveniles. The male, last in progressions and burdened with an active infant, has little success at insect foraging (even though insects are most abundant at this time of year).

As might be expected from the relative costs of lactation and pregnancy, behaviors of the pregnant female are less distinct from other group members. Fruit feeding rates are slower, and the female, less often the leader, often enters fruit trees second. Insect-foraging success rate per time decreases and mother, father, and juveniles have equal success rates per time. Pregnancy occurs when both insects and fruits are scarce.

It is clear that the costs of reproduction are high for small primate females, and sharing the burden of infant care with the father is to the female's advantage. But not all small primates have biparental care. Compared with *Aotus* and *Callicebus*, *Saimiri* has a higher litter/maternal weight ratio, infants gain weight more rapidly, and adult body size of females is smaller [Long and Cooper, 1968; Hall et al, 1977]. Although *Saimiri* females have a costlier reproductive burden than *Aotus* or *Callicebus* females, *Saimiri* males do not share parental care. To understand this paradox, the costs of biparental care to the male will be reviewed.

Costs to the Male

It is known that the costs of locomotion are proportionately greater for a small animal than a large one [Taylor, 1970]. Mothers in small species also give birth to proportionally heavier newborns [Leitch et al, 1959]. And as a general rule, offspring of smaller species gain weight proportionately faster than larger species [Eisenberg, 1981]. Carrying infants requires energy, particularly in small species.

In addition to the energy costs of carrying, there are also the costs of decreased foraging efficiency. When the infant is 1–3 months old, the father spends less time feeding and his fruit feeding rates are lower. Last in progressions, the male often enters fruit trees 15 min after the other three group members, and the fruit supply in these small-crowned trees may by then be depleted. When the infant is 1–3 months old, the father's insect-foraging success rate per time is not only less than that of other group members, but also less than the father's own success rates at times of the year when insect abundance is low and he is not carrying an infant.

The father's parental responsibilities do not terminate when the infant is independently locomoting. In these small family groups peer playmates are few or none. The father plays with the infant and juvenile four or five times a day in bouts of 5–20 min. This energy-expensive activity, rarely seen in mothers, continues throughout the time of food abundance, but ceases when resources are scarce (regardless of infant age).

An additional paternal duty in these two species is protection of the infant. At the Manu National Park there are seven species of hawks and eagles, and five of those species have been observed catching monkeys. There is evidence that these predators take a toll on infant monkeys, particularly on callitrichids. Dawson [Dawson and Dukelow, 1976] found that *Saguinus oedipus* in Panama lost 50% of its offspring, and A. Wilson and J. Terborgh (personal communications) in Peru observed 50% mortality of infants under a year of age in *Saguinus fuscicollis* and *Saguinus imperator*. I have also observed attacks on *Callicebus*, but none were successful. Also, large monkeys, especially *Cebus apella* and *Cebus albifrons*, chase *Callicebus* from fruit trees and *Aotus* from sleeping trees an average of twice a day in the wet season. *Cebus apella* is omnivorous and has injured opossums, silky anteaters (*Cyclopes*), squirrels (*Microsciureus*), and at least seven other species of land vertebrates (C.H. Janson, personal communication). I have never seen *Cebus* catch either *Aotus* or *Callicebus*, but close chases were observed where a male *Cebus* came within a half meter of both *Aotus* and *Callicebus* males with infants on their backs. The lactating female, already energy-stressed, probably could not have outrun *Cebus* for 100 m if she were carrying an additional weight on her back. Although an offspring can travel independently by the third month of age, it remains in close proximity to the father throughout the third and fourth month and jumps onto the father's back at any disturbance. It appears that there is a selective advantage to the infant for father as primary carrier in times of danger.

After examining the biparental care system in its natural habitat, I agree with Kleiman [1977] that small body size is an important factor in the evolution of this system. All the species in which the male is primary infant carrier have adult weights of a kilo or under. In larger monkeys male carriers may not be necessary since 1) cost of locomotion is not as expensive [Taylor, 1970]; 2) infant/maternal weight ratios are less; and 3) in large species males can effectively attack predators, whereas in small monkeys quick flight and carrying infants to safety are more effective against predators.

But litter/maternal weight ratio and small size may not be the primary factors influencing the system. *Saimiri* males do not carry offspring. Yet *Saimiri* has the highest litter/maternal weight ratio for a cebid species with single births [Leutnegger, 1973], and weight increases in *Saimiri* infants are faster than in *Aotus* [Long and Cooper, 1968; Hall et al, 1977]. In recent years correlations have been suggested between ecology and social behavior [Eisenberg et al, 1972; Clutton-Brock and Harvey, 1977, 1978], and the differences between *Saimiri* and *Callicebus* may be due to ecological constraints. For example, *Saimiri* feed in large-crowned fruit trees such as figs, which can easily accommodate groups of 30–50 animals. Females can afford to tolerate other females at these rich resources and form affiliative female groups [Wrangham, 1980]. The disadvantage to the female of losing male parental care because of parental uncertainty is offset by the advantage of having female subadult aid in carrying and peers for playing. The disadvantage of not having male carrying of infants in time of danger is offset by predator detection by multiple "ears and eyes" of large group size. Also, a synchronous breeding season ensures a female *Saimiri* that her infant will be born during the same month as all other *Saimiri* infants. This is an excellent strategy against predators, since the odds are in her favor that the infant preyed upon will not be hers and that they may be predator satiation.

In contrast, the callitrichids [Terborgh, 1983], and *Callicebus* use small-crowned fruit trees. Ninety-three percent of the fruit trees used by *Callicebus* had crown diameters of under 10 m. *Aotus* feed in large figs, but also rely on traplining small-crowned fruit trees. Most of these small, dispersed trees ripen a few fruits at a time. Therefore females using these trees cannot afford to tolerate other females (another adult female and her offspring actually means a doubling of group size), because small patches are not big enough to support large groups. Also these small-crowned fruit trees are dispersed such that variation among territories may not be large enough to "compensate second mated females for the costs associated with polygyny" [Wittenberger and Tilson, 1980]. Because of the energy costs of ranging more widely, it may not be economical for males to defend the territories of more than one female. Obligate monogamy results [Kleiman, 1977]. By repelling other females, the monogamous female loses the advantage of large group size (allomothers, peer playmates for offspring, predator protection by "more eyes and ears," and predator satiation), but gains a monogamous mate who is confident in his paternity and can invest heavily in offspring. The advantages to the female of male parental care are obvious. If the father provides energy-expensive services, such as carrying, playing, food sharing and protection, the female is then free to enter fruit trees first, and insect forage more successfully in order to meet the high energy costs of lactation. But what is the advantage to the male? How does this biparental care system maximize the male's reproductive success? It is usually to a male's advantage to protect and assist his offspring if this increases the offspring's chance of survival and if the possibility of obtaining matings with additional females is low [Trivers, 1972]. The data indicate that small species of monkey need aid in carrying because of the weight of offspring and cost of lactation, but there may be an additional factor. If fleeing from danger is the best protective strategy of small, monogamous primates, then it also may be more effective for the male to carry the infant. Without the high energy costs of lactation, the father is better equipped at any moment for a quick retreat with an extra weight on his back. If the survival of the offspring is at stake, it may be to the advantage of both male and female for the father to carry the infant.

ACKNOWLEDGMENTS

Completion of this project would not have been possible without the aid and attention of many. Special thanks to Warren Kinzey, John Oates, and John Fleagle for their expert advice and encouragement from the homefront. Without the able collaboration of Mary Woods, Tom Trocco, and Art Skopee, the data on captive *Aotus* would not have been possible. Many thanks to Patrick Daniels, Cirilo Luján Munares, David Sivertsen, and P. Stern for steadfast field assistance. I am indebted to Charles Janson for fruit trap data, and Martha Brecht, Charlie Munn, and C. Janson for insect abundance data. I thank

Robin Foster for invaluable instruction in plant identification in Peru, for lending me his Varo Noctron IV nightscope, and for his encouragement and support. ITT is gratefully acknowledged for lending me the ITT pocket scope image intensifier. Herb Appleby ably drew the figures. For their ecological expertise, stimulating discussions in the field, and criticisms of drafts of this manuscript, I thank John Terborgh and Charles Janson.

This research was supported by NSF grant BNS 81-15368, NSF grant BNS 77-24921, a grant from the World Wildlife Fund-U.S. Primate Program, and the Wenner-Gren Foundation for Anthropological Research grant 4282.

I am very grateful to the Peruvian Ministry of Agriculture, Forestry Institute, and ORDEMAD for permission to work in the Manu National Park. Dr. Susanna Moller-Herjt, Ing. Jose Purisaca, and Ing. Cardich were particularly helpful. Special thanks also to Ted, Chris, Maureen, Ed., and Julie Chapple, Betty and Jim Wright, Jill and Bob Parliament, Wilson McCagg, Barbara Maines, and most of all to Amanda Wright for her patience and good nature throughout this research, and to Kendra and Daphne.

REFERENCES

Altmann J. (1974): Observational study of behavior; sampling methods. Behavior 69:227–267.

Blackburn MW, Calloway DH (1976): Energy expenditure and consumption of mature, pregnant, and lactating women. J Am Diet Assoc 63:29–37.

Box HO (1977): Quantitative data on the carrying of young captive monkeys (*Callithrix jacchus*) by other members of their family groups. Primates 18:475–484.

Busse C, Hamilton WJ (1981): Infant carrying by male chacma baboons. Science 212:1281–1282.

Chivers DJ (1974): The Siamang in Malaya. Contrib Primatol 4:1–331.

Clutton-Brock TH, Harvey PH (1977): Primate ecology and social organization. J Zool Lond 183:1–39.

Clutton-Brock TH, Harvey PH (1978): Mammals, resources and reproductive strategies. Nature 273:191–195.

Crampton E, Lloyd L (1959): "Fundamentals of Nutrition." San Francisco: W.H. Freeman.

Dawson GA, Dukelow WR (1976): Reproductive characteristics of free-ranging Panamanian tamarins (*Saguinus oedipus geoffroyi*), J Med primatol 5:266–275.

Deinhardt F (1970): Nutritional requirements of marmosets. In Harris RH (ed): "Feeding and Nutrition of Nonhuman Primates." New York: Academic Press, pp 175–182.

Dixson AF, Fleming D (1981): Parental behaviour and infant development in owl monkeys (*Aotus trivirgatus griseimembra*). J Zool Lond 194:25–39.

Eisenberg JF (1981): "The Mammalian Radiations—An Analysis of Trends in Evolution, Adaptation and Behavior." Chicago: University of Chicago Press.

Eisenberg JF, Muckenhirn N. Rudran R (1972): The relationship between ecology and social structure in primates. Science 176:863–874.

Epple G (1975): The behavior of marmoset monkeys (Callithricidae). In Rosenblum LA (ed): "Primate Behavior," Vol 4. New York, Academic Press, pp 195–239.

Epple G (1977): Notes on the establishment and maintenance on the pair bond in *Saguinus fuscicollis*. In Kleiman DG (ed): "The Biology and Conservation of the Callitrichidae. Washington: Smithsonian Institution Press, pp. 231–237.

Fragaszy DM, Schwarz S, Shimosaka D (1982): Longitudinal observations of care and development of infant titi monkeys (*Callicebus moloch*). Am J Primatol 2:191–200.

Hall RD, Beattie RJ, Whychoff Jr (1977): Weight gains and sequence of dental eruptions in infant owl monkeys (*Aotus trivirgatus*). Walter Reed Army Inst (Ms).

205

Heltne PG, Turner DC, Wolhandler J (1973): Maternal and paternal periods in the development of infant *Callimico goeldii*. Am J Phys Anthropol 38:455–459.

Hoage RJ (1977): Parental care in *Leontopithecus rosalia rosalia:* Sex and age differences in carrying behavior and the role of prior experience. In Kleiman DG (ed): "The Biology and Conservation of the *Callitrichidae*." Washington: Smithsonian Institution Press, pp 293–305.

Hoage RJ (1982): "Social and Physical Maturation in Captive Lion Tamarins, *Leontopithecus rosalia rosalia* (Primates: *Callitrichidae*)." Washington: Smithsonian Institution Press.

Holdridge, LR (1967): "Life Zone Ecology." San Jose, Costa Rica: Tropical Science Center.

Ingram JC (1977): Interactions between parents and infants, and the development of independence in the common marmoset (*Callithrix jacchus*). Anim Behav 25:811–827.

Jenness R (1974): The composition of milk. In Larson BL, Smith VR (eds): "Lactation: A Comprehensive Treatise." New York: Academic Press, pp 3–107.

Kinzey WG (1981): The titi monkeys, Genus *Callicebus*. In Coimbra-Filho AF, Mittermeier RA (eds): "Ecology and Behavior of Neotropical Primates," Vol 1. Rio de Janeiro: Academia Brasileira de Ciencias, pp 241–276.

Kinzey WG, Wright PC (1982): Grooming behavior in the titi monkeys (*Callicebus torquatus*). Am J Primatol 3:267–275.

Kleiman DG (1977): Monogamy in mammals. Q Rev Biol 52:39–69.

Leitch I, Hytten FE, Billewicz WZ (1959): The maternal and neonatal weights of some Mammalia. Proc Zool Soc Lond 13:11–28.

Leutenegger W (1973): Maternal-fetal weight relationships in primates. Folia Primatol 20:280–293.

Leutenegger W (1980): Monogamy in callitrichids: A consequence of phyletic dwarfism? Int J Primatol 1:95–98.

Long JO, Cooper RW (1968): Physical growth and dental eruption in captive bred squirrel monkeys (*Saimiri sciureus*) (Leticia, Columbia). In Rosenblum LA, Cooper RW (eds): "The Squirrel Monkey." New York: Academic Press.

Mason WA (1966): Social organization of the South American monkey, *Callicebus moloch* A preliminary report. Tulane Stud Zool 13:23–28.

Millar JS (1975): Tactics of energy partitioning in breeding Peromyscus. Can J Zool 53:967–976.

Millar JS (1976): Adaptive features of mammalian reproduction. Evolution 31:370–386.

Mitchell G, Brandt EM (1972): Paternal Behavior in primates. In Poirier FE (ed): "Primate Socialization." New York: Random House, pp 173–206.

Moynihan M (1964): Some behavior patterns of platyrrhine monkeys. I. The night monkey (*Aotus trivirgatus*) Smithsonian Misc Collect 135(5):1–84.

Oftedal O (1980): Milk and mammalian evolution. In Schmidt-Nielson K, Bolis L. Taylor CR (eds): "Comparative Physiology: Primative Mammals. Cambridge: Cambridge University Press, pp 31–42.

Pook AG (1978): A comparison between the reproduction and parental behaviour of the Goeldi's Monkey (*Callicmico goeldii*) and of the true marmosets (*Callitrichidae*). In Rothe H., Wolters HJ, Hearn JP (eds): "Biology and Behaviour of Marmosets." Göttingen, West Germany: Eigenverlag Rothe.

Portman OW (1970): Nutritional requirements (NRC) of nonhuman primates. In Harris RH (ed): "Feeding and Nutrition of Nonhuman Primates." New York: Academic Press, pp 87–115.

Redican WK (1976): Adult male-infant interactions in nonhuman primates. In Lamb M (ed): "The Role of the Father in Child Development." New York: John Wiley and Sons, pp 345–385.

Robinson JG (1979): Vocal regulation of use of space by groups of titi monkeys Callicebus moloch. Behav Ecol Sociobiol 5:1–15.

Taylor CR, Schmidt-Nielson K, Raab JL (1970): Scaling of energetic cost of running to body size in mammals. Am J Physiol 219:1104–1107.

Terborgh JW (1983): "Five New World Primates: A Study in Comparative Ecology." Princeton: Princeton University Press.

Trivers RL (1972): Parental investment and sexual selection. In Campbell B (ed): "Sexual Selection and the Descent of Man, 1871–1971." Chicago: Aldine, pp 136–179.

Wittenberger JF, Tilson RL (1980): The evolution of monogamy: Hypothesis and evidence. Annu Rev Ecol Systemat 11:197–232.

Wrangham R (1980): An ecological model of female-bonded primate groups. Behaviour 75:262–300.

Wright PC (1978): Home range, activity pattern, and agonistic encounters of a group of night monkeys (Aotus trivirgatus) in Peru. Folia Primatol 29:43–55.

Wright PC (1981): The night monkeys, genus Aotus. In Coimbra-Filho AF, Mittermeier RA (eds): "Ecology and Behavior of Neotropical Primates," Vol I. Rio de Janeiro: Academia Brasileira de Ciencias, pp 211–240.

207

Effects of Patch Size on Feeding Associations in Muriquis (*Brachyteles arachnoides*)

Karen B. Strier

Beloit College

Key Words: Patch size, Group size, Feeding aggregate, Group cohesion, Muriqui, *Brachyteles*

Abstract: Data were collected on one group of muriquis, or woolly spider monkeys (*Brachyteles arachnoides*) during a 14-month study at Fazenda Montes Claros, Minas Gerais, Brazil to examine the effects of food patch size on muriqui feeding associations. Muriqui food patches were larger than expected from the availability of patch sizes in the forest; fruit patches were significantly larger than leaf patches. Feeding aggregate size, the maximum number of simultaneous occupants, and patch occupancy time were positively related to the size of fruit patches. However, a great number of individuals fed at leaf sources than expected from the size of these patches. Adult females tended to feed alone in patches more often than males, whereas males tended to feed in single-sexed groups more often than females. Yet in neither case were these differences statistically significant.

INTRODUCTION

The relationship between the size of food patches and primate grouping associations has been examined in a number of species. In extreme cases, groups split up into small, independent foraging parties to avoid intragroup feeding competition at small patches, and reunite at large patches that can accommodate a greater number of individuals. Such fission-fusion societies, known to occur in chimpanzees [1], bonobos [2, 3], and spider monkeys [4, 5], are attributed to the importance of patchy fruit resources in these species' diets.

Patch size also affects patterns of association in species that live in cohesive groups [6, 7]. While the significance of patch size for the formation of cohesive groups has been discussed [8], few studies have directly examined how cohesive groups respond to patchy food resources. This paper presents data on food patch size and grouping patterns in one group of muriquis, or woolly spider monkeys (*Brachyteles arachnoides*) in an effort to evaluate behavioral correlates of patch size.

STUDY SITE AND METHODS

Data were collected during June 1983 through July 1984 as part of an ongoing study of muriqui behavioral ecology at Fazenda Montes Claros, Minas Gerais, Brazil. The 80-ha forest, located at 19° 50' S, 41° 50' W, received 1,186 mm of rainfall during the study period. The forest supports two groups of muriquis in addition to three other primate species [9]. Observations focused on the larger group, which grew from 23 to 26 individuals and included 6 adult males and 8 adult females during this time [10]. The study group traveled together as a cohesive unit, maintaining vocal contact when individuals were visually separated.

Information on muriqui feeding patterns relative to food patch size was collected during 'feeding tree focal samples' (FTFS). I defined a patch as a tree or liana whose canopy is discrete from the canopies of other members of the same species. Individual trees and lianas constituted separate patches in all FTFS.

Samples were conducted opportunistically on preselected days between August 1983 and July 1984. An FTFS began when a muriqui was observed to enter and begin feeding in a patch. The time was noted, and the identity of the individual was determined in the majority of cases. When poor visibility prevented me from recognizing an individual by its natural markings, it was assigned a distinct code number. Similar data were obtained for all muriquis that subsequently arrived at the patch. As each muriqui left the patch, its identity (either actual or coded; see above) and the time were recorded. The sample terminated when the last muriqui left the patch. Entering and leaving a food patch were recorded instead of actual feeding times because these data could be reliably collected even when several animals were being monitored simultaneously. Other behaviors, such as brief resting bouts, were not distinguished. Patch occupancy times are therefore likely to overestimate actual feeding times except in cases when feeding began immediately upon entering a patch and ceased only when the animal(s) departed.

Individual occupancy time in a patch was determined by subtracting each individual's entrance time from its departure time; the total time a patch was occupied was obtained by summing the individual times over all animals observed during a sample. Feeding aggregates were defined as the total number of individuals that fed in a patch during a sample. The maximum number of individuals that simultaneously occupied a patch was determined by calculating changes in feeding group membership as individuals entered and departed from the patch during each sample.

Once all muriquis had left the patch, the patch was marked using surveyor's flagging tape and numbered aluminum tags, and its diameter at breast height (DBH) was measured. In the case of lianas, the DBHs of all supporting trees were measured and summed. The type of food eaten during the sample was described, collected whenever possible, and classified as fruit and/or seeds (n = 98), leaves (n = 95), or flowers (n = 21). In several cases, multiple FTFS were conducted at the same patch. In these cases, feeding aggregate size, the maximum number of simultaneous occupants, and occupancy time were averaged over samples conducted at the same patch to avoid biasing the results by repeated observations. Such average values were treated as single FTFS in the subsequent analyses. Together, 150 different patches were sampled, distributed among fruits (n = 58), leaves (n = 76), and flowers (n = 16). No distinction is made here between different species.

To evaluate the size of muriqui food patches relative to the availability of patch sizes in the forest, the DBHs of trees occurring in 20 randomly-placed 50 × 25 m vegetation plots were sampled. Transect lines were walked along both of the 50-meter boundaries of each plot and through the center of the plot parallel to these boundaries. The DBHs of all trees greater than 3 m in height that occurred within a strip 2 m wide of the transect line inside the plot were tallied and grouped into the following categories: small (< 6.8 cm); medium (6.8–25 cm); and large (> 25 cm). The DBHs of 3,846 trees were included in the plot sample of patch sizes.

DBH has been employed as an indicator of canopy volume or patch size in other studies [5, 7]. The ability of DBH to predict canopy volume in the present study was evaluated by measuring both variables for a sample of 50 randomly selected trees including known muriqui feeding trees (n = 26) and trees that were not utilized by the monkeys, but which occurred in the vegetation plots (n = 24). Canopy volumes were calculated by measuring the north-south and east-west projections of the canopy onto the ground and the distance from the upper to lower canopy margins using a standard metric tape and Suunto clinometer, and then applying a volume equation appropriate to the shape of the canopy.

RESULTS

DBH and Patch Size

Regression analysis of the measured canopy volumes against DBH for the sample of 50 trees showed that canopy volume can be reliably predicted by DBH from the equation: $y = 1.97x - 0.67$, where y = log canopy volume and x = log DBH (fig. 1). The correlation coefficient, $r = 0.87$, was highly significant (n = 50, $p \leq 0.0001$), thereby justifying the use of DBH as an index of relative canopy size, or patch size, in the following analyses.

Muriqui Food Patch Sizes

Comparisons between the DBH of trees in the FTFS and those represented in the vegetation plots indicate that feeding trees were significantly larger than expected from the distribution of available DBH size classes in the forest ($\chi^2 = 689.7$, df = 2, $p \leq 0.001$, 1-tailed) (fig. 2). The DBH measurements obtained for 145 different FTFS patches averaged 24.7 cm (SD = 21.3; range 1 – 108 cm). The average size of fruit patches ($x = 31.6$, SD = 26.1, n = 56) was nearly twice

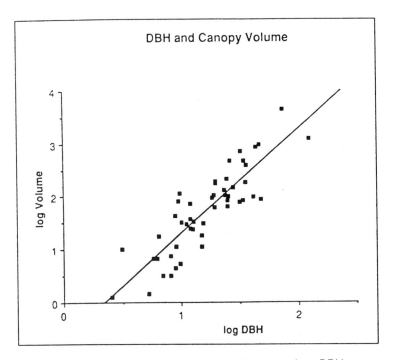

Figure 1. A logarithmic plot of canopy volume against DBH.

that of leaf patches ($\bar{x}$ = 16.8, SD = 13.6, n = 74). Overall, fruit patches were significantly larger than leaf patches (Wilcoxon z = 3.93, p ≤ 0.0001).

Relationship Between Feeding Group Sizes and Patch Sizes

Both feeding aggregate sizes and the maximum number of simultaneous occupants during the FTFS ranged from 1 to 20 individuals. The average aggregate size for all samples combined was 2.8 individuals (SD = 2.8, n = 150); the maximum number of simultaneous occupants averaged 2.6 individuals (SD = 2.4, n = 150).

Patch size correlated positively with both feeding aggregate size (r_s = 0.37, n = 145, p ≤ 0.0001) and the maximum number of simultaneous occupants (r_s = 0.38, n = 145, p ≤ 0.0001). Feeding aggregate size and the maximum number of simultaneous occupants during the FTFS were almost perfectly correlated (r_s = 0.99, n = 150, p ≤ 0.0001).

Feeding aggregates were larger at fruit patches ($\bar{x}$ = 3.4, SD = 3.4, n = 58) than at leaf patches ($\bar{x}$ = 2.4, SD = 2.4, n = 76). However, the difference in aggregate size at fruit and leaf patches was not significant (Wilcoxon z = 1.80, p ≤ 0.07). In contrast, the number of simultaneous occupants in fruit patches ($\bar{x}$ = 3.2, SD = 3.3, n = 58) was significantly greater than in the leaf patches ($\bar{x}$ = 2.1, SD = 1.6, n = 76; Wilcoxon z = 2.13, p < 0.03).

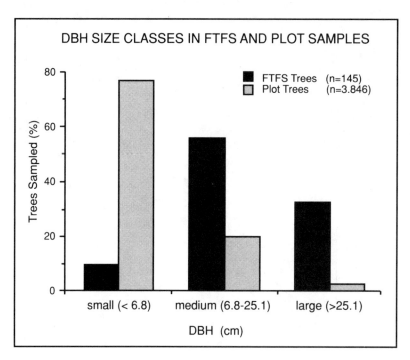

Figure 2. DBH size classes compared between FTFS and plot samples.

Both feeding aggregate size and the maximum number of simultaneous occupants were positively related to DBH in the fruit samples (r_s = 0.39, n = 56, p < 0.003 in both cases). However, neither of these variables correlated significantly with patch size in the leaf samples (r_s = 0.18, n = 74, p > 0.12 and r_s = 0.20, n = 74, p > 0.10, respectively). Fewer individuals fed simultaneously in leaf patches.

Patch Occupancy Times

FTFS lasted up to 478 min, and an average of 29.1 min (SD = 62.1, n = 150). Occupancy time was positively correlated with patch size (r_s = 0.46, n = 145, p ≤ 0.0001), and increased with both the size of feeding aggregates and the maximum number of simultaneous occupants (r_s = 0.86, n = 150, p < 0.0001 in both cases).

Individual muriquis spent more than twice as much time in fruit ($\bar{x}$ = 14.6, n = 358) than in leaf patches ($\bar{x}$ = 5.8, n = 227; Wilcoxon z = -11.42, p < 0.0001). Feeding aggregates spent significantly more time in fruit patches ($\bar{x}$ = 48.3) than in leaf patches ($\bar{x}$ = 14.3; Wilcoxon z = 3.09, p < 0.002). Occupancy times correlated significantly with patch size in all of the FTFS (fig. 3).

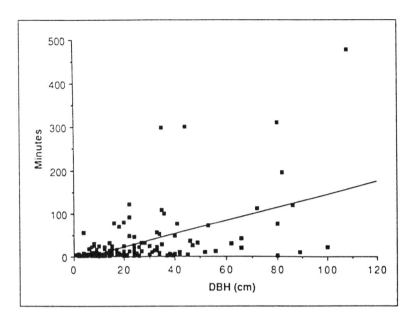

Figure 3. Relationship between patch occupancy time (min) and patch size (indicated by DBH).

Composition and Sex Differences in Feeding Aggregates

Although feeding aggregates with up to 20 individuals were observed during the FTFS, 139 of the samples involved only one individual. Adult females, either alone or in association with a semidependent offspring, accounted for 56% of all solitary feedings observed during the FTFs, whereas adult males accounted for only 30%. However, when compared to the expected frequencies based on the proportion of adult male and female muriquis in the group, no significant differences were evident $\chi^2 = 2.69$, df = 1, p $\leq$ 0.10).

Sixty-two percent of the feeding samples including two or more fully independent muriquis included only members of the same sex. In 24 cases, aggregates were composed only of adult or subadult males; in 14 cases, aggregates were composed only of adult females. Although males accounted for a greater proportion of single-sexed feeding groups than females, the differences were not significant when compared to the proportion of males and females in the group ($\chi^2 = 2.74$, df = 1, p $\geq$ 0.10).

DISCUSSION

Significance of Patch Size

The large size of muriqui food patches relative to the availability of different patch sizes in the forest suggest that muriquis may be selectively exploiting

213

these patches because of their size. However, other attributes such as the density and nutritional value of the food items in the patches may be more important than size in determining whether a patch is exploited. Comparisons of these variables between exploited and unexploited patches are needed to factor out the effects of species preferences before arguments about patch size selectivity in muriquis can be advanced.

Both the total number of individuals that fed during a sample and the maximum number of simultaneous occupants in a patch were employed as measures of feeding group size. Although these measures were strongly related to one another, the number of simultaneous occupants is a better indicator of the physical constraints of patch size on feeding group size, and therefore may be a better measure of the strength of intragroup feeding competition. Feeding aggregate size, in contrast, may imply more about the actual availability and desirability of food items in a patch. While both variables correlated significantly with patch size in the fruit samples, neither was related to patch size leaf samples.

Muriqui fruit patches were significantly larger than their leaf patches and, as the number of simultaneous occupants indicate, fruit patches supported larger aggregates. However, there were no significant differences in the total number of individuals that fed at fruit and leaf patches, even though fruit patches were much larger. Rather, it appears that a greater number of individuals fed at leaf sources than expected from patch size by feeding sequentially rather than simultaneously. Such behavior is not surprising, if leaves are generally less preferred food items, because of the longer processing times required to extract their nutrients [11]. Furthermore, the presence of secondary compounds in muriqui leaf sources [Strier, unpubl. data] may prevent individuals from consuming large quantities of certain leaves and thus depleting or substantially reducing the availability of food at leaf patches before departing.

Muriquis occupied fruit patches significantly longer than leaf patches. Although this finding may be related to the larger size of fruit patches, fruit generally comprised a smaller proportion of the canopy than leaves. Furthermore, muriquis devoted less of their feeding time to fruit (32%) than to leaves (51%) [9]. It is difficult, however, to distinguish between the effects of patch size, food availability, and food preferences on actual occupancy times.

Feeding Group Composition

Although females accounted for a greater proportion of solitary feeders, and males accounted for a greater proportion of single-sexed feeding groups, the sex differences were not significant when compared to expected frequencies based on the proportions of males and females in the group. The direction of these sex differences, however, was consistent with other measures of association obtained independently during the study period, which suggested that female muriquis avoided feeding competition with other group members more strongly than did males. In general, female muriquis maintained greater inter-individual distances while feeding than resting, and males spent a greater proportion of their time in proximity to other males than females spent to other females [12].

Another explanation for the lack of significant differences in male and female feeding associations may be related to the fact that muriquis are sexually monomorphic in body size, and therefore the nutritional requirements of males and females should be similar only when females are not pregnant or lactating. Because most of the females were weaning offspring for the majority of the study period, for energetic reasons their behavior may have more closely resembled that of males than might otherwise be the case. Indeed, although male and female activity budgets did not differ overall, significant behavioral differences were detected in paired comparisons of female muriquis in different reproductive states [13].

Implications for Understanding Primate Grouping Patterns

The data reported here raise questions about the ways primate groups are typically characterized. Multi-male polygynous groups are generally described either as fission-fusion societies or, more commonly, as cohesive units [8, 14]. However, treating these social systems as discrete categories may obscure an important underlying continuum between them. Primates such as the muriqui, which modify their grouping associations in response to patchy food resources and yet remain within calling proximity while resting and foraging, may represent an intermediate point on such a continuum. Taking this argument one step further, it is reasonable to predict that muriquis would adopt more fluid associations in habitats where large patches of preferred fruit are absolutely scarce. For example, a scarcity of large food patches may explain the small, fluid associations observed in muriquis at the only other site where this species has been studied systematically [15]. Similarly, a 50% increase in the present study group's size may lead to an increase in their tendency toward fragmentation [10, 16].

The importance of patch size availability to understanding intraspecific, and perhaps interspecific differences in grouping patterns is a testable hypothesis. If further studies yield supporting evidence, differences between fission-fusion and cohesive primate groups would be more appropriately viewed as facultative adjustments to the availability of large patches of preferred foods, rather than as distinct social and foraging strategies.

Acknowledgements

I am grateful to the Brazilian government and CNPq for permission to work in Brazil, and to Dr. Celio Valle for his sponsorship. E. Veado and R. Summers assisted in collecting the data reported here; S. Alexander provided technical assistance in the US. P. Garber, J. Mitani, J. Moore, and M. Strier contributed valuable comments on earlier drafts of the manuscript. The research was supported by NSF grants BNS 8305322 and BNS 8619442, the Fulbright Foundation, grant No. 213 from the Joseph Henry Fund of NAS, Sigma Xi, the World Wildlife Fund, and the L.S.B. Leakey Foundation.

References

1. Wrangham RW: Feeding behaviour of chimpanzees in Gombe National Park, Tanzania; in Clutton-Brock T (ed): Primate Ecology. Academic Press, New York, 1977, pp 503–538.
2. Kuroda S: Grouping of the pygmy chimpanzee. Primates 1979; 20: 161–183.
3. Badrian A, Badrian N: Social organization of *Pan paniscus* in the Lomako Forest, Zaire; in Susman R (ed): Evolutionary Morphology and Behavior of the Pygmy Chimpanzee. Plenum Press, New York, 1984, pp 325–346.
4. Klein LL, Klein DJ: Feeding behavior of the Columbian spider monkey; in Clutton-Brock T (ed): Primate Ecology. Academic Press, New York, 1977, pp 153–182.
5. McFarland MJ: Ecological determinants of fission-fusion sociality in *Ateles* and *Pan;* in Else JG, Lee PC (eds): Primate Ecology and Conservation. Cambridge University Press, Cambridge, 1986, pp 181–190.
6. Altmann S: Baboons, space, time, and energy. Am Zool 1974; 14:221–248.
7. Leighton M, Leighton DR: The relationships of size of feeding aggregate to size of food patch: howler monkeys (*Alouatta palliata*) feeding *Trichilia cipo* fruit trees on Barro Colorado Island. Biotropica 1982; 14:81–90.
8. Wrangham RW: An ecological model of female-bonded primate groups. Behavior 1980; 75:262–300.
9. Strier KB: The Behavior and Ecology of the Woolly Spider Monkey, or Muriqui (*Brachyteles arachnoides*) E. Geoffroy 1806). Doctoral dissertation, Harvard University, 1986).
10. Strier KB: Demographic patterns in one group of muriquis. Prim Conserv 1987; 8:73–74.
11. Parra R: Comparison of foregut and hindgut fermentation in herbivores; in Montgomery G (ed): The Ecology of Arboreal Herbivores. Smithsonian, Washington, 1978.
12. Strier KB: New world primates, new frontiers: insights from the woolly spider monkey, or muriqui (*Brachyteles arachnoides*). Int J Primatol, in press.
13. Strier KB: Activity budgets of woolly spider monkeys, or muriquis (*Brachyteles arachnoides*). Am J Primatol 1987; 13:385–395.
14. Terborgh J. Janson CH: The socioecology of primate groups. Ann Rev Ecol Syst (1986; 17:111–135.
15. Milton K: Habitat, diet, and activity patterns of free-ranging woolly spider monkeys (*Brachyteles arachnoides*) E. Geoffroy 1806). Int J Primatol 1984; 5:491–514.
16. Strier KB: Ranging behavior of woolly spider monkeys. Int J Primatol 1987; 8:575–591.

These are Real Swinging Primates

Shannon Brownlee

When I first heard of the muriqui four years ago, I knew right away that I had to see one. This is an unusual monkey, to say the least. To begin with, it's the largest primate in South America; beyond that, the males have very large testicles. We're talking gigantic, the size of billiard balls, which means that the 30-pound muriqui has *cojones* that look more fitting on a 400-pound gorilla.

But it wasn't prurience that lured me to Brazil. My interest in the muriqui was intellectual, because more than this monkey's anatomy is extraordinary. Muriqui society is untroubled by conflict: troops have no obvious pecking order; males don't compete overtly for females; and, most un-monkeylike, these monkeys almost never fight.

The muriqui is also one of the rarest monkeys in the world. It lives in a single habitat, the Atlantic forest of southeastern Brazil. This mountainous region was once blanketed with forest from São Paulo to Salvador (*see map, page 00*), but several centuries of slash-and-burn agriculture have reduced it to fragments.

In 1969 Brazilian conservationist Alvara Coutinho Aguirre surveyed the remaining pockets of forest and estimated that 2,000 to 3,000 muriquis survived. His data were all but ignored until Russell Mittermeier, a biologist, trained his sights on the muriquis ten years later. Known as Russell of the Apes to his colleagues, Mittermeier, an American, directs the primate program for the World Wildlife Fund. He hopscotches from forest to forest around the world looking for monkeys in trouble and setting up conservation plans for them. In 1979 he and Brazilian zoologist Celio Valle retraced Aguirre's steps and found even fewer muriquis. Today only 350 to 500 are left, scattered among four state and national parks and six other privately held plots.

In 1981 Karen Strier, then a graduate student at Harvard, approached Mittermeier for help in getting permission to observe the muriqui. He took her to a coffee plantation called Montes Claros, near the town of Caratinga, 250 miles north of Rio de Janeiro. Over the next four years she studied the social behavior of the muriqui there—and came up with a provocative theory about how the monkey's unconventional behavior, as well as its colossal testicles, evolved. She reasoned that the evolution of both could be explained, at least in part, by the muriquis' need to avoid falling out of trees.

Last June I joined Strier, now a professor at Beloit (Wis.) College, on one of her periodic journeys to Montes Claros—clear mountains, in Portuguese. We arrived there after a disagreeable overnight bus trip over bad roads. As we neared the plantation, I found it difficult to believe there was a forest—much less a monkey—within miles. Through the grimy windows of the bus I saw hillsides stripped down to russet dirt and dotted with spindly coffee plants and stucco farmhouses. There wasn't anything taller than a banana tree in sight. As the bus lurched around the last curve before our stop the forest finally appeared, an island of green amid thousands of acres of coffee trees and brown pastures.

Strier was eager to start looking for the muriquis—"There's a chance we won't see them the whole four days you're here," she said—so no sooner had we dropped our bags off at a cottage on the plantation than we set out along a dirt road into the forest. The trees closed around us—and above us, where they gracefully arched to form a vault of green filigree. Parrots screeched; leaves rustled; a large butterfly flew erratically by on transparent wings. By this time Strier had guided me onto a steep trail, along which she stopped from time to time to listen for the monkeys.

They appeared soon enough, but out first meeting was less than felicitous. After we had climbed half a mile, Strier motioned for me to stop. A muffled sound, like that of a small pig grunting contentedly, came from up ahead. We moved forward a hundred yards. Putting a finger to her lips, Strier sank to her haunches and looked up.

I did the same, twelve round black eyes stared back at me. A group of six muriquis squatted, silent, 15 feet above in the branches, watching us intently. They began to grunt again. A sharp smell with undertones of cinnamon permeated the air. A light rain began to fall. I held out my palm to catch a drop. It was warm.

"Hey, this isn't rain!" I said.

Strier grinned and pointed to her head. "That's why I wear a hat," she said.

My enthusiasm for the muriquis waned slightly after that. We left them at dusk and retired to the cottage, where Strier described her arrival at Montes Claros four years earlier. Mittermeier acted as guide and interpreter during the first few days of her pilot study. He introduced her to the owner of the 5,000-acre plantation, Feliciano Miguel Abdala, then 73, who has preserved the 2,000-acre forest for more than 40 years. His is one of the only remaining tracts of Atlantic forest, and he agreed to let Strier use it as the site of her study. Then Mittermeier introduced her to the muriquis, assuring her they would be easy to see.

They weren't, and observing them closely is a little like stargazing on a rainy night: not only do you run the risk of getting wet, but you can also spend a lot of time looking up and never see a thing. Mittermeier was adept at spotting the monkeys in the forest, and helped Strier acquire this skill.

But brief glimpses of the monkeys weren't enough. "My strategy was to treat them like baboons, the only other species I'd ever studied," she says. "I thought I couldn't let them out of my sight," She tried to follow on the ground as they swung along in the trees. "They went berserk," she says. They threw branches, shrieked, urinated on her—or worse—and fled.

Even after the muriquis grew accustomed to her, keeping up with them wasn't easy. They travel as much as two miles a day, which is tough for someone picking her way through thick growth on the forest floor. As Strier and a Brazilian assistant learned the muriquis' habitual routes and daily patterns, they cleared trails. These helped, but the muriquis could still travel much faster than she could. "I've often thought the thing to have would be a jet pack," Strier says. "It would revolutionize primatology. Your National Science Foundation grant would include binoculars, pencils, and a jet pack."

The monkeys move by brachiating, swinging hand over hand from branch to branch, much like a child on a jungle gym. Only one other group of monkeys brachiates; the rest clamber along branches on all fours. The muriquis' closest relatives are two other Latin American genera, the woolly monkeys and the spider monkeys—hence woolly spider monkey, its English name. But the muriqui is so unlike them that is has its own genus, *Brachyteles*, which refers to its diminutive thumb, an adaptation for swinging through the trees. Its species name is *arachnoides*, from the Greek for spider, which the muriqui resembles when its long arms, legs, and tail are outstretched.

Brachiating is a specialization that's thought to have evolved because it enables primates to range widely to feed on fruit. Curiously, though, muriquis have a stomach designed for digesting leaves. Strier found that their diet consists of a combination of the two foods. They eat mostly foliage, low-quality food for a monkey, but prefer flowers and fruits, like figs and the *caja manga*, which is similar to the mango. Year after year they return to certain trees when they bloom and bear fruit. The rest of the time the muriquis survive on leaves by passing huge quantities of them through their elongated guts, which contain special bacteria to help them digest the foliage. By the end of the day their bellies are so distended with greenery that even the males look pregnant.

We returned to the trail the next morning just after dawn. Condensation trickled from leaves; howler monkeys roared and capuchins cooed and squeaked; a bird sang with the sweet, piercing voice of a piccolo. Then Strier had to mention snakes. "Watch out for snakes," she said blithely, scrambling on all fours up a steep bank. I followed her, treading cautiously.

The muriquis weren't where we had left them the day before. Strier led me along a ridge through a stand of bamboo, where a whisper of movement drifted up from the slope below. Maybe it was just the wind, but she thought it was the muriquis, so we sat down to wait. After a couple of hours, she confessed, "This part of research can get kind of boring."

By noon the faint noise became a distinct crashing. "That's definitely them," she said. "It's a good thing they're so noisy, or I'd never be able to find them." The monkeys, perhaps a dozen of them, swarmed uphill, breaking branches, chattering, uttering their porcine grunts as they swung along. At the crest of the ridge they paused, teetering in indecision while they peered back and forth before settling in some legume trees on the ridgetop. We crept down out of the bamboo to within a few feet of them, so close that I noticed the cinnamon scent again—only this time I kept out of range.

Each monkey had its own feeding style. One hung upside down by its tail and drew the tip of the branch to its mouth; it delicately plucked the tenderest shoots with its rubbery lips. Another sat upright, grabbing leaves by the handful and stuffing its face. A female with twins—"Twins have never been seen in this species," Strier whispered as she excitedly scribbled notes—ate with one hand while hanging by the other and her tail. Her babies clung to the fur on her belly.

I had no trouble spotting the males. Their nether parts bulged unmistakably—blue-black or pink-freckled, absurd-looking monuments to monkey virility. I asked Strier what sort of obscene joke evolution was playing on the muriquis when it endowed them thus.

We were about to consider this question when a high-pitched whinnying began a few hundred yards away. Immediately a monkey just overhead pulled itself erect and let out an ear-splitting shriek, which set the entire troop to neighing like a herd of nervous horses. Then they took off down into the valley.

Strier and I had to plunge pell-mell into the underbrush or risk losing them for the rest of the day. "They're chasing the other troop," she said as we galloped downhill. A group of muriquis living on the opposite side of the forest had made a rare foray across the valley.

The monkeys we were observing swung effortlessly from tree to tree; we wrestled with thorny vines, and fell farther and farther behind. An impenetrable thicket forced us to backtrack in search of another route. By the time we caught up to the muriquis, they were lounging in a tree, chewing on unripe fruit and chuckling in a self-satisfied sort of way. The intruding troop was nowhere to be seen. "They must have scared the hell out of those other guys," said Strier, laughing.

Such confrontations occur infrequently; muriquis ordinarily tolerate another troop's incursions. Strier thinks they challenge intruders only when there's a valuable resource to defend—like the fruit tree they were sitting in.

Tolerance of another troop is odd behavior for monkeys, but not as odd as the fact that members of a muriqui troop never fight among themselves. "They're remarkably placid," said Strier. "They wait in line to dip their hands into water collected in the bole of a tree. They have no apparent pecking order or dominance hierarchy. Males and females are equal in status, and males don't squabble over females." No other primate society is known to be so free of competition, not even that of gorillas, which have lately gained a reputation for being the gentle giants of the primate world.

Strier's portrayal of the muriqui brought to mind a bizarre episode that Katharine Milton, an anthropologist at the University of California at Berkeley, once described. While studying a troop of muriquis in another patch of the Atlantic forest, she observed a female mating with half a dozen males in succession; that a female monkey would entertain so many suitors came as no surprise, but Milton was astonished at the sight of the males lining up behind the female "like a choo-choo train" and politely taking turns copulating. They continued in this manner for two days, stopping only to rest and eat, and never even so much as bared their teeth.

Primates aren't known for their graciousness in such matters, and I found Milton's report almost unbelievable. But Strier confirms it. She says that female muriquis come into heat about every two and a half years, after weaning their latest offspring, and repeatedly copulate during that five- to seven-day period with a number of males. Copulations, "cops" in animal-behavior lingo, last as long as 18 minutes, and average six, which for most primates (including the genus *Homo*, if Masters and Johnson are correct) would be a marathon. Yet no matter how long a male muriqui takes, he's never harassed by suitors-in-waiting.

Strier has a theory to explain the muriqui's benignity, based on a paper published in 1980 by Richard Wrangham, a primatologist at the University of Michigan. He proposed that the social behavior of primates could in large part be predicted by what the females eat.

This isn't a completely new idea. For years primatologist sought correlations between ecological conditions and social structure, but few patterns emerged—until Wrangham's ingenious insight that environment constrains the behavior of each sex differently. Specifically, food affects the sociability of females more than males.

Wrangham started with the generally accepted premise that both sexes in every species have a common aim: to leave as many offspring as possible. But each sex pursues this goal in its own way. The best strategy for a male primate is to impregnate as many females as he can. All he needs, as Wrangham points out, is plenty of sperm and plenty of females. As for the female, no matter how promiscuous she is, she can't match a male's fecundity. On average, she's able to give birth to only one offspring every two years, and her success in bearing and rearing it depends in part upon the quality of food she eats. Therefore, all other things being equal, male primates will spend their time cruising for babes, while females will look for something good to eat.

Wrangham perceived that the distribution of food—that is, whether it's plentiful or scarce, clumped or evenly dispersed—will determine how gregarious the females of a particular species are. He looked at the behavior of 28 species and found that, in general, females forage together when food is plentiful and found in large clumps—conditions under which there's enough for all the members of the group and the clumps can be defended against outsiders. When clumps become temporarily depleted, the females supplement their diet with what Wrangham calls subsistence foods. He suggests that female savanna baboons, for example, live in groups because their favorite foods, fruits and flowers, grow in large clumps that are easy to defend. When these are exhausted they switch to seeds, insects, and grasses. The females form long-lasting relationships within their groups, and establish stable dominance hierarchies.

Chimpanzees provide an illustration of how females behave when their food isn't in clumps big enough to feed everybody. Female chimps eat flowers, shoots, leaves, and insects, but their diet is composed largely of fruits that are widely scattered and often not very plentiful. They may occasionally gather at a particularly abundant fruit tree, but when the fruit is gone they disperse to forage individually for other foods. Members of the troop are constantly meeting at fruit trees, splitting up, and gathering again.

These two types of female groups, the "bonded" savanna baboons and "fissioning" chimps, as Wrangham calls them, pose very different mating opportunities for the males of their species. As a consequence, the social behavior of the two species is different. For a male baboon, groups of females represent the perfect opportunity for him to get cops. All he has to do is exclude other males. A baboon troop includes a clan of females accompanied by a number of males, which compete fiercely for access to them. For baboons there are few advantages to fraternal cooperation, and many to competition.

Male chimpanzees fight far less over females than male baboons do, principally because there's little point—the females don't stick together. Instead, the males form strong alliances with their fellows. They roam in gangs looking for females in heat, and patrol their troop's borders against male interlopers.

Wrangham's theory made so much sense, Strier says, that it inspired researchers to go back into the field with a new perspective. She saw the muriqui as an excellent species for evaluating the model, since Wrangham had constructed it before anyone knew the first thing about this monkey. His idea would seem all the more reasonable if it could predict the muriqui's behavior.

It couldn't, at least not entirely. Strier has found that the females fit Wrangham's predictions: they stick together and eat a combination of preferred and subsistence foods, defending the preferred from other troops. But the males don't conform to the theory. "Considering that the females are foraging together, there should be relatively low pressure on the males to cooperate," she says. "It's odd: the males should compete, but they don't."

She thinks that limitations on male competition may explain muriqui behavior. First, the muriquis are too big to fight in trees. "I think these monkeys are at about the limit of size for rapid brachiation," she says. "If they were bigger, they couldn't travel rapidly through the trees. They fall a lot as it is, and it really shakes them up. I've seen an adult fall about sixty feet, nearly to the ground, before catching hold of a branch. That means that whatever they fight about has got to be worth the risk of falling out of a tree."

Moreover, fighting may require more energy than the muriquis can afford. Milton has estimated the caloric value of the food eaten by a muriqui each day and compared it to the amount of energy she would expect a monkey of that size to need. She concluded that the muriqui had little excess energy to burn on combat.

The restriction that rapid brachiation sets on the muriqui's size discourages competition in more subtle ways, as well. Given that muriquis are polygynous, the male should be bigger than the female, as is almost invariably the case among other polygynous species—but he's not. The link between larger males and polygyny is created by sexual selection, an evolutionary force that Darwin first recognized, and which he distinguished from natural selection by the fact that it acts exclusively on one sex. Sexual selection is responsible for the manes of male lions, for instance, and for the large canines of male baboons.

In a polygynous society, the advantages to being a large male are obvious: he who's biggest is most likely to win the battles over females—and pass on his genes for size. But sexual selection's push toward large males has been thwarted in the muriqui, says Strier. Any competitive benefits greater size might bring a male would be offset in part by the excessive demands on his energy and the costs of falling out of trees.

She believes that the constraints on the males' size have had a profound effect on the muriquis' social behavior. Most important, says Strier, with males and females being the same size, the females can't be dominated, which means they can pick their mates. Most female primates aren't so fortunate: if they copulate with subordinate males, they risk being attacked by dominant ones. But a female muriqui in heat can easily refuse a suitor, simply by sitting down or by moving away.

Fighting not only doesn't help the male muriqui in his quest for cops; it may even harm his chances, since females can shun an aggressive male. Strier believes that females may also be responsible for the male muriquis' canine teeth not being oversized. As a rule, the male's canines are the same size as the female's only in monogamous primate species, but over the generations female muriquis may have mated more readily with males whose teeth were no bigger than their own. In sum, Strier thinks, for a male muriqui the costs of competing are far out-weighed by the benefits of avoiding it.

But he has the means to vie for reproductive success and still come across as Mr. Nice Guy: his sperm. Sperm competition, as it's called, is a hot new idea in sociobiology, originally proposed to explain male bonding in chimpanzees, and, as Milton was the first to suggest, it may explain why the muriqui has such enormous testicles.

The competition is something like a game of chance. Imagine a bucket with a hole in the bottom just big enough for a marble to pass through. People gather round, each with a handful of marbles. They drop their marbles in the bucket, mix them up, and one comes out the bottom. Whoever owns that marble is the winner.

In the sperm competition among male muriquis, the bucket is a female, the marbles are sperm, and winning means becoming a father. No male can be sure it will be his sperm that impregnates a female, since she mates with a number of his fellows. His chances are further complicated by the fact that the female muriqui, like all New World monkeys, gives no visible indication of ovulation; there may be nothing that signals the male (or the female) when during her heat that occurs. So it's to the male's advantage to continue mating as often as the female will have him.

This may sound like monkey heaven, but it puts the male on the horns of a dilemma. If he copulates as often as possible, he could run low on sperm just when the female is ovulating. On the other hand, if he refrains from copulating to save sperm, he may miss his chance at procreating altogether. Selection may have come to his aid, Strier reasons, by acting on his testicles.

Here's a plausible scenario. Suppose a male came along that could produce more sperm than the average muriqui because his testicles were bigger than average. That male would clean up in the reproductive arena. The ratio of testicle size to body weight has been correlated with high sperm count and repeated copulation over a short period in other mammals, and bigger testicles probably also increase the percentage of viable and motile sperm.

If the muriqui's testicles are anything like those of other species, then a male with extra big ones has a slight reproductive advantage. Like a player with more marbles to put in the bucket, a male that can produce more and better sperm has a better than average chance of impregnating females and passing on this advantageous trait to his sons. Just as important, the outsized organs probably don't cost him much in metabolic energy. Thus, over generations, the muriqui's testicles have grown larger and larger.

Strier's theory has five years of data behind it, and it's the kind of theory that will stimulate researchers to re-examine their ideas about other species. Yet it isn't her only concern; she concentrates equally on the muriqui's uncertain future. On our last day in the forest we watched the monkeys cross a six-foot gap in the canopy 60 feet above us. One by one they stood poised for a moment on the end of a branch before launching themselves. Strier counted them as they appeared in silhouette against a grey sky. The total was 33, including the twins. "They're up from twenty-two in 1982," she said. "That's a very fast increase."

The muriquis at Montes Claros make up almost one-tenth of the total population of the species, and they're critical to its survival—as are all the other isolated and widely separated troops. Each group's genetic pool is limited, and eventually the troops could suffer inbreeding depression, a decline in fecundity that often appears in populations with little genetic variability.

Strier and Mittermeier predict that one day muriquis will have to be managed, the way game species are in the U.S. They may be transported between patches of forest to provide some gene flow. But that's a dangerous proposition now. There are too few muriquis to risk it, and none has ever bred or survived for long in captivity. "Before my study, conservationists would probably have moved males between forests," Strier says. "That would've been a mistake. I have tentative evidence that in a natural situation the females may be the ones that do the transferring between groups."

For now, though, she thinks the biggest concern isn't managing the monkeys but preventing their habitat from disappearing. Preserving what remains of the Atlantic forest won't be easy, and no one knows this better than Feliciano Miguel Abdala, the man responsible for there being any forest at all at Montes Claros.

Abdala has little formal education, but he's rich; he owns nine plantations besides Monte Claros. His family lives in relative splendor in Caratinga, but he likes to spend the weekdays here. His house is just beyond the edge of the forest, and sunlight filters through the bougainvillaea vine entwining the front porch. Chickens can be seen through the cracks in the floorboards, scratching in the dirt under the house. Electric cords are strung crazily from the rafters, and a bare bulb dangles in the center of his office. Abdala removes his straw hat decorously and places it on a chair before sitting at his desk.

Abdala bought the 5,000 acres of Montes Claros in 1944. The region was barely settled then, and smoke still rose from the great burning heaps of slash left from clearing the forest. Abdala's land included one of the last stands of trees. I ask him why he saved it. "I am a conservationist," he says. "For a long time the local people thought I was crazy because I wouldn't cut the forest. I told them not to shoot the monkeys, and they stopped. Now all my workers are crazy, too."

I ask Abdala about his plans for his forest. He rubs his head distractedly and says, vaguely, "I hope it will continue."

Abdala believes the government should buy Montes Claros—plantation and rain forest—to create a nature reserve. He'll probably maintain the forest as long as he lives, but the land is quite valuable, and his heirs might not share his lofty sentiments.

As important as the muriquis have become to understanding the evolution of primate social systems, and as much as U.S. conservationists may wish to see these monkeys preserved, Strier thinks that in the end it's up to the Brazilians to save them. She's expecting a three-year grant from the National Science Foundation; part of the money will go toward allowing her to observe the monkeys in other forest patches, watching for variation in their behavior as a test of her ideas. Studies like hers will be critical not only for proving theories but also for ensuring that plans for managing the muriquis will work. The rest of the money will permit her to train seven Brazilian graduate students, because, she says, "the future of the muriqui lies with the Brazilians."

PART 3

Old World Monkeys and Hominoids

Reproduction—Anatomy, Behaviour, Physiology and Psychology

M. E. Stephens

How should a primate behave to enhance his or her reproductive success? What body parts should evolve to make mate competition or parenting competition more successful? How much energy should an individual of either sex devote to courtship and how much to parenting? All of these are good evolutionary questions. Few have simple or obvious answers and that is illustrated by the readings in this section of the text.

Members of the Catarrhini are used to illustrate aspects of primate reproductive strategies in this section. Seven articles barely do justice to either the subject or the many and varied species of old world monkeys and hominoids. Hominoids receive attention only in a survey article in this section but do receive further atten-

tion in the transitional section which follows.

Colobine members of the Cercopithecidae are only mentioned in the article on infanticide. These leaf eaters with their sacculated stomachs receive bad press but infanticide is an important subject in any discussion of reproductive strategies and Hanuman langurs present the best documented cases of infanticidal behaviour.

The reproductive advantages of some sexual behaviours are extremely difficult to discern. Multi-mount mating and homosexuality are two obvious examples of puzzling sexual activity. The articles in this section remove some of the mystery.

Competition for mates and sperm competition both receive attention in this section. Some obvious assumptions about male reproductive success are tested in some articles and the conclusions are often surprising.

Baboons and macaques dominate this section of the book. This merely reflects the fact that they are very well represented in the literature. After all, large primates are easier to study and large, terrestrial primates are the easiest of all.

Patas Monkey Copulations—One Mount, Repeat if Necessary

University of Rhode Island

Early, anecdotal reports of patas monkey (*Erythrocebus patas*) sexual behavior suggested that these primates were series-mount copulators. In 1975, limited evidence was presented in favor of single-mount copulations as the species-typical pattern for patas. The situation remained confused, however, as indicated by statements in a recent review article. This paper adds to our knowledge of patas sexuality by presenting quantitative data on the copulatory behavior of two additional adult males. Both males usually gave pelvic thrusts to intravaginal ejaculation once they had mounted a female and gained intromission. Mounts without ejaculation were clearly failed attempts at copulation, rather than segments of a stereotyped series-mount pattern. All of the available quantitative data indicate that the species-typical mating pattern for patas monkeys is copulation in a single mount.

Key words: patas monkeys, Erythrocebus patas, copulation pattern, mating pattern

INTRODUCTION

One of the most common objectives of studies of primate sexual behavior is to describe accurately the species-typical pattern of copulation. After a half-century of field and laboratory research, a considerable body of information on copulation patterns has been amassed [Hrdy & Whitten, 1987]. Sufficient data are now available for comparative investigations attempting to correlate mating patterns with type of society and ecogeography [Caldecott, 1986] and with anatomical features such as baculum length [Dixson, 1987].

In 1965, K. R. L. Hall and his associates [1965] noted that the adult male of their captive group of patas monkeys (*Erythrocebus patas*) showed series-mount copulations, similar in patterning to the mating behavior of rhesus macaques (*Macaca mulatta*). The description was not accompanied by supporting data, however, and so had to be taken at face value. Ten years later, at the completion of a study of captive patas at the Caribbean Primate Research Center (CPRC), I reported that adult males typically showed single-mount copula-

"Patas Monkey Copulations—One Mount, Repeat if Necessary" by James Loy, AMERICAN JOURNAL OF PRIMATOLOGY (1989). Copyright © 1989 Alan R. Liss, Inc. Reprinted by permission of John Wiley & Sons, Inc.

tions unless they had difficulty achieving intromission or their mounts were interrupted by harassment [Loy, 1975]. I supported my case by providing considerable data on the sexual behavior of one male and a few observations on two other males, and I concluded that patas monkeys could be tentatively classified as single-mount copulators [Loy, 1975].

A recent review article on African monkeys, however, showed that the issue requires further clarification. In that article, Bloomstrand and Maple [1987] repeated Hall et al.'s conclusion that during patas copulations ". . . repeated mounts are usually performed before ejaculation occurs" (p. 212). In the following paper, I provide further information on patas copulatory patterns by describing the sexual behaviors of two additional adult males. The new data strongly support the view that patas males are single-mount copulators unless something goes wrong with the mating.

MATERIALS AND METHODS AND ANIMALS

The data reported in Loy [1975] came mostly from one adult male, L173, who was observed from March 1972 to June 1974 at the CPRC. L173 was a member of a heterosexual group held in a large outdoor corral, and data on his sexual behavior were collected ad libitum [Altmann, 1974]. Although his exact age was unknown, L173 was fully adult and in his prime. Additional information on the CPRC patas group can be found in earlier publications [Loy, 1975, 1981].

Between 1983 and 1986, two additional adult males were studied at the University of Rhode Island (URI). These males lived successively in a heterosexual group held indoors in a large gang-cage. Adult male Rabbit was obtained from the patas colony at the University of California, Berkeley in 1983. He was 5 to 8 years of age during the period when his sexual behavior was studied at URI (1983–1986). Rabbit was replaced by 8-year-old male Blanco in July 1986, and Blanco's sexual behavior was observed until October 1986. Blanco was born at the University of Missouri and came to URI by way of the CPRC. Data on the copulatory behaviors of both Rabbit and Blanco were collected ad libitum. Further information on the URI patas colony can be found in Jacobus and Loy [1981].

It is important to note that in the studies of all three patas males, mounts were carefully distinguished from copulations. A *mount* consisted of a male holding an adult female by the waist and pressing his groin against her perineum. The male often, but not always, grasped one or both of the female's ankles with his feet. Once mounted, the male attempted to gain intromission and deliver deep pelvic thrusts. Neither intromission nor pelvic thrusting was necessary for a mount to be recorded, however, and many mounts lacked both. A *copulation* consisted of a mount that included intromission and deep pelvic thrusting, and ended with intravaginal ejaculation. Ejaculation was recognized by the cessation of rapid thrusting, and by body immobility and rigidity by the male.

RESULTS

Rabbit's sexual behavior is shown graphically in Figure 1. He was observed to mount adult females on 55 occasions. Thirty of those mounts included intromission, and once having achieved penetration, Rabbit pelvic thrust to ejaculation 27 times. In other words, 90% of the time when he mounted and gained intromission, Rabbit completed a copulation with the female. During two of his intromitted mounts that failed to result in intravaginal ejaculation, Rabbit and his partner were disturbed by the approach of another monkey. One mount with intromission ended without ejaculation for unknown reasons.

Twenty-five of Rabbit's mounts ended without intromission. In nine cases, this may have been due to intervention or harassment by other monkeys; in one instance, it was due to the female leaping away and terminating the mount; and in 15 cases, the reason for failure to intromit was unknown.

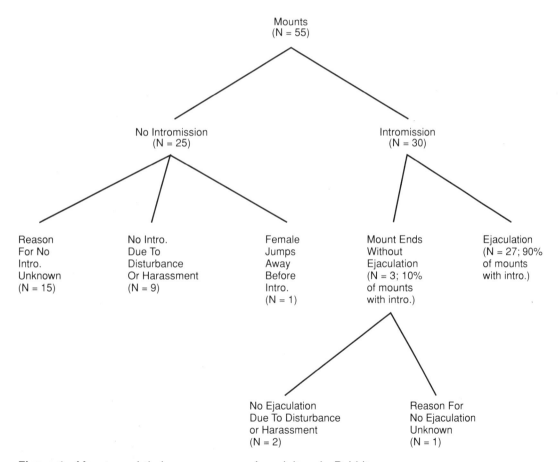

Figure 1. Mounts and their consequences for adult male Rabbit.

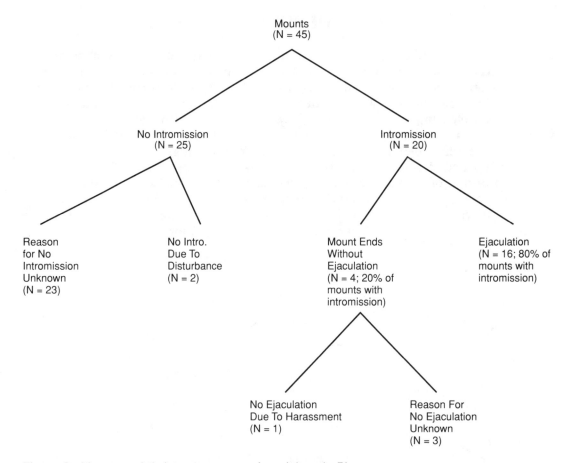

Figure 2. Mounts and their consequences for adult male Blanco.

Rabbit's copulatory behavior can be summarized as follows: he typically copulated in a single mount; mean number of intromitted pelvic thrusts to ejaculation was 12.1 (N = 24 cases); and mean time for an ejaculatory mount was 13.4 seconds (N = 7 cases).

Adult male Blanco was seen to mount adult females 45 times (Fig. 2). Twenty of these mounts included intromission, and once intromitted, Blanco pelvic thrust to ejaculation 80% of the time (N = 16 instances). Of the four mounts with intromission that failed to result in ejaculation, one was harassed by groupmates and three ended prematurely for unknown reasons.

Blanco failed to achieve intromission on 25 mounts. Failure to penetrate may have been due to disturbance by other monkeys on two of these mounts; in 23 cases, the reason for no intromission was unknown.

Blanco's copulatory behavior can be summarized as follows: he typically copulated in a single mount; mean number of intromitted pelvic thrusts to ejaculation was 10.4 (N = 15 cases); and mean time for an ejaculatory mount was 15.4 seconds (N = 13 cases).

The data from the URI males are in strong agreement with the earlier information gathered at the Caribbean Center [Loy, 1975]. CPRC male L173 was observed to mount females on 82 occasions. Twenty-seven (32.9%) of L173's mounts included intromission, and once intromitted, he thrust to ejaculation 70.4% of the time (N = 19 cases). About half (50.9%; N = 28 cases) of the time that L173 failed to gain intromission, it was due to harassment. Seven of the eight mounts by L173 that included intromission but failed to end with ejaculation were likewise terminated prematurely by harassment. L173's mean number of intromitted pelvic thrusts to ejaculation was 10.2 (N = 18 cases) and his mean time for an ejaculatory mount was 11.7 seconds (N = 12 cases).

In summary, all three males, L173, Rabbit and Blanco, usually (grand mean percentage = 80.5% of the time) gave pelvic thrusts to intravaginal ejaculation once they had mounted a female and gained intromission. If something went wrong with the mount (as it did about 66% of the time), such as disturbance by groupmates or failure to intromit due to improper posturing, etc., then the male dismounted without ejaculating (on one occasion, the female disengaged by jumping away). In these cases, males often quickly remounted the females and tried once again to copulate. Mounts without ejaculation were *failed copulation attempts*, however, not segments of a stereotyped, species-typical pattern of series-mounting.

DISCUSSION

Hall et al. [1965] described the copulations of the single adult male of the Bristol group as similar to the series-mount matings of rhesus monkeys. Since they gave no actual data on their male's copulatory patterns, it is impossible to test the accuracy of their comparison. As I noted in 1975, however, there is reason to suspect that the Bristol male was subject to frequent harassment that could have distorted his mating behavior [Loy, 1975].

Regardless of the ultimate accuracy or inaccuracy of the Hall et al. report, it is clear that the copulatory behaviors of the patas males observed at the CPRC and at URI differed dramatically from rhesus copulations. Rhesus copulations generally take several minutes to complete [Michael & Saayman, 1967]. They consist of a stereotyped series of mounts, and each mount usually involves intromission and a few deep pelvic thrusts. The rhesus male dismounts without ejaculating after all mounts except the final mount of the series. Between mounts, rhesus sexual partners continue to be involved with each other and may sit close together or touching, or they may groom one another. Carpenter [1942] and Altmann [1962] gave clear examples of rhesus copulations.

In contrast, as shown above, patas males mount females and attempt to copulate in a single mount. Judging from the three males for whom I have good data, over half of all copulation attempts fail immediately because intromission is not achieved. Lack of intromission may be due to improper posturing, harassment by other monkeys, or for other reasons. If a patas male does achieve intromission, however, he will pelvic thrust to intravaginal ejaculation about 80% of the time. Mounts with intromission that do not end in ejaculation usually are disturbed by other monkeys (10 of 15 observed cases).

The available data, therefore, strongly indicate that, contrary to the conclusion of Hall et al. [1965], the species-typical pattern for patas monkeys is copulation in a single mount.

CONCLUSIONS

1. The available quantitative data indicate that the species-typical mating pattern for patas monkeys is copulation in a single mount.
2. The report by Hall et al. [1965] of a series-mounting patas male may have resulted from their failure to recognize mating patterns that were distorted by harassment.

ACKNOWLEDGMENTS

My thanks go to the College of Arts and Sciences, University of Rhode Island, for supporting the URI patas colony.

REFERENCES

Altmann, J. Observational study of behavior: Sampling methods. BEHAVIOUR 49: 227–263, 1974.

Altmann, S. A. A field study of the sociobiology of rhesus monkeys, *Macaca mulatta*. ANNALS OF THE NEW YORK ACADEMY OF SCIENCES 102:338–435, 1962.

Bloomstrand, M.; Maple, T. L. Management and husbandry of African monkeys in captivity. Pp. 197–234 in COMPARATIVE BEHAVIOR OF AFRICAN MONKEYS. E. Zucker, ed. New York, Alan R. Liss, Inc., 1987.

Caldecott, J. O. Mating patterns, societies and the ecogeography of macaques. ANIMAL BEHAVIOUR 34:208–220, 1986.

Carpenter, C. R. Sexual behavior of free ranging rhesus monkeys (*Macaca mulatta*). I. Specimens, procedures and behavioral characteristics of estrus. JOURNAL OF COMPARATIVE PSYCHOLOGY 33:113–142, 1942.

Dixson, A. F. Baculum length and copulatory behavior in primates. AMERICAN JOURNAL OF PRIMATOLOGY 13:51–60, 1987.

Hall, K. R. L.; Boelkins, R. C.; Goswell, M. J. Behaviour of patas monkeys, *Erythrocebus patas*, in captivity, with notes on the natural habitat. FOLIA PRIMATOLOGICA 3: 22–49, 1965.

Hrdy, S. B.; Whitten, P. L. Patterning of sexual activity. Pp. 370–384 in PRIMATE SOCIETIES. B. Smuts; D. Cheney; R. Seyfarth; R. Wrangham; T. Struhsaker, eds. Chicago, The University of Chicago Press, 1987.

Jacobus, S.; Loy, J. The grimace and gecker: A submissive display among patas monkeys. PRIMATES 22:393–398, 1981.

Loy. J. The copulatory behaviour of adult male patas monkeys, *Erythrocebus patas*. JOURNAL OF REPRODUCTION AND FERTILITY 45:193–195, 1975.

Loy, J. The reproductive and heterosexual behaviours of adult patas monkeys in captivity. ANIMAL BEHAVIOUR 29:714–726, 1981.

Michael, R. P.; Saayman, G. S. Individual differences in the sexual behaviour of male rhesus monkeys (*Macaca mulatta*) under laboratory conditions. ANIMAL BEHAVIOUR 15:460–466, 1967.

Body Size, Sperm Competition, and Determinants of Reproductive Success in Male Savanna Baboons

Fred B. Bercovitch
Wisconsin Regional Primate Research Center,
University of Wisconsin

Abstract: One component of sexual selection is sperm competition. It has been reasoned that the intensity of sperm competition may be reflected in the relative testicular sizes of animals. Among males residing in multimale breeding systems, testicular size is relatively larger than among males residing is unimale mating systems. Information on whether differences in testicular size within a species can account for differences in male reproductive success is unavailable for natural populations of primates.

A population of six troops of savanna baboons in Kenya was surveyed for morphometric analysis, and one of these troops was the subject of extensive behavioral observations afterwards. Testicular weights could not be obtained, but measurements of linear dimensions were transformed into volumetric estimates. Male weight accounted for 30% of the variance in testicular volume. Neither body size nor testicular volume was associated with differences in male reproductive activity. The outcome of fights over access to females could not be related to male body size, and ejaculatory patterns of males were independent of testicle size. Both sperm competition and aggressive competition intensified during the four-day optimum conception period, but fights over access to consort females were infrequent.

Among savanna baboons, the probability of an ejaculation resulting in a conception is fairly low, which may account for the infrequency of injurious fights. Although testicle size influences sperm production, it does not influence either the timing of mating or the fertilizing capacity of spermatozoa, and both of these factors probably account for a substantial fraction of the variance in male baboon paternity. Sperm competition is an adjunct to agonistic competition as a mechanism affecting male baboon reproductive success. It is concluded that male reproductive success in baboons is affected more by social factors than by morphological traits associated with size.

Sexual selection contributes to differences in male and female reproductive tactics (Darwin, 1871; Trivers, 1972). Among most mammals, males are larger than females (see Ralls [1976] for exceptions), and this size dimorphism may be advantageous to males, because it can increase their access to sexually receptive females (Darwin, 1871; Trivers, 1972; Clutton-Brock et al., 1982; Anderson

"Body Size, Sperm Competition, and Determinants of Reproductive Success in Male Savanna Baboons" by Fred B. Bercovitch, *Evolution* 43 (7), pp. 1507–1521, 1989.

and Fedak, 1985). Body weight is correlated with probable reproductive success among male mammals residing in unimale mating systems (Clutton-Brock et al., 1982; Anderson and Fedak, 1985) but not among primate males living in multimale mating systems (Packer, 1979b; Smuts, 1982; Nieuwenhuijsen et al., 1987). In some species (e.g., bonnet macaques, *Macaca radiata* [Glick, 1979], stallions [Thompson et al., 1979], swamp buffalo, *Bubalus bubalis* [Bongso et al., 1984], and domestic boars [Schinckel et al., 1984]), adult male body weight is correlated with testicular size, but other species (e.g., dusky leaf monkeys, *Presbytis obscura* [Burton, 1981], chimpanzees, *Pan troglodytes* [Martin and Gould, 1981], and stumptail macaques, *M. arctoides* [Nieuwenhuijsen et al., 1987]) do not conform to this pattern. Testicular volume may be a nonagonistic mediator of male competition that acts via sperm competition (Popp and DeVore, 1979; Short, 1979, 1981, 1984; Harcourt et al., 1981; Smith, 1984; Kenagy and Trombulak, 1986). Sperm competition is a unique component of sexual selection, because it is a form of male competition that involves both nonagonistic male-male rivalry and conflicts among the gametes of a single individual for access to the egg. An adaptive strategy for males could be to deposit more sperm than their conspecifics as a method of increasing fitness.

Across primate species, body size accounts for over half the variance in testicular size (Kenagy and Trombulak, 1986), and both relative testicle size (Harcourt et al., 1981; Harvey and Harcourt, 1984; Kenagy and Trombulak, 1986; Moller, 1988) and male body size (Clutton-Brock et al., 1977; Leutenegger and Cheverud, 1982) are associated with the type of mating system. Multimale, polygynous mating systems are characterized by large males with relatively large testicles when compared to monogamous or unimale, polygynous mating systems. One explanation advanced for this pattern is that sperm competition is more intense in multimale mating systems than in unimale mating systems, with intense sperm competition favoring males with relatively large testicles (Popp and DeVore, 1979; Short, 1979, 1981; Harcourt et al., 1981; Moller, 1988). Understanding the relationship between sperm competition, testicular size, and reproductive strategies in primates is a burgeoning area of inquiry.

The objective of this report is to investigate the relationships between body size, testicular size, and reproductive activity in savanna baboons (*Papio cynocephalus anubis*). Baboons do not reproduce on a seasonal basis (DeVore and Hall, 1965; Packer, 1979a; Ransom, 1981; Nicolson, 1982), so testicular size does not change during the year as occurs during the mating season in many macaque species (Sade, 1964; Glick, 1979; Wickings and Nieschlag, 1980; Matsubayashi and Enomoto, 1983). In addition, testicular size in baboons is large, relative to most other primates (Schultz, 1938; Harcourt et al., 1981). Male savanna baboons obtain sexually receptive females from other males by a variety of techniques, including fighting, continuous harassment, formation of coalitions, chasing away the female, waiting for her mate to abandon her, or taking advantage of opportune situations (Packer, 1979b; Rasmussen, 1980; Collins, 1981; Strum, 1982; Bercovitch, 1986, 1988; Smuts, 1987), and male agonistic rank is not a reliable indicator of male mating success (Bercovitch, 1986). This report will present evidence suggesting that male variance in reproductive success among baboons is unlikely to be a consequence of variation in either testicular size or body size. It will be suggested that a primary determinant of reproductive success in male baboons is the timing of mating and the fertilizing capacity of males.

MATERIALS AND METHODS

The Study Site

The study site was an open-country, patchy scrub environment punctuated by nearly parallel outcroppings of volcanic cliffs located in the Central African Rift Valley of Kenya, about 115 km northwest of Nairobi. The study troops inhabited a cattle ranch (Kekopey Ranch) about 1,800 m above sea level near the town of Gilgil. Baboons obtained most of their water by drinking from cattle troughs or temporary puddles and ponds formed by broken water pipes.

Gilgil regularly experiences a long rainy season (April–June), a short rainy season (around November), and two intervening dry seasons (Harding, 1976). The flora was largely grassland, dotted with groves of acacia (*Acacia xanthophloea, A. drepanolobium, A. seyal*), sandpaper (*Cordia ovalis*), and grewia (*Grewia similis*) trees, thickets of leleshwa bushes (*Tarchonanthus camphoratus*), and clumps of succulent plants (*Opuntia* spp. and *Aloe* spp.).

At least six troops of baboons occupied Kekopey Ranch and the adjacent area. These six troops were the subjects of a biobehavioral study conducted between September 1978 and March 1979 (Byles and Sanders, 1981; Olivier et al., 1986). One troop, Pumphouse, has been the subject of behavioral observations since 1970 and was the focal troop for collection of data on reproductive tactics between August 1979 and March 1981.

Morphological Data

During the biobehavioral survey, baboons were immobilized and transported to a field laboratory where morphological measurements, saliva, and blood samples were obtained. Body weights were recorded to the nearest 0.1 kg, and most body measurements were taken to the nearest 0.1 cm (Bercovitch, 1987a). Only adult males or those with complete dental eruption are discussed in this report. Males attain full body size at 8–10 years in the wild (Altmann et al., 1981; Strum, 1982) and at 7–8 years in captivity (Glassman et al., 1984; Coelho, 1985). Males who were at least 11–12 years old are considered to be older males (Bercovitch, 1988).

Testicular measurements were obtained from supine, immobilized monkeys. The length of the left testicle and the total width across both testicles were recorded to the nearest 0.1 mm with a sliding caliper (this technique was followed in order to collect comparable data to that being collected by an investigator at another field site). As a consequence, it is assumed for this report that both testicles of a male had the same dimensions. Previous reports of primate testicular size have indicated that the correlation coefficient between the size of a male's two testicles is about 0.9 (Kinsky, 1960; Burton, 1981; Johnson et al., 1984), with the asymmetry in size less than 10%. Testicular measurements were taken from males in four of the six study troops.

Testicular volume has been estimated from linear dimensions by using the formula for a regular ellipsoid (Dixson et al., 1980; Wickings and Nieschlag, 1980; Steiner and Bremner, 1981; Plant, 1985):

$$\frac{\pi w^2 L}{6} \cdot$$

Volumetric estimates could not be converted to weights, but the two measurements are significantly correlated in rodents (Kenagy, 1979).

Behavioral Data

Focal subgroup samples (Altmann, 1974) were collected from adult consort females and their partners. A consort was defined as a continuous, close spatial association between a sexually receptive female and a male, with evidence of sexual activity by the male (Bercovitch, 1985, 1986). The average menstrual cycle length among savanna baboons in the wild ranges from 32.5 days (Hausfater, 1975) to 37.5 days (Bercovitch, 1985). Female baboons are in consort for about 5–7 days per cycle (Packer, 1979a; Rasmussen, 1980; Collins, 1981; Bercovitch, 1987b) and usually cycle 3–5 times prior to conception (Altmann et al., 1978; Rasmussen, 1980; Collins, 1981; Nicolson, 1982; Scott, 1984; Bercovich, 1987b). Baboons have enlarged sexual swellings during the follicular phase of their cycle, and conception is most likely during the nine-day period from –7 through +1, where day 0 designates the day of deflation of the sexual skin, or deturgescence (Hausfater, 1975). The optimum conception period occurs from cycle day –3 through day 0, and the last two days of sexual swelling are the most probable days of ovulation (Bercovitch, 1987b). All data reported here were obtained between days –7 and +1 (Bercovitch, 1986, 1987b).

Two observers collected 1,980 hours of focal consort data and 205 hours of focal data from nonconsort adult males when no females were in consort. Baboon troops are characterized by female philopatry and male migration (Packer, 1979a; Manzolillo, 1986), so some males that immigrated were not measured.

Measurements of Reproductive Activity

Reproductive activity was ascertained in a number of ways. Cycle-day selectivity measured the percentage of ejaculations achieved by males on the two most probable days of ovulation. Mating success was calculated as the proportion of ejaculations performed by a male with consort females during the nine-day fertile period. The ejaculatory rate of males was a record of their frequency (per hour) of ejaculating with a consort female, and masturbation rate was the frequency per hour of self-stimulation of the genitals during days when no females were in consort. Changeover success was calculated by dividing the number of occasions that a male was able to obtain access to a consort female from another adult male by the number of successful plus attempted changeovers. The probable sire was gauged by assuming that males that monopolized access to a female during her conception cycles by performing at least 60% of ejaculations between days –3 and 0 sired the female's offspring (Bercovitch, 1987b).

Data Analysis

Statistical procedures included analysis of variance, t test, Spearman's rank-order correlation, and Pearson's product-moment correlation (Zar, 1974; Sokal and Rohlf, 1981). Statistical significance was based upon a level of $P < 0.05$. Log-transformation of data did not alter results, so only the original data are reported. Because all males were not sampled for all measurements, the degrees of freedom varied in the analyses.

RESULTS

Body Size

Adult males weighed between 17.5 and 29.0 kg, with an average weight (±SD) of 22.4 ± 2.6 kg ($N = 56$). Male weight was significantly different between troops ($F_{[5.50]} = 7.99$, $P < 0.001$), but this result could be attributed to one troop with relatively small males (Fig. 1). The weight of males may have been affected by food availability. The lowest weights were recorded from the two troops that ranged in the more inhospitable and densely thicketed area called "The Badlands." The two troops that seemed to feed most often on human refuse piles yielded the heaviest males.

Leg length exhibited little variation among adult males. The smallest and largest males in the population differed by less than 5.0 cm (range = 19.4–24.0 cm), and the coefficient of variation was under 5% ($\bar{x} \pm SD = 21.7 \pm 1.0$ cm). A statistically significant correlation existed between body weight and leg length among adult males ($r = 0.412$, $N = 56$, $P < 0.002$). These findings suggested that it would be minimally productive to assess the influence of male size by using leg length, so analysis was confined to using body weight as a measure of size. Cycling adult females weighed an average (±SD) of 13.9 ± 1.5 kg ($N = 22$), or about 63% of male weight (Bercovitch, 1987a), whereas their leg lengths averaged 84% of male leg length (18.3 cm vs. 21.7 cm).

Neither male weight ($t = 1.126$, $d.f. = 23$, $P > 0.20$; Fig. 2A) nor leg length ($t = 0.430$, $d.f. = 23$, $P > 0.50$; Fig. 2B) differed between older and younger males, but the abdominal circumference of older males was significantly larger than that of younger males ($t = 2.390$, $d.f. = 23$, $P < 0.02$; Fig. 2C).

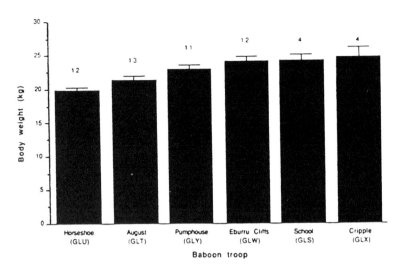

Figure 1. Male body weight of six troops of savanna baboons at Gilgil. Bars graph the mean (–SE), with sample sizes shown above each SE bar. Three-letter designations in parentheses are troop identities, as reported in the genetic analysis of this population (Olivier et al., 1986).

Testicular Size

Male weight was positively correlated with testicular volume ($r = 0.545$, $N = 32$, $P < 0.002$; Fig. 3), with weight explaining about 30% of the variance in testicular volume. Testicular volume showed no significant intertroop differences (Table 1) and averaged ($\pm$ SD) 55.3 ± 12.9 cm^3 ($N = 32$). Other adult males had significantly larger testicles than younger adult males ($t = 2.646$, $d.f. = 17$, $P < 0.01$; Fig. 2D). One male was omitted from the analysis, because he had one small, peanut-sized testicle and one rather large testicle. The volume of the larger testicle was 104.5 cm^3, twice the size of the population average for two testicles. Among rams, hemicastration results in the doubling of testicular weight in the remaining testicle (Voglmayr and Mattner, 1968) without affecting spermatogenic efficiency (Brown et al., 1986). The data from Gilgil suggest that testicular compensatory hypertrophy occurred in this male baboon (see also Nieuwenhuijsen et al. [1987]).

Body Size and Reproductive Activity

Body size had no measurable effect on male reproductive success (Table 2). Neither mating success ($r_s = 0.067$, $N = 9$, $P > 0.50$) nor cycle-day selectivity ($r_s = 0.050$, $P > 0.50$) was correlated with male weight. The proportion of sexually receptive females in the troop that a male consorted with was not associated with his weight ($r_s = 0.163$, $P > 0.50$). Other results not shown in Table 2 indicated that the proportion of successful changeovers was not correlated with

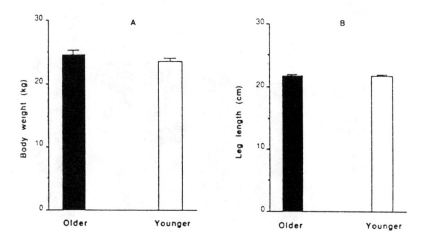

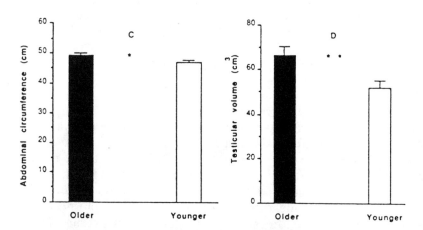

Figure 2. The influence of male age on morphometric measurements. Bars represent the mean (+SE) for each of four traits: A) body weight, B) leg length, C) abdominal circumference, and D) testicular volume. Older males are those at least 11 years old. Significant differences are indicated as follows: *$P < 0.05$: **$P < 0.01$.

body weight ($r_s = -0.433$, $P > 0.20$), nor was the proportion of consort losses resulting from aggressive interactions with other adult males correlated with male weight ($r_s = 0.021$, $P > 0.50$). The incidence of male copulation harassment was unrelated to body size. The rate at which copulating males were harassed by males was not correlated with the weight of the consort male ($r_s = 0.233$, $P > 0.50$), nor was the proportion of copulations in which the male was harassed related to body size ($r_s = 0.017$, $P > 0.50$).

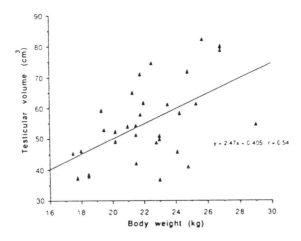

Figure 3. Adult male weight and testicular volume.

Males rarely fought each other for access to consort females, and only 11% of changeovers between adult males were due to fights between consecutive consort partners (Bercovitch, 1988). The patterns of fighting between adult males indicated that obtaining or retaining a female consort was not determined by male size. Thirteen pairs of adult males fought over access to a consort female, but weights were available for both males in only seven cases. In four of these, a successful consort changeover resulted from a fight. The heavier male obtained the female from the lighter male in two cases, and the opposite occurred in one case. The fourth case involved a pair who fought twice over access to a consort female and each male outfought the other on one occasion. In the three cases in which a challenger male failed to obtain a consort female in a fight, the challenger was the heavier individual.

Although body weight was not correlated with reproductive activity during this study, the heaviest male lost a consort only once in a fight, never lost a consort to a coalition of adult males, and was the challenger in all five cases where a challenger initiated a fight with a consort male and obtained the female as a result. However, this male once failed to obtain a female after fighting a male who was at least 3–4 kg lighter, and in an adjacent troop, the heaviest male in the population had a very low consort success (Smuts, 1982).

The probability of an aggressive changeover occurring was significantly greater during the four most likely days of conception than on other days (Bercovitch, 1985, 1988). In addition, the chances of an adult male obtaining a consort female from another male between cycle days–3 and 0 by using aggressive behavior was affected by cycle day (X^2 = 24.36, $d.f.$ = 3, P < 0.001). Aggressive changeovers peaked on cycle days –2 and –1, with no significant difference in the extent of aggressive changeovers between these two days (X^2 = 2.11, $d.f.$ = 1, P > 0.20). The highest proportion of changeovers due to aggressive interactions occurred on the final two days of sexual swelling in both conception and nonconception cycles (Bercovitch, 1985).

In summary, male weight was not associated with differences in male reproductive activity. One could not predict the outcome of a fight over access to a consort female based upon male weight, and lighter males were as likely as heavier males to utilize aggressive reproductive tactics. Heavier males did not mate more than lighter males on the likely days of conception. Aggressive consort changeovers were most likely to occur when the probability of conception was highest.

Testicular Size and Reproductive Activity

The average consort male ejaculatory rate during the nine-day fertile period was 0.83 times per hour (SD = 0.40, N = 12). The ejaculatory rate of the unitesticular male (0.99 times per hour) was equivalent to that of other males. Testicular volume was not correlated with ejaculatory rate when in consort (r_s = 0.314, N = 6, P > 0.20), with ejaculatory rate between cycle days –3 through 0 (r_s = 0.000, N = 6, P > 0.50), or with masturbation-to-ejaculation rate when not in consort (r_s = –0.600, N = 5, P > 0.20). The shortest interejaculatory interval recorded in consort was 4.67 minutes by a male whose testicles were not measured. The shortest interval between two successive masturbation-to-ejaculation events was 75 minutes. Male masturbation-to-ejaculation rates were not correlated with male consort ejaculation rates (r_s = 0.143, N = 8, P > 0.05). When no females in the troop were in consort, males masturbated to ejaculation at a rate about one-eighth that of their consort rate (i.e., 0.10 times per hour [SD = 0.05, N = 8]). One male masturbated to ejaculation while in consort with a female (see also Ransom [1981]).

The probability of conception affected male ejaculatory rates. The frequency of ejaculation was higher during the four-day optimum conception period than during the preceding four-day period. Of the ten adult males that consorted during both of these periods, nine increased their ejaculatory rates on days –3 through 0, compared with days –7 through –4 (sign test, P = 0.022). The ejaculatory rate of males during the four-day optimum conception period was significantly greater than the rate during the preceding four-day period (0.91 times per hour vs. 0.60 times per hour; paired t test, t = 3.06, $d.f.$ = 9, P < 0.02), but the frequency of ejaculation within the four-day period did not differ according to cycle day (Bercovitch, 1987b).

Testicular volume was neither related to mating success (r_s = –0.543, N = 6, P > 0.20; see Table 2) nor to cycle-day selectivity (r_s = –0.657, N = 6, P = 0.20). Males with larger testicles did not mate with a greater proportion of available females (r_s = 0.257, N = 6, P > 0.50). Larger testicle size was also not observed in the probable sires. During this study, six of 19 conception cycles occurred in which a male could be identified as a probable sire (Bercovitch, 1987b). In one case, the unitesticular male monopolized access to the female. In two cases, the probable sire could have had the smallest testicular volume, but this could not be established due to the presence of males with unmeasured

Table 1. A) The testicular volume (mean ± SD) of adult male baboons from four troops in Gilgil, Kenya. B) Results of analysis of variance on testicular volume.

A. Troop	N	Testicular volume (cc)
Eburru Cliffs	6	55.4 ± 14.5
Houseshoe	12	49.9 ± 11.3
School	3	63.3 ± 17.0
Pumphouse	11	58.9 ± 12.0
Combined:	32	55.3 ± 12.9

B. Source	d.f.	SS	MS	F	P
Volume	3	669.93	223.31	1.398	0.264
Error	28	4,471.55	159.70		
Total:	31	5,141.48			

testicles in the troop. In one conception cycle, the probable sire had intermediate (neither the largest nor the smallest) testicular volume, and in the final two cases, the probable sires' testicles were not measured.

In summary, testicular volume could not explain the variation in male reproductive activity. Neither the rate of masturbation-to-ejaculation nor the rate of ejaculations in consort is correlated with testicle size. No evidence surfaced to indicate that siring an offspring was related to testicular size in adult males. Male ejaculatory rates reached their zenith during the four cycle days when conception is most likely.

DISCUSSION

Body weight in savanna baboons accounted for close to one-third of the variance in testicular size. Although the current study had a limited sample size, neither body weight nor testicular volume strongly influenced male reproduction. The outcome of fighting for access to a consort female was independent of male weight, and relative consort success was not correlated with male body size. This study concurs with previous findings indicating that male size is a poor predictor of reproductive success in savanna baboons (Packer, 1979b; Smuts, 1982; but see Popp [1978]) and also demonstrates that testicle size is not associated with male reproduction.

Table 2. Adult male baboon size and measures of reproductive activity (see text for definition of terms). Male baboons' identifications are given using the same two-letter codes as in the author's other publications. Percentage females refers to the proportion of females in the troop that a male consorted with. Probable sire refers only to the study period.

Baboon	Body weight (kg)	Leg length (cm)	Testes volume (cm3)	Mating success	Ejaculatory rate (per hour)	Cycle-day selectivity	Percentage females	Probable sire
SL	28.3	23.1	–[a]	0.32	0.99	0.28	79%	yes
AT	26.8	24.0	–	0.12	0.63	0.00	75%	no
GA	24.1	21.2	45.8	0.21	0.63	0.27	95%	yes
FC	23.8	21.6	–	0.18	1.40	0.12	67%	yes
RD	22.0	22.8	61.5	0.01	0.41	0.04	25%	no
BO	21.8	21.5	71.1	0.15	1.46	0.04	100%	no
MQ	21.5	22.2	51.2	0.50	0.58	0.62	75%	yes
DV	21.3	21.3	64.9	0.14	0.66	0.12	90%	no
HO	20.2	21.1	49.1	0.24	0.85	0.19	53%	no

[a]Unitesticular male.

Sperm Competition, Testicle Size, and Baboon Mating Systems

A comparison of savanna baboons and hamadryas baboons corroborates Short's (1981) contention that the form of the mating system will exert secondary effects on testicle size beyond the primary effects of body size. Savanna baboons live in multimale polygynous mating systems, while the conspecific hamadryas baboons live in unimale polygynous mating systems within larger social systems (Kummer, 1968; Abegglen, 1984; Stammbach, 1987). Male savanna baboons average 1.3 times the weight of male hamadryas baboons (Kinsky, 1960; Phillips-Conroy and Jolly, 1981; Sigg et al., 1982), but their testicles are four times as heavy (Kinsky, 1960) and are 0.2–0.5% of body weight (Kinsky, 1960; Katzberg, 1969; Hill, 1970; Harcourt et al., 1981; Moller, 1988). The ejaculatory rate of savanna baboons is between 0.67 and 1.2 times per hour (Saayman, 1970; Hausfater, 1975; Seyfarth, 1978a; Rasmussen, 1980; Collins, 1981; Bercovitch, 1987b), whereas the reproductive activity of hamadryas baboons is so infrequent that it precluded a systematic assessment of ejaculatory rates (Abegglen, 1984). Male hamadryas baboons may not copulate for many consecutive months (Kummer, 1968), while male savanna baboons may masturbate to ejaculation daily. Gelada monkeys (*Theropithecus gelada*) live in a unimale mating system with a superficial structural similarity to the mating system of hamadryas baboons (Dunbar, 1983; Stammbach, 1987), and gelada males ejaculate at a rate of 0.18 time per hour (Dunbar, 1978), substantially below that of savanna baboons. Male hamadryas baboon reproductive strategies are designed to facilitate acquisition and control of a group of females, whereas male savanna baboon reproductive strategies involve acquisition and retention of a single female at sporadic intervals, a pattern that also characterizes differences in male pongid reproductive tactics (Harcourt, 1981). These comparisons within the genus *Papio* support the ideas that ejaculatory rates will reflect the intensity of sperm competition and that sperm competition will exert an influence on testicular size, which in turn indicates the type of mating system.

Sperm Competition, Testicle Size, and Male Fitness

Although sperm competition can account for relatively large testicles in multi-male mating systems, male fitness in baboons is not likely to be linked with testicle size. Testicle size has a very high heritability in other mammals (0.4–0.8, in mice, rams, and boars [Schinckel et al., 1984]), and traits with a high heritability generally have a minimal impact on fitness (Falconer, 1960 p. 167; Gustafsson, 1986). If the heritability of baboon testicle size were of the same magnitude, it would suggest that male reproductive success does not depend upon testicle size.

In addition to sperm quantity, sperm competition includes other factors relating to fertilizing ability (Parker, 1970; Dewsbury, 1982a, 1982b; Quiatt and Everett, 1982; Smith, 1984; Moller, 1988). The fertility of males may depend more upon rapidity of capacitation (molecular changes induced on spermatozoa in the female reproductive tract that enable sperm to penetrate the zona pellucida surrounding the ovum), speed of egg penetration, potency of acrosomal enzymes, sperm viability, sperm motility, or timing of insemination than upon sperm number (Beatty, 1975; Dewsbury, 1982a, 1982b; Mortimer and Templeton, 1982; Yanagimachi, 1982; Thornhill and Alcock, 1983; Mahadevan and Trounson, 1984; Smith, 1984; Parrish and Foote, 1985). When rabbit does are inseminated with approximately equal numbers of spermatozoa from two bucks, one of the males consistently fertilizes more eggs than the other (Parrish and Foote, 1985), and similar patterns occur in mice and bovines (Beatty, 1975; Dewsbury, 1982b).

Daily sperm production is positively correlated with testicle size (Amann, 1970, 1981; Johnson et al., 1984), but daily sperm output (i.e., the number of ejaculated spermatozoa in a day) is not necessarily indicative of testicle size (Amann, 1970; Synott et al., 1981). Frequent ejaculation decreases the sperm count per ejaculate (Freund, 1963; Schwartz et al., 1979; Oldereid et al., 1984; Levin et al., 1986) but has no effect on sperm-production rates (Amann, 1981; Berndtson and Igboeli, 1988). The sperm output of rabbits (Macmillan and Hafs, 1967) and bulls (Almquist, 1973) is increased by permitting noncopulatory mounts prior to intromission. Only sperm cells that have matured in the cauda epididymis for a few days are capable of fertilization (Bedford, 1974; Amann, 1981; Amann et al., 1976), so high ejaculatory rate can result in the emission of immature spermatozoa. In savanna baboons, the epididymis ranges from 14% to 23% of testicular size (Kinsky, 1960; Hill, 1970), and larger testicles need not have larger epididymides (Kinsky, 1960). Bedford (1977) has suggested that sperm storage in the epididymis may mediate sperm competition more than does testicle size.

The finding that older male baboons had larger testicles than younger adult males could indicate that testicle size is partly a consequence, not a cause, of difference in male reproductive success, because on average, older males probably have higher fitness. Sexually active rabbits have larger testicles than sexually rested rabbits (Amann, 1970). On the other hand, the age-related differences in testicular size may reflect an age-related pattern of fat deposition surrounding the testicles. In rhesus macaques, abdominal circumference is an accurate measure of body fat levels (Kemnitz and Francken, 1986), and the current study found an age-related difference in abdominal circumference. The scrotum of baboons contains much fat (Hill, 1970), and the tunica propria is larger in older male baboons (Katzberg, 1969). The testicles of older human males tend to be larger than those of younger males (Amann, 1981; Johnson et al., 1984), primarily due to a progressive fibrosis of tissue, resulting in increased tunic weight (Johnson et al., 1984).

Testicle size influences the rate of sperm production, but sperm count per ejaculate will depend upon age, frequency of ejaculation, epididymal volume, efficiency of epididymal emptying, and extent of sexual arousal. A higher sperm count tends to be associated with many seminal-fluid constituents that aid in fertilization (Bleau et al., 1984; Chan and Wang, 1987; Sebastian et al., 1987), and sperm count and ejaculate quality may covary (Moller, 1988), but a major element determining male baboon reproductive success is probably the timing of mating.

Upon ovulation, baboon ova remain in the ampulla for about 24 hours (Eddy et al., 1976; Edwards, 1980) and are fertile for less than 24 hours (Katzberg, 1967). The probability of conception is affected by the length of time that sperm have resided in the female reproductive tract (Tesh, 1969); Edwards, 1980), and a male that deposits relatively few motile sperm at the optimal time may have a greater probability of siring an offspring than a male who ejaculates a voluminous quantity of relatively nonmotile sperm at suboptimal times, regardless of the two males' relative testicular sizes.

Sperm Competition and Male Baboon Reproductive Tactics

The outcome of sperm competition has been linked to the temporal patterning of ejaculation in arachnids (Austad, 1982), insects (Thornhill and Alcock, 1983), birds (Moller, 1987), and rodents (Dewsbury, 1982b; Huck et al., 1985). In many cases, either the first or the last male to inseminate the female fertilizes the greatest number of eggs, but all of these species are polytocous (i.e., produce multiple offspring at one time), and multiple paternity among litters has been documented in polytocous species (Hanken and Sherman, 1981; Davies and Boersma, 1984; Huck et al., 1985). Most primates are monotocous, which creates conditions of more intense sperm competition. In addition, sperm competition will operate differently among eutherian mammals than among other animals, because the former are unique in requiring spermatozoa to undergo capacitation in the female reproductive tract before they can fertilize an egg (Yanagimachi, 1982; Bedford, 1983).

Savanna baboon females consort with an average of three to four adult males per cycle (Rasmussen, 1980; Bercovitch, 1987b) and consort for about a week during each cycle until they become pregnant (Packer, 1979a; Hausfater, 1975; Rasmussen, 1980; Collins, 1981; Bercovitch, 1985). The first and last males to consort with sexually receptive females on any given cycle are usually subadult males. Most adult males focus their reproductive efforts on those days when females are maximally swollen (Devore, 1965; Hausfater, 1975; Packer, 1979a; Rasmussen, 1980; Collins, 1981; Bercovitch, 1986, 1988). It is unlikely that there is a first- or last-male advantage in baboons, because such a condition would mean that subadult males are most likely to fertilize females and that matings during the most probable days of ovulation are unlikely to result in conception.

The timing of reproductive activity as a mechanism that influences sperm competition can involve three factors: cycle number, cycle day, and time of day. Savanna baboon females form consortships an average of four cycles prior to conception (Bercovitch, 1985), and laboratory data suggest that these cycles are probably ovulatory (Hendrickx and Kraemer, 1969; Wildt et al., 1977; Shaikh et al., 1982). If some males could predict a conception cycle in advance and could telescope their reproductive activity into those cycles, then these males would be timing their matings in a manner that increases their reproductive success. Neither behavioral nor physiological data indicate differences between conception cycles and nonconception cycles, which suggests that males cannot detect a conception cycle in advance (Bercovitch, 1987b).

Most adult males selectively consort during the most likely days of conception (Bercovitch, 1986), and aggressive changeovers are more likely on the four most likely days of conception than on all the other potential days of ovulation combined (Bercovitch, 1988). Male baboons may be capable of detecting ovulation, but it is more likely that males are acting in a manner that coincides with the chances of ovulation occurring, because the size of females' sexual swellings tends to indicate proximity to the day of deturgescence (Bercovitch, 1985, unpubl.). The outcome of sperm competition probably depends upon obtaining access to females on a likely day of conception, but the data do not indicate that larger males have a greater chance of mating on these days.

Most consort changeovers between males occur in the morning (Hausfater, 1975; Rasmussen, 1980; Smuts, 1985; Bercovitch, 1988), and some authors have suggested that this pattern could reflect male ability to assess the time of day that females ovulate (Hausfater, 1975; Rasmussen, 1980; Smuts, 1985). Data are unavailable on the diurnal distribution of ovulation time in baboons, but the two best-studied primates (rhesus macaques and humans) do not have a circadian rhythm regarding ovulation (Spies et al., 1974; Edwards, 1980; Johnson and Everitt, 1984). Spermatozoa from a single ejaculate are capacitated at staggered intervals (Bedford, 1983), and capacitation requires about 3–6 hours in rhesus macaques (Marston and Kelly, 1968). Given these data, it seems unlikely that the time of day mediates sperm competition in baboons. Therefore, a major factor influencing male baboon reproductive success involves timing matings so that they occur on days when conception is most likely.

During the optimum conception period, male baboons stay closer to their female consort partners, herd them away from other males, and groom them more often than at other times (Hausfater, 1975; Rasmussen, 1980). In addition, the present study has shown that ejaculatory frequencies are increased when females are most likely to be fertilized, that males increase the use of aggressive reproductive tactics during the four-day optimum conception period, and that the greatest incidence of fighting over access to females occurs on the last two days of sexual swelling in both conception and nonconception cycles.

In summary, male reproductive tactics are linked to the probability of conception, with escalated aggressive interactions and increases in ejaculatory rates occurring when the chances of fertilizing a female are greatest. Yet, male baboons usually do not fight to gain access to consort females, and injurious altercations are rare (Bercovitch, 1988).

The occurrence of multiple cycles in baboons probably decreases the likelihood of severe aggression, because it raises the uncertainty that any particular cycle will result in conception. As a consequence, the relative value of each ejaculation is reduced in terms of the likelihood that it will yield a fertilization. If the benefits of each ejaculation in terms of the probability of conception were low, then males may be reluctant to engage in costly competitive bouts to gain access to females (Bertram, 1975; Taub, 1980). A parallel situation seems to have molded the reproductive tactics of male lions (*Panthera leo*). The copulatory frequencies of lions are quite high, mating is nonseasonal, and females are polyestrous (Bertram, 1975). In addition, intragroup fights for access to sexually receptive females are infrequent (Packer and Pusey, 1982). Although the frequency of lions fighting for mating opportunities was once thought to be low due to the relatedness of males, more recent data have shown that the severity of fighting is not dependent upon relatedness (Packer and Pusey, 1982).

In both lions and baboons, the chances of an ejaculation yielding a conception are small enough that males seem reluctant to engage in high-intensity aggressive competition over access to sexually receptive females. The potential reproductive benefits arising from obtaining access to a sexually receptive female militate against costly or risky aggressive competition between males (see also Taub [1980]). Less than 5% of the fights during this study resulted in slash wounds, and only 25% of changeovers resulted from fighting (Bercovitch, 1985, 1988).

Sperm competition can be considered an adjunct to agonistic competition. The timing of ejaculatory output is a major factor affecting male baboon reproductive success, and males are more willing to escalate aggressive bouts on cycle days when the probability of conception is greatest. However, fighting is relatively uncommon among males, because the probability of any particular ejaculation resulting in a conception is fairly low. Male competition in baboons is intensified when females are likely to conceive, but the outcome of competitive bouts between males appears to depend less upon size than upon experience, dexterity, or mating preferences (Packer, 1979*b*).

Male baboon reproduction hinges not only upon the appropriate timing of mating, but also on the fertilizing capacity of males. Given that baboon eggs are fertile for less than 24 hours, that baboons are monotocous species, that capacitation occurs at staggered intervals among spermatozoa from a single ejaculate, that capacitation requires at least 3–6 hours, and that females usually mate with more than one male per day, it seems likely that spermatozoa from different males will be in the vicinity of the ovum simultaneously. The timing of mating is of utmost importance in fertilization, but the above conditions suggest that differences in spermatozoal ability to penetrate an egg could have an impact on male baboon reproduction.

Among baboons, social factors appear to affect male reproductive success in a more pronounced manner than do morphological factors. Among both hamadryas baboons (Bachmann and Kummer, 1980) and savanna baboons (Smuts, 1985, 1987); Bercovitch, unpubl.), males are reluctant to use aggression to challenge other males for access to a female if the pair are preferred partners. Dunbar (1984) reported that the behavior of female gelada monkeys was more influential in determining the outcome of male fights than was male size. Male savanna baboons affiliate with both anestrous females and infants, and these social behaviors could have reproductive consequences for males (Seyfarth, 1978b; Rasmussen, 1980, 1983; Smuts, 1983, 1985, 1987; Strum, 1983, 1984; Stein, 1984; Collins, 1986). Male baboons utilize a variety of reproductive tactics for gaining access to sexually receptive females (Strum, 1982; Bercovitch, 1986, 1988; Smuts, 1987), and the adoption of alternative mechanisms for enhancing reproductive output decreases the importance of body size as a determinant of male reproductive success.

In conclusion, both sperm competition and aggressive competition have molded male baboon reproductive tactics, but neither body size nor testicle size mediates male reproductive success. Fights between males for access to sexually receptive females are most likely to occur on the probable days of conception, but because the chances of fertilizing a female are relatively small, aggressive competition is kept to a minimum. Sperm competition has affected the evolution of male baboon reproductive tactics and the evolution of testicle size, but the variance in male baboon reproductive success depends more upon social relationships than upon morphological characteristics associated with size.

ACKNOWLEDGEMENTS

This research was funded by NSF Grant BNS 7806914 to R. H. Byles, S. C. Strum, and T. J. Olivier, as well as NIMH Grant 5T32MH15133 to R. H. Byles, D. G. Lindburg, and B. J. Williams. Field assistance in obtaining morphometric data was provided by G. M. Petersen, M. F. Sanders, E. E. Hunt, D. L. Manzolillo, J. G. Else, and the staff at the Institute of Primate Research (IPR), Kenya. My field assistant for collecting behavioral data was D. H. Bercovitch. Permission to work in Kenya was granted by the Office of the President of the Republic of Kenya, and logistic and moral support was provided by J. G. Else (IPR). Richard Dansie granted us permission to live on Kekopey Ranch. Critiques of this manuscript were provided by R. W. Goy, A. H. Harcourt, R. S. O. Harding, P. H. Harvey, J. M. Jones, A. P. Moller, M. J. Raleigh, M. M. Roy, and two anonymous reviewers. I thank E. Chan for her diligence in deciphering the multiple drafts of this manuscript and M. M. Roy for the figures. This is publication No. 28-018 of the Wisconsin Regional Primate Research Center, which is supported by NIH Grant RR00167.

LITERATURE CITED

Abegglen, J. J. 1984. On Socialization in Hamadryas Baboons. Bucknell Univ. Press, Lewisburg, PA.

Almquist, J. O. 1973. Effects of sexual preparation on sperm output, semen characteristics and sexual activity of beef bulls with a comparison to dairy bulls. J. Anim. Sci. 36:331–336.

Altmann, J. 1974. Observational study of behavior: Sampling methods. Behaviour 49:227–267.

Altmann, J., S. A. Altmann, and G. Hausfater. 1978. Primate infant's effects on mother's future reproduction. Science 201:1028–1030.

_____. 1981. Physical maturation and age estimates of yellow baboons. *Papio cynocephalus*, in Amboseli National Park, Kenya. Amer. J. Primatol. 1:389–399.

Amann, R. P. 1970. Sperm production rates, pp. 433–482. In A. P. Johnson, W. R. Gomes, and N. L. Vandemark (eds.), The Testis, Vol. 1. Academic Press, N.Y.

_____. 1981. A critical review of methods for evaluation of spermatogenesis from seminal characteristics. J. Androl. 2:37–58.

Amann, R. P., L. Johnson, D. L. Thompson, Jr., and B. W. Pickett. 1976. Daily spermatozoal production, epididymal spermatozoal reserves and transit time of spermatozoa through the epididymis of the rhesus monkey. Biol. Reprod. 15:586–592.

Anderson, S. S., and M. A. Fedak. 1985. Grey seal males: Energetic and behavioral links between size and sexual success. Anim. Behav. 33:829–838.

Austad, S. N. 1982. First male sperm priority in the bowl and doily spider, *Frontinella pyramitela* (Walckenaer). Evolution 36:777–785.

Bachmann, C., and H. Kummer. 1980. Male assessment of female choice in hamadryas baboons. Behav. Ecol. Sociobiol. 6:315–321.

Beatty, R. A. 1975. Genetics of animal spermatozoa, pp. 61–68. In D. L. Mulcahy (ed.), Gamete Competition in Plants and Animals. North Holland, Amsterdam, Neth.

Bedford, J. M. 1974. Biology of primate spermatozoa. pp 97–139. In W. P. Luckett (ed.), Reproductive Biology of Primates. Karger, Basel, Switzerland.

_____. 1977. Evolution of the scrotum: The epididymis as the prime mover?, pp. 171–182. In J. H. Calaby and C. H. Tyndale-Biscoe (eds.), Reproduction and Evolution. Australian Acad. Science, Canberra, Australia.

_____. 1983. Significance of the need for sperm capacitation before fertilization in eutherian mammals. Biol. Reprod. 28:108–120.

Bercovitch, F. B. 1985. Reproductive tactics in adult female and adult male olive baboons. Ph.D. Diss. Univ. California, Los Angeles.

_____. 1986. Male rank and reproductive activity in savanna baboons. Internat. J. Primatol. 7:533–550.

_____. 1987a. Female weight and reproductive condition in a population of olive baboons (*Papio anubis*). Amer. J. Primatol. 12:189–195.

_____. 1987b. Reproductive success in male savanna baboons. Behav. Ecol. Sociobiol. 21:163–172.

_____. 1988. Coalitions, cooperation, and reproductive tactics among adult savanna baboons. Anim. Behav. 34:1198–1209.

Berndtson, W. E., and G. Igboeli. 1988. Spermatogenesis, sperm output and seminal quality of Holstein bulls electroejaculated after administration of oxytocin. J. Reprod. Fertil. 82:467–475.

Bertram, B. C. R. 1975. Social factors influencing reproduction in lions. J. Zool. 177:463–482.

Bleau, G., J. Lemarbe, G. Faucher, K. D. Roberts, and A. Chapdelaine. 1984. Semen selenium and human fertility. Fert. Steril. 42:890–894.

Bongso, T. A., M. D. Hassan, and W. Nordin. 1984. Relationship of scrotal circumference and testicular volume to age and body weight in the swamp buffalo (*Bubalus bubalis*). Theriogenology 22:127–134.

Brown, J. L., L. D. Stuart, and P. K. Chakraborty. 1986. Testicular hypertrophy after hemicastration of prepubertal rams is not associated with altered spermatogenic efficiency. Biol. Reprod. 34. Suppl. 1:58. (Abstract).

Burton, G. J. 1981. The relationship between body and gonadal weights of the dusky leaf monkey (*Presbytis obscura*). Internat. J. Primatol. 2:351–368.

Byles, R. H., and M. F. Sanders. 1981. Intertroop variation in the frequencies of ABO alleles in a population of olive baboons. Internat. J. Primatol. 2:35–46.

Chan, S. Y. W., and C. Wang. 1987. Correlation between semen adenosine triphosphate and sperm fertilizing capacity. Fertil. Steril. 47:712–719.

Clutton-Brock, T. H., F. E. Guinness, and S. D. Albon. 1982. Red Deer: Behavior and Ecology of Two Sexes. Univ. Chicago Press, Chicago, IL.

Clutton-Brock, T. H., P. H. Harvey, and B. Rudder. 1977. Sexual dimorphism, socionomic sex ratio and body weight in primates. Nature 269:797–800.

Coelho, A. M., Jr. 1985. Baboon dimorphism: Growth in weight, length and adiposity from birth to 8 years of age, pp. 125–159. *In* E. S. Watts (ed.), Nonhuman Primate Models for Human Growth and Development. Liss, N.Y.

Collins, D. A. 1981. Social behavior and patterns of mating among adult yellow baboons (*Papio c. cynocephalus* L 1776). Ph.D. Diss. Univ. Edinburgh, Edinburgh, U.K.

_____. 1986. Interactions between adult male and infant yellow baboons (*Papio c. cynocephalus*) in Tanzania. Anim. Behav. 34:430–443.

Darwin, C. R. 1871. The Descent of Man and Selection in Relation to Sex. Murray, London, U.K.

Davies, E. M., and P. D. Boersma. 1984. Why lionesses copulate with more than one male. Amer. Natur. 123:594–611.

DeVore, I. 1965. Male dominance and mating behavior in baboons, pp. 266–289. *In* F. A. Beach (ed.), Sex and Behavior. Wiley, N.Y.

DeVore, I., and K. R. L. Hall. 1965. Baboon ecology, pp. 20–52. *In* I. DeVore (ed.), Primate Behavior. Holt, Rinehart, and Winston, N.Y.

Dewsbury, D. A. 1982*a*. Ejaculate cost and male choice. Amer. Natur. 119:601–610.

_____. 1982*b*. Dominance rank, copulatory behavior, and differential reproduction. Quart. Rev. Biol. 51:135–159.

Dixson, A. F., J. S. Gardner, and R. C. Bonney. 1980. Puberty in the male owl monkey (*Aotus trivirgatus grisemembra*): A study of physical and hormonal development. Internat. J. Primatol. 1:129–139.

Dunbar, R. I. M. 1978. Sexual behaviour and social relationships among gelada baboons. Anim. Behav. 26:167–178.

_____. 1983. Relationships and social structure in gelada and hamadryas baboons, pp. 299–307. *In* R. A. Hinde (ed.), Primate Social Relationships. Blackwell, Oxford, U.K.

_____. 1984. Reproductive Decisions: An Economic Analysis of Gelada Baboon Social Strategies. Princeton Univ. Press, Princeton, NJ.

Eddy, C. A., T. T. Turner, D. C. Kraemer, and C. J. Paverstein. 1976. Pattern and duration of ovum transport in the baboon (*Papio anubis*). Obstet. Gynecol. 47:658–664.

Edwards, R. G. 1980. Conception in the Human Female. Academic Press, N.Y.

Falconer, D. S. 1960. Introduction to Quantitative Genetics. Oliver and Boyd, Edinburgh, U.K.

Freund, M. 1963. Effect of frequency of emission on semen output and an estimate of daily sperm production in man. J. Reprod. Fertil. 6:269–286.

Glassman, D. M., A. M. Coelho, Jr., K. D. Carey, and C. A. Bramblett. 1984. Weight growth in savannah baboons: A longitudinal study from birth to adulthood. Growth 48:425–433.

Glick, B. B. 1979. Testicular size, testosterone level, and body weight in male *Macaca radiata*. Fol. Primatol. 32:268–289.

Gustafsson, L. 1986. Lifetime reproductive success and heritability: Empirical support for Fisher's fundamental theorem. Amer. Natur. 128:761–764.

Hanken, J., and P. W. Sherman. 1981. Multiple paternity in Belding's ground squirrel litters. Science 212:351–353.

Harcourt, A. H. 1981. Intermale competition and the reproductive behavior of the Great Apes, pp. 301–318. *In* C. E. Graham (ed.), Reproductive Biology of the Great Apes. Academic Press, N.Y.

Harcourt, A. H., P. H. Harvey, S. G. Larson, and R. V. Short. 1981. Testis weight, body weight and breeding system in primates. Nature 293:55–57.

Harding, R. S. O. 1976. Ranging patterns of a troop of baboons (*Papio anubis*) in Kenya. Fol. Primatol. 25:143–185.

Harvey, P. H., and A. H. Harcourt. 1984. Sperm competition, testes size, and breeding systems in primates, pp. 589–600. *In* R. L. Smith (ed.), Sperm Competition and The Evolution of Animal Mating Systems. Academic Press, N.Y.

Hausfater, G. 1975. Dominance and reproduction in baboons (*Papio cynocephalus*). A quantitative analysis. Contrib. Primatol. 7:1–150.

Hendrickx, A. G., and D. C. Kraemer. 1969. Observations on the menstrual cycle, optimal mating time and pre-implantation embryos of the baboon, *Papio anubis* and *Papio cynocephalus*. J. Reprod. Fertil. (Suppl.) 6:119–128.

Hill, W. C. O. 1970. Primates. Comparative Anatomy and Taxonomy, Vol. III. Cynopithecinae. Wiley, N.Y.

Huck, U. W., R. P. Quinn, and R. D. Lisk. 1985. Determinants of mating success in the golden hamster (*Mesocricetus auratus*). IV. Sperm competition. Behav. Ecol. Sociobiol. 17:239–252.

Johnson, L., C. S. Petty, and W. B. Neaves. 1984. Influence of age on sperm production and testicular weights in men. J. Reprod. Fertil. 70:211–218.

Johnson, M., and B. Everitt. 1984. Essential Reproduction. Blackwell, Oxford, U.K.

Katzberg, A. A. 1967. The developing ovum in the baboon, pp. 217–234. *In* H. Vagtborg (ed.), The Baboon in Medical Research. Vol. 1. Univ. Texas Press, Austin.

_____. 1969. Spermatogenesis in the wild East African baboon, pp. 56–60. *In* H. O. Hofer (ed.), Proceedings of the 2nd International Congress of Primatology. Vol. 2. Karger, Basel, Switzerland.

Kemnitz, J. W., and G. A. Francken. 1986. Characteristics of spontaneous obesity in male rhesus monkeys. Physiol. Behav. 38:477–483.

Kenagy, G. J. 1979. Rapid surgical technique for measurement of testis size in small mammals. J. Mammal. 60:636–638.

Kenagy, G. J., and S. C. Trombulak. 1986. Size and function of mammalian testes in relation to body size. J. Mammal. 67:1–22.

Kinsky, M. 1960. Quantitative untersuchungen an äthiopischen Säugetieren. Anat. Anz. 108:65–82.

Kummer, H. 1968. Social Organization of Hamadryas Baboons. Univ. Chicago Press, Chicago, IL.

Leutenegger, W., and J. Cheverud. 1982. Correlates of sexual dimorphism in primates: Ecological and size variables. Internat. J. Primatol. 3:387–402.

Levin, R. M., J. Latimore, A. J. Wein, and K. N. Van Arsdalen. 1986. Correlation of sperm count with frequency of ejaculation. Fertil. Steril. 45:732–734.

Macmillan, K. L., and H. D. Hafs. 1967. Semen output of rabbits ejaculated after varying sexual preparation. Proc. Soc. Exp. Biol. Med. 125:1278–1281.

Mahadevan, M. M., and A. O. Trounson. 1984. The influence of seminal characteristics on the success rate of human in vitro fertilization. Fert. Steril. 42:400–405.

Manzolillo, D. L. 1986. Factors affecting intertroop transfer by adult male *Papio anubis*, pp. 371–380. *In* J. G. Else and P. C. Lee (eds.), Primate Ontogeny, Cognition and Social Behaviour. Cambridge Univ. Press, Cambridge, U.K.

Marston, J. H., and W. A. Kelly. 1968. Time relationships of spermatozoan penetration into the egg of the rhesus monkey. Nature 217:1073–1074.

Martin, D. E., and K. G. Gould. 1981. The male ape genital tract and its secretions, pp. 127–162. *In* C. E. Graham (ed.), Reproductive Biology of the Great Apes. Academic Press, N.Y.

Matsubayashi, K., and T. Enomoto. 1983. Longitudinal studies on annual changes in plasma testosterone, body weight and spermatogenesis in adult Japanese monkeys (*Macaca fuscata fuscata*) in laboratory conditions. Primates 24:521–529.

Moller, A. P. 1987. Behavioural aspects of sperm competition in swallows (*Hirundo rustica*). Behaviour 100:92–104.

_____. 1988. Ejaculate quality, testes size and sperm competition in primates. J. Hum. Evol. 17:479–488.

Mortimer, D., and A. A. Templeton. 1982. Sperm transport in the human female reproductive tract in relation to semen analysis characteristics and the time of ovulation. J. Reprod. Fertil. 64:401–408.

Nicolson, N. A. 1982. Weaning and the development of independence in olive baboons. Ph.D. Diss. Harvard Univ., Cambridge, MA.

Nieuwenhuijsen, K., K. J. de Neef, J. J. van der Werff ten Bosch, and A. K. Slob. 1987. Testosterone, testis size, seasonality, and behavior in group-living stumptail macaques (*Macaca arctoides*). Horm. Behav. 21:153–169.

Oldereid, N. B., J. D. Gordeladze, B. Kirkhus, and K. Purvis. 1984. Human sperm characteristics during frequent ejaculation. J. Reprod. Fertil. 71: 135–140.

Oliver, T. J., D. H. Coppenhaver, and A. G. Steinberg. 1986. Distributions of immunoglobulin allotypes among local populations of Kenya olive baboons. Amer. J. Phys. Anthropol. 70:29–38.

Packer, C. 1979a. Inter-troop transfer and inbreeding avoidance in *Papio anubis*. Anim. Behav. 27:1–36.

_____. 1979b. Male dominance and reproductive activity in *Papio anubis*. Anim. Behav. 27:37–45.

Packer, C., and A. E. Pusey. 1982. Cooperation and competition within coalitions of male lions: Kin selection or game theory? Nature 296:740–742.

Parker, G. A. 1970. Sperm competition and its evolutionary consequences in insects. Biol. Rev. 45:525–568.

Parrish, J. J., and R. M. Foote. 1985. Fertility differences among male rabbits determined by heterospermic insemination of fluorochrome-labeled spermatozoa. Biol. Reprod. 33:940–949.

Phillips-Conroy, J. E., and C. J. Jolly. 1981. Sexual dimorphism in two subspecies of Ethiopian baboons (*Papio hamadryas*) and their hybrids. Amer. J. Phys. Anthropol. 56:115–129.

Plant, T. M. 1985. A study of the role of the postnatal tests in determining the ontogeny of gonadotropin secretion in the male rhesus monkey (*Macaca mulatta*). Endocrinology 116:1341–1350.

Popp, J. L. 1978. Male baboons and evolutionary principles. Ph.D. Diss. Harvard Univ., Cambridge, MA.

Popp, J. L., and I. Devore. 1979. Aggressive competition and social dominance theory: Synopsis, pp. 317–338. In D. A. Hamburg and E. R. McCown (eds.), The Great Apes. Perspectives of Human Evolution, Vol. 5. Benjamin Cummings, Menlo Park, NJ.

Quiatt, D., and J. Everett. 1982. How can sperm competition work? Amer. J. Primatol. (Suppl.) 1: 161–169.

Ralls, K. 1976. Mammals in which females are larger than males. Quart. Rev. Biol. 51:245–276.

Ransom, T. W. 1981. Beach Troop of the Gombe. Bucknell Univ. Press, Lewisburg, PA.

Rasmussen, K. L. R. 1980. Consort behaviour and mate selection in yellow baboons (*Papio cynocephalus*). Ph.D. Diss. Cambridge Univ., Cambridge, U.K.

_____. 1983. Influence of affiliative preferences upon the behaviour of male and female baboons during sexual consortships, pp. 116–120. In R. A. Hinde (ed.), Primate Social Relationships, Blackwell, Oxford, U.K.

Saayman, G. S. 1970. The menstrual cycle and sexual behaviour in a troop of free ranging chacma baboons. Fol. Primatol. 12:81–110.

Sade, D. S. 1964. Seasonal cycle in size of testes of free-ranging *Macaca mulatta*. Fol. Primatol. 2:171–180.

Schinckel, A. P., R. K. Johnson, and R. J. Kittok. 1984. Testicular development and endocrine characteristics of boars selected for either high or low testis size. J. Anim. Sci. 58:675–685.

Schultz, A. H. 1938. The relative weight of the testes in primates. Anat. Rec. 72:387–394.

Schwartz, D., A. Laplarine, P. Jouannet, and G. David. 1979. Within-subject variability of human semen in regard to sperm count, volume, total number of spermatozoa and length of abstinence. J. Reprod. Fertil. 57:391–395.

Scott. L. M. 1984. Reproductive behavior of adolescent female baboons (*Papio anubis*) Kenya, pp. 77–100. In M. F. Small (ed.), Female Primates: Studies by Women Primatologists. Liss, N.Y.

Sebastian, S. M., S. Selvaraj, M. M. Aruldhas, and P. Gouindarajulu. 1987. Pattern of neutral and phospholipids in the semen of normospermic, digospermic and azoospermic men. J. Reprod. Fertil. 79:373–378.

Seyfarth, R. M. 1978a. Social relationships among adult male and female baboons. I. Behaviour during sexual consortship. Behaviour 64:204–226.

_____. 1978b. Social relationships among adult male and female baboons. II. Behaviour throughout the female reproductive cycle. Behaviour 64:227–247.

Shaikh, A. A., C. L. Celaya, I. Gomez, and S. A. Shaikh. 1982. Temporal relationship of hormonal peaks to ovulation and sex-skin deturgescence in the baboon. Primates 23:444–452.

Short, R. V. 1979. Sexual selection and its component parts, somatic and genital selection as illustrated by man and the great apes. Adv. Stud. Behav. 9:131–158.

_____. 1981. Sexual selection in man and the great apes, pp. 319–341. In C. E. Graham (ed.), Reproductive Biology of the Great Apes. Academic Press, N.Y.

_____. 1984. Testis size, ovulation rate, and breast cancer, pp. 32–44. In O. A. Ryder and M. L. Byrd (eds.), One Medicine. Springer-Verlag, Berlin, W. Ger.

Sigg, H., A. Stolba, J. J. Abegglen, and V. Dasser. 1982. Life history of hamadryas baboons: Physical development, infant mortality, reproductive parameters and family relationships. Primates 23:473–487.

Smith, R. L. 1984. Human sperm competition, pp. 601–659. In R. L Smith (ed.), Sperm Competition and the Evolution of Animal Mating Systems. Academic Press, Orlando, FL.

Smuts, B. 1982. Special relationships between adult male and female olive baboons (Papio anubis). Ph.D. Diss. Stanford Univ., Stanford, CA.

_____. 1983. Special relationships between adult male and female olive baboons: Selective advantages, pp. 262–266. In R. A. Hinde (ed.), Primate Social Relationships. Blackwell, Oxford, U.K.

_____. 1985. Sex and Friendship in Baboons. Aldine, N.Y.

_____. 1987. Sexual competition and mate choice. pp. 385–399. In B. B. Smuts, D. L. Cheney, R. M. Seyfarth, R. W. Wrangham, and T. T. Struhsaker (eds.), Primate Societies. Univ. Chicago Press, Chicago, IL.

Sokal, R. R., and F. J. Rohlf. 1981. Biometry, 2nd Ed. Freeman, San Francisco, CA.

Spies, H. G., C. S. Mahoney, R. L. Norman, D. K. Clifton, and J. A. Resko. 1974. Evidence for a diurnal rhythm in ovarian steroid secretion in the rhesus monkey. J. Clin. Endocrinol. Metab. 39:347–351.

Stammbach, E. 1987. Desert, forest, and montane baboons: Multilevel societies, pp. 112–120. In B. B. Smuts, D. L. Cheney, R. M. Seyfarth, R. W. Wrangham, and T. T. Struhsaker (eds.), Primate Societies. Univ. Chicago Press, Chicago, IL.

Stein, D. M. 1984. The Sociobiology of Infant and Adult Male Baboons. Ablex, Norwood, N.J.

Steiner, R. A., and W. J. Bremner. 1981. Endocrine correlates of sexual development in the male monkey. Macaca fascicularis. Endocrinology 109:914–919.

Strum, S. C. 1982. Agonistic dominance in male baboons: An alternative view. Internat. J. Primatol. 3:175–202.

_____. 1983. Use of females by male olive baboons (Papio anubis). Amer. J. Primatol. 5:93–109.

_____. 1984. Why males use infants, pp. 146–185. In D. M. Taub (ed.), Primate Paternalism. Van Nostrand Reinhold, N.Y.

Synott, A. L., W. J. Fulkerson, and D. R. Lindsay. 1981. Sperm output by rams and distribution amongst ewes under conditions of continual mating. J. Reprod. Fertil. 61:355–361.

Taub, D. M. 1980. Female choice and mating strategies among wild Barbary macaques (Macaca sylvanus L.), pp. 287–344. In D. G. Lindburg (ed.), The Macaques. Van Nostrand Reinhold, N.Y.

Tesh, J. M. 1969. Effects of the aging of rabbit spermatozoa in utero on fertilization and prenatal development. J. Reprod. Fertil. 20:299–306.

Thompson, D. L., Jr., B. W., Pickett, E. L. Squires, and R. P. Amann. 1979. Testicular measurements and reproductive characteristics in stallions. J. Reprod. Fertil. (Suppl.) 27:13–17.

Thornhill, R., and J. Alcock. 1983. The Evolution of Insect Mating Systems. Harvard Univ. Press, Cambride, MA.

Trivers, R. L. 1972. Parental investment and sexual selection, pp. 136–179. *In* B. Campbell (ed.), Sexual Selection and the Descent of Man 1871–1971. Aldine, Chicago, IL.

Voglmayr, J. K., and P. E. Mattner. 1968. Compensatory hypertrophy in the remaining testis following unilateral orchidectomy in the adult ram. J. Reprod. Fertil. 17:179–181.

Wickings, E. J., and E. Nieschlag. 1980. Seasonality in endocrine and exocrine testicular function of the adult rhesus monkey (*Macaca mulatta*) in a controlled laboratory environment. Internat. J. Androl. 3:87–104.

Wildt, D. E., L. L. Doyle, S. C. Stone, and R. M. Harrison. 1977. Correlation of perineal swelling with serum ovarian hormone levels, vaginal cytology, and ovarian follicular development during the baboon reproductive cycle. Primates 18:261–270.

Yanagimachi, R. 1982. Potential methods for examining sperm chromosomes, pp. 225–247. *In* R. P. Amann and G. E. Seidel, Jr. (eds.), Prospects for Sexing Mammalian Sperm. Colorado Associated Univ. Press, Boulder.

Zar, J. H. 1974. Biostatistical Analysis. Prentice-Hall, Englewood Cliffs, N.J.

Social Relationships of Mountain Baboons—Leadership and Affiliation in a Non-Female-Bonded Monkey

R. W. Byrne, A. Whiten, and S. P. Henzi
University of St. Andrews, Scotland

Instead of close and differentiated relationships among adult females, the accepted norm for savanna baboons, groups of Drakensberg mountain baboons (*Papio ursinus*) showed strong affiliation of females towards a single male. The same male was usually the decision-making animal in controlling group movements. Lactating or pregnant females focused their grooming on this "leader" male, producing a radially patterned sociogram, as in the desert baboon (*P. hamadryas*); the leader male supported young animals in the group against aggression and protected them against external threats. Unlike typical savanna baboons, these mountain baboons rarely displayed approach-retreat or triadic interactions, and entirely lacked coalitions among adult females. Both groups studied were reproductively one-male; male-female relationships in one were like those in a unit of a *hamadryas* male at his peak, while the other group resembled the unit of an old *hamadryas* male, who still led the group, with a male follower starting to build up a new unit and already monopolizing mating. In their mountain environment, where the low population density suggests conditions as harsh for baboons as in deserts, adults in these groups kept unusually large distances apart during ranging; kin tended to range apart, and spacing of adults was greatest at the end of the dry, winter season. These facts support the hypothesis that sparse food is responsible for convergence with hamadryas social organization. It is suggested that all baboons, though matrilocal, are better categorized as "cross-sex-bonded" than "female bonded."

Key words: relationships, one-male groups, female-bonding, spacing, support, *Papio ursinus*, *Papio hamadryas*

INTRODUCTION

Baboons (*Papio ursinus*), inhabiting two temperate, montane sites, have been termed "mountain baboons" to distinguish them from typical "savanna baboons" [Anderson, 1982, for Suikerbosrand; and Whiten et al., 1987, for Giants Castle in the Drakensberg Mountains].

"Social Relationships of Mountain Baboons—Leadership and Affiliation in a Non-Female-Bonded Monkey" by R. W. Byrne, A. Whiten and S. P. Henzi in *American Journal of Primatology* 18:191–207(1989).

At both sites, mountain baboon patterns of behavior resemble some elements in the complex society of the desert baboon (*P. hamadryas*) [Kummer, 1968, 1984]; these apparent convergences with *hamadryas* are, in some but not all cases, similar at the two sites. Thus, fragmentation into subgroups which regularly reaggregate is seen at Suikerbosrand but not Giants Castle; small groups resembling *hamadryas* units in composition are found at both, and female transfer is known at one and suspected at the other, whereas only at Giants Castle do groups occur at population density as low as *hamadryas*, with a seasonal range shift into subalpine zones [Anderson, 1981a,b; Byrne et al., 1987; Whiten et al., 1987]. In other ways, these populations differ from *hamadryas*. Lone males are regularly found at Giants Castle; the fission-fusion of troops at Suikerbosrand is seasonal, not daily; and when one-male subtroops rejoin the large troops, sexual relations do not remain exclusively within the one-male group as in *hamadryas* [Anderson, 1981a, 1983; Byrne et al., 1987].

These two mountain baboon populations appear to differ from each other in their intergroup interactions with respect to the herding of females. This is a critical point, since herding by a male is the basis of a *hamadryas* one-male unit [Nagel, 1973]. At Giants Castle, encounters are frequent and characterized by the male's violent herding of females, his vigilance with respect to the other group, and his loud calling; after an encounter, the group subsequently travels diametrically away from the other group or lone male [Byrne et al., 1987]. At Suikerbosrand, encounters are significantly less frequent than chance, which implies active avoidance; agonism between groups is rare, and intragroup agonism is no greater when another group is present [Anderson, 1981b]. This difference between populations may, however, be illusory. Intergroup agonism is equally rare at Giants Castle, the encounters typically involving large separations between groups [Byrne et al., 1987]; if "an encounter" were instead defined by *close proximity* of groups, then such encounters would be rare and actively avoided by the groups at this site also. Conversely, for some of the time when other groups were "absent" at Suikerbosrand, the distant sight (by the baboons) of another group may have affected intragroup behavior; that is, "encounters," in the sense of sightings of other groups, may be common at Suikerbosrand. Thus the difference between the almost invariable herding of females in the (distant) presence of another group and rarity of herding at other times at Giants Castle, compared with fairly frequent herding of females by males of one-male groups at all times at Suikerbosrand, is likely to be a function of different definitions of an "encounter."

It seems, then, that mountain baboons are strongly convergent towards *hamadryas*. If this is so, it is important, since socioecological study of mountain baboons can then throw light on the evolution of the unusual social organisation of hamadryas [Byrne et al., 1987]. However, savanna baboon behavior is highly flexible, and isolated similarities to *hamadryas* do occur without an overall convergence in organization. Such similarities include the fragmentation of a troop into small parties during ranging, resulting in parties which, however, show inconstant membership and lack the consistent one-male composition of *hamadryas* [Hall, 1962; Aldrich-Blake et al., 1971; Sharman, 1980]; female

Table I. Two Modes of Baboon Social Structure

	Hamadryas	Savanna
Leadership (i.e., which animals determine choice of foraging route	Males [Kummer, 1968]	Females [Rowell, 1972]
Affiliation (indexed by distribution of grooming)	Chiefly female → male [Kummer, 1968]; but also female → female (Abegglen, 1984]	Chiefly female → female [Hall & DeVore, 1965; Melnick & Pearl, 1987] but also female → male [Ransom, 1971; Smuts, 1983]
Dominance (indexed by approach-retreat interactions and aggression)	Agonistic interactions rare, except for those of harem male towards females [Kummer, 1968], but female ranks linear [Abegglen, 1984]	Agonistic interactions common, female ranks linear [Hall & DeVore, 1965; Hausfater et al., 1982]
Coalitions (support from third party in agonistic interactions)	Uncommon, except for support of harem male [Kummer, 1968]	Common and important [Cheney, 1977]
Sexual behavior	One male has monopoly of sexual access in unit, even when more than one male in "one male unit" [Kummer, 1968, 1984]	Males compete for females: rank, coalitions, and friendship with females important [Packer, 1977; Hausfater, 1975; Smuts, 1983]

transfer [Ransom & Rowell, 1972; Rasmussen, 1981]; one-male groups [Stein & Stacey, 1981]; and males ranging alone for long periods [Altmann & Altmann, 1970].

In order to test whether the similarities in organization of mountain and hamadryas baboons represent genuine convergence, the full range of parameters which characterize baboon socioecology must be examined; this paper examines in particular the social relationships within two Giants Castle groups. Interest naturally focuses on social parameters which differ between hamadryas and savanna baboons, and Table I offers a summary of these [see also Stammbach, 1987; Melnick & Pearl, 1987].

The two modes of baboon society in Table I are closely related to patterns of intergroup transfer [see Smuts, 1987]. Almost all Old World monkeys are matrilocal and have been described as female-bonded [Wrangham, 1980], whereas, apart from hamadryas, only red colobus (*Colobus badius*) resembles African great apes in being non-female-bonded. Thus, if mountain baboons prove to have a society resembling hamadryas, then studying them will give much needed extra support to our knowledge of non-female-bonded primates; whether the dichotomy is useful in understanding *any* baboon groups will be considered in the Discussion.

MATERIALS AND METHODS

Study groups

Details of the Giants Castle study site in the Drakensburg Mountains and a general account of mountain baboons' ecology are given in full in Whiten et al. [1987]. Two groups chosen for detailed study had ranges centred on 2,250 m ("HIGH group") and around 1,835 m ("LOW group"). Both groups were smaller than the mean and median size of groups in the population, and comparable in size to each other; a full demographic profile of the population was not possible, for reasons given in Byrne et al. [1987]. During the period of detailed data collection (mid-July 1983–mid-January 1984), the groups naturally varied in size for demographic reasons, but for much of the time HIGH group consisted of 9 animals (range 7–11) and LOW group of 14 animals (range 13–14). All individuals are listed in Table II, along with weights and dates of birth where known, and estimated age class and kinship in all other cases. Weights were obtained in May 1983 when some individuals in LOW group were trapped for marking.

Where maternity was not obvious, grooming frequencies among adult females and young animals were used to deduce probable kinship [Walters, 1981]. For each possible pair, all occurrences of grooming A → B and B → A were summed to give a matrix of "closeness" of grooming relationship. These were analyzed by average-link cluster analysis, and the resulting dendrograms are shown in Figure 1. Cluster analysis successively clumps individuals into clusters, according to some measure of association—in this case, frequency of grooming each other. At each iteration, the pair of individuals with the highest grooming frequency (the "splitting level") are clumped. New association values are then computed between the clumped pair and all other individuals; the average link method substitutes, in each case, the average of the association values with each member of the new cluster [see Gorden, 1981, for choice of substitution method]. Extraction then continues with the new matrix until a splitting level of zero is reached. Interpretation of the three clusters obtained in each group as matrilineal families is supported by the pattern of approach-retreat interactions (see Results, below).

Although the study lasted from August 1982 to January 1984, habituation progressed slowly, and only in the last 9 months were data on individually recognized animals available from both groups. In this paper all quantitative data were collected during the final 6 months when observations were of the highest quality.

HIGH group was observed for 762 hours and LOW group for 297 hours during this period. Each independent individual was followed closely (20–30 m), on a schedule which balanced observation time over individuals, in order to collect focal feeding data by instantaneous samples at 2 min intervals. In addition, the unrestricted visibility in the open grassland habitat allowed all occurrences sampling to be used to record conspicuous social behaviors, and the very high average inter-animal spacing (see Results, below) made all triadic interac-

Table II. Group Composition*

	High group	Low group
Adult male	JG (prime)[a]	DV (21.6 kg, older)[a]
		HL (21.8 kg, younger)[a]
Adult female	PK	JA
	SP	ST (15.9 kg)
	ML	CH
Subadult male	JM (mother ML)	ME (20.4 kg, mother CH)
Older juvenile male	SK (mother SP)	SZ (17.0 kg, mother JA)
Older juvenile female	—	TR (10.2 kg, mother CH)
		CA (mother JA)
		PL (10.0 kg, mother ST)
Young juvenile male	PA (mother SP)	SF (8.4 kg, mother ST)
	DR (mother PK)	SY (mother CH)
Young juvenile female	—	SO (6.4 kg, mother JA)
Brown infant	RO (male, mother ML, born January 1983)	—
Black infant	JK (male, mother PK, born September 1983)	JJ (female, mother JA, born October 1983)
	JB (female, mother SP, born November 1983)	

*Age classes follow Altmann & Altmann [1970]: older juvenile corresponds to their "juvenile-2," young juvenile to "juvenile-1," brown infant to "infant-2," black infant to "infant-1."

[a]HL had brown pelage and appeared in his prime; DV was much greyer, his somewhat sunken cheeks implied an old animal, and his upper canines were perhaps more worn (2.7 cm) than those of HL (3.2 cm). JG was also greyish in pelage, but showed no other sign of old age.

tions, approach-retreat interactions, grooming, and copulation conspicuous. All of the infrequent cases of these behaviors were recorded. It was not possible to record durations of grooming bouts, and frequencies only are analyzed here; reversals of grooming role are treated as new bouts. Occasions on which one or more animals could not be monitored were a function of local topography, and as such were random across individuals. 10 × 40 Zeiss binoculars were used for all observations.

To measure overall dispersion, distance between each pair of adult animals was recorded at 30 min intervals, although not all pairs were visible at each sample time. To measure association, the nearest neighbour of each independently moving animal was recorded at intervals of 1 hour.

In order to determine which animal was most responsible for a particular move or change of direction of the group, certain diagnostic patterns of behavior were recorded whenever we could be sure of their occurrence. These are defined in Table III.

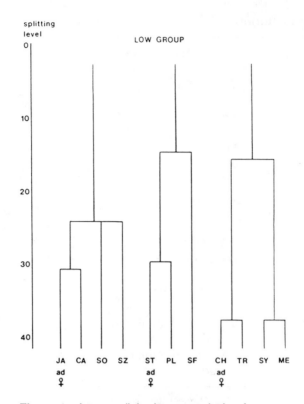

Figure 1. Average-link cluster analysis of grooming frequencies among adult female and young animals; the y-axis shows the splitting level, with stronger clusters extracted lower in the figure.

RESULTS

Leadership

It was not expected that clear cases of the behavior patterns which unequivocally point to a leader animal would be frequent; indeed, by contrast with *hamadryas* baboons, in savanna baboons such data has not been reported, although Rowell had evidently observed something of the kind since she distinguishes between animals who "suggest" possible routes and those who "decide" between them (1972, p. 34). The small group size and, in particular, the totally open grassland habitat at the present site were crucial in making this form of data available. Since such data have not been presented before for savanna baboons, Table III gives examples of each type that was recorded.

For the two-male LOW group, six clear cases of move determination were recorded, two each of types ii, iii, and iv. All imply that the older male, DV,

Table III. Examples of Determination of Travel Route

i. "Initiating"
Definition: One animal sets off purposefully, but others do not follow and this "initiator" [Kummer, 1968] returns to the group.

22.8.83 "PK sets off to the N and travels 150 m away from the rest of HIGH group. But the rest go E down a ridge and PK eventually swings round and joins them." (PK initiated but failed to determine move)

26.8.83 "At 1700 HIGH group arrives at SE plateau sleeping site. PK continues towards NE plateau site, but the rest remain and groom. 20 min later she returns to the rest of the group." (PK initiated but failure to determine move.)

ii. "Determining from behind"
Definition: One animal (initiator) sets off purposefully, but others do not follow until a particular animal, the "decision making" [Kummer, 1968] or "determiner" animal gets up, when the group moves as a whole.

2.9.83 "At 0740 all HIGH group are on broken ground just below their sleeping site of that night. SP approaches JG and grooms him, then continues moving to the S. No other animal moves. 1 min later, JG gets up and follows her, then suddenly all the group are following them. JG stops again, and the rest sit and look around. 5 min later, SP continues S and goes out of view, but no animals follow. 20 s later, JG gets up and follows her and the rest of the group immediately follows him." (SP initiated and JG determined move.)

iii. "Initiating and determining"
Definition: One animal sets off purposefully, others delay following or move in different directions, but the initiator does not return and in the end the others do follow, initially lagging behind the decision making animal. Here initiator and determiner are the same animal.

17.8.83 "LOW group are extending their known range to the N. DV leads this movement by 100 m from the nearest other animal. HL and CA follow him, but then return to the main group, whereas ME follows DV and both go another 200 m before returning to the group." (DV determined move.)

iv. "Reluctant following"
Definition: An animal who is well away from the others, apparently as a result of an incompletely observed case of iii, is followed (and thus "in the lead") with a considerable lag and apparent reluctance by the rest of the group.

17.10.83 "At 1800 most of HIGH group are quietly feeding near a sleeping site. However, PK moves rapidly W up to the rim of the valley with JM following close by and DR trailing behind. JG remains in the valley, watching this trio. Even lower, SP, PA, ML and RO feed near the sleeping site. However the party moving W do not stop moving and gradually all those in the valley follow, JG in front and ML in the rear, moving quite slowly with apparent reluctance. They were strung out along the ridge at 1855, when it was dark with moonlight. Next day they were found at a sleeping site on the main cliff to the W." (PK initiated and eventually, with JG, determined move.)

determined group movements. On no occasion was there any suggestion of determination of group movements by the younger male.

For the one-male HIGH group, ten cases were noted where a clear implication about the determiner of a move could be made, and these spanned all four patterns of behavior. In eight cases, the adult male, JG, was the determiner, whereas in two the highest-ranking adult female was successful in influencing JG to join her, and the two jointly determined the other animals' movements. In two other cases, she initiated but failed to determine movements. Thus the adult male alone determined travel in roughly 80% of disputed cases, and the top-ranking adult female influenced his leadership in the remaining 20%.

Kinship

In both groups, three main clusters were found (Fig. 1), each with one multiparous female, suggesting that the clusters are females. Generally, females groomed their (inferred) young more than the reverse, as would be expected [Walters, 1981]. However, in LOW group ST groomed the juvenile PL very little; thus, the "family" of ST, PL, and SF may be a result of compensation [Walters, 1981] after the death of PL and SF's true mother. Since older juveniles reciprocate more than young juveniles, the sum total of bouts for these female-juvenile pairs is greater, even when—as is usually the case—mothers groom their youngest juvenile most; thus where more than one immature clusters with a female, the greatest grooming reciprocity is usually not with the youngest. One oddity is the case of ME, a subadult male, and SY, a young juvenile, whose tight clustering results from the large amount of grooming given by ME to SY. They were often together, and even slept huddled together at night on the one occasion this could be observed. Frequent grooming of SY by adult CH and old juvenile TR supports the interpretation of SY as CH's son. But it is also possible that ME is unrelated to any of CH's family, but has built up a close relationship with the juvenile as a means of access to the adult female and her nulliparous but nearly adult daughter TR.

Affiliation

Affiliation among adult monkeys can be assessed by the extent and direction of grooming [Seyfarth & Cheney, 1984]. However, the presence of new infants inflates the amount of grooming of the mother (e.g., increases of 55% and 50% with two births during this study, chi square = 10.1 and 4.8, respectively at 1 df, both significant at $P < 0.05$). In order to compare the two groups, the period when HIGH group contained 3 infants was not used in this analysis (leaving 488 hours data); note that, even then, the two groups are not quite comparable, with a brown infant in HIGH group throughout, and a black infant born near the end of the study in LOW group. Similarly, in cycling females the period of full tumescence is known to be one of increased grooming with certain males [Saayman, 1971], and only in LOW group were females cycling during the study; their grooming interactions at full tumescence are excluded.

Table IV shows frequencies of grooming for average dyads of males and females, compared with frequencies expected if animals distributed their grooming at random. The comparison shows that grooming among females is about half that expected, and that grooming of males by females is about twice that expected, in both groups. Grooming of females by males differs between groups, being much higher (about that expected on a random distribution) in the one-male HIGH group; however, as noted above, this group differs in the presence of a brown infant throughout.

To examine the detailed pattern of adult affiliation, the frequency of bouts of grooming among all pairs of adults of both groups are presented as sociograms, with very low frequencies of grooming between pairs omitted for clarity (Fig. 2). Males are the focus of grooming among adults of both groups. In addition to adult animals, Figure 2 includes grooming interactions of the two older juvenile females in LOW group: TR, inferred daughter of CH, and CA, inferred daughter of JA. Whereas it is to the old male DV that the adult females direct their grooming, the two older juvenile females groom both DV and the young prime male HL.

In LOW group, 2 adults and 3 older juvenile females were cycling during the study, and any changes in affiliation to males with sexual state can be followed; see Table V. In all cases, tumescent females increased the proportion of their grooming devoted to the younger HL, who largely monopolized mating (see Sexual Behavior, below). No such increases occurred in the grooming devoted to the older DV, except in the case of the one female (CA) which he was able to mate with when HL was absent. Thus, the proportion of a female's grooming devoted to a male is closely associated with the likelihood of his mating with her.

Dominance Rank and Control

Approach-retreat interactions are infrequent in these groups: we found rates of 1.55 per 100 hours per dyad of adults in LOW group and 1.61 in HIGH group [excluding Herding: Byrne et al., 1987]. Breaking this down by sex shows that for an adult female in HIGH group the chance of being displaced by the male (3.9 acts per 100 hours observation) is much higher than that of being displaced by a given adult female in either group (0.6 in HIGH, 0.8 in LOW), or by a male in LOW group (0.7). Male-male displacement in LOW group (3.6 acts per 100 hours) was frequently over consortship of a female, while displacement of females in both groups was normally over prized food items. Adult males accounted for a disproportionate number of all displacements; indeed, the top-rank males of the two groups made 54% of all displacements.

The relative rarity of approach-retreat interactions is apparent from the matrices of pairwise interactions (Table VI). However, adult females rank linearly in both groups (no reversals) and when offspring are ordered below their inferred mothers, as has been done in both matrices, an essentially linear hierarchy can be seen. Thus a dominance structure is present in these small groups, though it is ill-differentiated.

267

TABLE IV. Grooming Frequencies of Adults*

	HIGH group		LOW group	
	Observed	Expected	Observed	Expected
Female → female	3.52 (1.85,n = 6)	5.90	0.56 (0.50,n = 6)	1.08
Female → male	5.50 (1.30,n = 3)	2.95	2.91 (1.89,n = 6)	1.08
Male → female	2.80 (2.25,n = 3)	2.95	0.22 (0.25,n = 6)	1.08
Male → male	0.00 (n = 0)	0.00	0.00 (n = 2)	0.36

*Observed frequencies of grooming are expressed as bouts per hundred hours given in an average dyad of each type, and (in parentheses) the standard deviation and No. of dyads; expected frequencies are calculated on the assumption that the same total No. of grooming bouts were distributed at random.

In the two-male group, the younger HL outranks the older DV; however, at the very start of the study, both males were noted with recent cuts and observers believed a change of status was just taking place. At this time, DV loud-called and herded females in the only intergroup encounter observed and on another occasion, whereas afterwards both these behaviors were restricted to HL (ibid.).

Herding of females in intergroup encounters has been analyzed elsewhere (ibid.), and in HIGH group this violent behavior was not seen at any other time, although on one occasion (28.8.83) a facial threat by the male JG resulted in a 2 m approach by female SP who then groomed the male. In LOW group, herding was noted in the absence of other groups at intervals throughout the study. In one case at the start of the study, it was the old male DV who herded females (11.5.83; herding of multiparous females JA and CH). From then on, it was always the younger HL; and on 8 of 10 occasions herding was directed at the older juvenile females, often when they showed full tumescence (five of eight occasions). Some of these interactions did not involve chasing and physical contact, but merely a fixed stare by the male. The proximity of the older male appeared to precipitate these interactions, and he would often actively avoid tumescent females in HL's presence, even a female with which he had just mated four times in HL's absence.

Coalitions and Support in Agonism

The giving and soliciting of support was rare; indeed, only 22 cases were seen during the study. Some of its more complex manifestations have been analysed separately [Byrne & Whiten, 1985]. Adult females supported their offspring, and subadult males supported younger relatives (three and five cases, respectively). In each group the leader male (i.e., the animal which determines most changes in group travel direction, see Leadership) supported young animals against external threats posed by the too close approach of observers (1 case each). Further, the leader male of HIGH group (JG) supported young animals against older ones, including their mothers (6 cases), and this pattern was once displayed by

Table V. Changes in Grooming of Males With Female Sexual State*

	Grooming of DV			Grooming of HL		
	%T	%D	%T – %D	%T	%D	%T – %D
CH	15 (26)	17 (59)	−2	23 (26)	3 (59)	+20
ST	0 (1)	25 (4)	−25	100 (1)	50 (4)	+50
TR	24 (68)	24 (59)	0	31 (68)	24 (59)	+7
CA	28 (72)	10 (41)	+18	40 (72)	15 (41)	+25
PL	3 (31)	6 (54)	−3	16 (31)	13 (54)	+3

*%T is the percentage of a female's grooming bouts that are given to a male while her sexual swelling is tumescent; %D is the percentage of her bouts given to a male when she is not swollen. Figures in parentheses denote total No. of grooming bouts given.

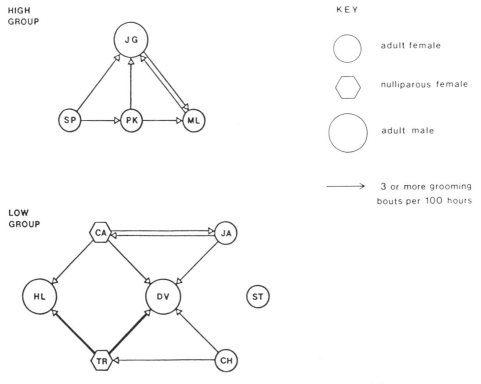

Figure 2. Sociograms of grooming rates between adult animals. Each directed arrow indicates 3 or more bouts of grooming given per 100 hours of total observation.

the dominant female of HIGH group and once by the dominant male (HL) of LOW group. The leader male of LOW group (DV) supported parous or nulliparous females against an aggressive subadult (5 cases) and when HL herded females, DV twice interfered on the females' behalf. In intergroup encounters [Byrne et al., 1987], he acted to protect juveniles. Thus, leader males support losers in agonism and generally act to protect vulnerable group members.

Sexual Behavior

In HIGH group, no adult female was cycling during the 9 months in which all animals were individually recognisable; however, as the group contained only one adult male during the entire 2 year study, he presumably had a monopoly of sexual access and fathered the three young conceived during this time (one to each female).

In LOW group, both adult and subadult females showed tumescence during this 9 month period, and 35 full copulations (that is, ones including a copulation call) were seen, but in most cases these were with older juveniles who continued to cycle regularly. These young females were at times mated by both adult males, the subadult and both juvenile males. However, all six full copulations between males and adult females were by the younger male HL, and all presentations by these females (an additional ten to those resulting in copulation) were to this male.

In summary, the younger adult male HL enjoyed a near monopoly of sexual access to potentially fertile females during the study, while the older DV could gain only occasional access to older juvenile females; thus LOW group, like HIGH group, was reproductively one-male.

Spatial Configuration

Although not a parameter on which a clear hamadryas/savanna baboon distinction is predictable (see Table I), the spatial configuration of individuals was felt important to social considerations and is presented here. Purely social effects in spacing are likely to be superimposed on a background of strong altitudinal and seasonal variation, the latter indicating ecological constraints on association (see Discussion).

Nearest neighbor analysis. Nearest neighbor data were collapsed to a triangular half-matrix for analysis: the samples in which A was B's nearest neighbor were pooled with the (independent) samples in which B was A's. Cases of contact between A and B were excluded to ensure independence from grooming data. Also excluded were all cases over 10 m, since it was felt that at such distances nearest neighbors were largely coincidental. The data (294 samples for HIGH group, 394 for LOW group) were subjected to average-link cluster analysis, and the resulting dendrograms are shown in Figure 3.

Table VI. Pairwise Approach-Retreat Interactions

HIGH group (762 hours)

	JG	PK	DR	SP	SK	PA	ML	JM	RO	
JG	—	20	2	23	6	2	16	7		76
PK		—	7	4	1		5			17
DR			—							0
SP				—			6			6
SK					—		2	1		3
PA						—				0
ML						1	—			1
JM						1		—		1
RO									—	0
Totals	0	20	2	30	12	3	29	8	0	104

LOW group (297 hours)

	HL	DV	ME	JA	SZ	CA	SO	ST	PL	SF	CH	TR	SY	
HL	—	17	6	1	3	7	4	7	8	3	4	20		80
DV	4a	—	12	1	7			1				1		26
ME			—	1	4	1	2	2		3				13
JA			1	—	1		2	7	2	3	6	2	1	25
SZ				1	—				2	1	2	2		8
CA						—			4	3	5			12
SO							—				1	1		2
ST								—						0
PL								1	—	1	2	2		4
SF										—	1	2		3
CH											—			0
TR					2	1						—		3
SY													—	0
Totals	4	17	19	4	16	8	8	17	16	13	18	35	1	176

aTwo of these were classed as counterchases [Hausfater, 1976] and thus do not imply reversal in dominance of HL over DV, while in the other two cases insufficient contextual information was obtained to be positive about their correct classification.

Patterns of association are similar in both study groups. Apart from the predictable clumping of mothers and infants, in both groups a cluster emerges of a single male with adult females. However, in general there is a lack of strong clusters, showing inconsistency in association during daytime ranging.

Do kin forage near each other during the day? With three matrilineal families in each group, and adult males and dependent infants excluded from the analysis, a maximum of 18 animals can be examined for such a tendency. Five animals were observed most often next to kin, but four of these involve the two youngest juveniles. If these latter are excluded, the number of kin neighbours during ranging becomes one out of a possible 16, while the chance level is just over five (chi square = 4.48 at 1 df; significant at $P < 0.05$). It seems that, beyond the early phase of development, kin avoid proximity while ranging.

Spacing of adults. The distance of an animal's nearest neighbour gives little clue as to the spacing of the group as a whole: for instance, if animals regularly form several tightly knit subgroups which range far from each other, all nearest neighbor distances will be low. To measure overall dispersion, the distances between all pairs of adult animals were used.

For HIGH group, data were sufficient to subject these median distances to ANOVA (between 802 and 982 samples per pair). Seasonal changes were examined by splitting the data into midwinter, late winter, spring, and summer periods such that each included approximately equal number of days of observation (but note that the transition from dry winter to wet spring is sharp in this temperate climate, so this boundary could not be chosen arbitrarily).

Within seasons, the data were split into 5 time bands of the same number of days of observation and each band used as a replicate in a repeated measures ANOVA. The data sample within each band was large enough to compute a reliable median value (for each pair, in each band, a mean of 44.8 ± 13.5 samples were used). Median distances were then used in an analysis of pairs (6) against seasons (4). A main effect was significant for pairs—$F(5,24) = 5.9$; $P < 0.01$—and seasons—$F(3,72) = 3.3$; $P < 0.05$—but there was no significant interaction.

Inter-animal distances decreased monotonically from late winter to summer (from 29.9 m in September to 22.1 m in December), while midwinter (June, 27.6 m) distances were slightly less than in late winter; Newman-Keuls tests showed a significant late winter/summer difference ($P < 0.05$), but no others.

For pairs of animals, the median distance of one female, SP, to the male (33.8 m) was the largest, and differed significantly from all other distances except for her distance to another female, ML (29.5 m). This itself is significantly larger than that of the closest two animals, PK and ML (21.1 m) (all Newman-Keuls, $P < 0.05$ or less), and reflects the often peripheral position of SP. Male-female distances (average 28.0 m) and female-female distances (25.2 m) were generally similar.

Perhaps of more significance than the differences between pairs is the consistently high spacing of all of them, bearing in mind that these data are aver-

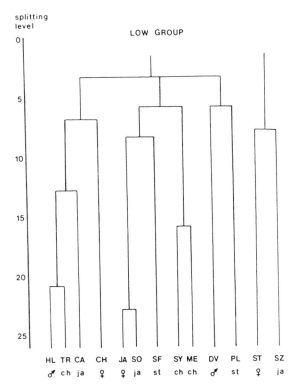

Figure 3. Average-link cluster analysis of
nearest neighbor frequencies among
independently mobile animals; the y-axis shows
the splitting level, with stronger clusters
extracted lower in the figure. Lowercase codes
indicate maternal kinship, as assessed from
Figure 1.

aged over all activities, not merely foraging: the grand mean is 26.6 m for HIGH group.

Even greater dispersion among adults is found in LOW group, with average separation of 66.9 m; unfortunately, sparser data on these animals precludes a full analysis (only between 26 and 129 samples per pair). Median distances were computed, in each season, for the male-male pair, for each male to all females, and among females (for each median, 41 ± 16.3 samples were used). Male-male distances were greatest (average median separation for the four time bands = 112.5 m), and male-female distances least (62.5 for DV and 56.9 for HL), with female-female distances intermediate (66.3 m). Male-male distances in early September, when the males conflicted over a tumescent female, were much larger than in any later time (230 m), whereas male-female and female-female distances varied only between 40 and 75 m, with no simple seasonal effects.

An unexpected finding was the high correlation between a female's median distances to each of the two males, in a given time band (for the 12 female by time band samples, r = 0.80; $P < 0.001$; 11 df). Which animals are responsible for this matching of a female's distance to each male is not known; however, since the older male determines travel direction, it seems likely to be the females or the young male.

DISCUSSION

Mountain baboons differ markedly in their social relationships from typical savanna baboons. Some aspects of this difference can be directly attributed to mountain baboons' unusual environment: subalpine and montane grassland [Whiten et al., 1987]. Spacing between foraging adults is very great, and a group of around ten animals is sometimes spread over an area 1 km across. The seasonal variations in these distances suggest food competition as the likely cause. In a predator-free open habitat with no discernible food patches, foraging apart from other animals is a good strategy for an adult, especially during the food bottleneck of the cold, dry season. The very low rates of approach-retreat interactions are presumably a consequence of this strategy; though infrequent, these interactions showed a linear hierarchy of dominance with offspring ranking below their mothers, just as in other baboons [Abegglen, 1984, for hamadryas; Hausfater et al., 1982, for yellow baboons]. The tendency of animals to avoid foraging adjacent to their maternal kin after their earliest years, found in this population, will effectively direct what little food competition remains, away from known close relatives.

To explain other differences in social relationships, the size and composition of mountain baboon groups must be taken into account, although these parameters may themselves be a product of ecology [Anderson, 1982; Byrne et al., 1987]. Groups at Giants Castle are unusually small [Whiten et al., 1987] and tend to be unimale in composition (Byrne et al., 1987]. Further, both groups in the present study contained several small maternal families, with low affiliation between the single parous females of each family, rather than the extensive matrilines typical of savanna baboons. Such a lack of female-female affiliation is consistent with the female transfer known for mountain baboons elsewhere [Anderson, 1981b], and would account for the absence of alliances and low rates of support in agonistic interactions seen at this site. In the few triadic interactions seen, females and juveniles support younger kin, but not members of other families.

Instead of close and differentiated relationships among adult females, mountain baboon groups at Giants Castle show strong affiliation of females towards a single male. Lactating or pregnant females focus their grooming on this male, producing a *hamadryas*-like radially patterned sociogram; the male supports young animals and those losing in agonism in the group, defends them against aggression and protects them against external threats. The same male is usually the decision-making animal in controlling group movements, and is usefully termed the "leader."

While a number of mountain baboon groups are demographically unimale one group studied in detail here contained two males. There appeared to be a marked age difference between the two males, and the leader was not the dominant animal. The younger, dominant male had sexual monopoly during the study and herded females both during intergroup encounters [Byrne et al., 1987] and at other times. Females increased their grooming of this male when sexually active, while at other times they chiefly groomed the older leader.

In both unimale and two-male groups, females (regardless of their sexual state) tended to range nearest to an adult male, and in the unimale group females were more often displaced from food sources by the male than any other animal. At first sight, for a female to belong to a two-male group would seem to incur disadvantage in such feeding competition, but other factors may balance this cost. In the two-male group studied here, adult females' distances to each male remained very similar, while the absolute distance varied widely with season, and these females were much less often displaced from food by a male than those in the one-male group. But despite this suggestion that the leader and the dominant males can be "played off" against each other to reduce their impact as food competitors, it should be noted that distances between foraging adults in this group were higher overall. As yet, we lack a metric for comparing these direct and indirect mechanisms for lowering food competition.

Convergence with *hamadryas* social organization has been suggested for mountain baboons [Anderson, 1981a, 1982; Byrne et al., 1987; Whiten et al., 1987]. The current study shows that convergences exist in intragroup social relationships as well as in intergroup organization. On all five social contrasts identified in Table I, Drakensberg mountain baboons matched hamadryas, not savanna baboons. In particular, the young, dominant male HL with his frequent aggressive herding of females and close affiliation with two not-yet-adult females can be compared with a *hamadryas* initial unit [e.g., Guy's unit, p. 71, and Fig. 35, Kummer, 1968]; male JG, who herds only in intergroup encounters yet has the strong affiliation and control of three parous females, can be compared with a *hamadryas* unit at its peak (e.g., Smoke's unit, p. 33 and Fig. 15b, ibid.); and old male DV, with control of group travel but no herding of females, who show strong affiliation towards him but mate with the young male HL "follower," resembles the unit of a male in old age (e.g., Rosso's unit, p. 75 and Fig. 37, ibid.).

Theoretical Implications

Theories for the origin of one-male groups in mountain baboons have been discussed elsewhere [Byrne et al., 1987]. What the current results show is that these groups in the Drakensburg resemble the one-male units of hamadryas more than superficially, so that an adequate theory should explain both. Unfortunately, there are very few data for comparative analysis on the small, one-male groups that occasionally form within more normal savanna baboon populations [Stein & Stacey, 1981; Stacey, 1986]. We propose that the key ecological variables must be the absence of predation in the Drakensberg and in Arabia [Byrne et al., 1987; Kummer et al., 1985], and the very low and similar densities of mountain and hamadryas baboons [Whiten et al., 1987]. Neither factor alone can be sufficient, since the decline to equally low densities in yellow baboons (*P. cynocephalus*) at Amboseli [Altmann et al., 1985] nor the common elimination of large predators from baboon habitat cause a switch to one-male groups. With no predators, and very low population density, one-male groups may be an inevitable consequence, and a multilevel society would then be a subsequent response to reinstated predation, as Kummer et al. [1985] argue for the case of Ethiopian hamadryas. The test, of reintroducing leopard to Giants Castle, has yet to be done, but at Suikerbosrand, Anderson (pers. comm.) has recently witnessed the results of a natural recolonization by leopard. Subtrooping decreased, but subtroop membership became nearly invariant in units which were largely unimale harems, and the males enjoyed more nearly exclusive mating even when their harems were together in the main troop.

This degree of flexibility, affecting not just group size and composition but a radical switch from matrilocal female-bonded groups to a hamadryas structure, seems very surprising. But is this surprise partly created by overreliance on the category of "female-bonded" primates (Wrangham, 1980)? This category, as defined by Wrangham, has to include savanna baboons, since they show male transfer and differentiated female relationships; however, they also display close relationships between particular males and females which are long-lasting and can modify the typically non-exclusive sexual relationships [Ransom, 1971; Dunbar, 1973; Seyfarth, 1978; Smuts, 1983]. Most recent studies of savanna baboons do not present data that allow a direct comparison of female-female and female-male affiliation. Those that do, fail to show that troops are socially structured around females: e.g., Collins [1981], in which female-female and female-male grooming closely resemble that expected from random allocation; and Saayman [1971], in which females groom each other less and males more than chance, as in the present study.

This apparent conflict can be resolved by a reformation of terminology. The term "female-bonded" clearly implies groups bonded together by close affiliative links between females. It does not necessarily suggest groups with female residence and breeding in natal groups. A term already exists for the latter, "matrilocal" groups. If all *matrilocal* primates formed female-bonded groups, the issue would be merely semantic, but baboons demonstrate that this is not the case, showing stronger *cross-sex bonding* in at least some and perhaps all populations.

We suggest that it may prove to be misleading, when searching for evolutionary explanations, to pigeon-hole baboons (and perhaps also macaques) together with Old World monkeys whose groups *are* female-bonded as well as matrilocal. Some of the latter are also multimale (e.g., vervets, *Cercopithecus aethiops*), yet apparently always lack male-female bonding [Henzi, 1985; Smuts, 1987], and thus have no basis for a switch to non-female-bonded organization. Recognizing this distinction among matrilocal monkeys, between cross-sex-bonded and female-bonded types, may help explain the quite different ecological circumstances in which typically multimale groups become one-male: high density in vervets [Gartlan & Brain, 1968] but low density in hamadryas and mountain baboons.

CONCLUSIONS

1. Small groups of mountain baboons lack the characteristic social relationships of female-bonded primates.
2. Instead, a single male usually leads and defends each group. This male is the social focus for females even when lactating or pregnant, and supports weaker animals in the occasional intragroup agonism.
3. A single male monopolized mating with potentially fertile females in both mountain baboon groups during the study; in the two-male group, it was the dominant, young male who mated adult females, not the older, leader male.
4. Detailed parallels are found between the social structure of particular mountain baboon groups and units of *hamadryas* baboon at different ontogenetic stages.
5. Inter-adult spacing during ranging is very great, especially at the harshest time of year, and kin tend to forage apart, suggesting that avoidance of food competition is the reason. Approach-retreat and triadic interactions are rare in mountain baboons.

ACKNOWLEDGMENTS

This research was supported by the Science and Engineering Research Council. We are grateful to the Natal Parks Board for permission to conduct this research, and in particular for the help of Dr. M. Brooks, D. & M. Yunie, R. & S. Physic, G. & W. Goody, W. Barnes, and W. Whitfield; to F. Benzies for help with collecting the data; to L. Miller for advice on data processing. We thank B. Smuts, R. I. M. Dunbar, A. Collins, J. Johnson, H. Kummer, and J. Graves for much helpful advice and discussion, and J. Altmann and three anonymous referees for many useful suggestions.

S. P. Henzi is now at Department of Psychology, University of Natal, Durban 4001, R.S.A.

REFERENCES

Abegglen, J. J. ON SOCIALIZATION IN HAMADRYAS BABOONS. Cranbury, NJ, Associated University Presses, 1984.

Aldrich-Blake, P.; Bunn, T.; Dunbar, R.; Headley, P. Observations on baboons, *Papio anubis*, in an arid region of Ethiopia. FOLIA PRIMATOLOGICA 15:1–35, 1971.

Altmann, S. A.; Altmann, J. BABOON ECOLOGY. Chicago, University of Chicago Press, 1970.

Altmann, J.; Hausfater, G.; Altmann, S. Demography of Amboseli baboons 1963–1983. AMERICAN JOURNAL OF PRIMATOLOGY 8:113–125, 1985.

Anderson, C. M. Subtrooping in a chacma baboon (*Papio ursinus*) population. PRIMATES 22:445–458, 1981a.

Anderson, C. M. Intertroop relations of chacma baboon. INTERNATIONAL JOURNAL OF PRIMATOLOGY 2:285–309, 1981b.

Anderson, C. M. Baboons below the Tropic of Capricorn. JOURNAL OF HUMAN EVOLUTION 11:205–217, 1982.

Anderson, C. M. Levels of social organization and male-female bonding in the genus *Papio*. AMERICAN JOURNAL OF PHYSICAL ANTHROPOLOGY 60:15–22, 1983.

Byrne, R. W.; Whiten, A. Tactical deception of familiar individuals in baboons. ANIMAL BEHAVIOUR 33:669–673, 1985.

Byrne, R. W.; Whiten, A.; Henzi, S. P. One-male groups and intergroup interactions of mountain baboons. INTERNATIONAL JOURNAL OF PRIMATOLOGY 8:615–633, 1987.

Cheney, D. L. The acquisition of rank and the development of reciprocal alliances among free-ranging immature baboons. BEHAVIORAL ECOLOGY AND SOCIOBIOLOGY 2:303–318, 1977.

Collins, D. A. SOCIAL BEHAVIOR AND PATTERNS OF MATING AMONG ADULT YELLOW BABOONS (*Papio c. cynocephalus*). Ph.D. thesis, University of Edinburgh, 1981.

Dunbar, R. I. M. SOCIAL DYNAMICS OF THE GELADA BABOON, *Theropithecus gelada*. Ph.D. thesis, University of Bristol, 1973.

Gartlan, J. S.; Brain, C. K. Ecology and social variability in *Cercopithicus aethiops* and *C. mitis*. Pp. 253–292 In PRIMATES: STUDIES IN ADAPTATION AND VARIABILITY. P. Jay, ed. New York, Holt Rinehart & Winston, 1968.

Gordon, A. D. CLASSIFICATION: METHODS FOR THE EXPLORATORY ANALYSIS OF MULTIVARIATE DATA. London, Champan-Hall, 1981.

Hall, K. R. L. The sexual, agonistic and derived social behaviour patterns of the wild chacma baboon, *Papio ursinus*. PROCEEDINGS OF THE ZOOLOGICAL SOCIETY OF LONDON 13:283–327, 1962.

Hall, K. R. L.; De Vore, I. Baboon social behaviour. Pp. 53:110 in PRIMATE BEHAVIOR. I. De Vore, ed. Holt, Rinehart and Winston, 1965.

Hausfater, G. DOMINANCE AND REPRODUCTION IN BABOONS (PAPIO CYNOCEPHALUS). Basel, S. Karger, 1975.

Hausfater, G.; Altmann, S.; Altmann, J. Long-term consistency of dominance relations among female baboons (*Papio cynocephalus*). SCIENCE 217:752–755, 1982.

Henzi, S. P. Genital signaling and the coexistence of male vervet monkeys (*Cercopithecus aethiops pygerythrus*). FOLIA PRIMATOLOGICA 45:129–147, 1985.

Kummer, H. SOCIAL ORGANIZATION OF HAMADRYAS BABOONS. A FIELD STUDY. Chicago, University of Chicago Press, 1968.

Kummer, H. From laboratory to desert and back: A social system of hamadryas baboons. ANIMAL BEHAVIOUR 32:965–971, 1984.

Kummer, H.; Banaja, A. A.; Abo-Khatwa, A. N.; Ghandour, A. M. Differences in social behaviour between Ethiopian and Arabian hamadryas baboons. FOLIA PRIMATOLOGICA 45:1–8, 1985.

Melnick, D. J.; Pearl, M. C. Cercopithecines in multimale groups: Genetic diversity and population structure. Pp. 121–134 in PRIMATE SOCIETIES. B. B. Smuts, D. L. Cheney, R. M. Seyfarth, R. W. Wrangham, T. T. Struhsaker, eds. Chicago, University of Chicago Press, 1987.

Nagel, U. A comparison of anubis baboons, hamadryas baboons and their hybrids at a species border in Ethiopia. FOLIA PRIMATOLOGICA 19:104–165, 1973.

Packer, C. Reciprocal altruism in olive baboons. NATURE 265:441–443, 1977.

Ransom, T. W. ECOLOGY AND SOCIAL BEHAVIOUR OF BABOONS (*Papio anubis*) AT THE GOMBE NATIONAL PARK. Ph.D. Thesis, University of California, Berkeley, 1971.

Ransom, T. W.; Rowell, T. Early social development of feral baboons. Pp. 105–144 in PRIMATE SOCIALIZATION. F. Poirier, ed. New York, Random House, 1972.

Rasmussen, D. Communities of baboon troops (*Papio cynocephalus*) in Mikumi National Park, Tanzania. FOLIA PRIMATOLOGICA 36:232–242, 1981.

Rowell, T. THE SOCIAL BEHAVIOUR OF MONKEYS. Harmondsworth, Penguin Books, 1972.

Saayman, G. S. Grooming behaviour in a troop of free-ranging chacma baboons. FOLIA PRIMATOLOGICA 16:161–178, 1971.

Seyfarth, R. M. Social relations among adult male and female baboons. II. Behaviour throughout the female reproductive cycle. BEHAVIOUR 64:227–247, 1978.

Seyfarth, R. M.; Cheney, D. L. Grooming, alliances and reciprocal altruism in vervet monkeys. NATURE 308:541–543, 1984.

Sharman, M. FEEDING, RANGING AND SOCIAL ORGANIZATION OF THE GUINEA BABOON, *Papio papio*. Ph.D. Thesis, University of St. Andrews, 1980.

Smuts, B. B. Special relationships between adult male and female olive baboons: Selective advantages. Pp. 262–266 in PRIMATE SOCIAL RELATIONSHIPS. R.A. Hinde, ed. Oxford, Blackwell, 1983.

Smuts, B. B. Gender, aggression and influence. Pp. 400–412 in PRIMATE SOCIETIES. B. B. Smuts, D. L. Cheney, R. M. Seyfarth, R. W. Wrangham, T. T. Struhsaker, eds. Chicago, University of Chicago Press, 1987.

Stacey, P. B. Group size and foraging efficiency in yellow baboons. BEHAVIORAL ECOLOGY AND SOCIOBIOLOGY 18:175–187, 1986.

Stammbach, E. Desert, forest and montane baboons: Multilevel societies. Pp. 112–120 in PRIMATE SOCIETIES. B. B. Smuts, D. L. Chency, R. M. Seyfarth, R. W. Wrangham, T. T. Struhsaker, eds. Chicago, University of Chicago Press, 1987.

Stein, D. M.; Stacey, P. B. A comparison of infant-adult male relations in a one-male group with those in a multi-male group for yellow baboons (*Papio cynocephalus*). FOLIA PIMATOLOGICA 36:264–276, 1981.

Walters, J. Inferring kinship from behaviour: Maternity determinations in yellow baboons. ANIMAL BEHAVIOUR 29:126–136, 1981.

Whiten, A.; Byrne, R. W.; Henzi, S. P. Behavioral ecology of mountain baboons. INTERNATIONAL JOURNAL OF PRIMATOLOGY 8:367–388, 1987.

Wrangham, R. W. An ecological model of female-bonded primate groups. BEHAVIOUR 75:262–300, 1980.

Male Age, Dominance, and Mating Success Among Rhesus Macaques

Carol A. McMillan
_____ *Wenatchee Valley College North, Washington* _____

Abstract: Some previous primate studies have found a positive correlation between male dominance and mating success when data from subadult males were included in the analyses. The information in this paper suggests that an unconscious bias may have been introduced when data on subadult males were included because of the lower dominance rank of these animals. Data from a study of rhesus monkeys on Cayo Santiago showed that subadult males mated significantly less than adults. Because these monkeys are not fully mature, data on them should not be used in any test for correlation between adult male dominance and mating success.

The only significant correlation found for adult male mating success was an inverse one with relation to age. Based on behavioral data young, fully adult males have the best chance of fathering offspring regardless of their dominance rank.

Key Words: Cayo Santiago, Subadult males, Dominance systems

Since the earliest primate behavior studies in the 1930s, researchers have been attempting to identify male characteristics that contribute to reproductive success. Not only basic biological factors (e.g., sperm production) but also social and developmental factors have been suggested to influence the likelihood that a given male will father offspring. The primary focus of most primate mating studies has been the relationship between mating and male dominance. In 1932 Sir Solly Zuckerman noted that the frequency of mating among captive Hamadryas baboon males was highly variable, and he concluded (1) that because dominant males are more aggressive they have greater access to estrous females than do lower ranking males, and (2) that the limit to the number of females held by any single male was determined by his dominance status (Zuckerman, 1932). Although many studies have attempted to verify or refute these statements, there is little agreement among the reports. Fedigan (1983) has written a comprehensive review of dominance and reproductive success in primates in which she points out the contradictory findings. She believes that some of the problems implicated in the mixed results include the difficulty in measuring male reproductive success and in conceptualizing dominance systems.

This paper presents new data on the extent to which mating success is related to both the age and the dominance status of rhesus males on Cayo Santiago and attempts to separate the effects of these two variables. Failure to separate these variables in some previous studies may be another factor that has contributed to the lack of agreement among researchers concerning the relationship of dominance and mating success in male primates. Young males generally produce sperm and ejaculate before they exhibit adult behaviors and mating patterns (Conaway and Sade, 1965; Hanby and Brown, 1974; Wolfe, 1978; Takahata, 1980). These "subadults" are generally low ranking (Hausfater, 1975; Wolfe, 1978). To include data on such males in analyses of dominance and mating success may give rise to illusory correlations when none actually exist.

MATERIALS AND METHODS

Mating data were collected for this study from mid-June through mid-December of 1980 at Cayo Santiago, Puerto Rico. Cayo Santiago is an L-shaped, 15.5 hectare island lying .94 km off the southeastern coast of Puerto Rico. The terrain is rugged and varied. Although rhesus monkeys are not native to Cayo Santiago, in many respects the island offers an environment similar to their natural one. For the purposes of this study one of the most important aspects of the site was the ability of the animals to range freely through varied terrain, much of it rugged and covered with vegetation. They thus had free access to secluded places at all times. They were, however, provisioned daily in three open-access feeding corrals, and rainwater was collected in catchment systems and dispersed at drinking fountains around the island.

During the 1980 mating season there were over 800 monkeys on the island living in one of six social groups, designated F, I, J, L, M, and O. Social groups of rhesus monkeys are composed of a stable core of females and their female offspring, their immature male offspring, adult males from other groups, and, in some cases, adult natal males (Sade, 1972). At irregular intervals, a social group undergoes "fission," splitting into two separate groups (Sade et al., 1977). A few exceptions to this basic group structure have been noted in the wild (Neville, 1968). On Cayo Santiago continuing sociometric studies of the population have resulted in almost complete knowledge of the female genealogical relationships of all individuals on the island. The genealogies of most of the animals living on Cayo Santiago in 1980 can be traced back through their matrilines to one of 15 females alive in 1956.

The group chosen for observation in this study was group I, a product of several fissionings of group B (Sade et al., 1977). No fission had occurred since 1961. The group ranged in size from 159 to 163 animals during the 7 months of this study. No births or deaths occurred in the troop during the mating season. The data on social group I were collected during 2,555 hours of observation by four observers. Modified focal animal samples (Altmann, 1974) were collected for adult females when they showed multiple signs of estrus based on behavior and body coloration (Kaufmann, 1965; Michael and Zumpe, 1970; Zumpe and Michael, 1970) and swelling (Czaja et al., 1975). Periods of most probable fertility were later calculated for each female based on a combination of two methods reported on by Riopelle and Hale (1975) and by Gordon (1981). Riopelle and Hale's formula was used to determine the fertile estrous cycle, taking into consideration the sex of the offspring, approximate weight and protein intake of the mother, and the daily temperature on the island. Gordon's method was used to determine the most probable day of ovulation within the fertile cycle. A period of "+" 4 days (1 S.D. in the estimated gestation length) was taken around the probable conception date and was considered to be a female's most probable fertile period.

Forty-eight of 57 females ranging in age from 2.5 to 21 years showed multiple signs of estrus. Thirty-five of these females subsequently gave birth to live offspring; one animal died before giving birth, and two aborted.

Thirty-nine males were observed to copulate with females in group I during the 1980 mating season. All 39 were members of the group for at least 1 month. A copulation was defined as a mating bout that ended in an ejaculation, as evidenced by a characteristic stiffening of the male and by residual ejaculate seen afterward on the male or female. Of all the males 6 years of age and older, only two (7.7%) failed to copulate, while of those 3.5 to 5.5 years of age five (22.7%) were never seen to copulate.

Male dominance relationships were defined by the direction of cowers (Gordon, 1981) between pairs of males. While attempting to determine the dominance hierarchy among the males, it became apparent that older males generally had established positions (although these may be subject to change) while younger males did not. The age of 5 years seemed transitional, with some 5-year-olds having established ranks while others seemed to have the indeterminate status of the younger males. Because of this uncertain status of 5-year-old males, they formed the cut-off point at which the age groups were divided: subadult, 3.5 to 5.5 years of age; adult, 6 years and older.

Only one rank reversal was observed among the 23 fully adult males between the months of August and November; that occurred at the beginning of the mating season, and thus the subsequent ranks were used for those two males in the analyses. Eleven males under 5 years of age were observed to copulate in group I; all ranked below these males but did not have clearly defined ranks among themselves. For this reason these 11 subadult males were given the same rank, which was equal to the mean of their pooled ranks. Five males who were 5.5 years old had achieved ranks that were stable during the 1980 mating season. Two of these males subsequently left the troop. All 5 were given their 1980 ranks for the analyses.

A core of 34 males was used for the analyses. These were all the males who were in the troop during at least the 4 months of the most intensive mating, mid-July to mid-November, who were seen to ejaculate at least once or who were 6 years of age or older. Every male with a stable dominance rank through-

282

out the season was included. Of the subadult males only those seen to ejaculate at least once were included.

Eight variables concerning mating behavior were calculated for the analyses. Since focal samples (Altmann, 1974) were taken only during estrous periods and since females had estrous periods of difficult duration and quantity, each female did not receive an equal number of hours of focal observation. The variables were calculated in such a way that any biases that may have resulted from unequal hours of observation would be eliminated. First, using Hausfater's method, (1975) the mean rate of mating by each male per hour of each female's focal observation was calculated. In other words, for each female the total number of matings by each individual male was determined; this number was then divided by the number of hours that the female was observed, giving a mating rate per hour for each male with each female. These rates were then averaged for each male across all females. Two variables were calculated in this manner: the mean number of mating bouts per hour and the mean number of ejaculations per hour for each male. The sample included 1,410 mating bouts and 656 ejaculations.

The six remaining variables were calculated from observation samples of data of uniform duration, thus correcting in a second manner for any possible biases resulting from differing amounts of observation on each female. Samples of 10 hours of observation during a female's probable fertile period and 15 hours of observation during a probable infertile period were taken from the data. The 10 hours of observation nearest her estimated day of ovulation were available for 25 females. The 15 hour samples were available for 33 females; these samples were taken from observations that were farthest from a female's time of probable fertility but that occurred during a period of active mating. Seventeen females had sufficient data available to be used in both the fertile and infertile period samples. The samples included 846 mating bouts and 402 ejaculations. Six variables were calculated from this sample: the number of mating bouts during probable fertile periods, the number of mating bouts during probable infertile periods, the number of ejaculations during probable fertile periods, the number of ejaculations during probable infertile periods, the total number of mating bouts, and the total number of ejaculations. Although sperm regeneration time may affect these variables, this study was based on focal animal sampling of the females, not males; therefore, the question of sperm regeneration could not be meaningfully incorporated into the analyses.

RESULTS

Age and Class Differences and Mating Success

Table 1 shows that fully adult males had significantly higher mean rates of mating bouts per hour of female observation than subadult males and significantly higher mean rates of ejaculation, engaged in significantly more mating

Table 1. Mann-Whitney U tests of association between male adult and subadult status and eight mating variables

Variable	U	P
Rate of mating bouts	44.0	≤0.001
Rate of ejaculations	41.5	≤0.001
Number of fertile period mating bouts	59.5	<0.01
Number of infertile period mating bouts	39.0	≤0.001
Number of fertile period ejaculations	58.5	<0.01
Number of infertile period ejaculations	36.0	≤0.001
Total number of mating bouts	49.5	≤0.001
Total number of ejaculations	49.0	<0.001

Table 2. Kendall's correlation coefficients for male dominance and eight mating variables

Variable	Adult and subadult male τ	P	Adult male τ	P
Rate of mating bouts	0.437	≤0.001	0.026	N.S.
Rate of ejaculations	0.475	≤0.001	0.092	N.S.
Fertile period mating bouts	0.527	≤0.001	0.214	N.S.
Infertile period mating bouts	0.478	≤0.001	0.257	N.S.
Fertile period ejaculations	0.518	≤0.001	0.181	N.S.
Infertile period ejaculations	0.564	≤0.001	0.341	<0.05
Total mating bouts	0.519	≤0.001	0.242	N.S.
Total ejaculations	0.568	≤0.001	0.313	<0.05

Table 3. Kendall's correlation coefficients for male age and eight mating variables

Variable	Kendall's τ	P
Rate of mating bouts	−0.151	N.S.
Rate of ejaculations	−0.069	N.S.
Fertile period mating bouts	−0.390	0.01
Infertile periods mating bouts	−0.076	N.S.
Fertile period ejaculations	−0.303	0.001
Infertile period ejaculations	−0.021	N.S.
Total mating bouts	−0.185	N.S.
Total ejaculations	−0.076	N.S.

bouts and ejaculations during females' periods of probable fertility and infertility, and achieved significantly more total mating bouts and ejaculations ($P<0.01$ in all cases, Mann-Whitney U test).

To determine the effect of age-class differences on the association of male dominance rank and mating success, Kendall's correlation coefficients were calculated for male dominance with the eight mating variables using data from both adult and subadult males. Second, the same tests were done using data only from the fully adult males. Table 2 shows that when adult and subadult males were considered together, significant positive correlations were found in all cases. However, all positive correlations with a probability less than 0.01 disappeared when data from only the fully mature males were analyzed. A correlation of $P<0.05$ remained for ejaculations during periods of probable infertility but not for ejaculations during periods of probable fertility. In other words, dominance rank was found to correlate significantly with mating success, as measured by all variables related to the likelihood of fertilization, only when data from subadult males were included in the analyses.

Age, Dominance, and Mating Success Among Fully Adult Males

No significant correlation was found between dominance rank and male age (Kendall rank order correlation coefficient = 0.185, P = 0.12, N.S.) among fully adult males. Since age was not related to dominance in adult males and since differences in age-class (i.e., adult vs. subadult status) largely account for differences in mating frequencies, the next question asked was whether age continued to affect the probability of mating success once a male became an adult. To answer this question, Kendall rank order correlation coefficient tests were done for male age with the eight measures of mating behavior for fully adult males who were in the troop throughout the mating season.

No significant correlations were found between male age and the rate of mating bouts, the rate of ejaculations, the numbers of infertile period mating bouts and ejaculations, or the total number of mating bouts or ejaculations (Table 3). Interestingly, however, negative correlations were found between the age of the male and the number of fertile period mating bouts (Kendall's rank order correlation coefficient = −0.390, P=0.012) and between male age and the number of fertile period ejaculations (Kendall's rank order correlation coefficient = −0.303, P =0.001). Indeed, the young adult males (6 to 8 years) engaged in significantly more ejaculations than older adult males (over 8 years of age) (Fisher's exact probability test, $P < 0.001$). Since the number of ejaculations observed during a female's most fertile period is probably the best estimate of a male's likelihood of fertilizing that female, these data suggest that a male's effective mating activity may peak during young adulthood and decline with age. However, this conclusion must be tentative because this is a cross-sectional rather than longitudinal sample.

285

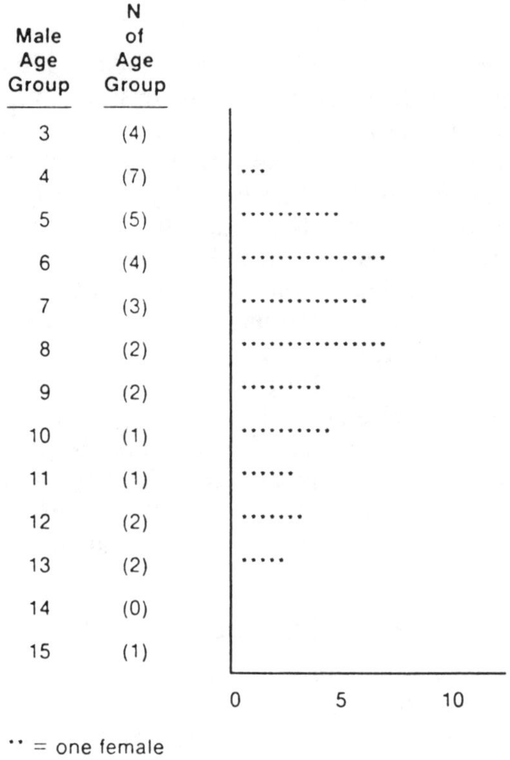

Male Age Group	N of Age Group
3	(4)
4	(7)
5	(5)
6	(4)
7	(3)
8	(2)
9	(2)
10	(1)
11	(1)
12	(2)
13	(2)
14	(0)
15	(1)

·· = one female

Figure 1. The mean number of females in probable fertile periods ejaculated with per male for each male age group. Two asterisks equal one female.

Male Age and Numbers of Mates

Each male ejaculated with a mean of 5.42 females (range, 0-14) when the females were in their probable fertile periods. Adult male age was negatively correlated with the number of probable fertile females with whom the male ejaculated (Kendall's rank order correlation coefficient = –0.316, $P=0.015$). Thus young males were not only more apt to ejaculate with probable fertile females than were older adult males, but they were also more apt to do so with a larger number of different individuals. Figure 1 shows that the number of fertile females with whom a male ejaculates appears to rise abruptly as he becomes fully adult, and then to decrease with time.

DISCUSSION

There are several reasons for the lack of agreement among researchers relating to the correlation or noncorrelation of dominance and mating success among primate males. One problem is differences in sampling techniques. Relatively early studies using ad libitum sampling methods on rhesus monkeys (Carpenter, 1942; Conaway and Koford, 1964; Kaufmann, 1965) showed positive correlations between male dominance and mating success. Drickamer (1974) later pointed out the problem of observability bias in ad libitum sampling. Using data from ad libitum sampling of a group of free-ranging rhesus monkeys, he found a positive correlation between male dominance rank and the number of matings observed. When he corrected for the differing degrees of observability of males of different ranks, however, the correlation disappeared. Thus the correlations observed in other studies using ad libitum sampling methods may reflect the fact that the matings of more dominant males are more easily seen.

Another problem causing disagreement in mating studies is that some researchers have based their conclusions on observed numbers of consortships and not on actual copulations (Carpenter, 1942; Conaway and Koford, 1964; Chapais, 1983, 1986). However, a male who spends a great deal of time grooming and sitting with an estrous female does not necessarily have sole access or even the most frequent access to her for mating. Quick copulations in the bushes "behind the back" of the consorting male were found to be very frequent occurrences among the rhesus monkeys on Cayo Santiago (McMillan, 1984).

A third source of discrepancy among mating studies may be differences in the environments in which the studies take place. A study by Smith (1981) found a positive correlation between dominance and mating success in rhesus males, but Smith's study was done in quarter-acre compounds, which may not accurately reflect a wild situation. Where there is little cover available covert matings by lower ranking males are less probable (Kaufmann, 1965; Loy, 1971; Hausfater, 1975; McMillan, 1984).

This paper presented evidence for a fourth reason for bias in mating studies: the inclusion of data on subadult males in an analysis of dominance rank and mating success. Among the fully adult males in this study, when considered by themselves, mating success (as measured by the number of ejaculations achieved during a period of probable female fertility) was not found to be correlated with dominance, but it was found to be inversely correlated with male age. The young adult males where shown to be the most sexually active during periods of highest female fertility. Overall, however, they were no more sexually active than were the older males. These data indicate that a male's effective mating activity may peak during his years of young adulthood. However, it was also shown that during the 1980 mating season the group I subadult males mated significantly less than the adults. Since subadults have low dominance rank, mating success was found to correlate with dominance rank only when these males were included in the analyses. When only the fully adult males were considered, the correlations were no longer present. Researchers who have included data on subadult males in their mating studies (e.g., Loy, 1971; Smith, 1981) may have introduced an unintentional bias into their analyses. Berkovitch (1986) and Dewsbury (1982) also point out that some anomalies in the literature can be explained because some researchers have included immature males in their analyses.

Sixteen studies of eight primate species (Jay, 1963; Reynolds, 1963; Simonds, 1965; Jolly, 1966; Baldwin, 1968; Goodall, 1969; Saayman, 1971; Sugiyama, 1971; Drickamer, 1974; Eaton, 1974; Enomoto, 1978; Bygott, 1979; Tutin, 1979; Coe and Levin, 1980; Wolfe, 1981; Johnson et al., 1982) found no correlation between male dominance rank and mating success even though most involved one or more methods that could have biased the results in favor of a positive correlation. Twelve studies of seven primate species (Carpenter, 1942; Tokuda, 1961–2; Conaway and Koford, 1964; Williams, 1968; Yoshiba, 1968; Loy, 1971; Suarez and Ackerman, 1971; Hanby and Brown, 1974; Struhsaker, 1975; Hausfater, 1975; Packer, 1979; Smith, 1981) did find positive correlations but all twelve had one or more of the above mentioned problems that introduced biases.

Despite the increasing evidence against a positive correlation between male dominance and mating success in most primate species, the assumption that such a correlation exists remains the basis for at least one current theory in primatology: infanticide by dominant males. Although this assumption is necessary in the theoretical argument for infanticide by dominant males, few, if any, researchers investigating infanticide have first tested the dominance/mating success question using unbiased methods. In fact, most have never tested it at all (Primate Information Center, 1982). The evidence against a correlation of dominance and mating success is certainly now great enough that the assumption of a correlation must never be used as a basis for further research without first being rigorously tested for the species being studied. Furthermore, evidence in this paper suggests that evolutionary hypotheses relating mating success to male age rather than to dominance rank many prove fruitful for future research.

ACKNOWLEDGEMENTS

Research for this article was supported in part by NIH grant DRR-ARG N01-RR-7-2115 to the Caribbean Primate Research Center of the University of Puerto Rico and by grants from the Department of Anthropology and the Graduate School of the State University of New York at Buffalo. I thank Cheryl Alongi, Phil Jackson, and Peter Killoran for their assistance in data collection and Carol Berman and Lois Uhl for their editorial assistance.

LITERATURE CITED

Altmann J (1974) Observational study of behavior: Sampling methods. Behavior 49: 227-264.

Baldwin JD (1968) The social behavior of adult male squirrel monkeys (Saimiri sciures) in a seminatural environment. Folia Primatol. 9:281–314.

Bercovitch FB (1986) Male rank and reproductive activity in savanna baboons. Int. J. Primatol. 7:533–550.

Bygott JD (1979) Agonistic behavior, dominance and social structure in wild chimpanzees of the Gombe National Park. In DA Hamburg and ER McGowm (eds): The Great Ape, Menlo Park. CA: Benjamin-Cummings.

Carpenter CR (1942) Sexual behavior of free-ranging monkeys (Macaca mulatta). J. Comp. Psychol. 33:113–142

Chapais B (1983) Reproductive activity in relation to dominance and the likelihood of ovulation in rhesus monkeys. Behav. Ecol. Sociobiol. 12:215–228.

Chapais B (1986) Why do adult male and female rhesus monkeys affiliate during birth seasons: In RG Rawlins and MJ Kessler (eds): Cayo Santiago Macaques. Albany: State University of New York Press. pp. 172–200.

Coe CL, and Levin RN (1980) Dominance assertion in male chimpanzees *(Pan troglodytes)*. Aggressive Behav. *6*:161–174.

Conaway CH, and Koford CB (1964) Estrous cycles and mating behavior in a free-ranging band of rhesus monkeys. J. Mammal. *45*:577–588.

Conaway CH, and Sade DS (1965) The seasonal spermatogenic cycle in free-ranging rhesus monkeys. Folia Primatol. *3*:1–12.

Czaja JA, Eisele SG, and Goy RW (1975) Cyclical changes in the sexual skin of female rhesus: Relationships to mating behavior and successful artificial insemination. Fed. Proc. *34*:1680–1684.

Dewsbury DA (1982) Dominance rank, copulatory behavior, and differential reproduction. Q. Rev. Biol. *57*:135–159.

Drickamer LC (1974) Social rank, observability and sexual behavior of rhesus monkeys *(Macaca mulatta)*. J. Reprod. Fertil. *37*:117–120

Eaton GG (1974) Male dominance and aggression in Japanese macaque reproduction. In W Montagna and WA Sadler (eds.): Reproductive Behaviour. New York: Plenum, pp. 287–298.

Enomoto T (1978) On social preference in sexual behavior of Japanese monkeys *(Macaca fuscata)*. J. Hum. Evol. *7*:283–293.

Fedigan LM (1983) Dominance and reproductive success in primates. Ybk. Phys. Anthropol. *26*:91–129.

Goodall J (1969) Some aspects of reproduction behaviour in a group of wild chimpanzees, *Pan trolgodytes* (sic) Schweinfurthi: At the Gombe Stream chimpanzee reserve, Tanzania, East Africa. J. Reprod. Fertil. [Suppl.] *6*:353–355.

Gordon TP (1981) Reproductive behavior in the rhesus monkey: Social and endocrine variables. Am. Zool. *21*:185–195.

Hanby J, and Brown C (1974) The development of sociosexual behaviours in Japanese macaques *(Macaca fuscata)*. Behavior *49*:152–196.

Hausfater G (1975) Dominance and reproduction in baboons *(Papio cynocephalus)*: A quantitative analysis. Contrib. Primatol. *7*:1–150.

Jay P (1963) The Indian langur monkey *(Presbytis entellus)*. In C Southwick (ed.): Primate Social Behavior. Princeton: Van Nostrand, p. 114-123.

Johnson DF, Modahl KB, and Eaton GG (1982) Dominance status of adult male Japanese macaques: Relationship to female dominance status, male mating behaviour, seasonal changes, and developmental changes. Anim. Behav. 30: 383-392.

Jolly A (1966) Lemur Behavior: A Madagascar Field Study. Chicago: University of Chicago Press.

Kaufmann JH (1965) A three year study of mating behavior in a free-ranging band of rhesus monkeys. Ecology *46*:500–512.

Lindburg DG (1971) The rhesus monkey in North India: An ecological and behavior study. In Rosenblum LA (ed.): Primate Behavior. New York: Academic Press, Vol. 2, pp. 1–106.

Loy JD (1971) Estrous behavior of free-ranging rhesus monkeys *(Macaca mulatta)*. Primates *12*:1–31.

McMillan CA (1984) Mating length and visibility. Paper presented to the American Society of Primatology, Arcata, CA, June 1984.

Michael RP, and Zumpe D (1970) Rhythmic changes in the copulatory frequency of rhesus monkeys (Macaca mulatta) in relation to the menstrual cycle and a comparison with the human cycle. J. Reprod. Fertil. 21:199–201.

Neville MK (1968) A free-ranging rhesus monkey troop lacking adult males. J. Mammal. 49:771–773.

Packer C (1979) Male dominance and reproductive activity in Papio anubis. Anim. Behav. 27:37–45.

Primate Information Center (1982) Infanticide in Non-human Primates. Seattle: Primate Information Center Press.

Reynolds V (1963) An outline of the behaviour and social organization of forest-living chimpanzees. Folia Primatol. 1:95–102.

Riopelle JA, and Hale PA (1975) Nutritional and environmental factors affecting gestation length in rhesus monkeys. Am. J. Clin. Nutr. 28:1170–1176.

Saayman GS (1971) Behavior of the adult males in a troop of free-ranging chacma baboons (Papio ursinus) Folia Primatol. 15:36–57.

Sade DS, et al. (1972) A longitudinal study of social behavior of rhesus monkeys. In Tuttle R (eds.): Evolutionary Biology of the Primate. New York: Aldine Press, pp. 378–398.

Sade DS (1977) Population dynamics in relation to the social structure of Cayo Santiago. Yrbk. Phys. Anthropol. 20:253–262.

Simonds PE (1965) The bonnett macaque in South India. In Devore I (ed.): Primate Behavior. New York: Holt, Rinehart and Winston, pp. 175–196.

Smith DG (1981) The association between rank and reproductive success of male rhesus. Am. J. Primatol. 1:83–90.

Struhsaker TT (1975) The Red Colobus Monkey. Chicago: University of Chicago Press.

Suarez B, and Ackerman DR (1971) Social dominance and reproductive behavior in male rhesus. Am. J. Phys. Anthropol. 35:219–222.

Sugiyama Y (1971) Characteristics of the social life of bonnett macaques (Macaca radiata). Primates 12:247–266.

Takahata Y (1980) The reproductive biology of a free-ranging troop of Japanese monkeys. Primates 21:303–329.

Tokuda K (1961–2) A study of the sexual behavior in the Japanese monkey troop. Primates 3:1–40.

Tutin CEG (1979) Responses of chimpanzees to copulation, with special reference to interference by immature individuals. Anim. Behav. 27:845–854.

Williams L (1968) Man and Monkey. Philadelphia: Lippincott, p. 116.

Wolfe L (1978) Age and sexual behavior of Japanese macaques (Macaca fuscata). Arch. Sex. Behav. 7:55–68.

Wolfe L (1981) Display behavior of three troops of Japanese monkeys (Macaca fuscata). Primates 7:55–68.

Yoshiba K (1968) Local and inter-troop variability in ecology and social behavior of common Indian langurs. In Jay P (ed.): Primates: Studies in Adaption and Variability. New York: Holt, Rinehart and Winston, pp. 217–242.

Zuckerman S (1932) The Social Life of Monkeys and Apes. London: Kegan Paul, Trench and Trubner.

Zumpe D, and Michael RP (1970) Ovarian hormones and female sexual invitiations in captive rhesus monkeys. Anim. Behav. 18:293–301.

Japanese Macaque Female Sexual Behavior—A Comparison of Arashiyama East and West

Linda D. Wolfe
University of Florida

INTRODUCTION

My interest in the Japanese monkeys *(Macaca fuscata)* of Arashiyama began in 1973 when I was searching for a dissertation project. In April 1973, I met with Claud Bramblett to discuss the possibility of studying the Arashiyama West troop in Texas for my dissertation. I was interested in studying sexual behavior since no other Arashiyama West researcher was currently investigating sexuality. Before beginning my dissertation research at Arashiyama West, I consulted with G. Gray Eaton, chief researcher of the Oregon troop of Japanese macaques, and a scoring schedule was developed. I collected data on the Arashiyama West monkeys during the 1973–74 and 1974–75 breeding seasons. The dissertation was completed in June 1976.

I had lingering questions, however, concerning the sexual behavior of Japanese monkeys, especially those behaviors involving female-female mounting interactions. The existence of female homosexual behavior had been previously documented for Japanese and other macaques [Hanby, 1972; Carpenter, 1942; Chevalier-Skolnikoff, 1974]. However, in my dissertation study of Arashiyama West monkeys there was an unusually high frequency of female homosexual interactions that demanded explanation [Wolfe, 1976, 1979]. Fortunately, Arashiyama B—the intact, genetically related troop which remained in the natural habitat in Japan—existed. I felt that many of those lingering questions I had concerning the sexual behavior of the transported troop could be answered if I were to investigate the sexual behavior of the Arashiyama B (Japan) troop using the same scoring schedule and sampling methods I had used with Arashiyama West (Texas). It was with those thoughts in mind that I observed the Arashiyama B troop between August 1977 and July 1978.

The purpose of this paper is to report on the findings of the research on the sexual behavior of adult females (≥6 years) of both the Arashiyama West and Arashiyama B troops of Japanese macaques.

MATERIALS AND METHODS

Study Subjects

Japanese researchers began studying, provisioning, and identifying the 47 individual monkeys living in the area of Arashiyama, Japan in 1954 [Hazama, 1964]. As a result of provisioning, the size of the troop continued to increase. In 1966, the troop fissioned into two new troops renamed Arashiyama A and Arashiyama B [Koyama 1967, 1970]. The two new troops were nearly equal in size with 98 monkeys in Arashiyama A and 87 in Arashiyama B; and they were similar in age and sex composition [Koyama et al, 1975]. Although the two troops continued to grow following the fission, the age and sex composition of the two troops remained very similar (see Figs. 1, 2). In 1972, 150 of the 158 members of the Arashiyama A troop were transplanted to a 42.2 ha electric fence enclosure located on a ranch 30 miles north of Laredo, Texas. Arashiyama A then became known as Arashiyama West. At the beginning of my study in August 1973 there were 136 monkeys, and at the close of my study in March 1975 there were 148. Within 7 months after transportation, 31 of the original members of Arashiyama West disappeared. This loss of monkeys and the continuing disappearance of monkeys and a low birth rate during the 1973 birth season changed the age and sex composition of Arashiyama West (see Fig. 1) [Clark and Mano, 1975; Wolfe and Noyes, 1981].

Arashiyama B, on the other hand, has remained in its natural habitat and did not experience a decline in the size of the troop (see Fig. 2). Rather, with continued provisioning, the size of the troop has increased, and at the beginning of my study Arashiyama B was composed of 285 monkeys.

Research Period

The Arashiyama West troop was studied between August and March of 1973–74 and 1974–75. This encompassed two breeding seasons and a total of 1,000 h of observations. Of that 1,000 h, 600 h were accumulated during the 1973–74 breeding season and 400 h during the 1974–75 breeding season. The data from the 1973–74 breeding season will be presented quantitatively. Generally, observations were made early in the morning for a minimum of 3 h.

The Arashiyama B troop was observed between mid-August 1977 and mid-July 1978 for a total of 1,000 h. Observations were made in the morning for a minimum of 3 h. The monkeys spent most of their time around the feeding station at the top of the Iwatayama Monkey Park where they are provisioned with various kinds of grains five times a day. Most of my observations were made around the feeding station. The monkeys were also followed on their foraging expeditions and to and from their sleeping sites.

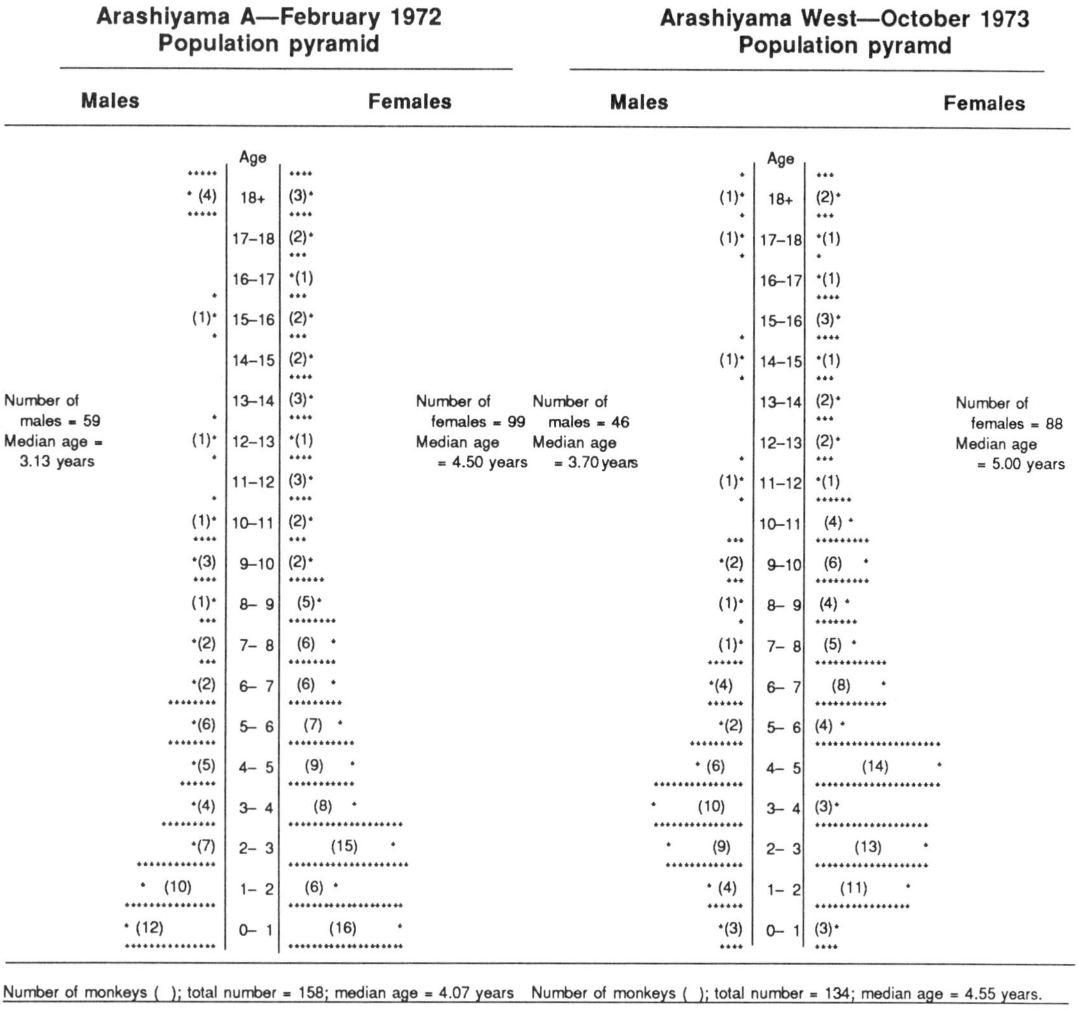

Arashiyama A—February 1972
Population pyramid

Arashiyama West—October 1973
Population pyramd

Figure 1. Population pyramid: Arashiyama A and West.

	Males	Age	Females	
Arashiyama A	(4)	18+	(3)	
		17–18	(2)	
		16–17	(1)	
	(1)	15–16	(2)	
		14–15	(2)	
Number of males = 59		13–14	(3)	Number of females = 99
Median age = 3.13 years	(1)	12–13	(1)	Median age = 4.50 years
		11–12	(3)	
	(1)	10–11	(2)	
	(3)	9–10	(2)	
	(1)	8–9	(5)	
	(2)	7–8	(6)	
	(2)	6–7	(6)	
	(6)	5–6	(7)	
	(5)	4–5	(9)	
	(4)	3–4	(8)	
	(7)	2–3	(15)	
	(10)	1–2	(6)	
	(12)	0–1	(16)	

	Males	Age	Females	
Arashiyama West	(1)	18+	(2)	
	(1)	17–18	(1)	
		16–17	(1)	
		15–16	(3)	
	(1)	14–15	(1)	
Number of males = 46		13–14	(2)	Number of females = 88
Median age = 3.70 years		12–13	(2)	Median age = 5.00 years
	(1)	11–12	(1)	
		10–11	(4)	
	(2)	9–10	(6)	
	(1)	8–9	(4)	
	(1)	7–8	(5)	
	(4)	6–7	(8)	
	(2)	5–6	(4)	
	(6)	4–5	(14)	
	(10)	3–4	(3)	
	(9)	2–3	(13)	
	(4)	1–2	(11)	
	(3)	0–1	(3)	

Number of monkeys ( ); total number = 158; median age = 4.07 years   Number of monkeys ( ); total number = 134; median age = 4.55 years.

Sampling Methods

Arashiyama West. Between August and November 1973, I learned the identity of individuals, a process facilitated by the presence of tattoos. During the 1973–74 and 1974–75 breeding seasons, with the predetermined scoring schedule, I used sequence sampling for recording data on sexual interactions [Altmann, 1974].

Data were coded in a notebook along with context information and later transferred to tally sheets. Monkeys that are sexually active, especially estrous females, are characteristically hyperactive, and it is easy to observe the majority of sexually active monkeys by the end of the 3-h observation period. Often there

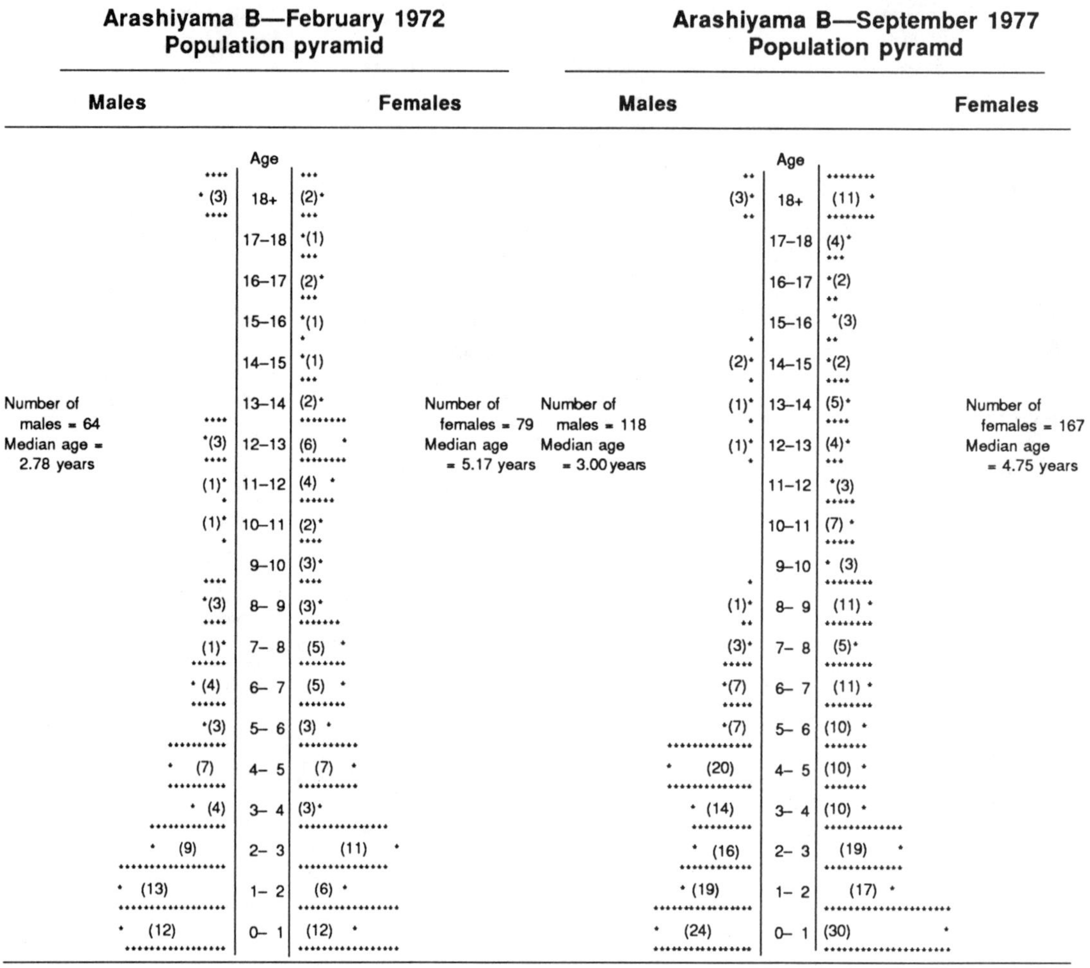

Arashiyama B—February 1972
Population pyramid

Males	Age	Females
(3)	18+	(2)
	17–18	(1)
	16–17	(2)
	15–16	(1)
	14–15	(1)
	13–14	(2)
(3)	12–13	(6)
(1)	11–12	(4)
(1)	10–11	(2)
	9–10	(3)
(3)	8– 9	(3)
(1)	7– 8	(5)
(4)	6– 7	(5)
(3)	5– 6	(3)
(7)	4– 5	(7)
(4)	3– 4	(3)
(9)	2– 3	(11)
(13)	1– 2	(6)
(12)	0– 1	(12)

Number of males = 64
Median age = 2.78 years

Number of females = 79
Median age = 5.17 years

Arashiyama B—September 1977
Population pyramd

Males	Age	Females
(3)	18+	(11)
	17–18	(4)
	16–17	(2)
	15–16	(3)
(2)	14–15	(2)
(1)	13–14	(5)
(1)	12–13	(4)
	11–12	(3)
	10–11	(7)
	9–10	(3)
(1)	8– 9	(11)
(3)	7– 8	(5)
(7)	6– 7	(11)
(7)	5– 6	(10)
(20)	4– 5	(10)
(14)	3– 4	(10)
(16)	2– 3	(19)
(19)	1– 2	(17)
(24)	0– 1	(30)

Number of males = 118
Median age = 3.00 years

Number of females = 167
Median age = 4.75 years

Figure 2. Population pyramid: Arashiyama B.

would be more than one sexual interaction taking place at the same time. During the 1973–74 breeding season the timing of male-female sexual interactions took precedence over the timing of female-female interactions, and during the 1974–75 breeding season female-female mounting interaction took precedence over male-female interactions. When there were two simultaneous adult heterosexual mount sequences occurring, the dyad for which I had the least amount of data was timed. When there was no sexual behavior occurring, visible changes in facial coloration or the presence of injuries or vaginal bleeding were recorded.

Arashiyama B. Between mid-August and mid-October, I learned to recognize the adult members of the troop with the help of a set of identifying photos and Japanese researchers who were familiar with the monkeys. During the

294

breeding season, I collected data on the sexual behavior of the troop as described for Arashiyama West. Yukio Takahata, a Japanese primatologist who was also studying the sexual behavior of the troop, and I freely exchanged data, and I have combined his data with mine where and when appropriate.

Breeding Season

Because the observation of semen is the most obvious, observable, and clear-cut characteristic of the breeding season, it has been chosen as the criterion of the onset and termination of the breeding season. The term breeding season is preferred over mating season because matings (ie, multiplemount copulations) can be observed all year long. Non-breeding-season matings are absent of semen and rarely lead to pregnancies [Kawai, et al, 1967].

The breeding seasons for Arashiyama West 1973–74 and 1974–75 were December 1, 1973, through April 4, 1974 [Linda Fedigan, personal communication] and October 9, 1974, through March 1, 1975, respectively. The Arashiyama B 1977–78 breeding season lasted from October 16, 1977, until March 5, 1978.

Estrus

Because adult female Japanese macaques do not experience a swelling of the perineum or other visible changes during ovulation, it is not possible under field conditions to define estrus by ovulation. Although the face of the adult female is bright red during estrus, the face will remain red for the duration of estrus whether the female is pregnant or not or in estrus for 1 day or 1 month. Therefore, a red face is not necessarily indicative of ovulation. In my research, I defined estrus as the time period in which a female is both proceptive and receptive [Beach, 1976; Carpenter, 1942]. During estrus, adult females are receptive to male attempts at mounting, mount males themselves, and mount and are mounted by other estrous females.

Interestrus Interval

The interestrus interval is the number of days from the beginning of one period of estrus to the beginning of the next period of estrus [Loy, 1981].

Mount Sequence

A copulation was defined as two or more mounts, in a series, between a sexually mature male and female, that terminated when the male ejaculated or failed to mount for 5 min [Hanby, 1972]. Data on the mount sequence was recorded as follows: First, I indicated if the first mount recorded was the beginning of the mount sequence. A mount sequence was scored as beginning if I observed the female approaching the male or the male courting the female immediately prior to the first mount observed. If I first observed the couple with the

295

male mounting the female, I scored the mount sequence as in progress at the initial observation. The time at the onset of observation was also recorded. Then I recorded each mount in sequence, the time in seconds between mounts, the number of thrusts during each mount, the length of each mount, and the activities between mounts. The time of the last mount was also recorded along with a notation of the presence or a absence of semen.

Reachback and Eye Contact

Toward the end of a mount sequence or during the final ejaculatory mount, females will often reach back and clutch and/or scratch the leg, shoulder, or face of the male or turn their heads and stare at the face of their male partners. This clutching is reportedly an indication of female orgasm and was therefore recorded [Zumpe and Michael, 1968].

Consortship

A consortship is an exclusive relationship between two monkeys (male-female, female-female) in which there is prolonged sexual interaction. During consortships, contact is maintained by mutual following and grooming. Prolonged sexual interaction is defined as 1) two or more mount sequences (ie, multimount copulations) in the case of a heterosexual adult pair; 2) two or more mounts in a series in the case of a female-female pair; and 3) two or more mounts in a series in the case of a sexually immature male-sexually mature female dyad [Wolfe, 1979]. Hereafter, the terms female-female mounting interaction and female homosexual consortship will be used interchangeably.

It should be noted that there is a difference between a mount sequence or copulation and a heterosexual adult consortship. While all consortships entail mount sequences, not all mount sequences take place within the context of a consortship. Because consortships seem to entail more intimate relationships and therefore a different behavioral pattern than a simple mount sequence, it is important to keep the two separate when collecting and analyzing data.

Female-female mountings are considered sexual for several reasons: 1) These reciprocal mounting interactions between females are confined to the breeding season. 2) The behavior occurs when the faces of the females are reddened as in heterosexual interactions. 3) The females reciprocate mounting in a series as in mountings between males and females. 4) Females mount each other in a series and using the same position(s) that females use to mount males, and males to mount females. 5) Between mounts females will groom each other, huddle, and forage together; this is similar to the heterosexual consortship. 6) Finally, just as females are usually not mounted by close matrilateral male relatives, they also avoid mounting interactions with close matrilateral female relatives. In addition, females rub, thrust, and press against one another, and occasionally reach back and make eye contact and grimaces during a mount. Primatologists have used these behavior patterns to argue for the existence of orgasm during homosexual mountings [see Chevalier-Skolnikoff, 1974].

Sexual Interactions

Specific data on a sexual interaction were collected as follows: 1) The date, time, names of individuals, and location of the interaction. 2) Male-to-female courtships: Courtship usually includes simultaneous staring, lip smacking, and eyebrow and ear flipping. 3) Female-to-male approaches: Japanese macaque females do not "present," but rather approach males by inching their way in a sitting position slowly toward a male. Females will approach a male as long as he sits passively. Should the male move abruptly, the females run away. Females will approach males both with and without being courted. 4) Mounting positions [Hanby, 1972]: a) double foot clasp position, which is the usual mount position of the adult male and is also used by females to mount both males and other females; b) ventral-ventral mounting; c) sit-on position, which is usually accompanied by thrusting or rubbing; and d) lie-on position, which appears to entail thigh pressure rather than rubbing or thrusting.

Masturbation

Masturbation by females is defined as any self-stimulation of the genitals either manually or by rubbing on inanimate objects. Because it occurred infrequently, data on female masturbation were collected using ad lib sampling methods [Altmann, 1974].

Vocalizations

Any vocalizations associated with sexual behavior were recorded according to Itani [1963].

RESULTS

Heterosexual Behavior

Arashiyama West. Approximately one-third of the mount sequences involving adults began with the female mounting the male an average of three times, in one of three positions—the sit-on, lie-on, or double foot clasp. The timing of the female-to-male mounts is the same as the male-to-female mounts, but if the female mounted in the sit-on position and rubbed her genitals on the male's sacrum she rubbed more times (X = 8) than males generally thrust (mode = 3). Females that mounted males had more male partners than females that did not [Wolfe, 1979].

Based on the 110 completed copulations observed from the very beginning of the mount sequence, the mount sequence lasted an average of 13.22 ± 7.05 min (excluding the female-to-male mounts), with the male mounting the female an average of 17.95 ± 8.97 times before ejaculating. The female clutching reac-

TABLE 1. Comparison of Arashiyama West and Arashiyama B Adult Females: Number of Mounting Partners

	Arashiyama B	Arashiyama West
Number of adult male mounting partners[1]	4.02 ± 2.22 (n = 66)	2.63 ± 1.56 (n = 41)
Number of young male mounting partners	1.38 ± 0.75 (n = 26)	2.0 ± 1.73 (n = 22)
Number of adult female mounting partners	2.3 ± 1.2 (n = 16)	2.25 ± 1.18 (n = 32)

't = 3.90 df = 102 P = 0.000.

tion was observed during 47% of the observed ejaculatory mounts. Between mounts, the female generally sat in front of the male, and the male placed his arms either around the female or off to one side of the female. In the absence of a consortship, dyads separated immediately after ejaculation or they separated after a short bout of allo-grooming. The 15 adult males averaged 8 ± 4.88 female partners and formed an average of 3.1 ± 2.1 consortships which lasted an average of 5.7 ± 5.14 days [Wolfe, 1978]. During the 1973–74 Arashiyama West breeding season, 53% of the adult females engaged in consortships with sexually immature males.

Arashiyama B. The pattern of adult heterosexual interactions among Arashiyama B monkeys followed the same pattern as described above for Arashiyama West monkeys. A major difference between these two troops is the occurrence at Arashiyama B of mount sequences between troop females and migrant males that appear only during the breeding season. The males advertise their presence by giving branch-shaking displays around the perimeter of the troop. Thirty percent of the adult females were observed leaving the troop in the direction of a displaying male and returning to the troop with ejaculatory plugs in their vaginas [Wolfe, 1981]. Furthermore, Arashiyama B females had more adult male partners than did Arashiyama West females (t = 3.90, df = 102, P = 0.000; see Table 1). Interestingly, fewer Arashiyama B females (23%) engaged in consortships with sexually immature males than did Arashiyama West females (53%). This difference is significant (x^2 = 7.21, df = 1, P = 0.01).

Based on 60 completed mount sequences that were observed from the onset, the average mount sequence lasted 14.47 ± 7.69 minutes and entailed the male mounting the female 16.58 ± 10.03 times. The 25 adult males observed mating had a mean of 10.50 ± 7.60 estrous female partners. Of the 176 completed mount sequences (not all of which were observed from the onset), 59% (n =105) ended with the female displaying the reachback during the final mount(s).

Adult females in this group also mounted adult males in the same manner as described for Arashiyama West monkeys. As predicted from the Arashiyama

West data, females that mounted males (n = 21) had more male partners (n = 4.76 ± 1.73) than females that did not (n = 45)(n = 3.67 ± 2.34 male partners).

Contrary to Fedigan and Gouzoules [1978], the difference in the number of mounting partners between those females that mounted males and those that do not is not an artifact of the presence or absence of recent offspring since the majority of females (n = 13) that mounted males had an offspring from the previous breeding season. Moreover, there was no significant difference in the number of adult male partners between females with a recent offspring (n = 4.1 male partners) and those without a recent offspring (n = 3.8 male partners, t = –0.58, df 65, P = 0.561). Females that mount males appear to be more sexually motivated and more stimulating and therefore more attractive to males than females that do not. Wolfe [1979] argued that if these females are capable of attaining orgasm, female-to-male mounting could facilitate orgasm because it would provide the females with direct female-controlled stimulation. The evidence presented here supports that contention.

Female Homosexual Behavior

Adult Arashiyama B females, like Arashiyama West females, also formed homosexual consortships. For both troops the average homosexual consortship lasted between 3 and 4 days (with a standard deviation of 3.5 days). Arashiyama West females formed 85 consortships during the 1973–74 breeding season while Arashiyama B females only formed 29 consortships during the 1977–78 breeding season. There were no significant differences in the number of adult female partners between the two troops (see Table 1). However, only 23% of the adult Arashiyama B females engaged in homosexual behavior as compared to 73% of the Arashiyama West females. This difference is significant (x^2 = 27.50, df = 1, P = 0.000).

Estrus

As has been reported for Arashiyama West [Wolfe, 1976, 1979] and the Oregon troop [Hanby, 1972] as well as for rhesus [Loy, 1971; McMillan, 1981] and Patas monkeys [Loy, 1981], there are no clear-cut estrus cycles for the Japanese macaque females of Arashiyama B (Table II). Rather, estrus occurs in "runs" [Hanby, 1972] and thus the phrase interestrus interval is more appropriate than the phrase estrous cycle [Loy, 1981]. The appearance of estrus in runs suggests that females are sexually active both midcycle and perimenstrually and are often sexually active during the interim phases of their menstrual cycle [Wolfe, 1976, 1979]. The presence of new males is an often cited social factor influencing female estrous behavior [Loy, 1981]. Given the lack of evidence for actual regular cycles in estrous behavior, it is concluded that the interval between runs of estrous behavior (ie, the interestrus interval) has little meaning as a stable parameter of reproductive biology.

Seventy-six percent of Arashiyama West females had at least one post-conception estrus (as determined by counting back 173 days from the day of birth)

Table 11. Arashiyama B: Mean and Standard Deviation Data on Estrus in Days: Adult Females (n=70)

	Adult females
Interestrus intervals	29.39 ± 16.9 (n = 129)
Number of estrus periods	2.8 ± 1.5 (n = 71)
Duration of estrus	8.0 – 8.9 (n = 198)
Mean number of days which passed after the onset of the breeding season before the female came into estrus	40.8 ± 28.3 (n = 70)
Mean number of days which passed after the onset of the breeding seaons before the female became pregnant[a]	53.0 ± 21.2 (n = 37)

[a]Calculated by backcounting 173 days.

and 66% of Arashiyama B females also had at least one postconception estrus (47% had one, 13% had two, and 6% had three). Of the 31 females of Arashiyama West that gave birth, 19% were recorded as having had one episode of postconception bleeding within 1 1/2 months from the estimated day of conception of about the same amount of vaginal discharge normally associated with a regular preconception menses. Of the 38 Arashiyama B that gave birth and were readily observable on a daily basis, 28% (n = 10) had one such postconception bleeding episode. The only difference at Arashiyama B in estrus between the postreproductive females and those females between 6 to 22 years of age is that the postreproductive females have a shorter duration of their estrus periods than do the younger adult females [Wolfe and Noyes, 1981].

Masturbation

During the 1-year Arashiyama B project, a total of 16% (n = 16) of the adult females and 18% (n = 2) of the prepubescent females were involved in a total of 27 observed incidents of masturbation. Of those 27 incidents, 18 involved the female manipulating her clitoris manually and nine involved the female rubbing on an inanimate object. None of the females that masturbated manually were involved in a mount sequence at the time of masturbation. On the other hand, 90% of the incidents involving the rubbing on inanimate objects did involve a mount sequence. Because of their different contexts, these behaviors will be discussed separately.

The majority (75%) of manual masturbations occurred while the female was not in physical contact with another monkey and the remaining occurred while the female was being groomed. If the masturbation occurred while the female was being groomed, the female would generally be lying on her side and manipulating her clitoris by reaching down over her hip. To masturbate when not in contact with another monkey, the female lay on her abdomen with her arm under her body and her hand placed between her thighs. The clitoris was then rolled against the side of her ischial callosity or pulled and rolled between her thumb and the side of her index finger. Manipulation of the clitoris in this manner usually lasted 1–2 min without interruption.

The possibility of orgasm among Japanese macaque females is intriguing. Of the 13 females that engaged in manual masturbation, six appeared to attain an orgasm. That is, among these six females, the clitoris became distended and darkened in color during stimulation, and flaccid and lighter in color following such stimulation. Furthermore, as the females ceased masturbating, muscle contractions of the vaginal muscles, anal sphincter, base of the tail, and, in one female, the thighs, were observed lasting 4–6 sec. This, interestingly, is the same length of time that an adult male displays signs of orgasm, whether the orgasm follows from masturbation or a mount sequence. The females, unless otherwise disturbed, usually slept after the orgasmic muscle contractions.

Autosexual behavior was not limited to the breeding season nor was it limited to females in estrus. Furthermore, adult females of all ages and ranks engaged in masturbation. On the other hand, masturbation occurred more often among females belonging to two matrifocal units. This finding suggests that masturbation may be a learned behavior passed from one generation to the next.

DISCUSSION

Sexual Novelty Hypothesis

Female homosexual behavior has been observed in most free-ranging and captive troops of Japanese macaques [Takahata, personal communication] However, as described for the Oregon troop of Japanese monkeys [Hanby, 1972; Eaton, 1978], female homosexual interactions are usually low in frequency and confined to a few particular females who engage in homosexual behavior each year. This was also nature of the female homosexual interactions of Arashiyama monkeys at the time of their initial habituation [Sugiyama, personal communication], but female homosexual interactions have increased especially among Arashiyama West females.

Pregnancy has been implicated in the homosexual behavior of Arashiyama West. As previously reported [Wolfe, 1974, 1976; Fedigan and Gouzoules, 1978], a majority of the Arashiyama West female-female mounting interactions occurred after conception. However, Takahata [1980], who studied the sexual behavior of Arashiyama B between 1975 and 1978, found that the majority of male-female mounting interactions also took place after conception. Furthermore, in other troops of Japanese macaques, for example, the Oregon troop [Hanby, 1972; Eaton, 1978], pregnancy does not lead to high frequencies of homosexual behavior. Thus, pregnancy per se does not directly affect the frequency of homosexual behavior.

The sex ratio among sexually mature monkeys during the Arashiyama West 1973–74 breeding season was one sexually mature male for 3.86 sexually mature females. This situation intensified during the second half of the 1973–74 breeding season when there were, in effect, 12 sexually mature males, since three males were ill and subsequently died, for the 58 sexually mature females for a sex ratio of one male for 4.83 females. Two questions arise from this set of data. First, to what extent is this an unusual sex ratio, and second, what might be the relationship between this sex ratio and the low number of adult male sexual partners per adult female and the high frequency of homosexual interactions and sexually immature male/sexually mature adult female consortships of Arashiyama West? If it were the case that mammalian males are (as popular myth might have it) sexually insatiable or that primate females had no desire for sexual novelty, then there would be no need to consider the relationship between sexual behavior and adult sex ratios. However, as recently argued by Nakatsuru and Kramer [1982], sperm is not cheap, and mammalian males can become sexually satiated [Dewsbury, 1981a, b; Allen and Lemmon, 1981].

Related to the issue of male sexual satiation are the observations that Arashiyama males will occasionally perform a courtship ritual in the direction of consorting females. However, the females ignore the males, and the males are not persistent in their courtship. Rarely do the males disrupt a homosexual consortship. These observations suggest that the males are less than serious when they perform the courtship ritual in the direction of consorting females, and do not necessarily indicate that those males are available to females as mounting partners.

Unfortunately, there are few data on the sex ratios of natural unprovisioned troops of Japanese monkeys. Sugiyama [1976] indicated that a sex ratio among sexually mature monkeys of one male to 3.5 females is not unusual. However, his data do not include nontroop migrant males that copulate with troop females, and all of the troops in his sample are provisioned troops with some capturing of "nuisance" males. Interestingly, Sugiyama's data indicate (excluding nontroop migrant males) a sex ratio among sexually mature monkeys of one male to two females for Arashiyama monkeys. In fact, the sex ratio of Arashiyama West's sexually mature monkeys at the time the troop was relocated was one male to 1.86 females. It was with the loss of peripheral and solitary males [Clark and Mano, 1975] that the sex ratio among sexually mature monkeys jumped to one male to 3.8 females by the beginning of the 1973–74 breeding season and then to one male for 4.83 females with the illness of three males during the same breeding season. Based on data presented by Hazama [1964], the sex ratio among the sexually mature (excluding nontroop migrant males) at the time of the 1954 habituation was approximately one male to two females. These data then indicate that during the 1973–74 Arashiyama West breeding season there was an unbalanced sex ratio, with fewer sexually mature males in the troop than females were accustomed to.

Several observations of Arashiyama B monkeys suggest that Japanese macaque females have a preference for novel males. For example, an old-appearing, low-ranking semicentral male that had joined the Arashiyama B troop in 1976 was observed mating with 30 different females during the 1977–78 Arashiyama B breeding season. In contrast, the long-term natal alpha male of Arashiyama B was observed mating with only nine different females during this same time period. Moreover, 30% of the adult females of Arashiyama B were observed leaving the vicinity of the troop and mating with migrant males [Wolfe, 1981]. Since there are foxes and wild domestic dogs in the area, leaving the troop alone entails some risk. There is also other evidence which suggests that Japanese macaque females prefer to mate with novel males. For the Oregon troop of Japanese macaques with a sex ratio of approximately 1 male for 1.8 females, a low frequency of female-female mountings was reported, and the females averaged ten male partners [Hanby, 1972]. Arashiyama West females during the early breeding season averaged between three and four male partners. Thus, given the opportunity, the evidence indicates that females will have more male partners than they did at Arashiyama West during the 1973–74 breeding season.

If we hypothesize that the high frequencies of female-female mountings among the Arashiyama West females during the 1973–74 breeding season represents a quest for sexual novelty, much of the seemingly disparate data begins to make sense. There are at least two forms of female homosexuality among Japanese monkeys: one form found in very low frequency among a few particular females is a partial, nonexclusive sexual preference for female partners; this would represent the low frequency form of female homosexual behavior usually observed among Japanese macaque females including the Oregon troop and the Arashiyama troop at the time of habituation. A second form might be termed "novelty deprivation homosexuality." That is, in the absence of novel male partners, either migrant males which are absent at Arashiyama West or large numbers of troop males, females will seek sexual novelty with sexually immature, untried males or with novel female partners.

Fedigan and Gouzoules provide evidence from their data gathered on Arashiyama West monkeys between 1972 and 1975 which support this hypothesis. They write: "Unlike the homosexual consorts, heterosexual partner choice showed significant similarities over the three years. Males and females took up significant amounts (.323, .247) of their opportunities for repeat consorts (binomial tests, p > .001)" [Fedigan and Gouzoules, 1978, p. 494]. This finding supports the hypothesis in that Arashiyama West females were engaging in repeated matings with the few available males and turning to other females with whom they had not engaged in a mounting interaction for sexual novelty.

Thus far in this discussion, all of the attention has been focused on Arashiyama West females. However, because there was more homosexual behavior among Arashiyama B females than among the females of the Oregon troop and more homosexual behavior during this study than at the time of their habituation, some attention needs to be given to the females of Arashiyama B. The current population pyramid of Arashiyama B is bottom-heavy, and the sex ratio among adults is skewed toward the females (Fig. 2). During the 1977–78 Arashiyama B breeding season, the adult sex ratio, including the ten solitary migrant males, was one male for 2.3 females. However, excluding the nontroop migrant males, it was one adult male to 3.2 adult females compared to 1954 when the adult sex ratio, excluding migrant males, was close to one male to two females. Within the past several years, there has been a capturing program designed mainly to control troop and nontroop "nuisance" males at Arashiyama, which is having an effect on the adult sex ratio and may be associated with the small increases in female-female mounting interactions since habituation.

Both the quantitative data and the anecdotal evidence support the hypothesis that the high frequency of female-female mounting interactions and sexually immature male-sexually mature female mounting dyads at Arashiyama West during the early postrelocation breeding seasons represented a quest for sexual novelty in the face of an altered sex ratio. The evidence suggests that adult females are attracted to the sexual novelty of unfamiliar males, and, therefore, alterations in the male/female sex ratio are important because 1) adult males can become sexually satiated, and 2) females are generally not attracted to well-known, familiar males.

ACKNOWLEDGMENTS

I thank L. Fedigan, H. Gouzoules, and S. Gouzoules for sharing their birth data from Arashiyama West with me, R. Kirk for the computer program which generated the population pyramids, A. Burstein for advice on demographic and statistical techniques, and G. Eaton for conversation. I am also grateful to Y. Takahata, N. Koyama, and the management of the Iwatayama Monkey Park for sharing their ideas and data with me.

REFERENCES

Allen M, Lemmon W (1981): Orgasm in female primates. Am J Primatol 1:3–34.

Altmann J (1974): Observational study of behavior: Sampling methods. Behavior 49:227–267.

Beach FA (1976): Sexual attractivity, proceptivity and receptivity in female mammals. Hormones Behav 7:105–138.

Carpenter CR (1942): Sexual behavior of free-ranging rhesus monkeys. J Comp Psychol 33:113–141.

Chevalier-Skolnikoff S (1974): Male-female, female-female, and male-male sexual behavior in the stumptail monkey, with special attention ot the female orgasm. Arch Sexual Behav 3:95–116.

Clark T. Mano T (1975): Transplantation and adaptation of a troop of Japanese macaques to a Texas brushland habitat. In Kondo S, Kawai M, Ehara A (eds): "Contemporary Primatology." Basal: S. Karger, pp. 358–361.

Dewsbury DA (1981a): Effects of novelty on copulatory behavior: The Coolidge effect and related phenomena. Psychol Bull 89(3):464–482.

Dewsbury DA (1981b): The Coolidge effect in northern grasshopper mice (Onychomys leucogaster). Southern Naturalist 26(2):193–197.

Eaton GB (1978): Longitudinal studies of sexual behavior in the Oregon troop of Japanese macaques. In McGill TE, Dewsbury DA, Sachs BD (eds): "Sex and Behavior." New York: Plenum, pp. 35–59.

Fedigan L, Gouzoules H (1978): The consort relationship in a troop of Japanese monkeys. I. Partner Selection. In Chivers DJ (ed): "Proceedings of the Sixth International Congress on Primatology." London: Academic Press, pp 493–495.

Hanby J (1972): The sociosexual nature of mounting and related behaviors in a confined troop of Japanese macaques. Dissertation, University of Oregon.

Hazama N (1964): Weighing wild Japanese monkeys of Arashiyama. Primates 5(3–4): 81–104.

Itani J (1963): Vocal communication of the wild Japanese monkeys. Primates 4(2)11–66.

Itani J (1972): A preliminary essay on the relationship between social organization and incest avoidance in non-human primates. In Poirier F (ed): "Primate Socialization." New York: Random House, pp 165–171.

Kawai M, Azuma S, Yoshiba K (1967): Ecological studies of reproduction in Japanese monkeys (Macaca fuscata). Primates 8:35–74.

Koyama N (1967): On dominance rank and kinship of a wild Japanese monkey troop in Arashiyama. Primates 8:189–216.

Koyama N (1970): Change in dominance rank and division of a wild Japanese monkey troop in Arashiyama. Primates 11:335–390.

Koyama N, Norikoshi K, Mano T (1975) Population dynamics of Japanese monkeys of Arashiyama. In Kondo S, Kawai M, Ehara A (eds): "Contemporary Primatology." Basel: S. Karger, pp. 411–417.

Loy J (1971): Estrous behavior of free-ranging rhesus monkeys (Macaca mulatta). Primates 12:1–31.

Loy J (1981): The reproductive and heterosexual behaviours of adult patas monkeys in captivity. Anim Behav 29(3):714–726.

McMillan C (1981): Synchrony of estrus in macaque matrilines at Cayo Santigo. Am J Phys Anthropol 54:251.

Nakatsuru K, Kramer D (1982): Is sperm cheap? Limited male fertility and female choice in the lemon Tetra (Pisces, Characidae). Science 216:753–754.

Sugiyama & (1976): Life history of male Japanese monkeys. In Rosenblatt JS, Hinde RA, Shaw E, Beer C (eds): "Advances in the Study of Behavior." New York: Academic Press, pp. 255–284.

Takahata Y (1980): The reproductive biology of a free-ranging troop of Japanese monkeys. Primates 21(3):303–329.

Wolfe LD (1974): The sexual behavior of the Arashiyama West troop of Japanese macaques. Presented at the American Anthropology Association Annual Meetings, 1974.

Wolfe LD (1976): Sexual behavior of the Arashiyama West troop of Japanese macaques. Dissertation, University of Oregon, 1976.

Wolfe LD (1978): Age and sexual behavior of Japanese macaques (Macaca fuscata). Arch Sexual Behav 7(1):55–68.

Wolfe LD (1979): Behavioral patterns of estrus females of the Arashiyama West troop of Japanese macaques (Macaca fuscata). Primates 20(4):525–534.

Wolfe LD (1981): Display behavior of three troops of Japanese monkeys. Primates 22(1):24–32.

Wolfe LD, Noyes MJS (1981): Reproductive senescence among Japanese macaque females. J Mammal 62(4):698–705.

Zumpe D, Michael R (1968): The clutching reaction and orgasm in the female rhesus monkey (Macaca mulatta). J Endocrinol 40:–123.

When the Bough Breaks
There may be method in the madness of infanticide

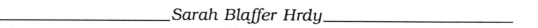

Sarah Blaffer Hrdy

Twenty years ago, John Calhoun, a researcher at the National Institutes of Health, built a minor metropolis for a few dozen Norway rats. He strewed the floor of a great ten-by-fourteen-foot cage with sawdust and strips of paper and partitioned it into four pens with an electrified fence. In each pen he installed a drinking fountain, a conical food hopper, and an artificial burrow for nesting. Ramps led over the electrified fence to connect the four pens, each of which was built to accommodate twelve adults. Altogether, the cage could comfortably house forty-eight rats; within a year, however, the population had multiplied to eighty.

From an observation window in the ceiling of the cage, Calhoun watched the rats' behavior deteriorate in the overcrowded pens. At first, healthy, pregnant females collected strips of paper from the floor, carried them to the nesting burrows, and arranged them in fluffy, cuplike nests. As the pens became more crowded, the females brought strips of paper to their burrows but stopped arranging them into nests. Rather they simply left the strips in heaps or trampled them into flat pads. Over time, the disturbed females collected fewer and fewer paper strips and, at last, bore their young on the cold comfort of the floor. They abandoned these infants, and as many as 96 percent of them died where they dropped and were devoured by adult rats. Slowly the population explosion leveled off.

"In the celebrated thesis of Thomas Malthus," Calhoun wrote, "vice and misery impose the ultimate natural limit on the growth of populations. Students of the subject have given most of their attention to misery, that is, to predation, disease and food supply as forces that operate to adjust the size of a population to its environment. But what of vice?" In the rats' maternal neglect, infanticide, and cannibalism, Calhoun saw the "vices" Malthus had envisioned: pathological behavior brought on by stress. Such behavior eventually might stabilize a population gone haywire.

These striking and influential observations fit in well with views of social behavior that were prevalent in the Sixties. Calhoun's crowded pens seemed the very image of our teeming cities, of our packed planet. Most researchers believed at the time that healthy animal societies are more or less harmonious systems in which each individual has a role to play. Among the Norway rats, each indi-

This article is reprinted by permission of *THE SCIENCES*; and is from Vol. 24(2): 44–50 1984 issue. Foreign individual subscriptions are $23.00 per year. Write to THE SCIENCES, 2 East 63rd Street, New York, NY 10021.

vidual has a role to play that helps ensure the colony's survival. According to this view, all animals, including humans, normally behave in ways that maintain the group's structure rather than disrupt it. Clearly, it was thought, strong inhibitions would prevent animals from killing their own kind, and no normal animal would do something so antisocial, so contrary to the survival of the species, as to kill young. Starting from such a premise, researchers concluded that infanticide could only be pathological and aberrant, beyond the pale and scope of normal behavior. It seemed likely that among Calhoun's rats—and, who knew, perhaps among humans too—easing stress of overcrowding would stop the killing.

It was in this fashion, too, that zoologists at that time interpreted conflicting reports about the behavior of an exotic species of Indian monkey, the Hanuman langur. These elegant, agile creatures are believed by the Hindus to be descendants of Hanuman, the monkey god. Victorian naturalists had recorded—in some of the most colorful prose to be found in the annals of primatology—grisly accounts of adult langurs maiming one another and of female langurs with infants desperately fleeing males who had invaded their troops. But the standard modern study of the species labeled this behavior pathological, dismissing the violent tales as "anecdotal, often bizarre, certainly not typical." In fact, in the early Sixties, langurs seemed to exemplify the normal and peaceful animal colony, as Calhoun's rats did the pathological and disturbed.

In 1965, however, the Japanese primatologist Yukimaru Sugiyama reported from Dharwar Forest, in southern India, that a band of langur males had invaded a troop of the animals, ousting the male that had reigned over it. Soon, all but one of the new males were also forced out, and the lone remaining male then attacked and killed infants in the troop. So stark was the contrast between these observations and prevailing ideas about the behavior of langurs that researchers looked for some peculiar feature of Dharwar Forest that might explain the discrepancy. The langurs of Dharwar lived at population densities up to forty times higher than those at the more peaceful site studied earlier; perhaps the langurs were so crowded, and thus under such stress, that they resorted to infanticide as a way of reducing their numbers.

The summer after my first year in graduate school, in 1971, I went to India to test this idea. I chose a relatively high-density population of langurs that lived on Mount Abu, in the state of Rajasthan. On and off over the next nine years, I followed the family histories and political upheavals of five troops of langurs, each with its own territory, and the roving all-male bands that lived nearby. What I found there stubbornly refused to fit the Calhoun model of infanticide.

The Langurs of Mount Abu live in groups of twenty or so. At the heart of each troop are several overlapping generations of closely related females (mothers, daughters, granddaughters) who stay together all their lives in the same range, roughly ninety acres. Young males, before reaching maturity, either wander off from the troop or are driven out, and join other males in nomadic bands of from six to sixty animals, which rove across vast ranges on the craggy, forested slopes of Mount Abu. The females of each troop are accompanied by one or sometimes several adult males who enter the troop from outside—by driving off the reigning male.

Like Sugiyama, I witnessed skirmishes when two troops met at the boundaries of their ranges and fierce fighting when invading males tried to break into a breeding troop. But nothing in the day-to-day life of these langurs—in spite of their relatively high population densities—suggested pathological behavior. The reigning adult males were very tolerant in their relations with mothers in their troops and with their own infants. Early in the course of my study, then, I had reason to question whether environmental stress was, in fact, upsetting the langurs' normal patterns of parental care. Over the years I saw many attacks on infants like those Sugiyama had seen at Dharwar, but they occurred only in one context: when invading males entered a troop.

By 1974, based on my work at Mount Abu and other researchers' studies, a clear pattern had emerged. The interloping male langurs did not kill their own infants, but those belonging to other males. What's more, males attacked only infants that were carried by unfamiliar females; they appeared to use their own past relations with the mothers to decide if the infants were their own, and so either to attack or to tolerate them. So the behavior of the infanticidal males appeared not pathological but highly goal-directed—and from an evolutionary perspective, it made sense. A female langur typically nurses her infant for as long as a year, thus delaying the conception of her next infant. She resumes sexual activity about the time of weaning. But a female whose infants were killed resumed her estrous cycle, became sexually receptive, and thus mated with the usurping male sooner than she would have had she continued to suckle. As a result, the usurping, infanticidal males increased their chance of reproducing, at the expense of the previously reigning male. The interlopers' behavior appeared to be a classic example of what Charles Darwin called sexual selection: competition between members of one sex (usually the male) for access to the other, a struggle in which the loser does not die but produces fewer offspring than the winner. For the male langurs who won, who eliminated the offspring of their competitors, infanticide seemed to be an exceedingly adaptive strategy for passing on their own genes.

Still, there were difficulties in interpreting the data, which fueled the controversy that followed my study. Because attacks by an infanticidal male langur can take place in a matter of seconds, scientists have actually witnessed only a few killings. Furthermore, at several study sites in India and Nepal, new males entered langur troops without behaving so aggressively. Even where infanticide occurred, not all the invading males attacked infants, and of those that did, not all succeeded in killing infants and mating with their mothers. Because some sites where male takeovers entailed intense fighting were more than ten times as densely populated as other, more peaceful locales, some researchers argued that the death of langur infants, like that of Calhoun's rats, was a by-product of strained social conditions. Finally, it was impossible to rule out the presence of humans as a factor.

Since that time, however, infanticide has proved to be widespread in primates. All told, researchers have now observed it in the wild in a dozen species of primates, in Africa, India, Southeast Asia, and South America. Although the practice is not common in any of these species, when it occurs it always follows a pattern: infants are attacked and killed only when a new male enters the breeding system. Thomas Butynski, of the New York Zoological Society, for instance, has observed this type of behavior among blue monkeys in the Kibale Forest, of Uganda. These monkeys roam about in the largest home ranges ever recorded for harem-dwelling monkeys, as many as 865 acres; they cannot be considered crowded. In a world increasingly overrun by humans, the Kibale is probably the wildest and most pristine forest in which monkeys have been given careful and prolonged study. Yet even though the blue monkeys are neither crowded nor unnaturally stressed, infanticide appears to be an integral part of their breeding system.

If the sexual selection hypothesis is correct, infanticidal behavior must be coded for, at least in part, in the genes. No one has yet demonstrated this with classic Mendelian breeding experiments, and so far there is no hard evidence for a genetic component of infanticide in primates. But Moshe Jakubowski and Joseph Terkel, of Tel Aviv University, have shown in the laboratory that various genetically distinct strains of mice differ substantially in their propensity to kill infants. Other scientists have demonstrated that behavioral differences of this type can be reflected in the reproductive success of infanticidal males—in other words, that the strategy works. In one set of experiments, Canadian zoologists Ron Brooks and Frank Mallory, both then at the University of Guelph, divided female collared lemmings and their litters into groups. In one group, a female and her young were exposed to a strange male; in a second, to a male with whom the female had previously mated; and in a third, control group, females were permitted to raise their litters without interference—no male was introduced. None of the infants were killed in the second and third groups. But in the first group, the strange males killed 42 percent of one-day-old pups. Furthermore, males that killed their rivals' infants managed to sire litters of their own within three weeks; males that did not, within four weeks. Where these lemmings evolved, the breeding season is confined to a brief Arctic summer, and a one-week head start is a significant reproductive advantage.

But how can an infanticidal male distinguish his own young from his rivals'? To date, the most detailed studies of this question have been undertaken with house mice. When a male house mouse is caged with a mother and her litter, one of three things happens. The male ignores the infants, attacks them, or helps care for them, licking the infants and huddling over them to keep them warm. If any of the infants are his, it is virtually certain that they will not be killed. Experiments suggest that there may be not one but several, sometimes redundant, systems at work her. Recently, William Huck, of Princeton University, found that in some strains of mice, males tolerate infants if they recognize the mother's scent (carried in the urine) as that of a former mate, and attack infants if they do not. In fact, males could be tricked into killing their own offspring by switching the pups to the nest of an unfamiliar female. And in other strains, merely the act of mating can make the difference. Fred vom Saal, of the University of Missouri, has shown that if after copulating with one female a male mouse is introduced to another female and her litter, he is far less likely to attack the pups than a virgin male would be. In the strain of mice vom Saal studied, 88 percent of males who had never mated were infanticidal, compared with only 15 percent of males who had recently mated. What's more, the inhibitory effects of mating last just about as long as the period of gestation and weaning, so that an infanticidal male is virtually certain not to kill his own offspring. These findings clearly support the sexual selection hypothesis.

But infanticide in nature is a protean phenomenon. Sexually selected infanticide in only one form. There may be a variety of evolutionary strategies at work, and females as well as males are often implicated. One particularly well documented case is that of Belding's ground squirrels, which make their burrows high in the California Sierra. Cornell University biologist Paul Sherman has made an extremely conservative estimate of the incidence of infanticide in these animals, counting only those cases where the killer dragged the kit above ground and not counting the attacks that likely took place out of sight, in the burrows. Even then, 8 percent of infant mortality could be attributed to murder by members of the infants' own species; and nomadic adult females, who constituted 7 percent of the population, were responsible for 42 percent of these deaths. Sherman thinks the females may kill infants to induce the victims' mother to abandon her burrow, thereby allowing the killer to move in and rear a litter of her own. It is as if an apartment hunter in Manhattan won herself a space by terrorizing tenants.

Infanticide may also be part of a competition for food. Among some species of birds, for example, murder in the nest is commonplace—one sibling kills another. Among great egrets along the Texas coast, University of Oklahoma ornithologist Douglas Mock has found, one-third of all hatchlings born each breeding season are killed by their older sibling. The firstborn chick relentlessly harasses and pecks the younger, and so pushes first in line for feeding. If there is enough food to go around, the younger chick may still survive. But among other birds—species of boobies, owls, skuas, eagles, pelicans, and cranes—the sibling last to hatch is *always* killed. The parents do not intervene; indeed, they may be said to preordain the killing by laying eggs at intervals, so that the first chick to hatch will be larger and stronger that the younger one. Mock believes the second egg may be a form of insurance for the parents, in case the first egg turns out to be infertile. Even if both chicks survived at this early stage, he says, there would not be enough food to raise them both until they were old enough to fly. To ensure that at least one chick will survive and carry on the family genes, then, it is to the parents' advantage, too, that the elder chick kills the younger.

Fratricide takes an even more extreme form in sand sharks. Like a few other species of fish, sand sharks do not lay eggs, but bear their young alive. Siblings begin to devour one another while still squirming inside the mother's oviduct. Here, the killer gains not only by elminating a competitor but at the

310

same time by procuring a meal. Among fish and insects, especially, the small and vulnerable young are in chronic danger from cannibalism. Similar patterns exist throughout nature. In fact, some biologists have argued that female hyenas, which are larger than males, evolved those extra inches and pounds to fend off males that might otherwise eat the females' pups.

In most mammals, however, parents do not inflict mortal injuries on their own young, except in unusual circumstances. In a famine, a mother lion may abandon a litter; hotly pursued by a predator, a mother kangaroo might jettison the young joey from her pouch. In the laboratory, female monkeys reared in isolation from other monkeys are often abusive to their infants, but in the wild, monkey and ape mothers almost never injure or abandon dependent young. In nature, the main exceptions to the extraordinary solicitude of primate mothers are to be found in our own species.

When a human infant is killed, the perpetrators are usually parents, not strangers. In "primitive" societies, close relatives—often the mother—may consciously calculate the cost of an infant, the demands it is likely to make on its parents, its prospects for survival and marriage, and its impact on the family as a whole. In fact, some parents readily articulate their reasons for sacrificing a newborn. Diamond Jenness, an anthropologist who lived for a time among the Copper Eskimo, of the Canadian Arctic, recorded in his diary on January 22, 1915, the birth—and fate—of a baby girl in the tribe. "Neither of the parents wanted to have any children at this time," wrote Jenness. "They were both young still, they said, and in all probability would have at least one more child later, a boy perhaps who could take care of them when they grew old. The woman therefore suffocated her child and laid it out on the ground a few yards from the camp where it was soon covered by drifting snow. Only a year or two previously, this couple had similarly exposed another little baby girl."

John Whiting, an anthropologist at Harvard University, has examined records from eighty-four different cultures in which the practice of infanticide is well documented. For one-third of these, ethnographies specifically mentioned as the motive for the killings the elimination of infants considered defective. The second most frequently cited reason was birth spacing. This rationale was cited most often among migratory peoples that subsisted by hunting, fishing, and gathering wild plants—which is perhaps not surprising, given the burden that carrying two infants imposes on a nomadic mother. Among the !Kung tribe, of the Kalahari desert, the practice of infanticide is spoken of as grave and disturbing, but as a fact of life.

Such practices are not confined to primitive or non-Western peoples. The second-century Greek physician Soranus included in his treatise *Gynecology* a chapter on "how to recognize a newborn that is worth rearing." A 1739 engraving by William Hogarth commemorates the construction of a foundling hospital in England "for the great numbers of newborn children daily exposed to Destruction by the cruelty of their parents." After only four years, swamped by nearly fifteen thousand abandoned children (most of whom died in infancy), the hospital was forced to close.

Human infanticide also may be indirect, delayed, or disguised. Indeed, human customs that ultimately decrease the chance that an infant will survive can be extraordinarily elaborate. The most common, however, is discrimination against unwanted children—often daughters—who are given less to eat. In peasant societies as distant in space and time as ninth-century France, nineteenth-century India, and contemporary Ecuador, sons have been, by custom, nursed up to twice as long as daughters, with predictable effects upon the sex ratios: more sons than daughters survived infancy.

Even child-rearing customs that are outwardly similar may mean quite different things to different cultures and social classes. Consider the practice of sending an infant to suckle from a woman other than its mother. Wealthy families in England in the sixteenth century and in Sicily as late as the nineteenth century often purchased the services of a poor woman as a wet nurse. This arrangement freed the mother from having to suckle her own child, enabling her to conceive again sooner than she could have otherwise (as with langurs and other mammals, in humans nursing inhibits ovulation so long as the mother nurses frequently). The wet nurse was carefully monitored—sometimes by paid family spies—so the babe's chances of survival were as good as if the mother herself were suckling it, and the custom allowed wealthy women to bear and raise more children. But in less priviledged homes, sending an infant to a wet nurse was the only way a working woman could keep her job, and survive. The wet nurse was usually an even poorer woman, who at any given time might be suckling as many as five infants, none of whom she could properly feed. Mortality in such cases was staggeringly high. Records kept by the lieutenant general of police in Paris for the year 1780 revealed that of twenty-one thousand recorded births, only one thousand of the infants were nursed by their own mothers. These practices continued for more than a century despite mortality rates that ranged from 40 percent to as high as 80 percent. According to one nineteenth-century report, of twenty-five thousand infants sent to wet nurses, twenty thousand died. Given the length of time and the numbers of people involved, it is inconceivable that mothers would not have been aware, at least in the later years, that sending their infants away to wet nurses placed them in jeopardy. In fact, in the slang of the day, wet nurses were known as "angel makers." It remains unclear, though, whether wet-nursing in Europe was a disguised form of infanticide or a desperate gamble by mothers who hoped that their offspring would be among the lucky survivors.

Customs such as these cannot be understood out of context. One must consider everything from a society's rules for inheritance of property (to avoid losing the family fortune, parents may favor children of one sex over the other) to a scarcity of food (which may doom a newborn of either sex). Because these conditions are almost endlessly variable, any understanding of infanticide in humans, just as in animals, demands case-by-case information concerning who is responsible and what, if anything, the killer stands to gain or to avoid losing.

The great question, of course, is this: Are these countless cases of infanticide, documented across long stretches of history and much of the planet, part of our evolutionary inheritance and influenced by genetic tendencies? No one takes seriously the idea of a gene for infanticide. But do humans inherit a predisposition to respond to certain circumstances by reducing or ending their investment in a particular infant? Or is infanticide entirely the result of environmental factors, cultural pressures, and historical trends? At present, there is no clear answer.

From a sociobiological perspective, parents, whether human or animal, are viewed as strategists whose ultimate goal is to increase the survival and lifetime breeding prospects of their whole family. This view assumes that each family has limited resources to channel into reproduction. Since the issue is long-term rather than immediate reproductive success, a particular infant might be killed if that would somehow enhance the family's overall opportunities to perpetuate its lineage—withholding food from a newborn, for instance, in order to feed an older child in whom more resources have already been invested, so that the older child would have a greater chance to reach adulthood and reproduce. Richard Alexander, an evolutionary biologist at the University of Michigan, believes that according to this view the way the family's resources are allocated among offspring should depend, statistically speaking, on how closely the parent (or step-parent) is related to an offspring; on how capable the offspring is of translating the parental investment into reproduction; and on what options the parent has for using the available resources (diverting them to an older or stronger child, for instance).

Recently, psychologists Martin Daly and Margo Wilson, of McMaster University, have attempted to apply this approach to the analysis of contemporary child abuse. In line with Alexander's evolutionary model, they found that children most likely to be abused and neglected tend to be those born to poor families, those with birth defects, those with several older siblings, and those with unrelated men in the household. One difficulty with this approach, however, is that other hypotheses would generate the same predictions about child abuse. For example, if such abuse is not an adaptive strategy but rather a pathological act brought about through stress, one would still expect it to occur most often among families with little money and many children. The parents' economic situation and their personal histories (the traditional domain of psychologists dealing with this problem) remain the best predictors of which parents are likely to be abusive, and most contemporary child abuse in this country must be regarded as pathological. In fact, in any society that has stringent legal sanctions against child abuse and in which children abandoned to institutions have good prospects for survival, it would virtually never be advantageous for parents to injure their own child.

Nevertheless, there might well be an evolutionary explanation for some portion of contemporary child abuse. As Daly and Wilson suggest, some parents may inherit a tendency to care less for particular infants—those with defects or those that are not their own—or to care less for infants under particular conditions, such as when food is scarce. Susan Scrimshaw, of the public health school at the University of California at Los Angeles, has speculated that some abused children, had they been born in other cultures or at other times, would not have been permitted to survive. If our society were very different and condoned child abuse (an idea we find repulsive), then psychological motivations leading to the neglect or abandonment of certain children might, however cruel or morally unacceptable, enhance the parents' long-term reproductive success.

Perhaps the most striking illustration of this paradox—how killing one's own offspring can somehow enhance the reproductive success of a family—is Mildred Dickemann's study of the Rajputs and other castes in northern India. Dickemann, an anthropologist at Sonoma State University, has applied sociobiological reasoning to explain the systematic slaying of daughters in precolonial India. The region endured recurrent famines, during which the poorest families perished; a lineage needed wealth and high social status to survive. Higher-caste families often killed their female infants, a practice Dickemann attributes to the society's marriage system. Families gave their daughters large dowries so that they might marry into a higher-caste family. But daughters in the highest caste could move no higher—and since wealth was inherited from father to son, when a wealthy daughter married, her large dowry would become her husband's property and leave her family forever. To prevent this, a family of the highest caste would direct all of its resources to the son to that he could keep his position, since maintenance of the family's rank over time was more important than the number of offspring produced in each generation. Under these circumstances, the daughters of the highest castes were doomed.

Considering such cases of human infanticide, some scholars have argued that the so-called maternal instinct must be a myth: If it exists, how could so many French mothers send their infants away to "angel makers"? How could Eskimo, !Kung, and Rajput mothers kill unwanted babies? Yet human mothers and infants do seem biologically designed to form strong attachments. When a mother suckles a baby, the effects of hormones, the powerfully pleasurable sensations of nursing, and the infant's smiles all help build a strong bond.

But there is a lag in the onset of this bonding, a gap of a day or so between birth and the start of regular nursing, when the mother's milk supply comes in. During that time, as scholars from a variety of disciplines have noted, a mother might in fact be able to decide against keeping an infant. In many societies, just such a neutral period is institutionalized by custom: the infant is not considered fully human until some ceremony or anointment, a baptism for instance. In !Kung tradition, a baby is a true person only when it is brought back into the village; a mother who abandons her newborn in the bush is not considered a murderer.

Thus, both biology and cultural traditions seem designed to permit mothers, for a brief period, to practice infanticide. The idea is only speculative—and, indeed, it is hard to imagine a way of proving or disproving it. Furthermore, even if infanticidal behavior should turn out to have been biologically adaptive for our ancestors, that does not necessarily make it desirable. It is a romantic notion indeed to imagine that what is natural is also good. Yet the lag in a mother's bonding to her baby, and ancient and widespread customs that leave the newborn briefly in limbo, raise intriguing possibilities. They are in line with the idea that infanticide has been part of the human adaptive repertoire for millions of years.

Apes of the World

Russell H. Tuttle

Anthropoidea, the suborder of human-like creatures, encompasses the living and fossil New and Old World monkeys, the apes, and the hominid primates. A traditional taxonomic scheme places the extant apes and humans in three families. The Hylobatidae, the so-called "lesser apes," includes all gibbons and the siamang; the Pongidae, the family of "great apes," is comprised of the orangutans, chimpanzees, bonobos, and gorillas; and humans are in their own family, the Hominidae.

Recently, biomolecular data have indicated that humans and the African apes are much closer to one another than any of them are to the orangutans (Goodman 1986). However, one study on the genetic distances among humans, chimpanzees, bonobos, gorillas, and orangutans suggest that the orangutans are no further distant from humans than the African apes are (Bruce and Ayala 1978). It will take a good deal more research to reveal which branches in hominoid taxonomic schemes and evolutionary trees will collapse and what will sprout in their stead.

The great apes of Africa include several subspecies of chimpanzees, the bonobo, and two or more subspecies of gorillas. Because they all share a unique mode of quadrupedal behavior—termed knuckle-walking—for which the forelimbs are specially adapted, the extant African apes are placed in the genus _Pan_, with two subgenera and three species (Tuttle 1986). Accordingly, the chimpanzees are formally designated _Pan (Pan) troglodytes_; the bonobos are _Pan (Pan) paniscus_; and the gorillas are _Pan (Gorilla) gorilla_. The orangutans are known taxonomically as _Pongo pygmaeus_.

The koolokamba or gorilla-like chimpanzee, _P. t. koolokamba_, is the least well known subspecies of chimpanzee. Captives have been confused with gorillas, and some authors have suggested that they are in fact hybrids between gorillas and chimpanzees (Shea 1984). To my knowledge, the question of hybridization between chimpanzees and gorillas has not been systematically tested experimentally. Rumors about the production of chimpanzee-gorilla hybrids (and even pongid-human ones) sometimes buzz through primatological conferences. Alas, these chimrillas, hupanzees, and gomans have the credibility of human clones. Yet the recent arrival of viable siabons should temper our skepticism regarding future possibilities (Shafer et al. 1984).

After the elusive koolokamba, the bonobo is the least familiar of the African apes. It has received notable attention because of suggestions that it might closely resemble the precursor of the hominid ancestor *Australopithecus* (Zihlman et al. 1978).

Bonobos are confined to the highly humid and swampy forests of central Zaire, south and west of the Zaire and Lualaba rivers and north of the Kasai River (Badrian and Badrian 1977, 1984). Although they closely resemble chimpanzees in many respects, bonobos also exhibit several characteristic features of their own. Observers have commented particularly on their narrow shoulders and slender, long-limbed physique (Badrian and Badrian 1977; Shea 1981).

Before 1965, there was a superfluity of taxonomic names for the hominoids, giving the impression that during the Miocene there had been an extensive radiation of fossil Eurasian and African apes. Then, in a major taxonomic revision, Simons and Pilbeam (1965) lumped many of the Miocene hominoid primates into two genera of apes (*Dryopithecus* and *Gigantopithecus*) and one of hominids (*Ramapithecus*).

These lumpophilic exercises were much applauded by the scientific community, because they reflected more accurately the biology of populations. They laid the groundwork for better-focused studies on functional morphology and adaptations. Refined dating techniques, paleoecological studies, and neontological behavioral and anatomical studies of primates and other mammals also gave new impetus to paleoprimatology.

Additional discoveries of fossil apes since 1965 have inspired another era of taxonomic splitting and concomitant phylogenetic ramifications, though in no way comparable to that of earlier decades. The field is somewhere between flux and fulmination now. We must conclude that because the fossil record is so badly broken, puzzles about where, when, and how the extant apes and humans evolved cannot be resolved at this point. Although the Miocene fossils are numerous, they have been obtained from a very small segment of our planet. Western and central Africa, the Arabian peninsula, southeastern Asia, and other major regions that may have been hot beds of hominoid evolution remain very poorly sampled. Unless these huge gaps are filled, we may never be able to document thoroughly the origins and deployment of gibbons, orangutans, chimpanzees, gorillas, and humans.

CLIMBING, SWINGING, AND WALKING

Modern field studies of apes generally confirm that there is a continuum from knuckle-walking gorillas to arm-swinging gibbons in the relative frequencies of terrestriality and arboreality. Gorillas are the most terrestrial apes, followed by chimpanzees, bonobos, and orangutans. The hylobatids—gibbons and siamangs—are the only elusively arboreal apes. All apes are adept vertical climbers; and all, except the massive gorillas, are quite versatile climbers in the crowns of trees (Tuttle 1986).

A survey of the largely impressionistic literature on arboreal behavior in the apes suggests that extensive brachiation—rapid, arm-by-arm progression along the underside of branches—is characteristic only of the hylobatids. It is a dramatic component of their displays during intraspecific altercations (Tuttle 1986). The rapid brachiation that has been attributed to chimpanzees and other anthropoid primates is probably vertical dropping and leaping between supports instead of true ricochetal arm-swinging like that which gibbons and siamangs exquisitely execute.

Arm-swinging along horizontal branches and vines seems to be a rare mode of locomotion in the gorillas. It is employed more frequently by orangutans and chimpanzees, and perhaps even more often by bonobos (Tuttle 1986). Sumatran orangutans evince brief bouts of brachiation during "show-off" displays (Rijksen 1978).

Quantitative and contextual information on the bipedal behavior of apes is still spotty and ambiguous. Hylobatid apes, bonobos, and chimpanzees run bipedally along horizontal boughs and branches, especially when they are excited by human intruders. There are no data in recent naturalistic literature that would allow us to rank the pongid apes in regard to their bipedal potentialities. Observations on captives indicate no clear-cut differences among chimpanzees, gorillas, and orangutans in their tendency to tire during terrestrial bipedalism.

A WIDE VARIETY OF DIET

Modern field studies support several generalizations about the feeding habits of the apes. The Asian apes, chimpanzees, and bonobos are great fruit-eaters, with a special predilection for figs in regions where they are available. Chimpanzees and bonobos are somewhat more omnivorous than Asian apes, and much more omnivorous than mountain gorillas. In addition to fruits, eggs, honey, gums, and a wide variety of arthropods and vertebrates, they eat many leafy, pithy, and fibrous foods, though not to the extent that gorillas do. Chimpanzees can also subsist chiefly on quantities of rather hard seeds and desiccated fruits over notable periods of time. With the exception of mountain gorillas, the apes subsist on a remarkable variety of plant species and parts. Because of seasonal fluctuations in availability, their staple foods vary dramatically over the year.

Gorillas are predominantly herbivorous, though they too have a taste for fruits and will forage for them if they are accessible. Some orangutans, gibbons, and gorillas actively prey on arthropods in addition to ingesting them inadvertently with plant foods. Chimpanzees and gorillas eat soil and, more rarely, their feces. Drinking is relatively infrequent. It is assumed that the Asian apes, chimpanzees, and bonobos obtain most of their fluids from juicy fruits and other foods, whereas gorillas obtain them mostly from lush herbage.

Food competition is a prime factor that may lead to niche differentiation among organisms living in the same area, such as the gibbons, siamangs, and orangutans of the Sumatran forest. Although all three apes complete for figs in the middle canopy of the forest, their different ranging patterns, times of activity, and modes of foraging tend to minimize hostile encounters. The gibbons have larger territories—about twice the size of those of the siamang—and each day they travel about 60% further than the siamang do. Gibbons are also the most selective feeders, rising earlier and feeding on choice fruits before the other two species arrive. The orangutan is probably the least selective feeder among the three species (Rijksen 1978). The siamang is in a difficult intermediate position between the orangutan (which usually travels about the same distance each day as the siamang and greatly reduces the quantity of preferred fruits in the area) and the gibbon, which often gets first pick of the high-quality foods that the two hylobatid apes must share.

Too little is known about the nutritional needs and digestive physiology of the African apes to permit firm inferences about the extent to which specific kinds of food, let alone individual plant and animal species, determine the ranging patterns and behavior of chimpanzees and gorillas in different regions of Africa. Further, gross comparisons among the diets of gorillas, chimpanzees, and bonobos are likely to be confounded by the notable variability among different populations of each species. For instance, of 286 potential foods that are common to both the Mahale region and Gombe National Park, chimpanzees of the two regions are known to share only 104, or 36.4% (Nishida et al. 1983).

TOOLS, SKILLS, AND COMMUNICATION

Yerkes and Yerkes (1929) gave chimpanzees the highest marks among apes for the construction and use, including throwing, of implements. The orangutan scored a distant second in these abilities, and the gorilla was ranked the least promising artisan and pitcher. The status of the chimpanzee as a pongid tool whiz has been underscored by contemporary workers (Goodall 1986); meanwhile, the gorilla, and more particularly the orangutan, have steadily earned more esteem as implemental apes (Lethmate 1979). This work has been summarized and discussed thoroughly by Beck (1980). Bonobos are also proving to be versatile tool-makers and -users (McGrew 1982).

A point for lively discussion has been the question of whether apes in the wild can learn to use tools by unobtrusively watching people. Captive Sumatran and Bornean orangutans in rehabilitation camps pick up a remarkable variety of tool behaviors, probably to some extent by watching their custodians or other orangutans that have learned by aping them (Rijksen 1978; Galdikas 1982; Beck 1980). A number of these behaviors are similar to those of wild chimpanzees. At Ketambe, where orangutans that had been kept illegally as pets were now being rehabilitated to live in the wild, Rijksen (1978) observed subjects using sticks to prize objects; to probe termite and ant nests, a wounded monitor lizard, and a caged clouded leopard; and to stab into the tough, prickly rind of the durian fruit. These orangutans also swat away swarming bees with leafy twigs and brandish sticks and throw stones and vegetation at camp pets, people, and living, dead, and dying reptiles. One orangutan even became a proficient catcher.

Galdikas (1982) notes that orangutans raised by humans are more inclined to imitate human tool behavior than those with less extensive human contact. If indeed apes imitate humans only when they are raised by them, then it is unlikely that wild chimpanzees would have acquired tool behavior by spying on human gatherers, hunters, and horticulturists. Perhaps the potential for wild chimpanzees to learn tool behavior by observing humans could be tested by a person who would learn insect probing and nut-cracking from chimpanzees in Tanzania and western Africa and then regularly ply these skills in a locality like the Budongo Forest where the chimpanzees do not use tools. Adventurous students should be warned, however, that even after spending months with chimpanzee termite fishers, Teleki (1974) remained as inept as a juvenile ape.

Observations that apes can versatilely employ a variety of objects as tools and communicate via artifactual symbols according to simple human rules have sparked questions about possible high-level neurological links between apes and humans. That is to say, are there specific areas of the central nervous system of apes that underpin these capabilities, and are they homologous with areas in the human central nervous system that are thought to make speech and other symbolically mediated behaviors possible? We are greatly hampered in the exploration of these questions by the fact that, to some extent, the "ape condition" must be interpolated from experiments on monkeys and clinical observations on humans, since ape brains are only crudely charted by direct studies. Further, the functional significance of human cerebral asymmetries in regard to object manipulation and language is still a question for refinement and debate.

LeMay and her co-workers document that, like humans, great apes exhibit a tendency for the left hemisphere to extend farther posteriorly and for the left occipital lobe to be wider than the right one. In addition, the right frontal lobe tends to be wider and the right hemisphere to project farther anteriorly than the left one in Pongidae and *Homo sapiens*. The asymmetries in length of the frontal and occipital lobes are reflected externally by the frontal and occipital bones of the skull (LeMay et al. 1982). This is contrary to the view (Groves and Humphrey 1973) that cranial asymmetry in the mountain gorilla might be ascribed to left-sided chewing.

As most people have heard, apes lack speech. Nevertheless, the asymmetries of their temporal region might have something to say about precursors of this high-flown human attribute. Research on cercopithecine monkeys indicates that pongid studies could be telling (Steklis 1985).

In the field of ape language projects, two camps are obvious—those researchers who have fostered their subjects (Fouts, Miles, Patterson, and the Gardners) and those who elected more traditional laboratory settings for their studies (the Premacks and the Rumbaughs).

The upshot of reactions to the past two decades of ape language research is that the great apes are generally thought not to have mastered syntax of the kind that allows humans to produce sentences creatively. Embedding has barely been explored, and it is unlikely to come under study until simpler sentence-like constructions are generated spontaneously by the subjects.

As investigators of two-way communication with apes realized the elusiveness of syntax, they turned to problems of semantics, just as linguists have shifted from a heavy concentration on syntx to questions of semantics in human speech. But it is much easier to demonstrate that great apes "know how" than that they "know that" (Ristau and Robbins 1982). Clearly apes can label objects with arbitrary and iconic symbols and remember a remarkable number of arbitrary signs. However, the skeptics argue cogently that apes have not exhibited comprehension of meaning such that the English glosses applied by investigators are the indisputable equivalents of human words. Thus, although apes can name and symbolize, we still do not know precisely what they know or whether their use of symbols is homologous with our own symbolic capabilities. A productive direction for future studies might involve more emphasis on symbolic communication in naturalistic social relations instead of focusing on food and paraphernalia of the Yankee bourgeois child's world (Ristau and Robbins 1982).

In a break from the language-oriented approach of comparative psychologists and the signal-oriented approach of ethologists, Menzel (1971) devised a group-oriented approach to chimpanzee communication. Menzel's experiments were conducted over a span of six years with five female and four male juvenile wild-born chimpanzees in a large enclosed field in southeastern Louisiana. Six of them had lived together in the field for one year before testing. They formed a cohesive and relatively compatible social group (Menzel 1971).

While the rest of the group was caged out of view, Menzel (1971) showed one chimpanzee, designated the leader, a cache of food or fearful object somewhere in the field. Five of the subjects served alternately as leaders. After the leader had been reunited with the group, they were released together into the field. If food was the incentive, the group followed the leader and sometimes even ran ahead of him. The followers seemed to orient more to *that thing out there* than to the leader. If the object to be found was something frightful, the group moved cautiously.

In trails in which one leader had been shown hidden fruit, which is the chimpanzees' preferred food, and another leader had been shown vegetables, the entire group tended to follow the fruitful leader. This indicated that there had been some sort of pooling of information in the holding cage. Further, the exchanges of information were quite subtle. Usually there were no conspicuous gestures, facial expressions, or vocalizations, except that single alarm calls were sometimes uttered when leaders first saw a frightful object.

Exactly how the chimpanzees communicated information in the holding cage or momentarily after release is a mystery. Indeed, the leader often wrestled with others or just sat by the door until they were freed. Menzel (1973) suggests that the "visual orientation and the locomotor postures and movements of 'the animal as a whole' contain sufficient information to account for the bulk of the communication about hidden objects."

Menzel (1971) notes that his subjects succeeded so well because they were well acquainted with one another. No less should be expected of relatively stable wild populations of chimpanzees and, perhaps, other social mammals. Needless to say, the more subtly a social group communicates during routine foraging, nesting, and other maintenance activities, the less likely it will be to attract predators and opportunistic competitors.

SELF-AWARENESS IN THE APES

Of all the arrogant conceits in which humans have indulged, among the greatest must be counted the claim that only we are aware of ourselves, have individual identities, and think about what we are doing, have done, and will do. It has been argued that consciousness and its concomitant, mind, are premised on human language. According to this dogma, thoughts are impossible in the absence of human language. During the past decade, however, these entrenched beliefs have been challenged vigorously by scientists from diverse disciplines. Suggestive evidence for self-awareness of a sort in apes has come in particular from studies using mirror-image stimulation.

Most animals react to their reflection in mirrors as if they are viewing other individuals of their species. Social reactions to mirror-image stimulation, commonly in the form of aggressive or sexual displays, have been elicited in a variety of fish, birds, monkeys, and other mammals (Gallup 1975).

Like monkeys, apes initially react socially to their mirror images. But after several days, young and adult chimpanzees begin to use the mirror to explore parts of their bodies that are normally out of view. They also use the mirror to inspect food wadges in their mouths, clean between their teeth, pick their noses, blow bubbles, and make faces. This led Gallup (1975) to conclude that they must recognize themselves in the mirror and that they may have a self-concept. To test these hypotheses he anesthetized subjects that had had prior experience with mirror-image testing, and other subjects with none, and placed spots of red dye on the superior aspects of their brow ridges and ears. The dye could not be felt locally after it had dried. Once alert and introduced to a mirror, the experienced subjects responded in many ways to the spots, including touching them and then looking at or sniffing their exploratory fingers. The mirror-naive subjects reacted socially to the mirror.

Despite the herculean efforts that must be exerted in order to explore the minds of apes, we should develop even more refined psychological probes and press on to establish the actual limits of their cognitive abilities. We need to learn whether their particular adaptive zones have endowed them with special mental skills that are less developed in humans. Here, knowledge from observations in the field must penetrate into the laboratory. Perhaps now that the drama of pongid field studies is winding down and animal welfare groups are limiting terminal studies on captives, there will be a resurgence of noninvasive comparative psychological studies that will culminate in a deeper understanding of ape mentalities.

MONOGAMY AND THE MERITS OF SOLITUDE

Unlike the Aves, in which monogamy is common, in the Mammalia it is a relatively infrequent mating pattern. Furthermore, within the primates, monogamy is uncommon (Rutberg 1983). The hylobatid apes, which by and large practice monogamy, appear even more unusual among primates now that Sussman and Kinzey (1984) have effectively excluded the marmosets and tamarins from the ranks of monogamous species.

Brockelman and Srikosamatara (1984) and Mitani (1984) concluded that in most, if not all, species the behavior of females is the key to understanding hylobatid territoriality and obligate monogamy. Because gibbons are selective feeders on high-quality foods that are not generally abundant, females stake claims to sections of the forest that are large enough to support themselves and their progeny, yet small enough to defend against other females. Males, which are similarly limited by the resources available, cannot successfully defend territories any larger than those holding a single female and her young; thus the males, too, are obliged to mate monogamously and repel intruders.

In marked contrast with hylobatid apes, adult orangutan males and females are rarely seen together in the forest. Instead, the most common social units are individual females with their dependent youngsters, lone adult and subadult males, and various small groupings of adolescents or singletons. In captivity, however, family groups are readily assembled and live together as compatibly as other primates for which cohesive bisexual families are the norm. Captive orangutans can be exceptionally affectionate, playful, and tolerant of one another (Maple 1980). Hence a major question for field behavioralists is how orangutans become so solitary.

Horr (1972) suggested that because adult orangutans are large animals that can consume most of the fruit in a particular tree, they forage in small units. They have no "serious natural predators" to induce them to seek group protection (Horr 1972). Since males are unencumbered by youngsters, they can roam more widely for food and have a better chance to breed with estrous females. The main limitation to the movements of adult females, even ones with clinging infants, seems to be juvenile tagalongs, which have trouble negotiating sections of the arboreal highway. If bulk alone were the drag, adult males would be expected to have smaller ranges than the females have.

Rodman (1979) elaborates why an incompatibility of lifeways separates the sexes most of the time. If a male were to try to keep up with a female, he would have to travel arboreally more often between feeding bouts, because females change feeding locations more often than males do. And if she were to follow him faithfully, she would sacrifice a degree of selectivity among food trees because of his formidable bulk and greater appetite.

Rijksen (1978) rejects this model in favor of MacKinnon's suggestion that the extreme arboreality and solitariness of present-day *Pongo* is the result of interactions with *Homo* (MacKinnon 1974). Thus, when faced with food competition and depredation by hunting *Homo sapiens* and perhaps *Homo erectus*, previously more terrestrial and banded *Pongo* took to the trees and dispersed in the canopy where they would be less conspicuous and more distant targets.

SOCIAL ORGANIZATION OF THE AFRICAN APES

At Gombe, providing the chimpanzees with bananas allowed Goodall to observe and film innumerable details of the relationships of known individuals and of social behaviors; such abundant data would have been acquired much more slowly, if at all, from shy peripatetics were it not for the lure of the bananas. Once subjects were habituated, they could be followed from camp to see how the behaviors were expressed in the forest. Whether provisioning perturbed their social relationships in degree or in kind could not be discriminated readily. We probably never will know how typical of pristine Gombe chimpanzees Goodall's subjects were (Wrangham 1974).

Goodall (1986) concludes that healthy adult Gombe males were dominant over all adult females and both classes were dominant over youngsters. The males did not have a strictly linear hierarchy. There was one top male, followed by six others whose ranks depended on which other males were present. Some individuals tended to assist one another if one of them was threatened by conspecifics or baboons (Goodall 1986).

Although alliances among females were rare, Gombe females also showed a relatively clear dominance ordering. Their boldness seemed to depend on the presence of an adolescent son and perhaps on their estrous cycle. The status of youngsters depended on the presence and status of their mothers (Goodall 1986).

Grooming behavior occupied a good deal of the leisure time in Gombe chimpanzees and was common among presumably unrelated adults, as well as siblings and parents. Although this was partly an artifact of provisioning (Goodall 1986), it is probable that in general wild chimpanzees are more inclined to groom one another than Asian apes are. Because both play and grooming entail intimate physical contact and mutualism, they probably contribute to the somewhat greater cohesiveness of chimpanzee over orangutan society.

Tutin (1980) documents that over a 16-month span the majority of Gombe females (9 of 14) were impregnated during restrictive associations with single males, rather than in gang sex with several opportunists. Tutin recognizes two forms of restrictive mating patterns: short-term possessiveness by high-ranking males, which prevents estrous females from mating with other males, and temporary consortships, in which breeding pairs actively avoid the company of other chimpanzees. The former is solidly a male-dominated relationship, whereas the latter requires notable cooperation from the female, wherein she may exercise choice. Further, the brevity of possessive mating periods suggests that female choice is operant there also.

Female chimpanzees must choose mates strategically, because they have a limited reproductive potential and a high level of parental investment (Tutin and

McGinnis 1981). On the basis of a 19-year accumulation of data from Gombe, Tutin (1980) finds that the theoretical lifetime reproductive potential of female chimpanzees is five or six offspring; the median is three births per female; and only two of the three offspring can be expected to survive to reproductive age. Teleki and his co-workers (1976) caution that the banana bonanza may have reduced the birth rate at Gombe National Park.

Consortships accounted for seven of the nine conceptions that occurred during restrictive matings. Tutin (1979) concludes that except for the alpha male, consortships are the most fecund arrangement for adult males and females. Although the universality of the Gombe chimpanzee mating pattern is not established, studies in the Mahale Mountains indicate that it is at least broadly comparable in other communities of Tanzanian chimpanzees. Nishida (1968) notes female choice at Mahale. Indeed, he reports that almost all the sexual interactions he observed were initiated by females and that frequently the males were unresponsive.

Latest to be studied and extra-elusive with humans, bonobos are the supreme bafflers concerning the nature and adaptive meaning of ape social organization and sexual behavior. Our knowledge is still sketchy, despite more than two decades of research at several localities in Zaire.

The first major advance in studies of bonobo social and sexual behavior came with the establishment of a base for long-term studies near Wamba village in the Salonga National Park (Kuroda 1979; Kano 1982). Like *Pan troglodytes*, *Pan paniscus* as observed at Wamba are organized into groups of between 50 and 120 individuals (Kano 1982), which usually forage in smaller subunits (Kuroda 1979). Lone individuals are seen infrequently. Small foraging subunits (<10 individuals) are usually quiet, nonvocal, and unaggressive toward one another, and sexually abstemious. They become excited and tend to vocalize in response to larger parties. The latter are clamorous, demonstrative, and given to copulatory frenzies and other sex acts that outdo the orgiastic reunions of chimpanzees. However, excited bonobos tend to be less aggressive than their Tanzanian congeners during reunions (Kuroda 1979).

Kuroda (1979) observes that bonobos have stronger affiliations between males and females than chimpanzees do; the core of the group is bisexual; and there is little difference between the ranging patterns of males and females. The sexes are quite tolerant of one another; interactions among females are particularly pacific. Kuroda (1980) notes that adult males were dominant over all females; there may also be a dominance order among Wamba bonobo males. Social grooming underscores the special affinities between adult males and females and among females.

Badrian and Badrian (1984) conclude that the core of bonobo society consists of strongly bonded females and the males associated with them. The survey of sites given here supports the further conclusion that bonobo society is unique among ape societies and should not be considered a mere variant of chimpanzee society or a compromise between their social pattern and that of gorillas (Badrian and Badrian 1984).

The first scientific accounts on the social grouping and behavior of free-ranging gorillas in natural habitats were concentrated primarily on *Pan gorilla beringei* (Schaller 1963). The most thoroughgoing follow-up studies are also focused on the mountain gorilla (Fossey 1983). We know much less about western and Grauer's gorillas, but available studies indicate that their sociality is at least grossly similar to that of the mountain gorillas.

Schaller's portrait of the silverback gorilla stresses attractiveness as much as peacefulness (Schaller 1963). The silverback, a mature male at the top of the social hierarchy, is the hub of the cohesive group. Females and youngsters cluster about him while other mature males are peripheral and peripatetic. All group members appear to be attuned to the silverback's activities; he leads them through their daily rounds of feeding, travel, resting, and nesting. When extra silverbacks are with a group, its members usually react only to the dominant silverback as their leader (Schaller 1963).

Because dominance is largely correlated with body size, the silverback supplants all other group members at choice sitting and feeding sites and on narrow trails. When more than one silverback is in a group, they form a linear hierarchy. Blackbacks and females are dominant over youngsters. In some groups, the females form a hierarchy among themselves (Watts 1985). Their relations with blackbacks are variably dominant and subordinate (Schaller 1963).

The silverback is highly attractive to youngsters, which also enjoy the company of peers. They freely use him as a play mound during adult resting periods. Older youngsters prefer the silverback over their mothers when the group moves and feeds. Even more remarkably, four youngsters, ranging from 2.5 to 3.8 years, were observed to survive the death or abandonment of their mothers because the silverback continued to protect them and even bedded them in his night nest. It is doubtful that they could have survived the nocturnal chill on Mt. Visoke without the silverbacked furnace (Fossey 1983).

The cohesiveness of gorilla groups seems not to be maintained by grooming or frequent sex. Schaller (19863) reports that Kabara gorillas rarely groomed and that grooming was never reciprocal. He concludes that adult grooming was chiefly utilitarian—that is, for the removal of irritants from otherwise inaccessible regions.

Harcourt (1978) and Fossey (1983) shatter Schaller's image of the silverback as a gentle giant highly tolerant of his neighbors. Apart from the brevity of his contacts with the Kabara subjects, it is possible that Schaller observed only stable groups that had well-established dominance relationships with one another during this visit. By contrast, on Mt. Visoke all hell broke loose during the formation of new groups (Harcourt 1978; Fossey 1983, 1984).

Harcourt (1978) considers that aggression is the main tactic used by a resident male against others to prevent their association with his females. Fossey (1984) notes that female transfers between established groups or from a group to a lone silverback almost always entail overt aggression between the dominant male in the female's current group and the seductive silverback. The presence of estrous females and copulations within a group seems to attract visitors and to set off displays and fights between the males of the different social units (Fossey 1982).

Yamagiwa (1983) suggests that the cohesiveness of gorilla groups may be premised on the strong affinities between the dominant silverback and youngsters. Females are bound to him through their children. Young females without youngsters have looser ties and are thus disposed to emigrate. Adventurous young silverbacks can break male-female bonds by killing the infants of parous females. If a young silverback kills a female's infant, she will likely join his budding breeding unit (Fossey 1984). Yamagiwa's scenario leaves unexplained how the father-daughter bond loosens, if, in fact she was bonded to him as a youngster.

There are several possible reasons for female choice among available silverbacks. Harcourt (1978) stresses the quality of the male's range and especially the success of the female in rearing offspring with the male as reasons for her staying in a new unit. If the male cannot protect the female against infanticidal males, she will leave him for one with recently demonstrated prowess—even the murderer of her child (Harcourt 1978; Fossey 1984).

Unfortunately, human encroachments and depredations have drastically reduced the populations of mountain gorillas since 1960 (Fossey 1983). Poaching and other destructive incursions into their habitat have accelerated new group formation among the Visoke gorillas. We cannot always discern which aspects of the process are characteristic of gorilla social dynamics in the absence of destructive agencies. We can only hope that some groups will be allowed to stabilize and develop naturally in large undisturbed tracts of Rwanda, Zaire, and Uganda.

Not only gorillas but chimpanzees, bonobos, orangutans, and many hylobatid apes now face the growing possibility that their way of life may soon disappear. The conservation of apes in the wild undoubtedly is the most vital issue confronting all scientists who would draw upon knowledge of the apes in order to understand the human career and to search for general biological principles among a spectrum of animals.

Without immediate moves to preserve the apes *and their habitats*, we will lose forever a wealth of information. This would be especially tragic now that we have many well-formulated hypotheses to test, incisive research tools and approaches, and the technology to process great quantities of data. We are on the threshold to move from viewing apes as amusements to considering them creatures which truly reveal things about ourselves.

REFERENCES

Badrian, A., and N. Badrian. 1977. Pygmy chimpanzees. *Oryx* 13:463–68.

_____. 1984. Social organization of *Pan paniscus* in the Lomako Forest, Zaire. In *The Pygmy Chimpanzee: Evolutionary Biology and Behavior*, ed. R. L. Susman, pp. 325–46. Plenum.

Beck, B. 1980. *Animal Tool Behavior: The Use and Manufacture of Tools by Animals*. New York: Garland STPM Press.

Brockelman, W. Y., and S. Srikosamatara. 1984. Maintenance and evolution of social structure in gibbons. In *The Lesser Apes: Evolutionary and Behavioral Biology*, ed. H. Preushoft, D. J. Chivers, W. Y. Brockelman, and N. Creel, pp. 289–323. Edinburgh Univ. Press.

Bruce, E. J., and F. J. Ayala. 1978. Humans and apes are genetically very similar. *Nature* 276:264–65.

de Waal, F. 1989. *Peacemaking Among Primates*. Harvard Univ. Press.

Fossey, D. 1982. Reproduction among free-living mountain gorillas. *Am. J. Primatol.*, suppl., 1:97–104.

_____. 1983. *Gorillas in the Mist*. Houghton Mifflin.

_____. 1984. Infanticide in mountain gorillas *(Gorilla gorilla beringei)* with comparative notes on chimpanzees. In *Infanticide: Comparative and Evolutionary Perspectives*, ed. G. Hausfater and S. B. Hrdy, pp. 217–35. Aldine.

Galdikas, B. M. F. 1982. Orang-utan tool-use at Tanjung Puting Reserve, Central Indonesian Borneo (Kalimantan Tengah). *J. Hum. Evol.* 10:19–33.

Gallup, G. G., Jr. 1975. Towards an operational definition of self-awareness. In *Socioecology and Psychology of Primates*, ed. R. H. Tuttle, pp. 309–41. The Hague: Mouton.

Goodall, J. 1986. *The Chimpanzees of Gombe*. Harvard Univ. Press.

Goodman, M. 1986. Molecular evidence of the ape subfamily Homininae. In *Evolutionary Perspectives and the New Genetics*, ed. H. Gershowitz, D. L. Rucknagel, and R. E. Tashian, pp. 121–32. Alan R. Liss.

Groves, C. P. and N. K. Humphrey. 1973. Asymmetry in gorilla skulls: Evidence of lateralized brain function? *Nature* 244:53–54.

Harcourt, A. H. 1978. Strategies of emigration and transfer by primates, with particular reference to gorillas. *Zeitschr. Tierpsychol.* 48:401–20.

Horr, D. A. 1972. The Borneo orang-utan. *Borneo Res. Bull.* 4:46–50.

Jolly, A. 1985. *The Evolution of Primate Behavior*. Macmillan.

Kano, T. 1982. the social group of pygmy chimpanzees *(Pan paniscus)* of Wamba. *Primates* 23:171–88.

Kuroda, S. 1979. Grouping of the pygmy chimpanzees. *Primates 20:161–83*.

_____. 1980. Social behavior of the pygmy chimpanzees. *Primates* 21:181–97.

Leighton, D. R. 1987. Gibbons: Territoriality and monogamy. In *Primate Societies*, ed. B. M. Smuts, D. L. Cheney, R. M. Seyfarth, R. W. Wrangham, and T. T. Struhsaker, pp. 135–45. Univ. of Chicago Press.

LeMay, M., M. S. Billing, and N. Geschwind. 1982 Asymmetries of the brains and skulls of nonhuman primates. In *Primate Brain Evolution: Methods and Concepts*, ed. E. Armstrong and D. Falk, pp. 263–77. Plenum.

Lethmate, J. 1979. Instrumental behavior of zoo orang-utans. *J. Hum. Evol.* 8:741–44.

McGrew, W. C. 1982. Recent advances in study of tool-use by nonhuman primates. In *Advanced Views in Primate Biology*, ed. A. B. Chiarelli and R. S. Corruccini, pp. 177-83. Springer-Verlag.

MacKinnon, J. 1974. The behaviour and ecology of wild orang-utans *(Pongo pygmaeus)*. *Animal Behav.* 22:3–74.

Maple, T. L. 1980. *Orang-utan Behavior*. Van Nostrand Reinhold.

Menzel, E. W., Jr. 1971. Communication about the environment in a group of young chimpanzees. *Folia Primatol.* 15:220–32.

_____. 1973. Leadership and communication in young chimpanzees. *Symposia of the Fourth International Congress of Primatology, Portland Oregon*, ed. E. W. Menzel, Jr., pp. 192–225. Basel: Karger.

Mitani, J. C. 1984. The behavioral regulation of monogamy in gibbons *(Hylobates muelleri)*. *Behav. Ecol. Sociobiol.* 15:225–59.

Napier, J. R., and P. H. Napier. 1985. *The Natural History of the Primates.* MIT Press.

Nishida, T. 1968. The social group of wild chimpanzees in the Mahale Mountains. *Primates* 9:167–224.

Nishida, T., R. W. Wrangham, J. Goodall, and S. Uehara. 1983. Local differences in plant-feeding habits of chimpanzees between the Mahale Mountains and Gombe National Park, Tanzania. *J. Hum. Evol.* 12:467–80.

Rijksen, H. D. 1978. *A Field Study on Sumatran Orang Utans* (Pongo pygmaeus abelii Lesson 1827). Wageningen, The Netherlands: H. Veenman and Zonen.

Ristau, C. A., and D. Robbins. 1982. Language in the great apes: A critical review. *Adv. Stud. Behav.* 12:141–255.

Rodman, P. S. 1979. Individual activity pattern and the solitary nature of orangutans. In *The Great Apes,* ed. D. A. Hamburg and E. R. McCown, pp. 234–55. Benjamin/Cummings.

Rutberg, A. T. 1983. The evolution of monogamy in primates. *J. Theoret. Biol.* 104:93–112.

Schaller, G. G. 1963. *The Mountain Gorilla: Ecology and Behavior.* Univ. of Chicago Press.

Shafer, D. A., R. H. Myers, and D. Saltzman. 1984. Biogenetics of the siabon (gibbon-siamang hybrids). In *The Lesser Apes: Evolutionary and Behavioral Biology,* ed. H. Preuschoft, D. J. Chivers, W. Y. Brockelman, and N. Creel, pp. 486–97. Edinburgh Univ. Press.

Shea, B. T. 1981. Relative growth of the limbs and trunk in the African apes. *Am. J. Phys. Anthropol.* 56:179–201.

_____. 1984. Between the gorilla and the chimpanzee: A history of debate concerning the existence of the *koolokamba* or gorilla-like chimpanzee. *J. Ethnobiol.* 4:1–13.

Simons, E. L., and D. R. Pilbeam. 1965. Preliminary revision of the Dryopithecinae (Pongidae, Anthropoidea). *Folia Primatol.* 3:81–152.

Steklis, H. D. 1985. Primate communication, comparative neurology, and the origin of language re-examined. *J. Hum. Evol.* 14:157–73.

Sussman, R. W., and W. G. Kinzey. 1984. The ecological role of the Callithricidae: A review. *Am. J. Phys. Anthropol.* 64:419–49.

Teleki, 1974. Chimpanzee subsistence technology: Materials and skills. *J. Hum. Evol.* 3:575–94.

Teleki, G., E. E. Hunt, Jr., and J. H. Pfifferling. 1976 Demographic observations (1963–73) in chimpanzees of Gombe National Park, Tanzania. *J. Hum. Evol.* 5:559–98.

Tutin, C. E. 1979. Mating patterns and reproductive strategies in a community of wild chimpanzees *(Pan troglodytes schweinfurthii)*. *Behav. Ecol. Sociobiol.* 6:29–38.

_____. 1980. Reproductive behaviour of wild chimpanzees in the Gombe National Park, Tanzania. *J. Repro. Fertil.*, suppl. 28:43–57.

Tutin, C. E., and P. R. McGinnis. 1981. Chimpanzee reproduction in the wild. In *Reproductive Biology of the Great Apes,* ed. Charles E. Graham, pp. 230–64. Academic Press.

Tuttle, R. H. 1986. *Apes of the World.* Noyes Publ.

Veit, P. 1983. Hope for the mountain gorilla? *Defenders* 58(1,2):20–27.

Watts, D. P. 1985. Relations between group size and composition and feeding competition in mountain gorilla groups. *Animal Behav.* 33:72–85.

Wrangham, R. W. 1974. Artificial feeding of chimpanzees and baboons in their natural habitat. *Animal Behav.* 22:83–93.

Yamagiwa, J. 1983. Diachronic changes in two eastern lowland gorilla groups *(Gorilla gorilla graueri)* in the Mt. Kahuzi region, Zaire. *Primates* 24:174–83.

Yerkes, R. M., and A. W. Yerkes. 1929. *The Great Apes.* Yale Univ. Press.

Zihlman, A. L., J. E. Cronin, D. L. Cramer, and V. M. Sarich. 1978. Pygmy chimpanzee as a possible prototype for the common ancestor of humans, chimpanzees, and gorillas. *Nature* 275:744–46.

PART
4

Transitions and
Ecological Overviews

Perspective on Models Linking
Non-Human and Human Primates

M. E. Stephens

Apes are humans' closest relatives in the animal world. Apes have been studied with a view to learning more about both modern humans and hominid ancestors. This section includes a sample of such studies.

There are also theoretical papers which attempt to summarize more universal aspects of primates. Are there correlations with primate social organization and ecological constraints? Can generalizations be made about primate social interactions or thought patterns? If so, may the human primate be included in such generalizations?

An Apes's View of the Oldowan

T. Wynn
University of Colorado at Colorado Springs

W. C. McGrew
University of Stirling

When in human evolution did our ancestors cease behaving like apes? In this article we address this question by interpreting the earliest known archaeological evidence, the Oldowan, in light of what primatologists know about modern apes, especially the chimpanzee *(Pan troglodytes)*. Our analyses consider aspects of Oldowan tools and tool-making and those aspects of Oldowan subsistence that can be reconstructed from artefacts. We conclude that all the behavior that can be inferred from Oldowan tools and sites falls within the range of the ape adaptive grade. There is nothing exclusively human-like about this oldest known archaeological evidence. However, the Oldowan did include two specific behavioral patterns that, while still within the ape adaptive grade, are almost unknown for modern apes and which point in the direction of adaptations found later in hominid evolution. These are carrying tools or food for thousands of metres and competing with large carnivores for animal prey.

INTRODUCTION

The question of the origins of culture is a central one to anthropology. While anthropologists acknowledge an evolutionary continuum with apes, we also recognize a huge difference between the cultural behavior of modern apes and the cultural acts of modern humans. When in human evolution did our ancestors cease behaving like apes? Humans and apes have been phylogenetically separate for several million years, but this does not mean that our ancestors had human-like behaviour for the same length of time. The anatomy of fossil hominids cannot fully answer this question because it tells us little about the kinds of behavior at issue. We must turn to the archaeological record.

The Oldowan Industrial Complex is the oldest known flaked stone technology. In east Africa tools from this complex date from as early as 2.5 million

"An Ape's View of the Oldowan" by T. Wynn and W.C. McGrew, *MAN* (NS)24, 383–398. Reprinted by permission of the Royal Anthropological Institute of Great Britian and Ireland.

years ago (Harris 1983) and by 2 million years ago they occur in archaeological sites associated with broken up animal bones (Leakey 1971; Isaac 1976). The archaeological record for the Oldowan is meager, however, when judged by the standards of more recent prehistory. From a few thousand tools and animal bones, and their geological context, archaeologists must try to reconstruct the behavior of a tool-maker generally assumed to be a precursor of modern humans. Because there are so few pieces in this archaeological puzzle, we must use other sources to complete the picture of Oldowan life. This is largely a matter of selecting appropriate analogies.

The traditional view of the Oldowan is one of a proto-human culture, a first step on the evolutionary trail leading to modern humans. Archaeologists have often used knowledge of modern hunters and gatherers as a source for understanding the archaeological patterns of the Oldowan (e.g. Isaac 1978). However, when one looks 'backward' to the Oldowan from the perspective of modern humans, or even from the perspective of recent Stone Age humans, one risks filling in the missing pieces with inappropriate analogies. The result may be an over-optimistic interpretation. For example, Parker and Gibson (1979) have attributed several behavioral patterns to Oldowan hominids such as aimed throwing, dividing carcasses into equal portions, and sharing. There is no tangible evidence of any of these in the archaeological record, but they are well known for recent hunters and gatherers. In a similar vein, Tobias (1983) has argued for a 'holistic picture of the lifestyle' that included language along with the behavior cited above. Neither the fossil record for hominids nor the archaeological data give direct evidence for language. Tobias presented this picture as a reasonable interpretation. And it is, if one assumes that the Oldowan was proto-human.

In the following analyses we take a different perspective. We look for what is 'ape' about the Oldowan. Based on knowledge on the modern Pongidae (the great apes), especially the chimpanzee, *Pan troglodytes*, we examine the archaeological patterns presented by the Oldowan tools and sites (cf. Tanner 1987).

We try to match these patterns with specific kinds of behavior known for modern apes and to assess if such behavior is congruent with the foraging, technological and mental competencies of apes in general, something we term an *ape adaptive grade*. Reference to an ape adaptive grade is necessary because many specific differences, especially in terms of subsistence, are to be expected between hominoids occupying different niches. However, the basic types of solution to adaptive problems are likely to be much the same, with the difference being merely variations on a theme.

At the outset we must mention a logical difficulty faced by all archaeologists: the problem of minimum necessary competence. In prehistory, one can assess only the minimal abilities needed to produce the archaeological patterns uncovered. This is especially maddening for the Oldowan, because, as we seek to show in this article, the minimum competence needed to produce Oldowan tools and sites is that of an ape adaptive grade. One solution to this problem is to assume the existence of behaviour that would have required a more human-like competence, but which is not evident in the archaeological record. We see no reason to assume the existence of such behavioral patterns, as the point of scientific archaeology is to use evidence, not make assumptions. Thus, for the purposes of this exercise, we accept minimal competence as being a reliable description of Oldowan behavior.

The article is organized into two main sections. The first addresses Oldowan tools and their counterparts in ape behavior. The second similarly treats the pattern of tool-use. Then follows a brief summarizing conclusion and a more speculative discussion.

TOOLS

The most direct way to compare Oldowan and chimpanzee technology is to compare the tools themselves (see table 1 and fig. 1). This approach has the advantage of dealing with more or less tangible phenomena. Here we will emphasize the cognitive prerequisites of the various tools. In assessments of the Oldowan the general presumption has been that it was a comparatively complex technology based on complex cognition (see., e.g. Gowlett 1984 or Toth 1985). After first considering the raw materials, we will examine the spatial concepts used in tool-making, the natural groupings of the tools and, finally, the manufacturing procedures.

All known Oldowan tools were made of stone; most chimpanzee tools are not. This distinction has maintained the status of a phylogenetic divide despite much documentation of ape too-use to the contrary. We question whether or not this simple difference in raw material deserves such significance. Chimpanzees use stones as weapons in agonistic encounters and in processing plant foods. True, chimpanzees do not flake stone, though they occasionally produce unintentional flakes when they crack nuts on stone anvils. These result from mishits when a hammer-stone clips the edge of the anvil (Hannah, unpublished data); apes have yet to be seen to use such flakes.

There is reason to suppose, however, that the use of intentionally flaked stone is within their range of abilities. A male orang-utan successfully completed an experimental task in which he had to strike a flake from a core using a hammer-stone and then use a flake to cut through a cord securing a box (Wright 1972). More recently, Kitahara-Frisch *et al.* (1987) reported that chimpanzees shown how to use hammer-stones to smash long-bones then used the resulting bone fragments to puncture a skin covering a bottle of sweetened drink. Thus, the lack of functional stone flaking in wild chimpanzees does not represent some behavioral or cognitive deficit, but rather a difference in the raw material used for most tools and, perhaps more importantly, a difference in the tasks performed by the tools. We must look elsewhere for evidence of greater complexity in the Oldowan.

One of the more direct ways to assess the cognitive ability employed in tool-use is through examination of spatial concepts. The advantage of this approach is that we can focus on the tools as products, particularly the geometric arrangement of elements on the tools, and do not have to see the sequence of

Table 1. Oldowan and chimpanzee tools compared.

Chimpanzee 1	Oldowan 2
1. Known subsistence tools termite probes ant probes leaf sponges wooden hammers stone hammers stone anvils tree-root anvils	1. Known tools stone hammers stone anvils flaked cores unmodified stone flakes modified stone flakes manuports flaked bone(?)
2. Spatial concepts Primitive spatial concepts of proximity, boundary, and order used to make tools of vegetation.	2. Spatial concepts Primitive spatial concepts of proximity, boundary, and order used to flake stone.
3. Natural groupings of tools Some standardization results from selection of raw material of appropriate size and strength for the task. Bitten to appropriate length. An 'ad hoc' technology.	3. Natural grouping of tools Some standardization results from selection of lava for large tools and quartz and quartzite for small tools. An 'an hoc' technology.
4. Manufacturing procedure selectivity of raw material modification by stripping, biting, chewing trial-and-error sufficient	4. Manufacturing procedure selectivity of raw material modification by flaking trial-and-error sufficient

1. (Boesch & Boesch 1983, 1984; Goodall 1968; Hannah & McGrew 1987; Hasegawa et al. 1983; McGrew 1974; McGrew & Collins 1985; Sabater Pi 1974; Sugiyama 1985; Sugiyama & Koman 1979; Teleki 1973).

2. (Bunn 1981; Harris 1983; Isaac 1976; 1981; 1984; Leakey 1971; Ohel 1984; Potts 1984; Toth 1985; Wynn 1978, 1981, 1989).

manufacture or use. The spatial concepts required for Oldowan tools are primitive. The maker need not have paid any attention to the overall shape of the tool; instead, his focus appears to have been exclusively on the configuration of the edges (Isaac 1981; Toth 1985). As a consequence one need not argue for the use of such relatively sophisticated ideas as perspective or symmetry. Examination of the arrangement of trimming on the edges suggests a fairly consistent set of three spatial notions, all of which fall under the purview of topological space. These are proximity, boundary and order. The simplest of these notions is *proximity* or 'nearby-ness'. By repeatedly bashing a cobble in more or less the same place knappers could create a number of sharp projections and intersect-

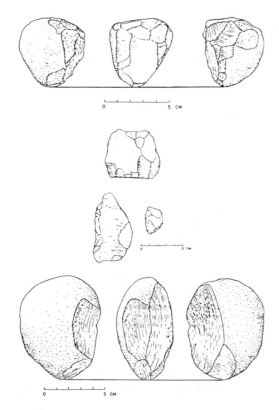

Figure 1. Sample of Oldowan flaked stone tools. Very simple concepts of space would suffice for positioning all of the modifications. These modifications altered the shapes of edges but apparently without any attempt to achieve an overall shape.

ing edges. Placing blows in proximity is a simple concept but it does require some coordination of motor patterns.

A more complex notion is that of *a boundary* in space. A boundary is a feature that divides a spatial field into two realms or areas. Bifacial flaking requires respect of a boundary. By trimming on alternating sides of a boundary on a cobble the Oldowan tool-maker could produce a single sinuous edge; the boundary in a sense divided the spatial field of the cobble into two realms.

The most sophisticated spatial notion used on Oldowan tools is that of *order*. When making unifacial scrapers the tool-maker had to coordinate proximity with a notion of constant direction of movement: one trimming blow after another along the edge of a flake or core. The result is a sturdy, relatively even edge.

Very few Oldowan artefacts have discontinuous sections of trimming. It appears that the initial trimming had a tyrannical control on later trimming. The first blow seems to have anchored the rest; concepts of proximity, boundary and order then extended the trimming from this starting point. For example, when making a bifacial chopper the first blow determined the location of the boundary that guided subsequent trimming. All in all, the patterns of trimming on Oldowan tools are very simple and indicate that hominids used simple spatial concepts to coordinate their stone knapping (Wynn 1981; 1989).

Unfortunately, a similar assessment cannot be applied to most chimpanzee tools. Many of their characteristics are largely determined by the raw material: the position of the leaves to be stripped from a twig is dictated by the plant, not the ape. However, all the conceptual or perceptual abilities needed for Oldowan tools appear in tools used by apes. Rigorous experimental studies have shown that when given a blank sheet of paper upon which to draw, chimpanzee 'artists' do not mark randomly. When given a sheet upon which a single geometric shape like a square is already present, they concentrate their marks on and around it, thereby showing the property of proximity (Smith 1973; Boysen *et al.* 1987). The property of boundary is exemplified in an unusual kind of termite-

336

fishing tool made only by the chimpanzees of Bilenge in Tanzania (McGrew & Collins 1985). The raw material is a sedge (*Cyperus pseudoleplocladus*), the stem of which is triangular in cross-section. For use as a fishing-probe, one of the three ridges is removed by careful longitudinal stripping, leaving a thinner more flexible tool which is trapezoidal in cross-section. Order is exemplified in the building of sleeping platforms ('nests'), something which all great apes in nature do every evening. For chimpanzees, the first major branch bent over determines the foundation, which is followed by the inter-weaving of side-branches and finally lining of the nest with detached leafy twigs (Goodall 1968). Unlike the stereotyped nest-building of songbirds, this construction by apes requires appropriate experience in ontogeny if it is to be manifest (Bernstein 1962).

In sum, all the spatial concepts needed for Oldowan tools can be found in the minds of apes. Indeed, the spatial competence described above is probably true of all great apes and as such does not make Oldowan tool-makers unique.

Another approach to the cognitive underpinnings of tools is through scrutiny of the natural groupings into which they fall. Do the tools fall into relatively discrete categories of kinds, or do they show a more continuous variation in features like size and shape? Such a search for natural 'types' is a perennial problem of archaeological methodology precisely because there is no way to know that the categories which we recognize in archaeological assemblages correspond to the mental categories of the artisans. As a result, many archaeologists avoid the question altogether by using problem-specific analytical types, for which no argument for correspondence is needed. Nevertheless, from the perspective of the evolution of cognition, the nature of natural groupings is important. How boundaries between groups are demarcated, and perhaps more significantly, how the resulting categories relate to one another tells us some interesting things about how the artisans organized their world. Such matters are at the core of behaviour and hence are worthy of investigation.

Leakey (1971) has argued that Oldowan tools fall into about two dozen types, including such types as side-choppers and end-choppers. While Leakey's familiarity with the artefacts is unmatched, it is unclear whether or not these types and sub-types represent categories that existed in the minds of their makers. If one lays out the artefacts on a table there is almost continuous variation in size and shape (Wynn 1978). The one clear discontinuity is between larger artefacts on lava cores and smaller artefacts on quartz flakes. Isaac (1984) and Toth (1985) saw this continuous variation as resulting from production of edges necessary to complete a task immediately to hand. In effect, the individual had a specific task to perform, chose a blank of the right size (or perhaps made one in the case of flakes) and chipped an appropriate edge. After finishing the task the tools were abandoned. The result of such an *'ad hoc'* technology would be a relatively continuous range of size and edge configurations corresponding to the range of specific tasks at hand. This interpretation better matches the variation seen in artefacts than does Leakey's claims for types and sub-types. From a more cognitive perspective, it seems that Olduvai's tool-makers need not have employed any standardized set of designs in the form of 'mental templates', or need not have used any concepts of types or sub-types.

Chimpanzees' tools present a pattern of variation that is directly comparable. The size and shape of chimpanzee tools seem to be tied to the task at hand. In making probes to 'fish' for termites, chimpanzees at Gombe in Tanzania select aptly sized stems or grass blades and often bite them to optimize their dimensions or to rejuvenate the stiffness of the end (Goodall 1968). When faced with a different task, of dipping for driver ants, chimpanzees bite the probes to a different length (McGrew 1984). In the Okorobiko mountains of Equatorial Guinea chimpanzees break open the termites' mounds rather than probe them, but again the tools are fairly uniform in features (Sabater Pi 1974). The uniformity of the artefact is governed by the uniformity of the task; it is still *ad hoc* technology. There is no reason to hypothesise a pre-existing image of an 'ideal' probe. One makes what will work at the time. There is also no evidence of types and sub-types in chimpanzees' tools. In sum, the chimpanzees' apparent lack of mental templates, formal classification and pre-existing types matches the kinds of tool-groupings seen in the Oldowan.

While we cannot watch Oldowan tools being made, we can identify some of the steps in procedure. Two are of special interest because they appear on the surface to be sophisticated: selectivity of raw material and the use of tools to make tools. In the Oldowan assemblages from Olduvai Gorge there is a marked tendency of the smaller tools to be made of quartz and quartzite and for the larger tools to be made of lava (Leakey 1971; Ohel 1984). The quartz and quartzite had to be carried for a distance of at least two kilometers. Thus, it seems that for reasons unknown the tool-users selected certain kinds of raw material for certain kinds of tools. This in turn implies a certain amount of foresight and suggests that tool-use was not entirely spur-of-the-moment. The knappers also needed to use stone hammers to make the flaked stone tools; in other words they used tools to make other tools. This striking point has achieved some notoriety in discussions of the evolution of intelligence (e.g. Parker & Gibson 1979) and has become a kind of threshold marker dividing ape from human technology.

From an ape's perspective neither of these is remarkable. Chimpanzees in the Tai Forest in Ivory Coast regularly use harder hammers of granite and quartzite on *Panda* nuts than on *Coula* nuts, which can be opened by softer hammers of laterite (Boesch & Boesch 1983). Moreover, they regularly carry such hammers to nut-cracking stations, sometimes for distances of over 500 metres. Such selectivity is directly comparable to that at Oldovai.

Apes in nature have not yet been seen to use tools to make tools. (Sugiyama (1985), has found chimpanzees in Cameroon using a 'brush-stick' to collect termites. It looks as if the frayed end of the stick has been beaten with a hammer, but the making of the tool remains to be directly observed). But is this such a significant failing? Two considerations argue against 'tools to make tools' as the great Rubicon of technological evolution. First, as noted above, it is possible to teach apes to use stone hammers to make tools with cutting edges; the procedure is well within ape capacities. Second, apes have efficient canines and incisors and for most of the tools that apes make these teeth are enough. However, one clearly cannot bite stone, so teeth alone would not suffice to make the tools used by Oldowan tool-makers. We cannot fault apes for not employing unnecessary techniques in making the tools needed in their subsistence.

Perhaps more enlightening than point-by-point comparisons between Oldowan and ape tool-making is a general comparison of the procedures used by both. For the Oldowan this means describing the least complicated procedure that would suffice for accomplishing the task (recalling that we must use minimum competence as a benchmark). Even the most complex Oldowan tool could be produced through trial-and-error. The tool-maker need only have had an image of the intended result such as a chopper and a repertoire of motor patterns for achieving it. She made a few modifications with trimming blows, checked the result to see if it would work for the task at hand, made a few more, checked again, and so on until she had produced an acceptable tool. Trial-and-error is not a haphazard, serendipitous kind of operation as the term may imply, but a procedure that employs well-defined intentions and techniques. What trial-and-error lacks is the use of contingencies for dealing with unanticipated problems. Moreover, trial-and-error procedures can control for only one variable at a time; that is, it cannot take account of the effect that an action may have on several variables at once or of the inter-relations between several variables (Piaget 1972; Wynn 1981). There is nothing about Oldowan tools that would require contingency plans.

Chimpanzees also use trial-and-error in making tools. Stripping leaves, peeling bark, splitting stems and biting vines to length requires a mental image and a set of motor patterns, but do not require contingency plans or simultaneous than one variable.

In sum, both specific and general comparisons place the tool-making procedures of the Oldowan well within the abilities seen in modern apes.

TOOL-USE

Even if Oldowan tools fail to show characteristics that would place them outside the range of ape technology, it is possible that they were *used* in a more complex way. Because we cannot observe Oldowan tool-use, as we can for apes, we must rely on inference for both specific and general comparisons. In the last few years, the sophistication of archaeological analyses of Oldowan refuse has increased dramatically and the result has been a more reliable, if not uncontroversial, picture of hominid subsistence. This picture appears to corroborate the ape-grade technology documented by the tools (see table 2).

Oldowan tool-makers processed small animals and parts of large animals with their tools. Sites excavated at Olduvai Gorge and at Koobi Fora have stone tools in association with broken-up bones of various sizes and species of animal (Leakey 1971; Isaac 1976). The variety of species and body-parts effectively eliminates the possibility that the bone accumulations resulted from known carnivores. Moreover, some of the bones have cut-marks that seen certain to have been made by stone tools (though note the cautionary findings of Behrensmeyer

Table 2. Tool-use compared.

Chimpanzee [1]	Oldowan [2]
1. What gets processed? termite mounds, bee hives, ant nests nuts water, brains, honey	1. What gets processed? body-parts of large and small animals
2. How is it processed? breaking open by pounding and prising inserting and luring guiding and concentrating sopping	2. How is it processed? breaking open by pounding and cutting slicing (e.g. tendons)
3. Where does processing occur? at termite mounds, ant nests, bee hives at nut-cracking stations	3. Where does processing occur? at death-sites at processing stations
4. What gets carried? raw materials hammers probes nuts body-parts	4. What gets carried? raw materials hammers manuports flaked cores body-parts

5. How far?
nuts - 265m
hammers - 500m
probes - 1km
body-parts - 6km
	5. How far?
	at Olduvai
	  gneiss (rare) 6-13 km
	  quartzie 2-5km
	  lava km
	at E. Turkana
	  from nearby stream bed

1, 2 See Table 1

et al. 1986). Exactly what products the butchers got from the carcasses is the subject of much current debate. Some argue that marrow was the main goal (Binford 1981), others that it was meat (Bunn 1981). Probably it was both (Potts 1984). While it is not yet possible to assess the relative importance of meat and marrow from large (i.e. greater than 100 kilograms body-weight) bovids in the overall Oldowan diet, their frequent presence is enough to distinguish Oldowan foraging from that of chimpanzees.

Chimpanzees also consume small animals and parts of large animals. Apart from eggs and nestlings, the prey are usually other primates and the young of ungulates (McGrew 1983). The largest recorded prey of which parts are eaten is adult bushbuck *(Tragelaphus scriptus)* which weigh from 25-80 kilograms (Haltenorth & Diller 1977). However, with one notable exception, no ape has been seen to use a tool to obtain meat. The exception involved an old male chimpanzee at Gombe who threw a stone at a defensively massed sounder of bush-pigs *(Potamochoerus porcus)*, hitting one of them. Soon after the pigs broke ranks and in the ensuing melee the chimpanzees captured piglets which they ate (Plooij 1978).

This apparent contrast in tool-use in processing meat deserves further development. Oldowan extractive foragers used stone tools to break into things. Most obvious was their use of tools to break into the diaphyses of long bones in order to get the marrow, but the idea of 'extraction' can be extended to butchery as well (Parker & Gibson 1979). The carcass of the prey must be 'broken into' in order to get at the edible tissues inside the skin container. Butchery marks on the epiphyses suggest that other products such as tendons may also have been a goal but the many comminuted bones at sites such as FLK suggest that extraction, especially of marrow, was a common procedure in the tool repertoire (Potts 1984). Parker and Gibson were the first to emphasize the evidence for extractive procedures in Oldowan tool-use, but perhaps they inadvertently masked its importance by adding to it several hypothetical behavioral patterns such as aimed throwing.

Chimpanzees also employ extractive procedures in their natural tool-use. Probing for termites, breaking open nuts, and using sponges to swab out fluids or brains are all extractive tasks; all entail removing embedded food from a container. Conceptually this is no different from extracting marrow from bones or meat from carcasses. Use of sponges to extract brains (Teleki 1973) seems indistinguishable from the kinds of procedures that Oldowan meat-eaters used to get at edible portions of carcasses. The behavioral patterns are similar enough to suggest that extractive foraging in the archaeological record can be just as readily interpreted as homologous or analogous. It certainly does not distinguish hominids from pongids.

Much has been written about the significance of the hominid re-use of sites, but again close examination reveals an ape-like pattern. Recent work by Potts (1984; 1986) and Toth (1985) stresses that Oldowan sites such as FLK and KBS[1] were places to which foragers carried tools and food. These were not death sites, so the acquisitors must have carried carcasses or parts of them to these places for further processing or consumption. However, these sites do not appear to have been 'home-bases' as some archaeologist maintained initially and enthusiastically (e.g. Isaac 1978). (Evidence of whether the consumers slept there or even spent long periods there would be hard to obtain, however.) By studying weathering patterns on the fossilized bones, Potts (1986) has shown that the bones at FLK accumulated over a period of five to ten years. Over the same period the site was visited repeatedly by carnivores. Also, most of the body-parts taken to FLK were small; few seem large enough to share. The East Turkana site of FxJj 50 (Bunn *et al.* 1980) consists of several dense scatters of bone associated with stone tools, suggesting several episodes of use spanning a period of not more than a year (authors' estimate). Like FLK, the site was also visited by carnivores during the period of bone deposition. All this suggests that Oldowan sites such as FLK were picnic-sites (such as groves of trees?) to which foragers carried parts of prey however acquired to be consumed in relative safety and comfort (Potts 1984). Other sites such as the HAS site at Koobi Fora (Isaac *et al.* 1976) and the 'Deinotherium' site at Olduvai (Leakey 1971) appear to have been acquisition sites from which the hominids removed body-parts. In addition to take-away foods, they also carried tools and unmodified stone (Ohel 1984). Some of the stone was carried from as far away as six kilometers, though shorter distances of less than two kilometers were far more common. In sum, Oldowan foraging seems to have included acquisition of parts of prey, which were then carried to another place for further processing with tools, which had also been carried, for consumption.

Chimpanzees practice a directly comparable kind of foraging. They use hammers to crack open nuts and select hammers of particular sizes and raw materials to fit the task (Sugiyama & Koman 1979; Boesch & Boesch 1983; 1984; Kortlandt & Holzhaus 1987). Because stone is relatively rare in the Tai forest it must be carried to most nut-cracking stations. In most cases processing occurs near the nut trees. However, when suitable anvils or roots or stones are not nearby, then chimpanzees transport nuts as well. In a study of wild-born chimpanzees released from captivity who spontaneously took up nut-cracking, the apes carried nuts several hundred metres to suitable anvils (Hannah & McGrew 1987). However, the extensive data-set from Tai shows that only about 5 percent of hammer-transports exceeded 200 metres, and the modal distance was only 5-20 metres (Boesch & Boesch 1983). Chimpanzees re-use nut-cracking stations for years, in some instances producing impressive accumulations of refuse. Finally, chimpanzees sometimes carry away animal food for later consumption: an adult female occasionally nibbled at a piece of bushbuck pelvis which she carried for two days while travelling six kilometres (Hasegawa *et al.* 1983).

In sum, the spatial pattern of this foraging is the same as can be reconstructed for the Oldowan: carrying tools and food to processing stations that are re-used over time. The specifics differ but the general pattern and its cognitive demands are the same. The important point is that both hominoids carry objects to goals that are out of sight.

Neither the food processed nor the spatial arrangements of processing places Oldowan foraging outside the range of ape behavior. These two aspects of foraging are relatively amenable to study in prehistory, but they do not exhaust the topic of foraging. How did the meat-eaters acquire the body-parts of prey in the first place? There is much debate among archaeologists on this point (e.g. Shipman 1986). If they simply scrounged bones for marrow, then their foraging might have been largely indistinguishable from chimpanzees' foraging for nuts. If, at the other extreme, Oldowan tool-users killed and butchered large mammals using projectiles and elaborate tool-kits, then their foraging *was* outside the known range of ape behavior. Few argue for either of these extremes. Most opinion focuses on a flexible meat-getting strategy combining scavenging with hunting as the behavior behind the bone accumulations (Tooby & DeVore 1987). Whether the former was 'early' scavenging soon after the prey's death, or 'late' scavenging of carrion is not yet clear (Bunn 1981; Potts 1984). Whether such hunting involved bringing down healthy adults of large body-size or despatching injured or aged prey or immatures remains to be determined.

So, how do chimpanzees obtain their meat? Goodall's (1968) and Teleki's (1973) descriptions of their hunting (that is, stalking, pursuit, capture, killing) followed by processing (that is, dismembering, sharing, eating) are well-known. Gombe's apes also show 'early' scavenging in pirating most of their bushbuck fawns from the baboons who have just killed them (Morris &Goodall 1977). More recently, Hasegawa *et al.* (1983) have reported that chimpanzees at Kasoje in Tanzania scavenge ungulates, probably the cached kills of solitary carnivores. Conspicuously absent in all this is the use of tools to *obtain* meat, except for Plooij's report (1978) noted above.

To be meat-eaters, early hominoids and living apes must compete with large carnivores; that is, Canidae, Felidae and Hyaenidae. That early hominoids had such competition is clear from the fossil record, but how they coped is yet unknown. For chimpanzees, evidence shows that they can deal with solitary big cats such as leopards *(Panthera pardus)*. This is known from extensive field experimentation (e.g. Kortlandt 1965) and from a striking recent report in which a party of chimpanzees mobbed an adult female leopard and killed her offspring (Hiraiwa-Hasegawa *et al.* 1986). However well they cope with solitary large carnivores by mobbing, this is a different proposition from dealing with large carnivores in groups; then the apes retreat to the trees (Tutin *et al.* 1981). Thus, lion *(Panthera leo)*, spotted hyaena *(Crocuta crocuta)* and wild dog *(Lycaon pictus)* probably provide sterner tests. The ape's solution is on of indirect competition, to be active by day, while the social carnivores are largely crepuscular or nocturnal hunters.

In sum, what we know about Oldowan foraging seems to be within the capabilities of apes. The details differ, but this might be expected given local differences in habitat. Oldowan foraging appears to have been that of a hominoid who lived in a semi-arid, open grassland habitat and who combined scavenging of carcasses and hunting of small game. There is no evidence for a dramatic re-ordering of general hominoid foraging, nor for a evolutionary leap in the cognitive capabilities underlying it.

CONCLUSIONS

When we consider the archaeological record of the Oldowan from the perspective of the behavior of modern apes it seems very familiar. The spatial concepts employed to manufacture tools, the natural grouping of tools and even the general procedures for tool-making can all be found in the repertoire of living apes. Moreover, Oldowan foraging patterns such as extractive foraging and the re-use of processing sites are typical of ape patterns of foraging too. The specifics of the Oldowan adaptive niche differ from those of modern apes, but the general pattern is the same. There is nothing about the Oldowan which demands human-like behaviour such as language, ritual, shared knowledge of arbitrary design, or other sophisticated material processes. At most one can argue that the Oldowan pushed the limits of ape grade adaptation; it did not exceed them.

DISCUSSION

The preceding conclusion has relevance for both our understanding of hominoid adaptation and for our understanding of human evolution. In the first case, the analyses rc-emphasize the breadth and potential of an ape grade of intelligence and culture. We tend to assume that the range of ape adaptive solutions extends only to those that we see in the modern world, while at the same time we inflate the human range with prehistoric examples. From the fossil record, especially that of the Miocene, we know that hominoids were much more diverse and successful in the past (Pilbeam 1986). This diversity could well have included varieties of technological and foraging patterns not seen in modern pongid populations. We do not disparage Oldowan hominids by placing them in the company of apes; apes were successful for a long time. The use of flaked stone makes the Oldowan look new, but it appears to be a variation on an old theme.

In its general features Oldowan culture was ape, not human. Nowhere in this picture need we posit elements such as language, extensive sharing, division of labour or pair-bonded families, all of which are part of the baggage carried by the term *human*. The same conclusion applies to the specific elements of behaviour which can be reconstructed. However, this does not mean that the Oldowan tells us nothing about the emergence of human behavior. The importance of an ape's perspective for human evolution is that it allows us to factor out what is *not* new about the Oldowan and identify what *is* new. When we factor out the apelike patterns, two others remain that are foreign to modern apes: carrying objects for thousands of metres and competing successfully with large carnivores for large animals. Neither is beyond the competence of an ape adaptive grade, but both point in the direction of advances later in human evolution that eventually clearly distinguish humans from our near cousins.

At first the difference in distances that objects are habitually carried may seem unremarkable: the cognitive prerequisites for carrying objects for 300 metres are presumably no different from those for carrying objects for 3000 metres. However, the difference is one order of magnitude. This suggests several points. First, hominid bipedalism which frees the upper limbs is much more efficient for carrying objects than is pongid tripedalism or quadrupedalism, as recognized long ago by Hewes (1961). Second, Oldowan foragers had to *organize* larger units of geography than do modern chimpanzees. The overall home-ranges need not have been larger, but the Oldowan tool-makers clearly planned tool-use that incorporated areas of hundreds of square kilometers. We have no evidence that their spatial repertoires were any different from those of apes, given, for example, the simple geometry of the stone tools, but the management of large geographic spaces may have called for different sorts of spatial abilities from those of apes. Later, soon after the Oldowan, we do find evidence for more complex spatial concepts. Early Acheulean bifaces, 1.5 million years old, required rudimentary ideas of spatial measurement and symmetry (Wynn 1989). Neither concept is known for apes and both suggest a more abstract spatial frame of reference than any used in the Oldowan. Interestingly, neither appears necessary to the mechanical performance of the tools. Perhaps they were borrowed from the repertoire used to organize geographic space, where such abstraction might have been highly selected for. In other words, the relatively complex spatial competence of early Acheulean hominids may have been a response to a situation first encountered in the Oldowan.

Competition with carnivores seems a more daunting problem. If Oldowan meat-eaters scavenged, then they probably had to employ strategies to deal with large, social carnivores. One possible strategy not often mentioned in the speculative literature is deception. Recent studies of non-human primates suggest that deception in social behaviour may have been an important factor in the selection for intelligence (Byrne & Whiten 1988). A shift from its use in within-species competition to across-species competition seems plausible. Moreover, deception probably became a useful tool later in human evolution when full-scale co-operative big-game hunting became prominent. Deception of competing carnivores (e.g. by concealing weapons or by feigning indifference before snatching a prey) would be the kind of behaviour that might well be selected later for intelligence of a human grade.

Although we have focused exclusively on the archaeological record in these analyses, the fossil evidence needs mentioning too. If the Oldowan tool-maker was *Homo habilis*, our conclusion that it had an ape grade adaptation may seem counter-intuitive. After all, the brain of *Homo habilis* falls between that of living apes and humans in terms of its size and shape (Passingham 1982; Holloway 1981; 1983). This need not mean, however, that *Homo habilis* must have had a *culture* that was equally intermediate. If we were to reject archaeological evidence because it was inconsistent with our interpretation of the anatomical evidence, we would come perilously close to circular reasoning: the Oldowan must have been sophisticated because its makers had big brains, therefore culture selected for big brains. (A further cautionary note about the difficulties of assigning tools to purported makers based on anatomical grounds comes from Susman's (1988) analyses of *Paranthropus* fossils. He concludes that they, and not sympatric *Homo*, were the makers.) We do not question the evidence for brains but instead think that scholars must not reconcile the 'inconsistency' by promoting the Oldowan to insupportable cultural levels. The evolutionary pressures for encephalisation may have been unrelated to culture. If one uses archaeological evidence, it must speak for itself, and the Oldowan argues for an ape adaptive grade.

NOTES

An earlier version of this article was delivered by Wynn at a conference, 'Tools compared: the material of culture', sponsored by the Royal Anthropological Institute, London, 1988.
[1] FLK is the abbreviation established by Louis Leakey for Frieda Leakey Korongo, one of the archaeological localities in Bed 1 at Olduvan Gorge. KBS and HAS are abbre-

viations for specific Oldowan sites at Koobi Fora in northern Kenya. FxJj50 is the designation for another Oldowan site at Koobi Fora, in this case labelled by a formal site enumeration system used throughout Africa.

REFERENCES

Behrensmeyer, A. K., K. D. Gordon & G. T. Yanagi 1986. Trampling as a cause of bone surface damage and pseudo-cutmarks. *Nature, Land.* 319, 768–71.

Bernstein, I. S. 1962. Response to nesting materials of wild born and captive born chimpanzees. *Animal Behav.* 10, 1–6.

Binford, L. R. 1981. *Bones: ancient men and modern myths.* New York: Academic Press.

Boesch, C & H. Boesch 1983. Optimization of nut-cracking with natural hammers by wild chimpanzees. *Behavior* 83, 265–86.

_____, 1984. Mental map in wild chimpanzees: an analysis of hammer transports for nut cracking. *Primates* 25, 160–70.

Boysen, S. T., C. G. Berntson & J. Prentice 1987. Simian scribbles: a reappraisal of drawing in the chimpanzee *(Pan troglodytes). J. Comp. Psychol.* 101, 82–9.

Bunn, H. T. 1981. Archaeological evidence for meat-eating by Plio-Pleistocene hominids from Koobi Fora and Olduvai Gorge. *Nature, Land.* 291, 574–80.

_____, J. W. K. Harris, G. Isaac, Z. Kaufulu, E. Kroll, K. Schick, N. Toth & A. Bechrensmeyer 1980. FxJj50: an early Pleistocene site in northern Kenya. *Wld. Archaeol.* 12(2), 109–39.

Byrne R. W. & A. Whiten (eds) 1988. *Machiavellian intelligence: social expertise and the evolution of intellect in monkeys, apes, and humans.* Oxford: Univ. Press.

Chiarelli, B. & R. S. Corruccini (eds) 1981. *Primate behavior and sociobiology.* Berlin: Springer.

Coppens, Y., F. C. Howell, G. Isaac & R. Leakey (eds) 1976. *Earliest man and environments in the Lake Rudolph Basin.* Chicago: Univ. Press.

Foley, R. (ed.) 1984. *Hominid evolution and community ecology: prehistoric human adaptation in biological perspective.* London: Academic Press.

Goodall, J. L. 1968. The behaviour of free-living chimpanzees in the Gombe Stream Reserve. *Animal Behav. Monogr.* 1, 161–311.

Gowlett, J. 1984. Mental abilities of early man: a look at some hard evidence. In Foley 1984.

Haltenorth, T. & H. Diller 1977. *A field guide to the mammals of Africa including Madagascar.* London: Collins.

Hannah, A. C. & W. C. McGrew 1987. Chimpanzees using stones to crack open oil palm nuts in Liberia. *Primates* 28, 31–46.

Harris, J. W. K. 1983. Cultural beginnings: Plio-Pleistocene archaeological occurrences from the Afar, Ethiopia. *Afr. Archaeol. Rev.* 1, 3–31.

Hasegawa, T., Hairaiwa, M., Nishida, T. & H. Takasaki 1983. New evidence on scavenging behavior in wild chimpanzees. *Curr. Anthrop.* 24, 231–32.

Hewes, G. W. 1961. Food transport and the origin of hominid bipedalism. *Am. Anthrop.* 63, 687–710.

Hiraiwa-Hasegawa, M., Byrne, R. W., Takasaki, H. & J. M. E. Byrne 1986. Aggression towards Large carnivores by wild chimpanzees of Mahale Mountains National Park, Tanzania, *Folia primat.* 47, 8–13.

Holloway, R. L. 1981. Exploring the dorsal surface of hominoid endocasts by stereoplotter and discriminant analysis. *Phil. Trans. R. Soc. Lond.* B292, 385–94.

_____ 1983. Human brain evolution: a search for unites, models and synthesis. *Cana J. Anthrop.* **3,** 215–30.

Isaac, G. L. 1976. Plio-Pleistocene artifact assemblages from East Rudolph, Kenya. In Coppens *et al.* 1976.

_____ 1978. The food-sharing behavior of protohuman hominids. *Sci. Am.* **238**(4), 90–108.

_____ 1981. Archaeological tests of alternative models of early hominid behavior: excavation and experiments. *Phil. Trans. R. Soc. Lond.* **B292,** 177–88.

_____ 1984. The archaeology of human origins: studies of the lower Pleistocene in East Africa 1971-1981. *Adv. Wld Archaeol.* 3, 1–86.

Kitahara-Frisch, J., Norikoshi, K. & K. Hara 1987. Use of a bone fragment as a step towards secondary tool use in captive chimpanzee. *Primate Rep.* **18,** 33–7.

Korlandt, A. 1965. How do chimpanzees use weapons when fighting leopards? *Yb. Am. phil. Soc.* **1965,** 327–32.

_____ & E. Holzhaus 1987. New data on the use of stone tools by chimpanzees in Guinea and Liberia. *Primates* **28,** 473–96.

Leakey, M. 1971. *Olduvai Gorge,* vol. **3.** Cambridge: Univ. Press.

McGrew, W. C. 1974. Tool use by wild chimpanzees in feeding upon driver ants. *J. hum. Evol.* **3,** 501–08.

_____ 1983. Animal foods in the diets of wild chimpanzees (*Pan troglodytes*): *why cross-cultural variation? J. Ethol.* **1,** 46–61.

_____ & D. A. Collins 1985. Tool use by wild chimpanzees (*Pan troglodytes*) to obtain termites (*Microtomies herus*) in the Mahale Mountains, Tanzania. *Am. J. Primat.* **9,** 47–62.

Morris, K. & J. Goodall 1977. Competition for meat between chimpanzees and baboons of the Gombe National Park. *Folia primat.* **28,** 109–21.

Ohel, M. 1984. Spatial management of hominid groups at Olduvai: a preliminary exercise. *Palacoecol. Africa* **14,** 125–46.

Parker, S. T. & K. R. Gibson 1979. A developmental model for the evolution of language and intelligence in early hominids. *Behav. Brain Sci.* **2,** 367–408.

Passingham, R. E. 1982. *The human primate.* Oxford: W. H. Freeman.

Piaget, J. 1972. *The principles of genetic epistomology* (trans.) W. Mays, London: Kegan Paul.

Pillbeam, D. 1986 Distinguished lecture: hominoid evolution and hominoid origins. *Am. Anthrop.* **88,** 295–312.

Plooij, F. X. 1978. Tool-use during chimpanzees' bushpig hunt. *Carnivore* 1(2), 103–06.

Potts, R. 1984. Hominid hunters? Problems of identifying the earliest hunter/gatherers. In Foley 1984.

_____ 1986. Temporal span of bone accumulations at Olduvai Gorge and implications for early hominid foraging behavior. *Paleobiol.* **12,** 25–31.

Sabater, Pi, J. 1974. An elementary industry of the chimpanzees in the Okorobiko mountains. Rio Muni (Republic of Equatorial Guinea). West Africa. *Primates* **15,** 351–64.

Shipman, P. 1986. Scavenging or hunting in early hominids: theoretical framework and tests. *Am. Anthrop.* **88,** 27–43.

Smith, D. A. 1973. Systematic study of chimpanzee drawing. *J. compar. physiol. Psych.* **82,** 406–14.

Sugiyama, Y. 1985. The brush-stick of chimpanzees found in south-west Cameroon and their cultural characteristics. *Primates* **26,** 361–74.

_____ & J. Koman 979. Tool-using and -making behavior in wild chimpanzees at Bossou, Guinea. *Primates* **20**, 513–24.

Susman, R. L. 1988. Hand of *Paranthropus robustus* from Member 1, Swartkrans: fossil evidence for tool behaviour. *Science* **240**, 781–84.

Tanner, N. M. 1987. The chimpanzee model revisited and the gathering hypothesis. In *The evolution of human behaviour: primate models*. (ed.) W. G. Kinzey. Albany: State Univ. of New York Press.

Teleki, G. 1973. *The predatory behavior of wild chimpanzees*. Lewisburg: Bucknell Univ. Press.

Tobias, P. V. 1983. Hominid evolution in Africa. *Can. J. Anthrop.* **3**, 163–85.

Tooby, J. & I. DeVore 1987. The reconstruction of hominid behavioral evolution through strategic modelling. In *The evolution of human behavior: primate models*. (ed.) W. G. Kinzey. Albany: State Univ. of New York Press.

Toth, N. 1985. The Oldowan reassessed: A closer look at early stone artifacts. *J. Archaeol. Sci.* **12**, 101–120.

Tutin, C. E. G., W. C. McGrew & P. J. Baldwin 1981. Responses of wild chimpanzees to potential predators. In Chiarelli & Corruccini 1981.

Wright, T. 1972. Imitative learning of a flaked stone technology—the case of an orangutan. *Mankind* **8**, 296–306.

Wynn, T. 1978. Tool-using and tool-making. *Man.* (N. S.) **13**, 137–8.

_____ 1981. The intelligence of Oldowan hominids. *J. hum. Evol.* **10**, 529–41.

_____ 1989. *The evolution of spatial competence*. Champaign: Univ. of Illinois Press.

Une vue anthropoïde de l'Oldowan

Rèsumé

Dans l'évolution humaine, quand nos ancêtres on-ils cessé de se comporter comme des anthropoïdes? Dans cet article, nous considérons cette question en interprétant la première évidence archéologique connue, l'Oldowan, à la lumière de ce que les primatologues connaissent des singes modernes, particulièrement du chimpanzé *(Pan troglodytes)*. Nos analyses considèrent des aspects des outils d'Oldowan et leur fabrication et les aspects de la subsistence d'Oldowan qui peuvent être reconstruits à partir d'objets fabriqués. Nous concluons que toute la conduite qui peut être déduite des outils et des sites d'Oldowan tombe parmi la portée de la catégorie d'adaptation du singe. Il n'y a rien d'exclusivement humain à propos de cette évidence archéologique la plus anciennement connue. Néanmoins, l'Oldowan comprit deux types de comportement spécifiques qui sont presque totalement inconnus pour les singes modernes, tout en étant parmi la catégorie d'adaptation du singe, et qui indiquent la direction des adaptations troveés plus tard dans l'évolution hominienne. Ce sont le transport d'outils ou de nourriture sur des milliers de mètres et la compétition pour la proie animale avec de gros carnivores.

From Ape's Nest to Human Fix-Point

Colin P. Groves
Australian National University

J. Sabater Pi
Parque Zoologico, Barcelona

Nests of gorillas, chimpanzees and orang utans show similarities in basic construction, but also characteristic differences in use of material, site and location preference, and so on; the behaviour of the different ape species in and around nests also differs from species to species. The campsites of human nomads, and by extension the fix-points of humans in general, have the same basic plan as those of apes, and the social organization that lies at the base of the 'nest' and campsite organization is derivable from the common denominator of the apes' societies. The peculiarly human aspects of 'nesting' are no less remarkable for being essentially elaborations on the generalized ape pattern.

INTRODUCTION

Anyone however slightly familiar with Great Apes in their natural environment will have been struck by their elaborate nests: their ubiquity, the regularity of their construction, the skill required to make them, and in many cases their apparent incongruity. This is especially the case for the gorilla, the only ape to construct its nest usually on the ground. One of us (J. S. P.) has collected a mass of data on gorilla nests in Equatorial Guinea, and has made comparative observations on nests of the same species in Rwanda, in quite a different habitat; observations on gorilla nests in Rwanda have also been made by C. P. G. A large number of chimpanzee nests were observed by J. S. P., but more cursorily mainly for conservation reasons (Jones & Sabater Pi 1971; Baldwin *et al.* 1982). We feel that the full data on these nests should be published, with a survey of published data on nesting patterns across the Hominoidea, taking advantage at the same time of recent theoretical advances (Hediger 1977; Isaac 1978; P. C. Reynolds 1981) to draw conclusions as to the functional and pattern regularities across species.

"From Ape's Nest to Human Fix Point" by Colin P. Groves and J. Sabater Pi, *MAN* (NS) 20, 22–47. Reprinted by permission of the Royal Anthropological Institute of Great Britian and Ireland.

The Great Apes—*Pongo, Pan, Gorilla*—are the only 'higher' non-human primates (Anthropoidea = Simiiformes) which construct nests. At first sight such behaviour links them to certain Strepsirhini (specifically, members of the genera *Galago, Microcebus, Cheirogaleus, Hapalemur, Varecia, Lepilemur* and *Daubentonia*). As Hediger has pointed out, however, the nests of the two groups are quite different functionally. The strepsirhine nest would be a 'fix-point' in a territory: it is a place of maximum security, a sleeping place, and a place for rearing young (more especially the last), although, in the light of the finding of Bearder and Martin (1980) of multiple nest sites per home range in *Galago senegalensis*, the designation 'fix-point' seems not always strictly appropriate. The hominoid nest, however, is made afresh each evening and abandoned the next morning, there being no fix-point; it is a sleeping-place only. In Hediger's terminology, the strepsirhine nest is a Home; that of the apes is not—nor indeed is it a true Nest, but something new and unprecedented in mammalian evolution.

The human home-base would seem at first sight to have aspects of the strepsirhine Home. Or does it? We shall examine this proposition below.

NESTS OF APES

Briefly, we may make the following generalizations about nest-making in each of the three Great Apes: a nest is built each evening by each animal above about three years of age. Nests are not shared, except by females and their infants, except as an anomaly; but co-bedding would seem to be much less anomalous in *Pan paniscus* than in other apes, involving a male and an oestrous female, or two females (Kuroda 1980). The nest is made of vegetation which is pulled towards the marker, held down with some twisting into place, pieces being also broken off and inserted. A cup and a rim can commonly be differentiated. Nest-building takes one to five minutes. The nest is slept in for one night only; the following day it is abandoned and left to disintegrate, and a new one is constructed the following night, even if the maker has not travelled very far that day.

Nests are not uncommonly left unused, by both gorillas and chimpanzees, but under what circumstances is not known. On rare occasions nests may be re-used; such a case is recorded by Sabater Pi and de Lassaletta (1958), and Fang assistants assured one of us (J. S. P.) that re-use occurs. Dyce Sharp (1927) records a case where (in the Cross River District of Cameroun) a troop were bottled up in a small area by floods yet went to some pains to build new nests each night only a few yards from the previous night's, or in the same tree.

Bernstein (1967) found that wild-born chimpanzees will make nests from an early age in captivity if given suitable material, whereas captive-born adults will not, even if caged with wild-born chimpanzees who are able to make them. Even chimpanzees caught at about one year of age will make some kind of nest. Later (1969) the same author found that all three species of Great Ape will make nests if given the opportunity, when still immature; the quality of the nest improves with age, up to maturity—to some extent, at least, independent of practice. He found difference between the three species: chimpanzees would make the 'standard' ape nest, and sleep entirely within it; gorillas were less elaborate, and often slept partly draped over the rim; orangs made the best nests, and not only slept within them but even (in most cases) covered themselves up inside it. All three species would transport material to the nest-building site if none was available in the vicinity; they would use synthetic material, such as hosepipe and sacking, as well as vegetation; they would sometimes sit alert, or eat food, in the nest, as well as sleeping in it.

From the wild it is clear that chimpanzees, at least, learn not only how to make sturdier nests, but even where to make them for best results (Goodall 1968). There is both maturation and learning involved, as one of us (J. S. P.) has observed additionally in the Barcelona Zoological Gardens.

NESTS OF GORILLAS AND CHIMPANZEES

(1) Size and shape. In the Equatorial Guinea sample, the nests of gorillas were nearly always oval, but sometimes round. The greatest diameter of nests made by silverback males was 1.3 to 1.35 m; by adult females and blackback males, 1.1 to 1.2 m; by juveniles, 0.7 to 0.8 m. These figures agree well with those published by Casimir (1979) and Schaller (1963) for mountainous areas (table 1); Dyce Sharp (1927) is alone in giving figures as much as 9 ft by 6 ft (2.75 x 1.8 m) for the male's nest, though this could be an estimate rather than a measurement.

Chimpanzee nests are also oval; in Equatorial Guinea and in Senegal (data courtesy P. J. Baldwin; see Baldwin *et al.* 1981) the mean sizes are somewhat less than those of juvenile gorillas, while in the Kasakati basin (Izawa & Itani 1966) the mean values are larger (table 1). There are unfortunately no data on the sizes of the 'double beds' reported for *Pan paniscus* (though one was described as 'large' (Kuroda 1980)), nor is it stated whether one or both occupants constructed them—i.e. whether the structure was planned as such, or simply became a bed for two when a second bonobo climbed in.

(2) Pattern of nest site (a) Size of nesting site. As the whole troop nests together each night in all known populations of gorillas, the number of nests at a site is the number in the troop minus the number of infants, except that a few infants make tentative nests even in their first year. The site may be long and the nests strung out, but more usually there is an oval plane to the site. The greatest diameter of the site is approximately 10-30 m (Schaller 1963) though both larger and smaller diameters were recorded in Rio Muni; the site area is of the order of 160-170 m^2 (table 1). Elliott (1976) found that a small group nested within 20m, reducing to about 13 m when the group lost a juvenile, and remaining at 13 m or so even when joined by another female. Casimir (1979) states that the area of the nest site increases according to the size of the

group; inspection of his fig. 6 suggests that any such correlation is very weak. It might appear that only when a peripheral male is in temporary association with the troop is the nest site area much expanded (C. P. G., personal observations; and inference from Schaller 1963).

Three nest sites (containing 10, 4 and 11 nests respectively) were surveyed by Butzler (1980) near Mouloundou, S. E. Cameroun. The greatest diameter of the site in both the first two cases was about 10 m (measured from his fig. 4); in the third case, 16 m, one of the nests being well apart from the others, which were together in an oval space some 9 m across. This evidence, too, suggests little correlation between size of group and that of nesting area.

(b) Spacing of nests. Within the site, a nest could be from 1.5 to 15 m from its nearest neighbor (C. P. G.'s observations). Schaller (1963) finds that most of the troop nest 1.5 m apart from each other, the medium-sized nests being never more than 6 m apart; but silverbacks nest an average of 4 m from other troop members, and 10 m from each other if there are more than one. Juveniles' nests are some 3.8 from each other. Jones & Sabater Pi (1971) agree that nearly all nests are less than 10 m from their nearest neighbour. Casimir (1979) gives very much greater mean distances between nests than other authors. The data suggest a regularity of a sort in the pattern of nesting found at any given site; Elliott's data suggest, too, that there might be traditions within a single troop for such patterns, which we agree is very plausible.

Chimpanzees' nests average a minimum of 4 m apart in two regions (Baldwin *et al.* 1981); clustering seems to vary slightly according to habitat, there being less distance between nests in secondary forest (Rio Muni) and in woodland or grassland (Senegal), but more in gallery forest (Senegal). Fifty per cent. of chimpanzee nests in Rio Muni are 3-4 m apart, but 30 per cent. are over 10 m from their nearest neighbors (Jones & Sabater Pi 1971). The greater dispersal of the nests may simply reflect the nature of the substrate, or may relate to the less cohesive nature of the society. In Rio Muni there is nearly always one nest only per tree, but in Senegal two—but a median of 5 nests per tree in woodland in Senegal. Baldwin *et al.* (1981) note that despite this the similar absolute spacing of nests suggests that there is an optimal distance effect at work.

(c) Other factors. It has been suggested from time to time (Blower 1956; Osborn 1957; Sabater Pi 1960) that there is a certain element of organization in the nest site, relating to the location of the nest of the silverback. Neither Schaller (1963) nor Casimir (1979) are in agreement with this proposition, although the latter does note a tendency for the silverback to bed down at the base of a large tree, where, surprisingly, he makes only the most rudimentary of nests; but such is not the case in Rio Muni.

For the present study, we have accepted that the silverback's nest is a 'special position' if it is in the most elevated position, central, or peripheral, or with a clear view of the total group. Out of 40 nest sites the silverback's position is 'special' in 21, not 'special' in 19. However, in the medium-sized groups

Table 1. Sizes of nests in African apes.

	Locality	Source	n	Mean Diameter of individual nests (m) Adult male	Adult female	Juvenile	Mean Diameter of nest site (m)
Gorilla							
G.g. gorilla	Rio Muni	J.S.P., this paper	23	1.32	1.15	0.75	16.3 × 11.5
	Cross River	Dyce Sharp (1927)	1	2.75 × 1.80	—	—	—
G.g. graueri	Mt. Kahuzi	Casimir (1979)	63	1.25	1.05	0.79	19.4 × 10.1
G.g. beringei	Kabara	Schaller (1963)	?			0.60	20?
		Elliot (1976)		1.50			
Chimpanzee							
P.t. verus	Assirik	Baldwin et al. (1981)	157		0.80 × 0.60		—
P.t. troglodytes	Okorobiko	J.S.P., this paper	8		0.80 × 0.62		22.7 × 9.7
P.t. schweinfurthii	Kasakati	Izawa & Itani (1966)	9		1.12 × 0.89		—

(5-8 nests) there was such a 'special' position in 13 out of 14 cases; more data would be needed, and perhaps the different kinds of 'special position' should be taken separately. In Butzler's (1980) study, in his two large groups (10 and 11 nests), one of the nests in each case was larger and stood apart from the rest (very markedly so in one case, as noted earlier). Dyce Sharp (1927) notes that in his experience the nests of all other troop members are visible from the male's.

Some nest sites are divided into two or more units by bushes or by *Aframomum* stands. This was recorded for 52 nest sites (26 each for wet and dry seasons); the group was divided in such a way in 15 cases of which 10 were for the rainy season. This initially promising finding, with its small sample size, fails to attain 5% significance.

(3) Structure and techniques of construction. The nests are really very simple structures, whose method of construction can be deduced from analysis of their components. Those of chimpanzees are more complex than those of gorillas; Dyce Sharp (1927) seems to be alone in describing gorilla beds as the more elaborate of the two, this being in the isolated (as far as gorillas are concerned) Cross River region.

The commonest type of bed made by gorillas in Equatorial Guinea is made on flat ground in patches of *Aframomum* sp. The stalks of the plant are bent and arranged around the body, while sitting or standing, to make the rim; the centre is then filled with branches pulled in or broken off from all round. The most leafy plants are used, providing a springy, comfortable platform. The next commonest type of bed is made on steeply sloping ground, again in *Aframomum*. There is here a barrier of stems of the plant, preventing the body from sliding down the slope during the night; the structure is finally levelled all over with more branches and leaves, to give the usual circular shape. Despite these precautions, gorillas do sometimes slide down the slope at night. Casimir (1979) also notes that nests are 'propped up' when made on slopes; he reports that silverbacks nest more often on slopes than do other troop members, juveniles less so. The third type of bed is constructed in bushes (*Harungana sp.*, *Vernonia* sp., etc) one to two metres above the ground. The smaller branches are bent, the larger ones forcefully split, to make a solid platform; the center is then filled in with fine, soft, leafy branches. The resulting bed is very good and springy. A few nests are made in trees, especially *Musanga cecropioides*. In these cases branches are bent over to fill in a platform made by the branching of the major forks to form the canopy. In all cases, there may be some interweaving as well as simple bending into place. The cup-and-rim shape is generally evident. Chimpanzee nests in general resemble those of gorillas that are made in trees, though more elaborate.

In 37 cases the number of leaves was roughly estimated for the first type of gorilla bed (J. S. P.), with the intention of investigating whether there were any differences in insulation between wet and dry season nests. The results seemed promising: of 18 dry season nests, 10 had under 200 leaves, while of 19 rainy season beds only 3 had under 200 leaves, while 12 had over 400 (in one case, over 600). This is significant at $p < 0.05$, but should be taken cautiously nonethe-

Table 2. Plants used for construction of gorilla nests in Rio Muni.

Plant	No. of nests	Plant	No. of nests
Aframomum	366	Branches(indet.)	5
Sacrophrynium	66	*Hypselodelphys*	4
Costus	26	Leaves(indet.)	4
Musanga	24	*Halopegia*	3
Harungana	22	*Oncocalamus*	2
Haumannia	12	*Cissus*	2
Palisota	12	*Cyathea*	1
Manihot	11	*Anodinium*	1
Grewia	10	*Scleria*	1
Vernonia	6	*Mussaenda*	1
Lophira	5	*Macaranga*	1

less because of the small sample size. It does suggest, then, that the gorilla gives some attention to climatic factors in nest-building; it is of course possible that there are simply more leaves available during the wet season, though we do not think this the probable explanation given the nature of the vegetation in the two seasons.

Day nests, commonly constructed during the inactive hours of the day, are simple structures, sometimes limited to only two or three stems of *Aframomum* (in the case of gorillas), bent and arranged on the ground in the basic plan of the first night-nest described above.

(4) Materials used in construction. Table 2 shows the plants identified in 448 gorilla beds studied by J. S. P. Of the main plants utilized, *Aframomum* (5 species), *Sarcophrynium* and *Costus* are grasses, *Musanga* and *Harungana* are trees; of the rest there are one shrub, three trees and three lianes, the rest being grasses.

Among the five *Aframomum* species, *A. giganteum* and *A. sanguineum* were by far the most utilized, occurring in 366 beds. They and the two grasses that are next most used are all tall species growing at the forest edge and in secondary growth, and are eaten by gorillas. 'Two species of *Aframomum*' were the exclusive material utilized in the nests studied by Butzler (1980).

Table 3 shows the percentages of plants among those (305 out of 488) beds in whose construction only a single plant type was used. Here again *Aframomum* predominates, followed by *Sarcophrynium*; but here the order changes, and it appears that some plants *(Costus)* are never used alone in construction, while others *(Lophira)* are never used in conjunction with any others. Most beds are made with a single species, or only two; only 3.7 per cent. of the total contain as many as 5 or 6 different plant species.

Table 4 gives the distribution of nests in different biotopes. From table 4a can be seen the extraordinary dependence of gorillas on regenerating fallow

Table 3. Gorilla nests in Rio Muni constructed with only plant species.

Plant	No. of nests using that plant alone	Plant	No. of nests using that plant alone
Aframomum	243	Green leaves, sp. indet.	4
Sacrophrynium	15	Dry leaves, sp. indet.	3
Harungana	15		
Lophira	5	*Vernonia*	2
Musanga	5	*Oncocalamus*	1
Flexible branches, sp. indet.	4	*Anonidium*	1
Grewia	4	*Ampelocissus*	1
Cyathea	1	*Scleria*	1

Table 4. Biotopes of ape nests in Rio Muni

(a) General figures

	Gorilla		Chimpanzee	
	No. of nests	Percent	No. of nests	Percent
Forest regrowth	316	70.53	23	11.79
Secondary forest	88	19.64	38	19.48
Dense or primary forest	36	8.03	134	68.71
Plantations	8	1.78	0	0.00
	448	99.98	195	99.98

(b) Relation between biotope and season

	Forest regrowth	Secondary forest	Dense forest	Plantations	Total
Gorilla					
Dry season	233	20	3	8	264
Rainy season	83	68	33	0	184
	316	88	36	8	448

$p < 0.05$, d. f. = 3

	Forest regrowth	Secondary forest	Dense forest	Plantations	Total
Chimpanzee					
Dry season	1	14	70	0	85
Rainy season	22	24	64	0	110
	23	38	134	0	195

$p < 0.005$, d. f. = 2

land, or tertiary forest (in which, of course, Aframomum predominates), and the contrasting dependence of chimpanzees on dense forest. Table 4b shows that these dependences are more marked in the dry season (p<0.005). During the rainy season the gorilla is more often in dense forest and in secondary forest, taking advantage of the fruiting abundance, while chimpanzees by contrast nest more in secondary and agrologicla areas at this time. Of 11 day nests, 5 were in tertiary or regrowth forest, 4 in secondary forest, 2 in dense forest. Twelve examples of nests being used twice were found; but these were not on consecutive nights.

Gorillas in Rio Muni are, therefore, rather discriminating in their use of plants to make nests: they appear not simply to nest beside their latest meal, but to choose among the plants growing nearby those which experience has shown to make the most satisfactory nests. What they are feeding on towards dusk will of course influence where they nest in so far as it may itself provide suitable bedding, or is growing in an area suitable for nest-making, or is growing in association with other suitable materials. The food itself may be the commonest plant in the given region, or a rare plant but favored by gorillas, and so on. Thus, the nesting site choice involves the presence of food supply, but does not depend on it.

Casimir (1979) states that in Kahuzi the frequency of use of a plant species for a nest is a pure reflection of its frequency in the biotope; inspection of his table 1 suggests, however, that this is not the whole story: for example, the commonest tree in the area is only half as much utilized in nest building as the next commonest, while food plants are not predominant in nest building at all.

(5) Siting of nests: (a) Height above ground. Table 5 (a,b) shows the height above the ground of nests found in Equatorial Guinea. Overwhelmingly, gorillas nest on the ground. Nests that are not on the ground may be on tree stumps or on fallen trees (n=13), over the branches of fallen trees (14), or on rocks (2), as well as in trees or bushes as described above; two were on a very large trunk at the very edge of a river bank—an anomaly considering that gorillas are supposed to be much afraid of water, though in Barcelona and other zoos the gorillas make regular use of a pool in summer, and Fang guides maintained to J. S. P. that they have many times seen gorillas bathing in forest streams.

Casimir (1979) has summarized everything published about the height of gorilla nests. In different areas, 43.5 to 97.1 per cent. of beds are directly on the ground; in Equatorial Guinea the figure is 77 per cent. Undoubtedly there is a very important effect from simple ecological factors; but, as Goodall & Groves (1977) have emphasized, there are also behavioral factors with cultural connotations. Gorillas make their beds at nightfall, more or less wherever they happen to be feeding. Siting of nests, like material utilized, will therefore depend on a variety of factors mainly related to food supply.

In sharp contrast to gorillas, chimpanzees nest high in the trees (table 5b). In Equatorial Guinea (Jones & Sabater Pi 1971) they are rarely below 3 metres above

Table 5a. Height above ground of gorilla nests (n=448) in Rio Muni.

Approx. height (metres)	Number of nests
<1	349
1	50
2	24
3	5
4	7
5	4
6	1
7	4
8	2
15	2

the ground, though relatively few were above 11 m, and the mode is 5-6 m; in other localities they tend to be above this level—between 4 and 14 m in Guinea (Bournonville 1967), usually 4 to 24 m with a mode of 9-10 m, in Senegal (Baldwin *et al.* 1981), between 4.5 and 25 m in Gombe (Goodall 1968), and commonly even above 30 m in th Budongo Forest (Reynolds & Reynolds 1965). Mean heights are greater in the wet season than in the dry, in both Rio Muni and Senegal; and in Senegal higher in gallery forest than in woodland (Baldwin *et al.* 1981). There is also the curious finding that in Senegal nests are built in the crowns of trees, but

Table 5b. Height above ground of chimpanzee nest (n=195) in Rio Muni.

Approx. height (metres)	Number of nests	Approx. height (metres)	Number of nests
0	8	15	21
1	3	16	1
2	3	17	3
3	5	18	6
4	11	19	0
5	18	20	10
6	16	21	2
7	11	22	0
8	17	23	1
9	8	24	1
10	18	25	1
11	2		
12	18	30	1
13	4		
14	5	40	1

in Rio Muni generally in the first fork; Baldwin *et al.* (1981) speculate that the abundance of leopards at the Senegal site may influence this. Day nests may however be made on the ground; Goodall (1971) also records that a wounded young female made a ground nest to lie in and dab her wounds with leaves.

The nests may take up to 30 minutes to make but usually only 1 to 5 minutes (Goodall 1962); in Senegal, the mean time is 4 minutes (Baldwin 1979). Like gorillas' tree nests, they are mainly in tree forks (82 per cent.), or sometimes where two horizontal branches cross. Smaller branches are bent over and held in place with the feet, then leafy twigs are pushed in round the rim. A further handful of leafy twigs may be placed under the head or body after the nest has been tried out.

(b) Use of overhead cover. In the Equatorial Guinea study, 25 per cent. of gorilla (but 83 per cent. of chimpanzee) nests were made beneath tree foliage which provided the users with a certain amount of protection from the rain and the night dew. The remainder were in the open with no protective cover. Casimir (1979) found that on Mt Kahuzi only 5.5 per cent. of gorilla nests were under cover. The gorilla seems deliberately to seek open areas for nest-building, the chimpanzee closed areas.

When the data are split up by season, however, a different picture emerges (table 6): the gorilla does build under cover rather more in the wet season. Such a finding is in conflict with both Casimir (1979) and Kawai & Mizuhara (1959), both of whom report no correlation. One solution could be the nature of the habitat: the more open nature of the forest as a whole, and the rarity of cultivated land and consequent regrowth, in the eastern areas, and the more closed nature of the forest—the gorilla's prime wet season refuge—in west Africa. As the gorilla tends actually to remove overhead cover as a by-product of the bed-making activity (Jones & Sabater Pi 1971), there is a possibility that a choice to leave some intact under certain circumstances could be involved.

In nests observed by C. P. G. in the open-canopy *Hagenia* woodlands of the Virunga Volcanoes, Rwanda, there appeared to have been attempts in a few cases to construct the nests under banks or tree-root formations, but most remarkable was the case of a juvenile female of Group 5 who on at least four occasions (over a 2-week period) had obviously pulled down overhead vegetation to form a kind of roof. This, as far as we know, remains the only record of a covered nest in the gorillas.

Unlike gorillas, chimpanzees do not remove overhead plant cover when nest-building, so they are generally protected to some extent from the weather. There was much less overhead cover to nests in Senegal than in Rio Muni, perhaps simply because of the nature of the vegetation; and they are built less undercover in the rainy season (see discussion in Baldwin *et al.* 1981). Day nests are most usually made in response to rain (Goodall 1971). Like gorillas, chimpanzees almost never re-use old nests, but construct a new one each night. Goodall (1968) reports the case of one juvenile female chimpanzee who appeared deliberately to construct a 'roof' over her nest during the rains. Partial body covering appears to be common in at least some groups of Bonobos (Kano

Table 6. Incidence of cover over ape nests in Rio Muni.

(a) General figures

	Gorilla	Chimpanzee
Cover	113	162
Absence of cover	335	33
	448	195

Gorilla:	p<0.01, d. f.=1
Chimpanzee:	p<0.001, d. f.=1

(b) Relationship between cover and season

	Cover	Absence of Cover	Total
Gorilla			
Dry season	53	211	264
Rainy season	60	124	184
	113	335	448

p<0.05, d. f.=1

	Cover	Absence of Cover	Total
Chimpanzee			
Dry Season	81	4	85
Rainy Season	81	29	110
	162	33	195

p<0.005, d. f.=1

1982): a specialized use of leafy twigs, generally in day nests, in contact with the body (a raincoat more than a roof) and, in Kano's opinion, not in fact very effective in keeping the rain off!

(c) Orientation of nest site. Jones & Sabater Pi (1971) claimed in an early study that there was a significant tendency for gorilla and chimpanzee nests in Equatorial Guinea, if constructed on slopes, to be on east and south facing slopes (gorilla 46 per cent., chimpanzee 62 per cent.) rather than north and west facing (21 per cent., 15 per cent.), the remainder being on flat ground. In view of the failure of other authors to find such a tendency (see, for example, Goodall & Groves 1977), we feel that it is time to examine the question again, using more extensive data and a X^2 test (table 7). It appears that the correlation does not survive this new test; separating the data by season, the probability is above 5 per cent. of the null hypothesis for gorillas (but only just), but below this level for chimpanzees. There may still, therefore, be some element of fore-knowledge of possible thermal benefit in orientation. Casimir (1979) found a similarly equivocal result.

Table 7. Orientation of ape nests in Rio Muni.

(a) General figures

	Flat ground	Sloping ground	Total
Gorilla	222	226	448
Chimpanzee	68	127	195

Gorilla: p < 0.05, d. f. = 1
Chimpanzee: p < 0.05, d. f. =1

(b) Relationship between orientation and season

	Flat	Facing SE,SW,S,W	Facing NW,NE,N,E	Total
Gorilla				
Dry season	143	66	55	264
Rainy season	79	53	52	184
	222	119	107	448

p<0.05, d. f.=2

	Flat	Facing SE,SW,S,W	Facing NW,NE,N,E	Total
Chimpanzee				
Dry season	27	33	25	85
Rainy season	41	42	27	110
	68	75	52	195

p > 0.05, d. f. = 2

Jones & Sabater Pi (1971) reported that 22 per cent. of chimpanzee nests are constructed where the terrain is flat, 63 per cent. where the slope faces east or south, and only 15 per cent. facing west and north. In view of the modifications which become necessary to draw similar conclusions for gorillas (see above), this proposition needs to be re-tested for chimpanzees also. In chimpanzees, of course, the overhead cover will diminish any thermal benefit of orientation.

(6) Faeces in nest. The presence of faeces in the gorilla's nest at night has been much discussed. Schaller (1963) found that 73 per cent. of nests in the Virunga Volcanoes contained faeces, contrasting somewhat with the findings of A. Goodall (1974), who found only 14.2 per cent. and 2.4 per cent. in two regions of Mt. Kahuzi. Goodall suggests that gorillas in colder climates deliberately defecate in their nests to insulate the beds against freezing or near-freezing night temperatures. In Equatorial Guinea, 316 out of 395 nests contained faeces (80 per cent.). There is no correlation with season, although in Goodall's hypothesis one might expect some. It was not always clear, however, whether the faeces had been in the nests most of the night, or were emitted at dawn; in the latter case they would, of course, afford no thermal advantage.

The explanation we now think most probable would be the following: the gorilla is a large mammal whose whole lifestyle is characterized by an economy of energy expenditure. Its largely herbivorous diet is at once low in nutrient content and heavily fibrous; defaecation takes place about five times per 24 hours (Schaller 1963). Faeces are not messy and adherent like those of most other primates, but of the consistency of horse dung. Gorillas defaecate frequently; considering that they are likely to do so at least once during the night, the energetic cost of waking up and unrolling (with loss of heat) in order to defaecate might well exceed the disadvantages of lying on the faeces, which would not be great given the nature of the gorilla's dung balls. In simple terms, it is just not worth the gorilla doing it! As for chimpanzees, the position of their nests, high in the trees, and perhaps the smaller size of the nest, makes it much easier to eliminate over the side with just a slight movement. One of us (J. S. P.) has, however, a few records of faeces within the chimpanzee nest.

(7) Size of nest groups. As noted above, the size of the nest group in gorillas is the same as the size of the troop, except that infants below about 3 years of age share their mothers' beds, and solitary males may nest on the periphery of the troop. For Equatorial Guinea the size of gorilla groups varies between 2 and 16 individuals (Harcourt et al. 1981), but they are usually small, so that we can say that a nest group larger than 7 beds corresponds to two or more groups nesting conjointly where their home ranges coincide; an aspect of gorilla life noted also by Schaller, and made the subject of speculations as to the nature of the social group by Goodall & Groves (1977).

In chimpanzees, the size of the nest group is not that of the 'troop', which only rarely comes together. From 1 to 12 chimpanzees may nest together. In Rio Muni there is no seasonal difference (mean of rainy season 2.8, of dry 3.1), but in Senegal, where the seasons are more marked, the respective means are 2 and 7—that is, foraging groups, hence nesting groups, are considerably larger in the dry season corresponding, presumably, to either a coarser-grained environment or reduced predation or both.

(8) Relation to human settlements. Returning to the positioning of the nest groups, the distance from the nearest human habitation was examined, with relation to the size of the group (table 8a). It appears that among gorillas the smaller nest groups are located further from human settlements. Perhaps the larger groups are less frightened to sleep in proximity to human habitation. For chimpanzees, there is no correlation between size of nesting group and distance from human habitation. The distance from settlements for both species is greater in the wet season (table 8b).

(9) Timing of nest construction and abandonment. Nests are made at nightfall. They are often constructed in great haste because of failing light, and nests are made earlier when the sky is darkened with cloud. The activity begins some time between 1726 and 1834 hrs (mean 1800 hrs), but is normally com-

Table 8. Distance of gorilla nest sites from human habitation.

(a) According to size of group

	Distance to settlement (m)				
	0-2000	2000-4000	4000-6000	6000-8000	Total
Gorilla					
Size of groups					
1-4	2	7	5	7	21
5-8	1	6	3	3	13
9-12	2	8	1	1	12
13-16	0	3	0	0	3
	5	24	9	11	49

$p < 0.05$

	Distance to settlement (m)				
	0-2000	2000-4000	4000-6000	6000-8000	Total
Chimpanzee					
Size of groups					
1-2	15	2	10	1	28
3-4	4	5	1	0	10
5-6	5	0	2	0	7
7-8	0	1	1	0	2
9-10	1	0	0	0	1
11-12	1	0	1	0	2
	26	8	15	1	50

$p = 0.01$

(b) According to season

	Distance to Settlement(m)				
	0-100	101-1000	1001-4000	4001-8000	Total
Gorilla					
Dry Season	15	96	29	16	156
Wet Season	19	71	11	38	139
	34	167	40	54	295

$p < 0.05$, d. f. $= 3$

	Distance to Settlement(m)				
	0-100	101-1000	1001-4000	4001-8000	Total
Chimpanzee					
Dry Season	0	28	34	18	80
Wet Season	0	38	11	33	82
	0	66	45	51	162

$p < 0.05$, d. f. $= 2$

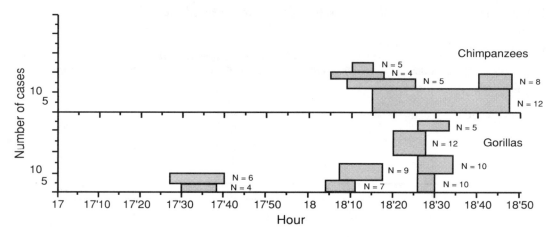

Figure 1. Timing of nest construction in chimpanzees and gorillas in Rio Muni.

plete by 1835 (fig. 1). It takes longer in groups that are larger: up to 14 minutes, while in smaller groups it can be as little as 4 minutes. The silverback is usually the first to begin nesting. Individual nests take from under a minute to 5 minutes to make.

Gorillas rise from their beds when there is light enough to permit easy movement and feeding, between 0555 and 0650 hrs (fig. 2); the later times correspond to days of morning fog or cloudiness. The first up is usually a juvenile, but the nest site is not abandoned until the silverback or an old female leaves the place.

There appears to be no moving around at night, but vocalizations and (in gorillas) chest-beating do occur. As fig. 3 shows, there is much chest-beating up till 2000 hrs. Odd vocalizations recommence after 0400, and chest-beating begins to be heard again after 0600 hrs.

In chimpanzees, the nest area falls quiet after about 1930 hrs, with a few scream vocalizations heard up to about 0100, after which there is an increasing noise level—predominantly pant-hoots—up to 0330 or 0400; a further hour of quiet gives place, after 0500, to further, more varied, vocalizations as the day's activity begins.

(10) Conclusions. Gorilla nesting patterns are much the same everywhere they have been studied; mainly on the ground, unelaborated, of well selected plants (often, food plants), in a fairly tight group especially the adult females, and with some seasonal variation. These generalities can be used as a basis for comparison with the less ample data for chimpanzees and orang utans.

Chimpanzee nests were first reported in the literature by Du Chaillu (1861), whose account of them, however, is a veritable goldmine of misinformation. He attributes nests to a special species, *Troglodytes calvus*, known to the Fang as *Nshiego mbouvé*. The nests he reports as usually 15 to 20 ft above the

364

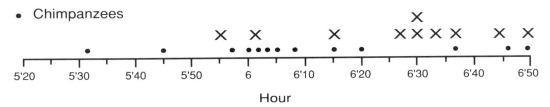

Figure 2. Timing of morning abandonment of nests by gorillas and chimpanzees in Rio Muni.

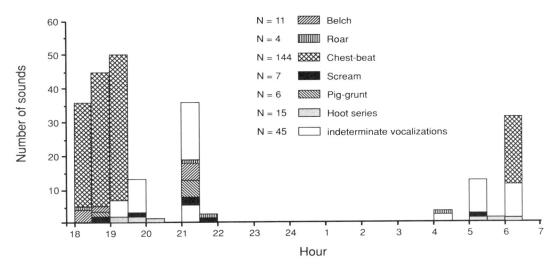

Figure 3a. Nocturnal vocalisations and chest-beats by gorillas in Rio Muni.

ground, invariably on a tree standing a little apart from the others, with no limbs below the one bearing the nest. The male and female cooperate in gathering leafy branches, and vines with which they tie them to the tree: the female brings the vines to the male, who does the actual building, one nest for each of them but in different trees. The nest is interpreted not as a platform but as a roof (in fact, it is rounded at the top to throw off the rain); the animal sits on the branch below, its head reaching into the domed roof, its arm clasped about the trunk. The nest is said in one place to be inhabited for 8 to 10 days, in another for 10 to 15 days—as long as the nearby supply of wild berries lasts.

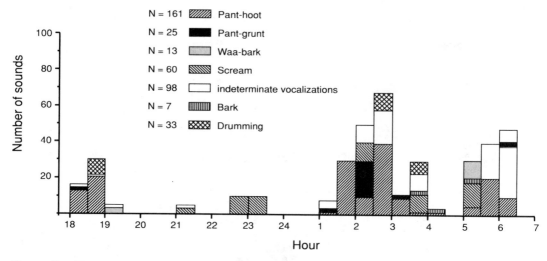

Figure 3b. Nocturnal vocalisations and drumming by chimpanzees in Rio Muni.

ORANG UTAN NESTS

Orang utan nests are made at heights of 19.5m (MacKinnon 1971, for Sabah), 13-15m (Rijksen 1978, for Aceh), or thereabouts. Unlike chimpanzees and gorillas, the nests are not necessarily made at or near the evening feeding site: they may travel considerable distances to suitable nesting areas, and indeed Rijksen states that only day-nests are made in food trees. Again unlike the African apes, nests are re-used on occasion: but the inner lining is always reconstructed according to Rijksen (1978). As in captivity, so in the wild, the orang frequently covers itself up in its nest: holding or balancing loose branches above its head as a roof (MacKinnon 1971), or covering itself with loose branches and twigs, which it may leave the nest to go and collect (Rijksen 1978). And in captivity too, orang utans cover their head with sacks when sleeping or the whole body with straw or material when available.

MacKinnon's (1971) detailed description of nest-building gives the distinct impression that the finished affair is much more sturdily made than a chimpanzee's, despite taking only 2-3 minutes. There is much more use of branches from above or below, tucked in to give extra stability ('hanging' and 'pillaring' in MacKinnon's terminology). Nests are often built in vantage points, as on slopes or ridges, according to both MacKinnon and Rijksen. A drizzle during the day sends an orang back to the previous night's nest, or else a new one is made; day nests are often made to process awkward fruits, like durian and mango, in comfort; females with young may build several nests in a day. As orangs are 'solitary' (with all the social complexity that in fact implies), a single nest generally makes up the whole nest site.

Just as the greater arboreality of the orang utan cannot by itself explain the greater elaboration of its nest-building activity compared to the chimpanzee, neither can the additional dexterity of its prehensile feet. The same intellectual attributes are reflected in Parker's (1974) finding that, in manipulations of a rope, of all non-human primates the orang utan shows much the greatest 'Secondary' behaviours—using the rope in reference to another object or to the animal's own body. For the moment we simply draw attention to what appear to be the facts of the matter, and will not speculate further.

HUMAN NESTS

We must be perfectly clear why we feel justified in searching for a common origin of human and great ape nesting/camping patterns. First of all there is Bernstein's demonstration that there is an unlearned component to nest-making in apes; in what sense this might be true for humans as well is something we cannot be sure of. More important, however, is the matter of continuity. If four species—orang utan, chimpanzee, gorilla, human—perform a certain activity whose motor components and end result are similar, parsimony suggests that their last common ancestor was itself doing something of the kind, and that its descendants have been so doing ever since, the practice having been maintained from generation to generation because it was somehow advantageous. We cannot be sure, naturally, that at some point during the evolution of, say, the chimpanzee the activity ceased to be advantageous and so was discontinued, only to be reinvented later—because, after all, chimpanzees are intelligent and inventive—when it became advantageous again. Put like this, the loss-and-reinvention scenario sounds cumbersome and unnecessary. Substitute 'human' for 'chimpanzee', and to some readers the same idea would be more plausible; though one cannot think of any cogent reason why.

Baldwin *et al.* (1981) note that there is a common pattern in the way all apes build their nests, and that is not the only conceivable way in which it might be done; 'Since', they write, 'all species of Great Apes build nests in the same manner, it seems likely that the behavior evolved millions of years ago in their common ancestor and that it was already a stable and consistent pattern before the different pongid lines diverged'. Since the orang utan is less closely related to the gorilla and chimpanzee than are humans, this behavior would have been present in the proto-human stock as well.

We propose that the most fruitful comparison in this context is likely to be hunter-gatherer camps. This is not because we suppose that these are somehow unchanged from a proto-hominid type, but because being those of nomads such camps will be subject to many of the same environmental constraints as the nest sites of the great apes. Data on such camps, as given by Yellen (1977) for the Dobe !Kung, by Harako (1976) and Tanno (1976) for the Mbuti, and by Gould (1977) for the Pitjantjajara, are summarized in table 9.

Among all hunter-gatherers there seem to be favoured spots, even to the extent that there may be occupation there most of the time, and there are casual encampments for a day or two. The big differences from all great apes are

Table 9. Comparisons of 'nests' of Hominidae.

	Orang Utan	Gorilla	Chimpanzee	Human (Nomadic)
Existence of permanent sites	No	No	No	Yes
Duration of occupancy	1 night	1 night	1 night	1 night to 1 month
Re-use of nests	Occasional	No	Occasional	Yes
Occupancy of a nest	Individual	Individual	Individual (rare 'co-bedding' in Bonobo)	Social group or individual
Usual diameter of a 'nest'	?	1.3 m (adult) 1.1 m (medium) 0.7 m (juvenile)	0.70 m	2 m
Area available per individual	?	15 m²	38 m²	6.5 m²
Area of nest (camp) site	?	160–170 m²	210 m²	120 m² (!Kung)
Distance between nests	No applicable	1.5 m	4 m rainy 2–3 dry 3–7	4 m
No. occupying a nest site	1	About 12		ca. 17 (!Kung) ca. 45 (Mbuti) ca. 45 (Pitjantjajara)
Overhead cover as part of nest	Usual	Very rare	Very rare	Usual
Use of natural overhead cover	Yes	Rare: but esp. when wet	Common: esp. in dry season	Yes
Location of nests	15–20 m up tree	Ground	5–6 m up tree	Ground
Deliberate selection of suitable nest site	Yes?	No	No?	Yes
Relation to natural vegetation	Part of it	Part of it	Part of it	Free-standing

368

that (1) it is not anomalous for a group to stay more than one night running at a camp, and (2) good sites are often known about, and made for, rather than 'ad hoc', though the Mbuti do seem to be unusual among hunter-gatherers in that all their camps are at known sites, which are occupied in turn (Harako 1976; Tanno 1976).

It has been seen that any variation according to season is hard to find in apes (except for chimpanzees in a woodland habitat in Senegal); but it has constantly been noted in humans. The camps of the !Kung were larger in the dry season, and people would stay in one place longer, providing greater continuity of occupation (Yellen 1977); dry-season camps have huts that are better made and more evenly arranged. Dry-season camps also tend to be larger in the Hadza (Woodburn 1966). Among the Mbuti on the other hand, it is the rainy season camp which is occupied for longest and by the largest number of people (Harako 1976). Among the Pitjantjara winter camps are significantly larger in area than summer camps, but tend to be occupied by fewer people (Gould 1977).

In the rainy-season camps of the Dobe !Kung the huts are for storing possessions in, not for sleeping in, unless it is raining, but are also used for shade during the day; a hut and the associated area is occupied by a nuclear family and averages 4.9m in diameter (range 2.2 to 8.2) (Yellon 1977). The camps of !Kung, Mbuti and Pitjantjajara are generally circular, with the huts (or other dwelling places) on the circumference, their entrances facing towards the centre of the camp. The !Kung camp has an area of 26-326m^2 (mean 122), and is 7.0 to 25.2m in diameter (mean 15.6); 'a single social unit occupies 2.2-8.2 (mean 4.9). Hut-to-hut distances around the circumference vary from 2 to 15.3m., with a mode of 4-5m (Yellen 1977). Pitjantjara camps are much smaller than this.

The myth of the patrilineal, patrilocal horde in hunter-gatherers has died hard; but the essential flexibility of the social group is now clear. The number of people occupying a campsite varies from day to day, so that figures can be given on average only. Yellen gives a mean of 4.6 social units per site (these being more or less nuclear family groups), or 16.7 people, making 3.7 people occupying an individual area. Within each campsite, therefore, there is a theoretical area of 24.8m^2 available to each social unit (range 11.3 to 47.8), and 6.5m^2 (range 2.4 to 13.6) available to each individual. Mbuti camps would seem to contain 30-62 people, in 5-12 social units (broadly, families); camps of net-hunting bands were larger (37-62, mean 49, n=3), and the social units were larger (mean 7.2 people, n=21), then those of archers (30-45, mean 36, n=3; 3.9 people per unit, n=28) (calculated from data in Harako 1976). The Pitjantjara campsite has 3 to 17 social units in summer, 2 to 6 in winter; 14 to 107 individuals in summer, 9 to 54 in winter. A social unit consists of 3.6 people: almost exactly the same as among the !Kung. The Gielli or Bayele camp (pygmoids of Rio Muni) has 5 to 20 social units year round, showing no difference between rainy and dry seasons (J. S. P. personal data).

What has been claimed as the earliest trace of a human habitation has been discovered at Olduvai (Leakey 1971). The famous Stone Circle at DKI^A, discovered in 1962, is a structure of blocks of basalt, piled loosely to nearly one foot (30cm) in places, enclosing a space of 3.6 × 4.2 metres diameter, i.e. about

12.5 m^2 (calculated as the area of a circle 4 m diameter). There are small stones scattered over the enclosed surface; and on one side a number of small stone heaps spaced at intervals of 60-75cm 'as if supports for branches or poles supporting a windbreak'. The circle is on a gentle slope; the ground inside is slightly lower than that outside. Careful excavation of the surrounding area failed to reveal any similar structure.

It must be admitted that the dimensions of the Olduvai Stone Circle fit quite well in the !Kung data for individual camps. Such a small area could not possibly accommodate multiple social units. Yet its elaborateness suggests it was more than a temporary shelter or hunting blind, such as Gould (1977) describes. It was apparently, on its own. Can this be taken as evidence for a stage in human evolution when social units were independent of one another? We will return to this topic below.

Isaac (1980) has thoroughly considered all the data on human social organization and 'nesting' behavior, and concluded that the following features are characteristic of the human pattern:

1. The sleeping place is a home base. Each day, the members of the social group move rapidly from it.
2. Males and females have separate trajectories; there may be more than one party of each sex.
3. On any given day, some individuals will stay at the home base.
4. Many (not all!) foodstuffs are transported back to the home base, there to be shared out.
5. The whole group shifts its home base at intervals.
6. The group may undergo reversible fission or fusion.

Of these characteristics, the most fundamental from our point of view, as from Isaac's is the first: the Home Base. As Hediger (1977) and P. C. Reynolds (1981) note, a 'fix-point'—even an artificially modified one—is nothing exceptional in the animal kingdom; but its evolution among the Hominoidea is unexpected. The question to be asked is surely, why did nests become re-usable and long-lasting? The answer given, implicitly, by Isaac, is that there were ecological/economic reasons, based on the division of labour.

Isaac considers what could be archaeological traces of home bases, and suggests they might be what he calls 'Type-C' sites, characterized by an accumulation of discarded tools and broken bones. These include the bones of larger mammals, which are one type of food not utilized by other savannah or savannah-woodland primates (e.g. chimpanzees)—the others being deep tubers, scavenged meat and, unexpectedly, tortoises. Binford (1977) has strongly criticized the basis on which an early big-game hunting culture is based: if this is justified, it rather knocks away the putative archaeological basis of Isaac, and leaves us back with the Olduvai Stone Circle.

We have noted the sort of argument that can be advanced for homologizing nest-making behaviour in humans and apes; we must now examine possible origins for human social organization, to see who might be expected to occupy a common 'nest site'.

THE SOCIAL ORGANIZATION OF EARLY HOMININES

The evidence to date of the bases of social organization in the apes has been set out in a recent book (Hamburg & McCown 1980). The orang utan has a system of widely overlapping female home ranges overlain by a shifting network of male ranges: according to the state of the food supply, a prime male will either establish a temporary territory, from which rivals are excluded by vocal display backed up by actual aggression where necessary, or becomes nomadic, returning to his familiar area when conditions are right. MacKinnon (1980) notes that old males become sterile but continue to behave territorially, and hypothesises that each is maintaining an exclusive area on behalf of a younger male relative (son?).

Understanding of chimpanzee social organization has been in a state of flux ever since the early studies (Goodall 1963: V. & F. Reynolds 1963) described it as 'flexible'. Wrangham (1980) reviews the evidence, and proposes that the reality is not of a social community of males and females occupying a community range, and forming and dissolving daily subgroups of different composition, but one of two models:

1. The females within each community do not range throughout the community range, but each tends to stay within her own relatively restricted, but not exclusive, area.
2. The females are not strictly affiliated to a community at all, but occupy their own ranges as under (1) above, irrespective of where the communities of males are located.

In effect, the two models do not differ greatly in their practical consequences. Females are certainly associated more with one community of males than with another, and can be looked on as 'belonging' to a community. A female will generally shift her range—transferring between communities—on achieving her first oestrus, and sometimes again during subsequent oestrus periods. A male, on the other hand, may emigrate (alone or with other males) but does not transfer between communities.

Gorilla social organization is more rigid than that of the other apes. A troop generally has a single mature (silverback) male and several females; younger silverbacks may emigrate and try to kidnap females from other troops, or may stay in the troop and mate with specific females (those not mates of the old male, and not their full sisters). It may be specifically the sons of the troop male who stay in the troop, and the sons of passing wanderers who emigrate (Harcourt *et al.* 1978). Females tend to transfer as do chimpanzees.

It is easy to see potential homologies between orang and chimpanzee social organization, especially under Wrangham's second model: all we need is to have the male travelling in groups and associating for longer periods with female groups. To associate gorillas with such a scheme is more difficult. Goodall & Groves (1978) suggest that gorillas, too, may have local communities, and that their troops are simply the chimpanzee's flexible subgroups made permanent.

The social organization of human nomadic peoples is thoroughly flexible: the composition of camps, as we have seen above, changes from day to day. There is however the vexed question of the nuclear family. Make the polygynous family more independent, and you have the gorilla troop; or dissociate the male-female pairs and you have the chimpanzee community. How, then, to explain the separating out of human male-female couples, or of one-male harem units?

The male-female unit in the human nuclear family has been called a pair-bond. It is not, for the following reasons:

1. It is potentially polygynous. The fact that, even in societies where polygyny is countenanced, the usual union is monogamous, makes no difference. No pair-bond-living species is ever polygamous in any sense (see P. C. Reynolds 1981:245).

2. It does not exclude other kin, or indeed other, unrelated individuals. The pair-bond of birds, gibbons, etc. is the highest unit of social organization. The nuclear family of human society, even where —as in twentieth-century industrial countries—it is neolocal and an independent entity for purposes of day-to-day subsistence, is never free of ties to other kin, and preserves a complex network of rights and obligations with respect to them. In most societies, of course, including our nomadic hunter-gatherers, the nuclear family is neither neolocal nor economically independent.

3. It is not permanent. Divorce and adultery 'give every indication of being as venerable as marriage' (P. C. Reynolds 1981). Woodburn (1966) emphasizes this for the hunter-gatherer Hadza: the divorce rate is 49 per 1000 years of marriage, higher than in the typical industrial society. Splitting up and re-pairing is not known for certain under natural conditions, and extremely difficult to organize experimentally, in pair-bonded species.

4. The presence and degree of sexual dimorphism in the human species is much more consistent with the idea that male-female bonds have arisen within a multi-male group, with its concomitant dominance relationships (Martin & May 1981).

Chimpanzees form consortships, lasting sometimes for weeks, resulting in fertilization (Tutin 1975). Troop-leader silverback gorillas mate only with certain females, leaving others to be mates to their sons or to the wandering silverbacks (Veit 1982); but mating is a rare event among gorillas in any case. The human nuclear family is clearly derived from a long extension of a consortship, and has retained many of the same characteristics (dissolubility, existence within a wider social group, etc.). Chimpanzee consort pairs—and orang consort pairs, when they occur—separate from the social group for long periods. Human consort pairs do likewise, for still longer periods.

It is interesting that Itani (1977) has argued that the basic social organization of the Hominoidea is what he calls 'pair type'. If this viewpoint is acceptable, our argument above still makes it most unlikely that human social structure is of this type; a partial reversion, on a very superficial level, is 'all that can be said for it'.

DISCUSSION

If we are correct in deriving the human social organization from the common denominator of apes, the human camps from ape nest sites, then we must be clear about exactly what factors are in common and what the differences are. Human social groups are of the same general size (20-80) as those of chimpanzees and the hypothesized ones of gorillas: in theory, at least, they would be derivable from the dispersed organization of orang utans (see, for example, the model of Calhoun 1966). Within the social group, subgrouping takes place with much of the same flexibility as the chimpanzee exhibits, with this one exception: that consortships are longer-lasting and tend to form a consistent basic minimum of association. Like the gorilla but unlike the chimpanzee (as far as we know), a male forms multiple concurrent consortships (polygny): rarely, though not in apes, a female does the same (polyandry). A consortship, in all cases, is a potentially reproductive relationship in that it is the usual way infants are conceived, and the male partner claims social paternity even if not the biological father; and so is to be distinguished from the promiscuous sex that is such a misleadingly conspicuous feature of chimpanzee social life, and some human societies, but does not normally result in the birth of infants.

In a subsistence system in which sharing, while it occurs, is not pervasive, the major resources being available to all, a lengthening of consort bonds could easily result in the spatial separation of the consort pair for longer periods than occur in chimpanzees, whether this is total separation from other groups or merely remaining together during travel from one camp to another. As a bush/savannah ape, the early human ancestor would require an enormous memory store, a highly developed reasoning ability to follow the fluctuation of environmental vicissitudes, and enhanced learning ability: not new capabilities for a new set of requirements, but an elaboration of the same skills as are already highly developed in apes (Menzel 1970; Rodman 1975), and for the same reasons magnified—to be able to predict the location of resources in a fluctuating environment and so save crucial energy. The further reduced predictability of relevant causal processes, in a still less productive environment than inhabited by apes, demands a much wider home range and so selects the more intensely for learning ability and for the continued distalward expansion of iconic manipulation, as P. C. Reynolds (1981) expresses it. And so learning becomes supplemented by teaching, and intensified by rearing in an extended consortship.

A study of table 9, with due acknowledgement of the slenderness of the human data, shows that the campsites/nest sites of Hominidae (here used to cover humans and great apes) are similar. The number of individuals occupying the site varies, but the size and shape (though not necessarily the internal organization) of the site are similar, the spacing of the individual nests/camps is alike. In their social ordering, the major differences are two: the individual camps are arranged around the periphery in the human case, with a communal area and perhaps also an area for adolescents in the middle; and, still more strikingly, the individual camps are occupied by an entire nuclear family, not as in apes by single individual or, at most, a mother-infant pair. Consort pairs nest close together in chimpanzees, but do not share a common nest, except, it would seem, in *Pan paniscus* in some instances (Kuroda 1980); otherwise only extreme peer-dependence has resulted in nest-sharing: and this concerned not consorts but brothers (Riss & Goodall 1976).

Functionally, the nest of apes has taken on aspects of the Home but for only *one* night. The human 'nest' is a place for reconvening, both of the consort pair and of different social units. No ape nest-site is definitely known about and re-used, although there is a possibility that orang utans may in fact select in this way; whereas good sites are deliberately made for by human nomadic bands, and in many cases there is even a major base-camp. It is a place of maximal security, a fix-point. No doubt, the elaboration of food-sharing and division of labor (Isaac 1980) intensified these aspects of the nest. What is noteworthy, as Hediger (1977) has pointed out, is that at no point did the nest assume the functions of a breeding-place: this had to await the coming of permanent dwellings.

Structurally, too, the individual 'nests' have much in common between all species, but there are characteristic differences. In their simplest form, a scraping away of substrate to form a depression for the body is a shared feature. The more usual, more complex structure involves skilful interlacing and tying together of sticks and flexible plant material; there are very decided preferences, based presumably on experience, perhaps on tradition as well, for particular plant species from which to make the nest. Yet the ape uses material at hand or nearly always, as far as we know; the human collects it from a distance. Related to this, the ape makes its nest around it; the human may do this, but as frequently constructs it first, then enters it. Finally, the ape's nest is anchored to the growing vegetation structure, while the human's is a new structure; even such a superficially simple construction as a windbreak involves breaking off sticks and inserting them in the ground, supporting them if necessary with stones moved into place for the purpose—which is exactly what is supposed to have happened 1 3/4 million years ago to create the Olduvai Stone Circle.

P. Reynolds (1981) proposes nest-construction as a test of his 'distalward migration of conscious control' hypothesis. Apes, he observes, consciously control their hand movements in such a way as to place their hands in planned configurations, as for example in the gestures of sign-language. They can also manipulate and alter objects on and *ad hoc* basis, as in termite-fishing or other food-getting activities. No cercopithecoid monkey has anything like these activities. What apes do not do, however, is plan object configurations: they do not collect sticks for later use in termite-fishing, nor use objects to manipulate other objects. Nor, he surmises, does the ape work to a consciously controlled blueprint in nest-building: only in the human case has the distalward migration of conscious control reached so far.

All the evidence summarized above supports Reynolds's hypothesis. An ape does not collect suitable materials before beginning construction. It does not break off sticks, move them to a new location, and use them as supports for a superstructure. It does not construct a nest, then enter it. It does not, as far as can be deduced, design a structure capable of containing two bodies (though here we may be going beyond the evidence). It does not coordinate its building activities with all other troop members in such a way as to stamp a regular pattern on the nest site. It does not choose a site for its camping possibilities, and return to it again and again (orang utans perhaps excepted). The human, with its fully developed ability to visualize objects in new configurations, and to bring these configurations into being on the basis of that mental picture, does all these things.

By examining closely the regularities of nesting patterns in apes, especially gorillas, we believe that a groundwork can be laid from which it is possible to argue more securely to the origins of human camps. Both structure and function must be considered. The basic structure has changed extraordinarily little from the nest sites of apes to the camps of modern hunter-gatherers; but analysis of those aspects of structure which have changed, and of the differences in function, offers clues for the origins and selective advantages of human social organization, and places in focus the cognitive similarities and differences between ape and human.

NOTES

J. Sabater Pi was supported during fieldwork by the National Geographic Society and Tulane University. Colin P. Groves would like to acknowledge useful discussions with Dr. Nicolas Peterson and Dr Peter Reynolds. The figures were drawn by R. Pena and J. Oriol.

REFERENCES

Baldwin, P. J. 1979. The natural history of the chimpanzee *(Pan troglodytes verus)* at Mt. Assirik, Senegal. Thesis, University of Stirling.

_____, J. Sabater Pi, W. C. McGrew & C. E. C. Tutin 1981. Comparisons of nests made by different populations of chimpanzees *(Pan troglodytes)*. *Primates* 22, 474–86.

Breader, S. K. & R. D. Martin 1980. The social organization of a nocturnal primate revealed by radio-tracking. In *A handbook on telemetry and radio tracking* (eds) C. J. Amianer & D. W. Macdonald. Oxford: Pergamon Press.

Bernstein, I. S. 1967. Age and experience in chimpanzee nest building. *Psychol. Repts* 20, 116.

_____ 1969. A comparison of nesting patterns among the three Great Apes. *The Chimpanzee* 1, 393–402.

Binford, L. R. 1977. *Olorgesailie* deserves more than the usual book review. *J. anthrop. Res.* 33, 403–502.

Blower, J. 1956. The mountain gorilla. *Uganda Wildl. Sport* 1, 41–52.

Bournonville, D. de 1967. Contribution à l'étude du chimpanzee en République de Guinée. *Bull. Instu. franc. Afr. noire* 29, 1189–1269.

Butzler, W. 1980. Présence et répartition des gorillas, *Gorilla gorilla gorilla* (Savage & Wyman 1847), au Cameroun. *Säugetierkundl. Mitt.* 28, 69–79.

Calhoun, J. B. 196 . The social use of space. In *Physiological mammalogy* (eds) W. W. Mayer & R. G. van Gelder. New York: Academic Press.

Casimir, M. J. 1979. An analysis of gorilla nesting sites of the Mt. Kahuzi region (Zaire). *Folia primatol.* 32, 290–308.

Cipriani, L. 1966. *The Andaman islanders.* London: Weidenfeld & Nicolson.

DuChaillu, P. 1861. *Exploration and adventures in equatorial Africa.* London: John Murray.

Dyce Sharp, N. A. 1927. Notes on the gorilla. *Proc. zool. Soc. Lond.* 1927, 1006–8.

Elliott, R. C. 1976. Observations on a small group of mountain gorillas *(Gorilla gorilla beringei).* *Folia primatol.* 25, 12–24.

Goodall, A. 1974. Studies on the ecology of the mountain gorilla. Thesis, University of Liverpool.

_____ & C. P. Groves 1977. The conservation of the eastern gorillas. In *Primate conservation* (eds) G. A. Bourne & H. S. H. Rainier, New York:

Goodall, J. 196 . Nest building behaviour of the free-ranging chimpanzee. *Ann. N. Y. Acad. Sci.* 102, 455–67.

_____ 1968. Behavior of free-ranging chimpanzees in the Gombe Stream Reserve. *Anim. Behav. Monogr.* 1, 161–311.

_____ 1971. *In the shadow of man.* London: Collins.

Hamburg, R. A. & E. R. McCown (eds) 1979. *The great apes.* Menlo Park, Ca.: Benjamin/Cummings.

Gould, R. A. 1977. Puntutjarpa Rockshelter and the Australian desert culture. *Anthrop. Pap. AMNH* 54, 1–187.

Harako, R. 1976. The Mbuti as hunters: a study of ecological anthropology of the Mbuti pygmies. 1. *Kyoto Univ. Afr. Stud.* 10, 37–99.

Harcourt, A., D. Fossey & J. Sabater Pi 1981. Demography of *Gorilla gorilla.* *J. zool. Soc. Lond.* 195, 215–33.

Hediger, H. 1977. Nest and home. *Folia primatol.* 28, 170–87.

Isaac, G. Ll. 197 . The activities of early homonids. In *Human origins: Louis Leakey and the east African evidence* (eds) G. Ll. Isaac & E. R. McCown. Berkeley: Univ. of California Press.

_____ 1980. Casting the net wide. In *Current argument on early man* (ed.) L. K. Konigsson. Oxford: Univ. Press.

Itani, J. 1977. Evolution of primate social structure. *J. hum. Evol.* 6, 235–43.

Izawa, K. & J. Itani 1966. Chimpanzees in Kasataki Basin, Tanganyika. *Kyoto Univ. Afr. Stud.* 1, 73–156.

Jones, C. & J. Sebate Pi 1971. Comparative ecology of *Gorilla gorilla* (Savage & Wyman) and *Pan troglodytes* (Blumenbach) in Rio Muni, west Africa. *Bibl. primatol.* 13.

Kano, T. 1982. The use of leafy twigs for rain cover by the pygmy chimpanzees of Wamba. *Primates* 23, 453–7.

Kawai, M. & H. Mizuhara 1959. An ecological study of the wild mountain gorilla. *Primates* 2, 1–42.

Kuroda, S. 1980. Social behavior of the pygmy chimpanzees. *Primates* 21, 181–97.

Leakey, M. D. 1971 *Olduvai gorge,* vol. 3. Cambridge: Univ. Press.

MacKinnon, J. 1971. The orang utan in Sabah today. *Oryx* 11, 141–91.

_____ 1979. Reproductive behavior in wild orangutan populations. In *The great apes* (eds) R. A. Hamburg & E. R. McKown. Menlo Park, Ca.: Benjamin/Cummings.

Martin, R. D. & R. M. May 1981. Outward signs of bleeding. *Nature, Lond.* 293, 7–9.

Menzel, E. W. 1973. Chimpanzee spatial memory organization. *Science* 182, 943–5.

Osborn, R. M. 1957. Observations on the behavior of the mountain gorilla. *Symp. zool. Soc.* 10, 29–37.

Parker, C. C. 1974. The antecedents of man the manipulator. *J. hum. Evol.* 3, 493–500.

Reynolds, P. C. 1981. *On the evolution of human behavior.* Berkeley: Univ. of California Press.

Reynolds, V. & F. Reynolds 196 . Chimpanzees of the Budongo forest. In *Primate behavior* (ed.) I. DeVore. New York:

Rijksen, H. D. 1978. A field study on Sumatran orangutans. *Meded. Landbouwhogeschool Wageningen* 78: 2. Holt, Rinehart & Winston.

Riss, D. & J. Goodall 1976. Sleeping behavior and associations in a group of captive chimpanzees. *Folia primatol.* 25, 1–11.

Rodman, P. S. 1979. Individual activity patterns and the solitary nature of orang-utans. In *The great apes* (eds) R. A. Hamburg & E. R. McCown. Menlo Park, Ca.: Benjamin/Cummings.

Sabater Pi, J. 1970. Beitrag zur Biologie des Flachlandgorillas. *Z. Saugetierk* 23, 108–14.

_____ & L. de Lassaletta 1958. Beitrag zur Kenntnis des Flachlandgorillas. *Z. Saugetierk.* 23, 108–14.

Schaller, G. B. 1963. *The mountain gorilla.* Chicago: Univ. Press.

Tanno, T. 1976. The Mbuti net-hunters in the Ituri forest, eastern Zaire: their hunting activities and band composition. *Kyoto Univ. Afr. Stud.* 10, 101–35.

Tutin. C. E. G. 1975. Exceptions to promiscuity in a feral chimpanzee community. *Contemp. Primatol.* 445–9.

Veit, P. G. 1982. Gorilla society. *Nat. Hist. N. Y.* 91, 48–59.

Woodburn, J. 1966. Stability and flexibility in Hadza residential groups. In *Man the hunter* (eds) R. B. Lee & I. DeVore. Chicago: Aldine.

Wrangham, R. 1979. Sex differences in chimpanzee dispersion. In *The great apes* (eds) R. A. Hamburg & E. R. McCown. Menlo Park, Ca.: Benjamin/Cummings.

Yellen, J. C. 1977. *Archaeological approaches to the present.* New York: Academic Press.

War Among the Chimps

_____ Michael Ghiglieri _____

Five apes silently crested the ridge from the south. They peered intently into the valley beyond, craned their necks, and shifted positions uneasily. A grunt drifted up from below. All five apes retracted their lips in nervous grimaces, and they shifted slightly to touch one another in reassurance. Then they quietly hurried down the slope. They had marked their prey.

The male and female eating fruit in the valley were on the southern periphery of their community's territory. It was the only place where the male could hope to mate with this female away from competition from his fellow males. It was more dangerous here, but that was a small price to pay.

Suddenly the five intruders surrounded the couple's tree. Two climbed its trunk while the others positioned themselves to block escape routes. The female shrieked and fled; the male guarding her route let her pass, but he tackled her consort. Then the others converged. One grabbed his leg, another his arm, the third pummeled and bit him, while the fourth stomped on his back. After ten minutes of this brutal attack, the bloody male was inert. The interlopers stepped back to study him. One ran a circle around him and hooted. Two others joined in. Then, abruptly, they returned up the hill.

The female emerged from hiding. Only the faintest hiss of breath indicated that her mate still lived. She tentatively touched him, and he tried to rise. But his spine was broken, and he sank back to the forest floor. She stayed with him until the next day, brushed flies from his wounds, and groomed him. After he died she returned north.

This scene is constructed from about a dozen observations made by several scientists during repeated lethal chimp attacks in Tanzania in the 1970s. As a graduate student in biological ecology, I was intrigued enough by the stories that I decided to travel to Uganda, observe the chimpanzees firsthand, and try to make scientific sense of the killing. Now, years later, I have returned to the United States with many stories to tell and a few conclusions about chimpanzee warfare.

Chimpanzees as killer apes may shock or even smack of heresy. During most of this century the popular media have bestowed on chimpanzees the innocent aura of a natural clown, a good-natured caricature of man, one whose ancestors reached the evolutionary threshold leading to *Homo sapiens*, then tripped over it.

In contrast, gorillas seemed natural heavies. Endowed with the strength of several men, and with a fierce and forbidding glower, gorillas became trapped in a King Kong image. Their cousins the orangutans fared no better. Edgar Allan Poe had one lethally wielding a straight razor in the Rue Morgue. And today's image is dominated by obese males confined to zoos. How is it that, instead of these seeming ne'er-do-wells, the happy-go-lucky chimpanzee has turned out to be the most lethal ape—an organized, cooperative warrior who seizes opportunities to outflank and murder males unrelated to him?

Most primatologists now agree that social systems result from the interplay of two basic processes: behavioral ecology and sexual selection (the type of natural selection that operates on one or the other *sex* of a species). Of these two, it is ecology—specifically as it relates to the animal's diet—that makes the most obvious difference. Indeed, when it comes to social systems, "you are what you eat" is more true than one might guess. Part of the wisdom gleaned from hundreds of field studies focusing on the behavioral ecology of mammals indicates that specializing in certain foods influences social life profoundly. Mountain gorillas, for example, require an especially abundant food supply; adult males consume up to 66 pounds of leaves, shoots, and bark each day. Despite the swath of greenery a group can gobble up daily, however, their foods are so abundant that a family group of a dozen or so can normally find all the food it needs. In terms of competition, gorillas can easily afford one another's company.

In complete contrast, orangutans apparently cannot afford even one adult friend; the cost of competition is simply too high. Though the animals eat primarily fruit, their diet may also include bark, flowers, young leaves, insects, and anything else they can digest. They are physically designed to forage for these foods almost exclusively in trees. So highly adapted are they that their feet are a second pair of permanently hooked hands. This leaves them so clumsy on the ground that they can travel only a few hundred yards each day (only 10 percent the normal range of a chimpanzee). Limited mobility restricts each orangutan to visiting only a few rare fruit-trees daily. Survival then demands that each tree be monopolized. This means traveling alone.

Chimpanzees are the anomaly. During my two years in the Kibale Forest of Uganda, I observed two communities of wild chimpanzees, one numbering nearly 60 members. Like the orangutan, they eat a broad range of foods, though fruit accounts for the majority. But unlike their red-haired cousins, chimpanzees travel efficiently both in trees and on the ground. Because they can travel so much faster, they can visit many more fruit trees and can afford to travel with several companions—up to two dozen during times of plenty in Kibale (although 44 percent of the parties I saw, especially during lean seasons, did consist of solitary chimps or just a mother with her dependent offspring). Daily the chimps dissolved and recemented social bonds as the food supply permitted. But because being social still exacts *some* cost in competition for food, even in seasons of abundance, the big question remains: Why do they bother? What do they gain from their elaborate fusion-fission society?

I believe that the best explanation for why apes are social at all is sociobiological. It is likely that each ape is social not simply for company, but for selfish reasons. And those reasons go to the very heart of its genetic imperative to reproduce. In fact, at least from a male perspective, the social system of the chimpanzee seems tailor-made for maximum reproductive success.

Evolution should be looked at as a long-term reproductive contest, and it is fair to assume that most individuals are genetically programmed to try to win it. Female apes must invest four to seven years (the shortest time is among gorillas, the longest among orangutans) exclusively in *each* of their offspring to give it a good chance of survival. Because females mature at about age 15 but quit producing infants at around age 40 (if they live that long), each can hope to raise no more than four or five healthy children. Males live just as long, but because they invest very little besides the time that it takes them to mate, theoretically they can sire hundreds of offspring. They are limited only by the number of females available to them. And because males and females exist in nearly equal numbers, males end up competing fiercely with one another for very limited opportunities to mate. Sexual selection occurs when certain types of males (large, aggressive, intelligent, sneaky, handsome, or whatever) are more successful than others in winning females. In essence, sexual selection is a natural arms race.

Dominating other males is the key to success. Among orangutans and gorillas the system is simple: one-on-one competition. Among chimpanzees, however, things are very different. Males are much more tolerant of competition from other males within the community and often share their mates. But they compete in cooperative teams against all other males *outside* their community. The reason for this unusual behavior again has its basis in genetics.

Nearly all male primates remain in their natal social groups only during childhood and adolescence. Upon reaching adulthood they abruptly break their early bonds and wander off to seek entry into another established group. Hundreds of field studies have revealed that among nearly all social primates, females form the cores of groups; they remain during maturity and become the group's bearers of tradition and repositories of collective knowledge. Among chimpanzees, however, this social system has been turned completely upside down.

Toshisada Nishida and Jane Goodall independently observed that males in the Mahale Mountains never emigrated from their natal community, while females normally did. Observations from other studies of chimpanzees, including my own, indicate the same thing. The genetic consequences of this are enormous.

Because the males of a community have all descended from the same male forebears, they are much more closely related to one another than to alien males—or to their own mates. When any one of them breeds, a large number of genes shared by the others are reproduced. Male chimps *within* a community

380

share genetically in one another's reproductive success, just as do humans with the birth of siblings, cousins, nieces, and nephews. This process, in which an individual increases its genetic reproductive success by assisting close relatives to breed more, was termed inclusive fitness by British biologist W.D. Hamilton, who noted that among social insects no other valid explanation could account for workers' suicidal defense of their queen. Because of inclusive fitness, it is even possible that a male chimpanzee who never breeds but who assists his relatives to breed *more* can himself be reproductively successful. The sexual selection arms race has somehow allowed male chimpanzees to retain imperfect copies of themselves as allies.

Still, most male chimpanzees prefer to do their own mating, and they sometimes try to escort a female away to monopolize her during her rare periods of receptivity. However, Jane Goodall observed that, strangely, most females resist this and manage to mate with most or all adult males in their community during the peak of their ovulatory periods. One explanation for this behavior holds that since the genetic difference between the males in the community is small, so is the importance of discriminating between them. But I suspect that the female chimpanzee is promiscuous for an entirely different reason: by mating with every male, she may ensure that each of her mates will later suspect he is the father of her infant and protect it. No mater which reason is true, the fact remains that, with the possible exception of South American spider monkeys, whose social system is still unclear, chimpanzees are the only one of 181 species of nonhuman primates in which it is known that males routinely remain in the social group of their birth, cooperatively share mates, and, significantly, are communally territorial, willing to go to war to protect their turf.

The nettlesome question, of course, is *why* are they territorial? Where is the survival advantage in risking one's life for land? The answer appears to be that winning more habitat enhances a group's mating success. Because ecological resources limit the number of females who can live in any region, the success of males in expanding, or at least holding, their territory determines the upper limit of their reproductive potential. No wonder they are territorial; if they were pacifists, or even individualists, their more coordinated neighbors would carve their territory into parcels and annex them. Thus armies are introduced into the natural arms race. Once this happens, solidarity between a community's males becomes essential.

In stark contrast to their brutality toward alien males, the behavior of a community's males toward one another is a blueprint for cooperation. Male chimpanzees in Kibale, even as young as juveniles, overwhelmingly preferred to travel with one another than with females. They also groomed one another (an important hygienic exchange service) much more frequently than they groomed females—and for longer sessions. Also, males were at least ten times more likely than females to give resounding pant-hoots, a vocalization carrying as far as two miles and the main means by which separated chimps keep in touch. Sonographic analysis by Peter Marler and Linda Hobbet of Rockefeller University indicated that pant-hoots from chimps in Gombe National Park in Tanzania were distinctive enough to be recognized individually. Choruses of pant-hoots in Kibale communicated how many chimps were calling and the identities of some of them; when repeated during travel, they also revealed the direction the callers were going. These pant-hoots not only invited other community members to join the caller, they also probably warned alien males of a potential rumble.

But the chimpanzees of Kibale surprised me by going beyond merely advertising their companionship: they also advertised the best places to eat. When males first arrived at large trees laden with fruit, they often pant-hooted wildly and pounded on the tree's resonant buttresses, sometimes for several minutes. At first I could not imagine what, beyond sheer exuberance over the prospect of so much food, prompted them to create such a din. But eventually I noticed that other community members seemed to appear more often after these calls. I began to suspect that the apes were actually advertising the presence of food. When I finally analyzed my data, I found these pant-hooting choruses indeed were food calls that did attract other apes more often. At first this seemed rather big-hearted generosity.

It was anything but. Because chimpanzees are generally too self-centered for genuine altruism, I looked at my data more closely. Males never gave food calls at small trees (and females never gave food calls at all), only at bonanzas of fruit. So they really were not inviting much in the way of competition. And what they did get was grooming partners, traveling companions, and occasionally a sexually receptive female. Males also stood to gain in the reproductive contest simply by improving the nutrition of their fellow community members, especially when the cost to them was so small. Males in Tanzania also gave food calls and shared meat, albeit grudgingly, from kills of small mammals. All of this sharing—meals, mates, company—promotes solidarity to a degree unknown among other male apes.

Such is life from the view of a male chimpanzee. Females face entirely different challenges. The first of these is choosing a new community with a future. To be successful, a female must accurately gauge the territory's food resources *and* she must accurately guess whether the males of the community are strong enough to hold their own against neighbors. A new immigrant must also be prepared to hold *her* own against the aggression of resident females, who sometimes cooperate to repel newcomers trying to carve out a home range in their territory. Because (in Tanzania) the community's males sometimes attack the infants of females living on the territorial periphery—even if they have mated with them—but protect infants of core females, it is imperative for a female to stake her new turf claim not just at the periphery of the new community, but in its core. And each female must accomplish this before her prime has ended: adult males in both Mahale and Gombe recruited young females but attacked and sometimes killed those beyond their prime. Immigrating females face a formidable range of obstacles, but when they pass them, life becomes relatively secure.

One way they assure this security is through another surprising social behavior I observed in the Kibale Forest. Unlike most female chimpanzees in Tanzania, who socialized largely with males, females in Kibale groomed, traveled, and otherwise socialized mostly with one another. Mothers especially favored other mothers. Such friendships may provide multiple advantages, one of which is the ability to present a more solid front against young immigrants trying to squeeze into an already saturated territory. To raise infants successfully in the chimpanzees' competitive world, nothing should be left to chance.

The demands of chimpanzee society equip them with a natural aggression vital for survival. This trait may grow even more pronounced when the chimps are taken from the wild, where much of their time is spent finding food, and transplanted into unfamiliar captivity, where easy food allows them to concentrate fully on raising their dominance status. Indeed, their fierce independence and competitiveness makes them especially unreceptive to learning what to them are the utterly meaningless tricks their trainers try to teach them for the entertainment of an audience.

Wallace Swett, director of Primarily Primates, a San Antonio halfway house for abused primates, explains that the biggest difficulty trainers face is that the chimpanzees' natural tendency to try to dominate other chimpanzees is simply transferred to the trainers. Far from being eager, receptive students, chimpanzees often ignore their handlers, threaten them and sometimes even attack them. Frequently trainers respond with such coercive methods as beating the animals with blackjacks or jolting them with cattle prods. After Twentieth-Century Fox released the film *Project X*, which featured several chimpanzee performers, the studio was accused of hiring trainers who beat the animals when other training techniques proved ineffective. Though Fox continues to deny the charges, a number of groups, including the People for Ethical Treatment of Animals, in Washington D.C., insist they are true.

Sociobiologically, I find it hard not to compare wild chimpanzees with warlike tribes of humans. Not only do males of both species wage war, they even do it for similar reasons. For the apes, these are territorial expansion and more females for mates. Among humans, modern wars have often been fought for economic reasons. Even wars I observed being waged with axes and spears in modern Papua New Guinea were fought to monopolize rare lands suitable for growing coffee, the most valuable crop. Combatants in modern wars hope that economic gain will bring power, wealth, and secure borders. As with the apes, this security translates directly or indirectly into reproductive advantage. Lest doubt still exist that humans are not the only primates who engage in full-scale war aimed at annihilating the enemy's males, annexing their territory, absorbing their economy, and possibly stealing their women, I should report on the magnitude of the conflicts between chimpanzees in Tanzania.

Jane Goodall began her amazing work on chimpanzees in 1960 at Gombe National Park and eventually came to know at least 50 apes, most of whom visited her camp for free bananas. By 1968 the banana feeding had become both a logistical nightmare and a scientific problem. Goodall cut back the feeding, and the chimps, left to fend for themselves, gradually split into two factions: the larger Kasakela community, which continued to visit camp, and a slightly smaller faction containing about a dozen apes, which moved south to the Kahama Valley. A few years after the split, parties of Kasakela males began making repeated forays south, brutally killing at least five of the Kahama males, plus one old female, thus annihilating the Kahama community.

This annihilation was unprecedented in the annals of primate behavior. Goodall told me that she suspected the murder might have been spurred by a shortage of sexually receptive females in the Kasakela community. I suspected that the loss of the banana supply produced a catastrophic ecological crunch and that the Kasakela males were moving south to expand their resource base. Now I think both of us may have been right; soon after the Kahama males were eliminated, the Kasakela community annexed part of the Kahama territory, foraged in it, and bred with its remaining females. Recently a more powerful community from the south forced them north again. And, even more recently, Nishida reported a similar, brutal intercommunity annihilation in the Mahale Mountains.

It would be comforting to think that being human places us above this kind of savagery, but our track record indicates that we're even more warlike. Nor is it reassuring to contemplate that, based on careful comparison of DNA, it appears that not only are chimpanzees and bonobos our nearest relatives, we are also *theirs*. It seems that warfare is our common biological legacy. *Does* war run in our genes like baldness and diabetes? Or could it be only a cultural legacy? Has sociobiology even advanced far enough to answer these questions?

Shortly after Edward O. Wilson of Harvard University ushered in sociobiology as an independent branch of evolutionary science in 1975, it fell under attack by people who questioned the soundness of calling nearly all behavior gene-driven. Sociobiology does suffer from two current weaknesses. The first is an inadequacy of comparative data on *lifetime* reproductive success of individuals using different survival strategies—for example, cooperating socially or going it alone. Its second weakness is the lack of physical identification of genes and the metabolic pathways responsible for behavioral predispositions. These problems not withstanding, it still seems to me that sociobiology offers the best set of testable hypotheses that attempt to explain the biological roots of social behavior. Its challenge is to test these hypotheses fully.

No matter what sociobiology uncovers about the darker sides of human and animal behavior, there is no doubt that there are gentler sides, sides that-gene-driven or not—may represent the best in all creatures. I was deeply impressed by a ragged old female chimp named Gray. During a quarter of the many times I observed Gray, she was accompanied by a little juvenile female named Zane. Due to Gray's age and several other factors, I became convinced that Zane could not be Gray's daughter. She had to be an orphan Gray had adopted. (Later I learned that Goodall had also observed two similar cases of adoption).

Near the end of my research in Kibale I watched old Gray lead Zane away from a huge fig tree to find shade for a midday rest; but the route Gray chose was difficult. At one point she reached the end of a horizontal tree arching across a swamp, then leapt through space, grabbed the top of a smaller tree, and climbed down to earth. When Zane reached this gap, however, she could not make the jump—it was just too much for her. Gray stared at her foster daughter, blinked once, then slowly climbed back up the slender tree and pumped it to and fro until it swung close enough for her to grab a branch of the tree in which Zane was stranded. Gray then spread-eagled her self to grip both trees and act as a living bridge—over which Zane immediately scrambled. Then they traveled together like mother and daughter into the shady forest. I watched them disappear, and when they were gone, I couldn't help concluding that perhaps there is hope for all of us.

The Ecology of Social Relationships Amongst Female Primates

C.P. Van Schaik

University of Utrecht

SUMMARY

1 The aim of this paper is to develop a framework in which to explain inter-specific variation in the patterning of female social relationships among diurnal primates (and hopefully some other mammals as well).

2 It is suggested that female social relationships reflect competition among females for food and safety. Competition for food can be of the scramble and of the contest type, and can occur both within and between groups.

3 For each meaningful combination of the three important components (between-group scramble is ignored), a set of predictions is derived for the social structure among the females in a group or society.

4 It is hypothesized that where high predation risks force primates to live in cohesive groups, within-group competition predominates. This can be mainly by scramble or by both scramble and contest. In the former case, females develop individualistic and egalitarian ranking systems, in which female bonding varies, while in the latter they develop nepotistic and despotic ranking systems, accompanied by female residence.

5 The majority of folivores, and at least one gregarious insectivore, belong to the first type, whereas frugivores and omnivores belong to the second.

6 Among species of low vulnerability to predators, between-group competition predominates, and females should form nepotistic but egalitarian ranking systems, accompanied by female residence, provided that they can still live in sizeable groups. Primates on oceanic islands without predators, and some of the larger arboreal and the largest (semi-)terrestrial primates, are expected to show this pattern.

7 When high potential within-group competition precludes the formation of female groups, variable relationships are expected depending on the options open to males.

INTRODUCTION

There is very wide variation in the social organization of primate species. Ecological explanations have been sought for this. So far, these theories (see van Schaik & van Hooff 1983; Terborgh & Janson 1986; Wrangham 1987) have been successful mainly at the level of global features of social organization, such as the presence or absence of gregariousness, and, for gregarious species, group size and composition. This variation is even more pronounced at the level of social relationships, but there are no generally accepted theories accounting for the ecological determinants of social relationships among the members of a primate society (Silk 1987). Are relationships also determined by external conditions, or are they basically arbitrary variations related to chance events in the evolutionary history of the species?

Wrangham (1979) suggested that relationships among females should be linked more directly to ecological conditions than those among males or those between males and females. The two latter kinds depend primarily on the behaviour and spatial distribution of the females (cf. Emlen & Oring 1977), and are mainly related to mating competition and mate choice, respectively. Of course, we oversimplify if we look to the ecological conditions alone to account for the variability in female social relationships, because interactions between male and female strategies may result in different female relationships from those found in the absence of any male influence. This is most striking in species in which the male contribution to rearing offspring is considerable (for example, the callitrichids). However, if we limit ourselves to species with multi-female groups, female relationships form a very useful starting point for an enquiry into the role of ecological factors in social relationships, and this paper will concentrate on them.

The most influential attempt at an ecological theory for variation in female social relationships was made by Wrangham (1980). He distinguished two types of social structure, namely female-bonded (FB) and non-female-bonded structures. Females in FB societies are surrounded by genetic relatives, maintain strong grooming bonds, and are actively involved in agonistic encounters with other societies. Such societies were thought to have developed where females formed groups in order to cooperatively defend their food, occurring as defensible high-quality patches, against other groups and so needed relatives as reliable coalition partners. Thus, on this view, the evolution of group living in primates and female-bondedness are both ascribed to competition between groups (societies), and frugivores should live in FB-groups whereas folivores should be non-FB.

On the first score, the evolution of group living, Wrangham's theory turns out to have little empirical support (van Schaik 1983; Terborgh & Janson 1986; Dunbar 1988). First, it leaves unexplained why many non-FB primate species also live in groups (for example, hamadryas baboons, *Papio hamadyas*; red colobus, *Colobus badius*; gorilla, *Gorilla gorilla*). Second, in at least a number of species competition for food appears to increase monotonically with group size rather than being greatest in the smallest and perhaps the largest groups (van Schaik & van Hooff 1983). Third, a quantitative test in brown capuchins (*Cebus apella*) has shown that competition between groups is far less important than within groups (Janson 1985), something also suspected for various macaques and baboons (van Schaik, in preparation). Fourth, as a consequence of this, the predicted relationship between birth rate and group size is found in a few species only (van Schaik 1983): most species show declining birth rates as group size increases whereas an increase or a humped relationship would have been expected. The data on most species agree best with the idea that predation risk sets the lower limit to group size, whereas within-group competition, related to the sizes of food patches used (see, for example, Terborgh & Janson 1986), sets the upper limit. Female fitness is maximized at some intermediate group size.

Perhaps then, competition between groups was not the only, or even the major factor influencing female social relationships in most primate species. Indeed, many species also do not conform to the second part of the theory. Frugivores are expected to form FB groups, but not all do: chimpanzees (*Pan troglodytes*) and spider monkeys (*Ateles* spp.) live in fission—fusion societies in which males rather than females defend the area and adult females do not form strong bonds (see, for example, Goodall 1985, McFarland Symington 1987). Likewise, most of the highly frugivorous gibbons (*Hylobates* spp.) form monogamous pairs rather than multifemale groups; so do several Neotropical cebids and callitrichids. There are also various species without female emigration in which groups avoid each other rather than fight over area or food sources (for example, mangabeys, *Cercocebus albigena*: Waser 1976), or in which females take little or no part in between-group conflicts, which are often quite rare as well (for a review, see Cheney 1987; see also Terborgh & Janson 1986). In fact, female residence and natal dispersal by males is also found in the majority of solitary mammals (Waser & Jones 1983), in which between-group competition is notably absent. Finally, we would not expect steep ('despotic') linear hierarchies if conflicts between groups would be the major determinant of female social relationships (see below; cf. Vehrencamp 1983).

In its present form, therefore, Wrangham's (1980) theory can not provide an ecological explanation for female social relationships in primates. However, the approach is sound and I will merely propose two extensions. First, the notion of competition has to be diversified. Not only is there food competition between groups, but also, and often far more prominently, within groups; and in the latter case it can be of the scramble or contest type. Second, we also have to take into account that competition within groups may concern safety from predators.

To make clear why we should look to competition as the factor structuring female social relationships, consider the following argument. In a stable population, a female's fitness is approximated by the number of offspring she raises to reproductive maturity, in other words, her birth rate times the length of her reproductive career times the survival rate of her offspring. These variables are vitally affected by two factors. First, birth rate and offspring survival are strongly influenced by the quantity and quality of food a female can acquire (see, for example, Mori 1979; Wrangham 1979). Second, both her own survival,

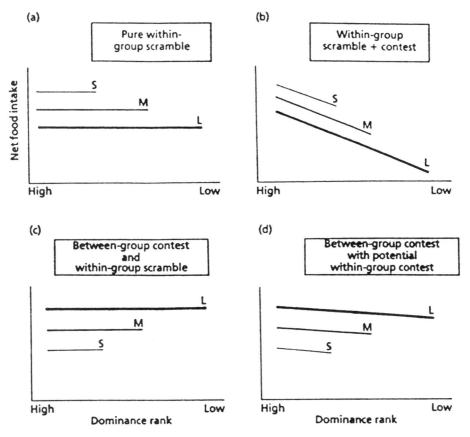

Figure 1. Various combinations of the three relevant components of food competition among group-living mobile organisms to illustrate the main competitive regimes distinguished in Table 1, namely pure WGS (type A), WGC with a variable mix of WGS (type B), and strong BGC with WGS (type C) and strong BGC with potentially strong WGC (type D). S = small group; M = medium group; L = large group.

and hence the length of her reproductive career as well as that of her offspring, is strongly influenced by the level of safety she can maintain (see, for example, van Schaik 1983; Dunbar 1988). Therefore, a female's social relationships with other females in a group should serve these vital interests. It is suggested that among non-human primates, group living by females apparently evolved originally as a defence against predators (van Schaik 1983; Terborgh & Janson 1986; Dunbar 1988). If this is so and spatial clumping is enforced by extrinsic factors, we can expect females to form affiliative relationships when this raises their inclusive fitness by enhancing either their own competitive power or that of their relatives.

This paper is organized as follows. First, I define the main competitive regimes to which primate females are subjected and establish in which ecological conditions these are found. Next, I systematically explore the effects that each of these competitive regimes should have on female social relationships. Finally, I compare the predicted patterns with those found among primates, and look at more intermediate situations, which can realistically be expected in nature.

COMPETITIVE REGIMES

The Three Modes of Feeding Competition

Competition for food among free-moving animals can take on two forms: scramble and contest (Nicholson 1957). Scramble occurs when the net food intake of all individuals in a population is about equally affected by an increase in the population's density. All animals share the same food supply, and none of them are able to obtain more than the others through overt behavior, for example by evicting others from high-quality food sources or by staking out an exclusive territory. Whenever the distribution of the food and other factors allow it, competition will be by contest (also: interference), with territory owners or winners of interactions usurping a greater share of the critical resource than floaters or losers. In all but the most extreme conditions the competition experienced by an animal is a combination of both kinds.

If animals are living in groups, or are at least organized into distinct societies (i.e. unstable spatial coherence but stable membership), the situation becomes more complicated. Scramble and contest can now occur at two levels, both within the group or the society and between different groups or societies. In gregarious non-human primates competition therefore has four different faces: within-group scramble (WGS), within-group contest (WGC), between-group scramble (BGS) and between-group contest (BGC) (Janson & van Schaik 1988; see also Fig. I). WGS occurs when animals foraging in a group have to share a limited supply of food with others and all of them suffer roughly equal reductions in foraging efficiency. It is expected when food is dispersed in patches that are either very small but cannot be monopolized or very large relative to group size, so at least among animals that graze or go after cryptic food in small patches (insects). WGC occurs when some group members are able to obtain a higher net food intake, hence when food occurs in well-defined patches, the access to which can be monopolized. Thus, it should at least be found among frugivores. WGC reflects the dominance effect in competition and WGS reflects the group size effect with the dominance effect removed.

Between-group contest occurs when the members of dominant groups obtain more food than the members of subordinate ones because the former aggressively displace the latter or are avoided by them, or because they defend a bigger or better territory. BGS occurs when groups overlap extensively in area and suffer a reduced foraging efficiency due to each other's removal of food, or when groups show mutual avoidance while occupying more or less exclusive ranges. Its quantitative importance depends on the potential for BGC, because, as between individuals, contest is likely to replace scramble whenever the conditions allow it. BGS basically represents the effect of population density on net food intake. Since I can see no way in which it may affect female social relationships, I shall ignore it in the rest of this paper.

Competitive Regimes

The effects of competition on an individual female's net food intake will always be a combination of these three components and in some cases an additional component due to the advantages of social foraging. If we divide each component into just two categories, a weak (W) or a strong (S) effect on net food intake, this gives us eight possible competitive regimes (Table 1). However, this number can be reduced for three reasons, the last two of which can be made clear only after we have examined the social consequences of the competitive regimes in detail. First, diurnal primates are unlikely to experience weak effects of all three components in nature (column 8, Table 1), since that would require a population density and a degree of spatial clumping that are low enough to preclude all food competition. Second, strong WGC and strong BGC have incompatible effects, so columns 6 and 7 can be eliminated. Third, the effects of strong WGC override those of WGS, so columns 2 and 3 are indistinguishable.

Hence, we can start our analysis with four competitive regimes (types A—D in Table 1), namely competition mainly by WGS (A), competition by WGC and a variable intensity of WGS (B), competition mainly by WGS and BGC (C), and competition mainly by BGC, usually with an unexpressed potential for strong WGC (D). Figure 1 illustrates these four regimes.

Ecological Conditions and Competitive Regimes

Clearly, the next question to be answered is whether we can identify the characteristic ecological conditions for each of these competitive regimes. Strong competition within groups, be it through WGS or WGC, is generally predicated on group cohesiveness: the continuous close presence of conspecifics automatically exacerbates competition for food. Among primates, the occurrence of cohesive groups is clearly associated with high vulnerability to predators (see above). Thus, arboreal primates of small body size and (semi-)terrestrial primates of all but the largest body size form groups that are usually fairly cohesive.

Conversely, as predation risk decreases, animals tend to live in groups that are much less cohesive and often split up in parties of variable size and composition (see, for example, van Schaik & van Hooff 1983; Terborgh & Janson 1986). Party size in such fission—fusion groups varies directly with food supply and patch size, and thus inversely with the potential within-party competition (see, for example, McFarland Symington 1988). Thus, within-group competition is clearly limited in these species with a fission—fusion type of social organization.

Strong BGC should occur when it is both necessary due to a high population density relative to the environment's carrying capacity (K) and possible, i.e.

Table 1. The eight possible (1–8) and four realized (A–D) competitive regimes amongst non-human primates (S = strong, W = weak effect on net food intake). See text for full explanation

Possible combinations	1	2	3	4	5	6	7	8
Within-group scramble	S	W	S	S	W	W	S	W
Within-group contest	W	S	S	W	W	S	S	W
Between-group contest	W	W	W	S	S	S	S	W
Realized combination	A	B	B	C	D			

when groups or societies are able to defend territories against their neighbours or to at least defend the access to valuable food sources.

This allows us to characterize the ecological conditions conducive to each competitive regime (see Table 2 for a summary). First, type A (predominance of WGS) is expected among those primates living in cohesive groups that rely on cryptic insects or foliage rather than fruit or whose food occurs in patches large enough to feed all group members. Second, type B (predominance of WGC) is expected among those primates living in cohesive groups whose food is distributed in clear-cut patches that are usually too small to accommodate all group members. Types C and D (strong BGC with and without strong WGS, respectively) are expected where primates live at a high density relative to K and have defensible resources or where the population density is lower but the resources are (at least seasonally) distributed in rare, but large patches. Unfortunately, although food does play a role in limiting primate population (see, for example, Anon. 1981), little is known about the role of other factors. For instance, high rates of density-independent mortality generally lead to population levels well below K. They can be caused by periods in which only low-quality food is available or the weather is inclement, either or both of which may lead to very narrow energetic margins and occasionally mass-starvation (see, for example, Milton 1982). Also, in at least some species, predators may take more than just the 'doomed surplus', destined to die from starvation.

For type C groups we thus require either cohesive groups occurring at a high density, or cohesive groups with food distribution in rare, scattered, but large, patches. We simply do not know how frequently the first combination of factors occurs under natural conditions. The second condition might apply to species that specialize on larger fruit trees, for example strangling figs, and forage for scattered food items in between.

Type D (strong BGC only) occurs when primates form groups of flexible party size that are nonetheless able to defend their range or high quality food sources against neighbouring groups. Such a condition may arise in two different kinds of species: (i) those of intermediate or large body size and a safe lifestyle, and (ii) those that are living in a predator-poor environment. The first condition is found among large primates (more than c. 30 kg) that are semi-terrestrial and forest-living, and among primates of perhaps more than c.8 kg liv-

392

Table 2. Competitive regimes and ecological conditions in diurnal primates

Competitive regime	Type	Vulnerability to predators	Food distribution	Population density (N)	BGC potential
Strong within-group scramble only	A	High	Dispersed, or clumps>GS^o	N<K^t, or [N≈K and Low]	
Strong within-group contest only	B	High	clumped, clumps<GS	N<K, or [N≈K and Low]	
Strong within-group scramble and strong between-group contest	C	Intermediate/ high	Dispersed, or clumps>GS	N≈K	Highs
				or	
			Scattered clumps>GS	N<K	High
Strong between-group contest only	D	Low	Clumped	N≈K	High

^{GSo} = group size.

^{Kt} = carrying capacity.

ing entirely in the canopy that are too large for the monkey-eating raptors. This size threshold could be lower for exclusively arboral primates living in Asia, where large raptors are absent. The second condition is found among primates of intermediate to large body size (more than c. 3–6 kg; depending on degree of terrestriality) living on oceanic islands, where carnivores and large raptors are characteristically absent (see also Sondaar 1977).

We shall treat the two cases in turn; first, the situation when within-group competition is strong and, next, the one in which between-group competition prevails.

FEMALE RELATIONSHIPS WHERE WITHIN-GROUP COMPETITION IS STRONG

Theory

Social relationships Let us now examine the social relationships expected under the first two competitive regimes, namely WGS alone and WGC plus WGS (types A and B). In a food contest situation, dominance rank (i.e. the ability to supplant other group members from resources) affects net food intake and so birth rate. Hence, dominance relationships will be consistent (i.e. aggression in a dyad is directed primarily from one partner to the other) and primarily transitive (i.e. the dominance hierarchy will tend to be linear or 'steep'). Since rank is so important, females who give agonistic support to maturing and adult relatives, in order to help them outrank other females, raise their inclusive fitness. Thus, the hierarchy will become nepotistic, because daughters will, as they mature, obtain ranks close to their mothers (Fig. 2). Ranks among adults will also tend to be stable because (i) relatives support each other, so that temporary variations in individual fighting power are not translated into rank changes, and (ii) the importance of rank to reproductive success (RS) will make animals very reluctant to give it up without escalated fights, (thus) making challenges to established higher-ranking group members risky (cf. Parker 1974).

In a food scramble situation a female's RS depends primarily on group size, and aggression over food is not often effective in increasing it. There is so little advantage to supporting female kin in attaining high rank that relatives do not support each other and agonistic coalitions are very rare. There may be short-lasting or context-dependent social advantages to dominance, for instance when it allows a female to protect young infants or to immigrate into a group. Dominance relationships will consequently be relatively unstable and inconsistent (i.e. within dyads there is a low asymmetry in the direction of aggression), and the dominance hierarchy will be weakly differentiated or 'shallow' and not necessarily linear. It is easier to recognize social strata than exact rank positions. These hierarchies will be individualistic, since in contrast to the nepotistic situation adult relatives need not occupy adjacent ranks (Fig. 2). The difference between the social effects of the scramble and contest situation are summarized in Table 3.

Let us now turn to the question of migration by females: how often and in which patterns should females decide to emigrate from their natal group? We assume that populations are relatively stable and at some level below K. In the food contest situation emigration by individual females from groups that have reached a size well over the optimum should be rare. First, as shown by many experimental studies, a lone immigrant female invariably enters at the bottom of the hierarchy, because she has the double disadvantage of having to enter a new group and to fight alone against female coalitions. Second, without relatives she has no prospects of ever rising in rank, while there is some likelihood for this to occur in her lifetime if she remains with relatives (cf. Gouzoules, Gouzoules & Fedigan 1982). Hence, only low-ranking females without relatives are expected to emigrate. However, when the shortfall in RS relative to a small group becomes too great low-ranking females could emigrate together with relatives, either to set up their own group or to join existing groups. Because such female clusters threaten the rank positions of the incumbents if they migrate into an existing group, they are most likely to set up their own small group. Thus, if groups grow too large, they will often shrink by group splitting rather than by losing single female members.

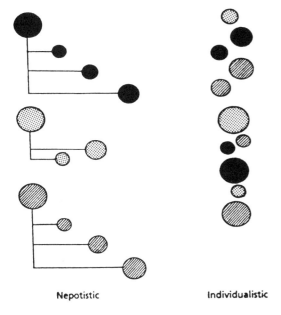

Nepotistic   Individualistic

Figure 2. A schematic representation of a typical nepotistic (left) and a typical individualistic (right) female hierarchy. Size of the circles corresponds to female age; relatives have similar shading.

In a food scramble situation, a female's RS depends on the size of the group she is in, regardless of whom she is with. This in itself is sufficient to lower the emigration threshold for females, since there is no social incentive to stay, unless other factors interfere (e.g. infanticide avoidance through female coalitions). Neither will there be pressure to emigrate together with relatives. Thus, whenever a female finds herself in a group well above or below the optimal size she should be willing to move, provided that migration costs (m) are not prohibitively high. The value of m depends on the risk of predation outside a group, and the ease of settling in existing groups or of finding others with whom to found a new group. We are assuming that there is space available, that females can reduce the risk of predation by teaming up with other females and can easily found new groups or enter existing ones, since group sizes are generally small.

Emigrants are most likely to be young females, for if a female moves into a group in which she can attain a higher birth rate, her benefit will be larger the earlier in her career she moves. If the expected increase in RS by migration exceeds m, females should migrate. However, it is important to note that WGS predicts conditional natal dispersal by females, not obligatory emigration. The proportion of migrants should depend on population growth, it being higher during phases of strong increase or decrease. Thus, within a given species, it should be possible to find some populations with a predominance of female residence and other with high rates of female dispersal.

Where females live in cohesive groups, in which they scramble, but also derive a net benefit from defending their range or food sources against other groups (type C), a slight change in social structure is expected. If females perform an essential role in between-group conflicts and have to perform cooperative attacks on other groups, they should prefer kin as allies (Wrangham 1980). Thus, females are expected to remain in their natal group in this case.

In conclusion, two interrelated factors determine the nature of female social structure, namely the type of food competition and the relatedness among the females. Table 4 shows the expected female social structure under the various regimes. This classification is only consistent in part with the FB versus non-FB dichotomy (Wrangham 1980). Type B clearly corresponds to the FB category.

Table 3. A summary of female social behaviour in primate groups experiencing either within-group scramble or within-group contest (+ scramble) competition

	Female social relationships	
	Within-group scramble	Within-group contest (+ scramble)
Female reproductive success depends on:	Group size	(Group size +) dominance rank
Displacements over food	Rare	Common
Spontaneous' aggression	Rare	Common
Agonistic support by relatives	Rare	Common
Dominance relationships	Inconsistent	Unidirectional
Stability of ranks	Low	High
Dominance hierarchy	Non-linear, egalitarian, individualistic	Linear, despotic, nepotistic
Groups mainly change by	Female migrations	Group splitting

Dominance relationships are consistent, transitive and stable, giving rise to dominance hierarchies that are steep and linear ('despotic', see Vehrencamp 1983). In type A dominance relations are weakly consistent, often intransitive and relatively unstable over time, giving rise to dominance hierarchies that are weakly linear and shallow ('egalitarian'). Thus, type A corresponds to the non-FB category, but only if the females are the dispersing sex. If they remain resident, they would probably form grooming bonds, albeit weak ones. Type C groups, if they occur, would be intermediate between FB and non-FB, because females are expected to form grooming bonds in an egalitarian hierarchy.

An important prediction is that the combination of strong WGC and female natal dispersal should be extremely rare, only occurring if a factor other than food exerts an overriding selective pressure towards female dispersal.

Species experiencing different kinds of within-group food competition are also expected to differ with respect to patterns in aggression, allomothering, sex differences in juvenile mortality, and female life history. These predictions are still to be worked out in detail.

Scramble or contest for safety Where there is a large variance in predation risk depending on the position in the group, we may expect contest for these positions, which will usually not involve overt agonistic behaviour. Females may increase their safety by being surrounded by as many others as possible, or by being close to certain individuals that are able to deter predators. Marginal predation (Hamilton 1971) is probably most important to terrestrial primates living in large groups on open plains. Thus, in savannah-living yellow baboons (*Papio cynocephalus*) high-ranking females tend to be in the centre (Collins 1984). It is probably less important among arboreal forest primates where groups are often

Table 4. A summary of female social structure in cohesive multifemale primate groups.

Type	Competition for food	Females resident (grooming bonds)	Hierarchy despotic/ egalitarian	Nepotistic/ individualistic	Examples (tentative)
A	Within-group* scramble	+ or −	Egalitarian	Individual	*Gorilla(?)*, some spp. of *Saimiri, Colobus, Alouatta, Presbytis*
B	Within-group contest	+	Despotic	Nepotistic	Several spp. of *Macaca Cercopithecus, Papio, Cebus, Cacajao, Chiropotes, Lemur catta,* etc.
C	Within-group scramble + within-group contest	+	Egalitarian	Individualistic	Some *Presbytis* spp.?
D	Between-group contest	+	Egalitarian	Nepotistic	*Macaca nigra* group *Pan paniscus* (?)

*Competition for safety also of the scramble type, otherwise groups should turn into type B groups.

small and where, due to the greater cover, predators can approach the group from more directions. However, among species living in larger and less compact groups, females may still contest for the safer positions, as in wedge-capped and brown capuchins (*Cebus olivaceus*: Robinson 1981; Janson 1985). Where groups fission at times of food scarcity, there should be contest for membership of the largest party, as in long-tailed macaques (*Macaca fascicularis*: van Noordwijk van Schaik 1987). Females living in small groups in open areas, may contest for proximity to the much larger adult male, as in geladas (*Theropithecus gelada*: Dunbar 1980) and hamadryas baboons (Sigg 1980).

Among species in which within-group competition for food is mainly by scramble but competition for safety is by contest, we should expect a social structure closer to the contest than to the scramble type, although rank inheritance may become imperfect as some weak or aging relatives require more support or do not reap sufficient reproductive benefits from the support.

The Primate Evidence

Who scrambles for food? Animals grazing on a continuous vegetation are obviously scrambling for food because a displaced animal does not encounter less food or food of a lower quality. Scramble is also expected where food is dispersed, clumps are small, and handling times are short, so that feeding sites cannot be monopolized, even provided that they can be recognized by the animals. Thus, no rank effect on the net intake of dispersed food is found among vervets (*Cercopithecus aethiops:* Whitten 1983), brown capuchins (Janson 1985), and yellow baboons (Altmann 1980; Post, Hausfater & McCusky 1980). Browsing arboreal folivores may also scramble when the spatial variation in the quality of feeding sites is low, and so displacements are ineffective. This may happen in the lean season when they feed on a poor food supply, and feeding efficiency can be raised by decreasing the costs rather than by increasing the quantity or quality of food. They also scramble when the amount they eat at any given patch is limited by detoxification of secondary compounds, rather than patch size. Unfortunately, no studies have yet examined variation in net food intake among female folivores. By contrast, competition is by contest when the spatial variation in quality of resources is high and clumps can be recognized and are large enough to defend. Then, dominants attain much higher intake rates on fruit (Whitten 1983); Janson 1985) or water (Wrangham 1981). As expected, aggression rates during foraging on dispersed food are far lower than during feeding on clumped food sources (see, for example, Janson 1985). Many authors have noted that food-related displacements are very rare among folivores.

Where feeding competition is by contest, high ranking females should have a higher birth rate than low ranking ones, provided the effect of age is controlled for. Although the relationship between dominance rank and reproductive success has recently received considerable attention in field studies, the complementary behavioural data are often lacking. However, among yellow baboons, food intake and energy budgets are not dependent on dominance rank and neither is birth rate, although age of first reproduction is lower for daughters of high ranking females (Altmann 1980). By contrast, among long-tailed macaques, low ranking females have a less favorable energy budget and also give birth at slightly lower rates than high ranking ones (van Noordwijk & van Schaik 1987). Likewise, when the degree of food clumping changed after provisioning by humans was terminated, the rank effect on birth rates among Japanese macaques (*Macaca fuscata*) decreased (Sugiyama & Ohsawa 1982). Among folivores, rank is often strongly correlated with age, and thus correlations with birth rate may be caused by either of the two. However, RS is often negatively correlated with rank because young, high ranking females lose many of their infants soon after birth in howler monkeys (*Alouatta palliata:*) Jones 1980; Clarke & Glander 1984) and in langurs (*Presbytis entellus:* Hrdy 1977; Dolhinow, McKenna & vonder Haar Laws 1979).

Primate female hierarchies and dispersal Because the bonding among female depends on their dispersal tendency we shall first review the effects that scrambling has on female emigration, and then the effects it has on female social relationships.

Natal emigration by single females has been recorded in many well-studied species, but female emigration is far more common among arboreal folivores than among species with other diets (Moore 1984; Pusey & Packer 1987). Female emigration is also common in Costa Rican squirrel monkeys (*Saimiri oerstedi*), which are strongly insectivorous (Boinski 1987). In a number of folivores all females usually emigrate from their natal group, an evolutionary development perhaps made possible by the lower migration threshold for females in scramble conditions. Although female emigration is rare among gregarious non-folivores, group splitting has often been reported in fast growing populations. These groups all tend to split along matrilinies (see Moore 1984). Single female emigrants are either returning to their natal group from a group that broke away from it (references in Rasmussen 1981; unpublished observations) or are, as expected, females without relatives in the group (see, for example, Sugiyama & Ohsawa 1982). By contrast, among folivores, group splitting is rare compared with emigration by single females, but when it occurs is usually related to takeovers, i.e. social events (see, for example, Sugiyama 1967; Davies 1984). In fast growing population of folivorous howler monkeys, high rates of female emigration and immigration are reported, but group splitting is not (Clark & Glander 1984; Crockett 1984).

Nepotistic ranking systems, well-defined female relationships, and a linear dominance hierarchy form a cluster of interrelated traits found in a great variety of diurnal, gregarious non-folivorous cercopithecines (Hinde 1983), at least one cebid (brown capuchins, Janson, personal communication) and even lemurs (*Lemur catta*: Taylor & Sussman 1985). The individualistic ranking system, with generally unstable ranks, poorly defined relationships and a frequent lack of linearity of the dominance hierarchy, is found among Costa Rican squirrel monkeys (S. Boinski, personal communication) and among many folivores of various taxonomic affinity which do not live in open areas: langurs, colobus, howlers, sifakas (*Propithecus* spp., and gorillas (Jay 1965); Dunbar & Dunbar 1976; Oates 1977; Dolhinow, McKenna & vonder Haar Laws 1979; Harcourt 1979; Jones 1980; Davies 1984), regardless of whether they are close relatives or not. There exists appreciable variation in the strength of grooming bonds, which, at least in the cases where this is known, depends on genetic relatedness among the females. It is my impression that where females remain in their natal groups, grooming bonds are less strong in individualistic than in nepotistic societies, but quantitative comparisons are sorely needed.

Gregarious primates that scramble for food but may contest for safety were expected to be intermediate. Hamadryas females tend to disperse from their natal groups, contrary to expectation. In geladas high ranking females can monopolize access to the large harem male; the females have a peculiar ranking system in which relatives often occupy adjacent ranks but young females rank highest within families (Dunbar 1980). Although savannah baboons follow the rules of the nepotistic ranking system, Moore (1978) remarked that these rules seemed to be less rigid than among macaques.

FEMALE RELATIONSHIPS WHEN COMPETITION
IS MAINLY BETWEEN GROUPS

Theory

Females experiencing low predation risk form less cohesive groups, if they form groups at all, and may tend to live at high densities. Hence, competition between groups or societies will turn into BGC whenever food sources are defensible. Since females are most directly affected by feeding competition (cf. Wrangham 1979), their social relationships should in this situation reflect the effects of BGC.

First, let us consider the situation that females can still form groups, even though these are often fissioned into parties. In the latter case, these parties should at least occasionally be able to coalesce and have contests with other groups or societies over access to prime food sources that are big enough to accommodate many or all group members. Female groups for BGC may be expected where large primates of low vulnerability to predators specialize on food that occurs in patches of variable size, but at least sometimes big enough to allow for sizeable female parties. They should also be expected on oceanic islands or other situations without large predators; these primates will generally be smaller and therefore be more likely to maintain groups on a fruit supply of a given mean patch size than larger species.

What social relationships should prevail among the females that cooperatively defend their range or access to prime food sources? We assume that females play an essential role in the defence and do not leave the task entirely to the males even though (some of) the latter are expected to take part as well. We further assume that the number of participating females is an important determinant of the outcome of the contest. We can note two things. First, in more or less cohesive groups strong BGC almost inevitably would imply strong WGC. This might prompt subordinates to leave the group and parasitize on the group's defence of the food, or to refrain from joining in the contests but still harvest some of the fruits of their labour. An alternative option that is even more damaging to the remaining group members would be to join another group and increase its contest power. Thus, the subordinates can force the dominants not to exert to the full their power to suppress the subordinates' food intake through WGC. This leads to female dominance hierarchies that are becoming fairly egalitarian rather than despotic (cf. Vehrencamp 1983; *pace* Wrangham 1980), despite the potential for great fitness differences within the group.

Second, females should prefer relatives as alliance partners (Wrangham 1980), because an alliance with kin is a greater contribution to inclusive fitness than one with non-kin (especially if this would imply that they are directed against kin) and because they are more stable in the long run (since defection against kin is more costly). Hence, female residence will be the most likely outcome, and the dominance hierarchy will be nepotistic (due to the small WGC that can remain) but egalitarian (type D in Table 4). Obviously, if groups exist

Table 5. A summary of female social structure when female diurnal primates forage alone or in ephemeral parties

Range defence feasible for:			
females	+	−	−
males	+	+	−
Social system	Monogamy/resource defence polygony	Fission-fusion society	Semi-solitary lifestyle
Female social structure	Resident, nepotistic despotic	Non-resident, individualistic, despotic	Resident, nepotistic, despotic
Examples	Gibbons (*Hylobates* spp.)	Chimpanzee (*Pan troglodytes*)	Orang-utan (*Pongo pygmaeus*)

Applicable only to polygynous situation

whose food supply leads to WGS but yet allows for BGC through defence of feeding areas (territories), then social relationships should be of type C (see Table 4).

It is difficult to predict whether a gradual increase in BGC relative to WGC should lead to a gradual or to a sudden change towards an egalitarian system, but I suspect intermediate situations would show intermediate ranking systems.

When females no longer form cohesive groups, the range of outcomes is quite large. This is because the role of males in the female social structure can no longer be ignored. So far we dealt with cohesive groups of females, and the almost universal male strategy in response to female groups among primates is female defence polygyny (cf. Emlen & Oring 1977). When females are more dispersed, among primates the optimal male strategy is most likely to shift to resource defence polygyny, thus the establishment of territories by males, either alone or in alliance with other males.

Table 5 depicts the expected outcomes for the situation when the potential within-group competition leads to females being basically solitary for some or most of their time. They are still expected to defend their range against other females. Likewise, males are expected to become territorial among each other (cf. Wrangham 1979). Thus, various outcomes ensue depending on whether females and males, only males, or neither of the sexes can defend their range. It is impossible to give generalizations about the ecological conditions in which each of these outcomes is expected, although the size of food patches relative to female size, their density and the mobility of both males and females are clearly involved.

Yet, in all cases there will be some pressure towards female residence, either because mothers can assist their daughters in setting up a territory, or because they can share (part of) their range with daughters and tolerate them or even form alliances when food sources are available that can hold several individuals.

If both males and females can defend a territory, the result is either monogamy or resource defense polygyny, depending on how strong the advantage to the female of services by the male can be (see Table 5). If a single male can defend a range, while females cannot profitably do so and thus share it with other females, the result will be a nepotistic and despotic hierarchy among females who rarely meet. Alternatively, only a group of males is able to defend a territory containing a number of dispersed females. These males are likely to be relatives for the same reason as cooperatively defending female groups are. Groups of related males are formed most readily when maturing males remain in their natal area, and this provides strong pressure towards female natal emigration. Hence, dominance hierarchies among the females are expected to be individualistic, while still despotic. Finally, when neither males nor females can defend their range, discrete societies may disappear altogether. However, females may still benefit from staying near their natal range if mothers selectively tolerate their daughters or even form alliances with them if occasionally coalitions for access to food sources are possible, i.e. groups can be maintained for some time.

The Primate Evidence

Very few primates have been studied on oceanic islands. Some data are available on the macaques off the Sunda shelf. It is interesting to note that, where densities are known, they are very high (MacKinnon, MacKinnon & Chivers 1979; van Schaik & van Noordwijk 1985), consistent with the prediction. What little is known about their social behaviour supports the theory. Group size is clearly smaller than of comparable species in similar habitats on the Sunda shelf (MacKinnon et al. 1979; Whitten & Whitten 1982; van Schaik & van Noordwijk 1985), and groups are often fragmented into small parties, which in the case of the Simuleue macaques also have different composition than among their Sumatran counterparts. Sulawesi macaques have a social structure that is dramatically more egalitarian than that of other macaques (Thierry 1985). Although the aggression frequencies are not so low as among folivores, there is often symmetric aggression within dyads, resulting in inconsistent dominance relationships. In addition, the tension caused by agonistic interactions is defused by very frequent reconciliation behaviour. Aggression is often redirected towards non-group members. In contrast to all other macaques living in multimale groups (cf. Herzog & Hohmann 1984), the males in these species have loud inter-group vocalizations, which suggests that BGC is important (Whitten & Whitten 1982; van Schaik & van Noordwijk 1985; Watanabe & Brotoisworo 1982). Physical attacks are most common during inter-group conflicts (Watanabe & Brotoisworo 1982).

The variability in social organization among large species with low vulnerability to predation is clearly greater than among the vulnerable species. For example, all possible outcomes expected by the above considerations are found among the apes (see Table 4 and 5). Thus, female bonobos (*Pan paniscus*) form parties of varying sizes that may serve to cooperatively defend food sources and to which males attach themselves temporarily (White, this volume); gibbons are largely monogamous and territorial; among chimpanzees females are more or less solitary while cooperative groups of males defend a range; orang-utans (*Pongo pygmaeus*) are semi-solitary, and neither males nor females can maintain exclusive ranges. Gorillas, however, do not fit into this scheme, because unrelated females tend to form cohesive groups around a single adult male. More detailed discussion of ape social structure and their ecological determinants is provided by Wrangham (1979, 1986), van Schaik & van Hooff (1983), Rodman (1984) and Dunbar (1988).

DISCUSSION

Within-Group Competition

WGS is predicted to give rise to female social relationships that are very different from those found under WGC conditions. The main distinction is the one between an individualistic egalitarian, and often non-FB ranking system and a nepotistic, despotic, FB one. An individualistic, despotic system is not expected to occur among primates. Such a system should obtain where animals in a contest situation have a short lifespan (no maternal support possible) or female dispersal is enforced by some other factor.

Arboreal folivores fit into the scramble pattern with regard to their egalitarian and individualistic social structure. Although the crucial test (measuring the effect of rank on female food intake) has not yet been performed, they also show very low rates of food-related aggression, no relationship between rank and RS, and their groups do not often split. The occurrence of very much the same pattern in the strongly insectivorous Costa Rican squirrel monkey suggests that it is not taxonomy or folivory *per se* that is responsible for this pattern.

Although the theory developed here is the only one proposed so far to account for this whole range of characters, several alternative hypotheses have been proposed to explain some of the differences in female relationships treated here. We shall consider them in turn. Hrdy (1977), refers to the WGS type dominance hierarchy as an altruistic one, which is found in harem systems with a high mean and a low variance in genetic relatedness among the females. Older females gain in inclusive fitness by giving up their ranks in favor of younger close relatives with higher expected future reproductive output whether these are daughters or not. Younger females thus outrank older, much heavier females. This argument assumes that it is the harem system rather than scramble competition that gave rise to the individualistic ranking system. If so, we can predict that this altruistic ranking system should also be found in other harem-living species regardless of diet but should not occur among folivores in multi-male groups, or in harems of immigrant females. Unfortunately, it is not clear whether other non-folivorous harem-living guenons (*Cercopithecus* spp.) have nepotistic ranking systems (Cords 1986) but harem-living geladas have some form of nepotistic ranking system (Dunbar 1980). The female hierarchies of langurs or other folivores (e.g. howlers) do not seem to differ where groups are multi-male (Jay 1965) or where females are immigrants (Jones 1980; cf. Sigg 1980). Thus, the comparative data do not support this hypothesis.

An alternative interpretation for the lack of female agonistic support to maturing daughters among folivores would be that they are incapable of it due to early senescence. Although folivore females may show earlier senescence, this possibility does not seem to be correct, because aging langur females who are low-ranking among the females are the most vigorous in defending the group against external threats such as other groups, predators and infanticidal males (Hrdy 1977), and not even middle-aged females are observed to support their (sub) adult daughters.

A simpler variation of this theme is that folivores refrain from aggression because the narrow energetic margins allowed by a folivores existence necessitated the evolution of non-damaging conflict resolution (Jones 1980). Many authors have indeed ascribed the low levels of aggression among folivores to their diet. However, although high costs of aggression would raise the threshold of escalated fighting, they do not preclude the development of consistent dominance relationships within a dyad or of linear dominance hierarchies. Moreover, damaging fights are quite common among male folivores contesting access to the breeding group (see, for example, Sugiyama 1967; Crockett 1984). Thus, when a resource can be contested folivores are quite capable of escalated fights just like other mammals.

Competition Between Groups

One of the key points of this chapter is that BGC has not exerted a significant effect on female social relationships in most of the smaller gregarious primate species (*pace* Wrangham 1980). Yet, the primate literature is replete with accounts of between-group conflicts among several of these very species. How can this paradox be resolved? First, it is possible that BGC, although groups often meet, does not have any strong quantitative effects (cf. Janson 1985). Second, BGC may be an important component of food competition without having a strong effect on social relationships. Obviously, strong BGC does not radically change female relationships where within-group competition is by scramble, but it also need not always do this where within-group competition is by contest. For instance, as a result of female preferences for males that defend the food supply (cf. Smuts 1987), males may play the decisive role in interactions between groups in species with considerable sexual dimorphism in body size and canine length. At present, our knowledge of the role of males is mainly anecdotal. Finally, recent increases in population density may have caused an increased BGC, without, however, immediately changing the female social relationships since these largely represent evolved adaptations rather than direct behavioural choices. We would, for instance, expect not all females to be equally involved in between-group contest in such species, but rather that high-ranking females are most heavily involved since they derive the greatest benefits in a type B social structure. This is in fact found among the vervet monkeys of Amboseli (Cheney 1987), which is the only vervet population studied to date in which females actively participate in between-group conflicts. It is also inhabiting a shrinking habitat, and may thus live at a density that is larger than the carrying capacity, a situation likely to give rise to strict territoriality.

BGC may be the predominant mode in a group of species that are of small or intermediate body size, and thus clearly vulnerable to predators, and live in relatively small groups, yet seem to have relationships that were hypothesized to reflect a predominance of BGC. Known examples include white-fronted capuchins (*Cebus albifrons:* Janson 1986) and stump-tailed macaques (*Macaca arctoides:* de Waal, this volume). However, it is possible that here WGC is strongly reduced because they rely on large fruit trees to which access is communally defended. As Janson & van Schaik (1988) note, above a certain patch size contest seem to be reduced, and the intake of all individuals tends to be similar (cf. Janson 1985). Since at least white-fronted capuchins are known to specialize on large fig trees, this may account for the apparent predominance of BGC effects on their social relationships. However, nothing is known about stump-tailed macaques in the wild.

Testing the Framework

Obviously, even the most ingenious theory will not make correct predictions for all primate species, and the present framework is bound to have its exceptions in cases where other factors override the social effects of competition for food or safety. It is not difficult to find cases that are seemingly at odds with the framework. We should, however, be aware that some of those may merely represent intermediate situations, which should of course predominate in nature rather than the extreme competitive regimes I considered here. For instance, the possible lack of strongly differentiated female relationships among guenons noted by Cords (1987), may perhaps be due to the relatively strong BGC component. Likewise, Srikosomatara & Robinson (1986) found an important effect of between-group competition among Venezuelan wedge-capped capuchins, although WGC is not negligible. In most cases, we simply do not know enough about the competitive regime of a species to decide, and the question is evidently how to test the framework. What we need are detailed field studies on a single species in which the competitive regime is characterized by precise estimates of the strength of the three components of food competition and on reproductive rates and survival or female fitness (see Janson & van Schaik 1988 for methods) and in which contest for safety is estimated. These data should then be compared with data on female social relationships: female dispersal or residence, consistency and stability of dominance relationships, linearity of the hierarchy, occurrence of grooming bonds, and coalitions and the female role in between-group conflicts.

Within species, there is usually a strong relationship between the density of a population and the occurrence of aggressive encounters between groups (Cheney (1987). Thus, there may be problems with testing the framework where recent ecological changes have led to increased population densities and thus to an increased importance of BGC. After all, for a proper assessment one needs to study the species at the density that prevailed during most of its evolutionary history.

Primate populations under study often increase, because the continuous presence of the researchers discourages hunting by natural predators, or because the latter are disappearing from nature reserves and parks due to human pressure and island-effects. Such recent increases in population densities may be responsible for some of the discrepancies between theory and observation. The high female emigration rates among the red howlers (*Alouatta seniculus*) observed by Crockett (1984) may also be an indication of high population growth, rather than a typical feature of the species. Likewise, the competition for group membership observed by Jones (1980) in a population of mantled howlers (*A. palliata*) inhabiting an isolated forest patch may reflect unusual crowding. Female residence, nepotistic hierarchies and group splitting would seem a much more plausible adaptive response to such conditions.

Changes in the distribution of food may also affect the results. The village langurs studied by Hrdy (1977) had more consistent and stable dominance relationships than those found among langurs in forested areas (see, for example, Jay 1965; Sugiyama 1967).

These reservations are clearly speculative. However, if they are substantiated, it means that testing the relationships proposed here will be increasingly difficult because the pristine habitats this requires are rapidly disappearing.

ACKNOWLEDGEMENTS

I thank Charles Janson, Willem Netto, Ronald Noë, Maria van Noordwijk, Han de Vries, and in particular Jan van Hooff for helpful discussion, Sandy Harcourt, and the editors for comments on the manuscript, Sue Boinski for allowing me to cite her unpublished data, and Greg Grether for linguistic advice. During the writing of this chapter the author held a senior fellowship of the Royal Netherlands Academy of Arts and Sciences.

REFERENCES

Altmann, J. (1980). *Baboon Mothers and Infants*. Harvard University Press, Cambridge, Massachusetts.

Anonymous (1981). *Techniques for the Study of Primate Population Ecology*. National Academy Press, Washington D.C.

Boinski, S. (1987). Mating patterns in squirrel monkeys (*Saimiri oerstedi*), implications for seasonal sexual dimorphism. *Behavioral Ecology and Sociobiology*, **21**, 13–21.

Cheney, D.L. (1987). Interactions and relationships between groups. *Primate Societies* (Ed. by B.B. Smuts, D.L. Cheney, R.M. Seyfarth, R.W. Wrangham & T.T. Struhsaker), pp. 267–81. Chicago University Press, Chicago, Illinois.

Clarke, M.R. & Glander, K.E. (1984). Female reproductive success in a group of free-ranging howler monkeys (*Alouatta palliata*) in Costa Rica. *Female Primates* (Ed. by M.F. Small), pp. 111–26, Alan Liss, New York.

Collins, D.A. (1984). Spatial pattern in a troop of yellow baboons (*Papio cynocephalus*) in Tanzania. *Animal Behaviour*, **32**, 536–53.

Cords, M. (1987). Forest guenons and patas monkeys: male-male competition in one-male groups. *Primate Societies* (Ed. by B.B. Smuts, D.L. Cheney, R.M. Seyfarth, R.W. Wrangham & T.T. Struhsaker), pp. 98–111, Chicago University Press, Chicago, Illinois.

Crockett, C.M. (1984). Emigration by female red howler monkeys and the case for female competition. *Female Primates* (Ed. by M.F. Small), pp. 159–73, Alan Liss, New York.

Davies, A.G. (1984). An ecological study of the red lead monkey (*Presbytis rubicunda*) in the dipterocarp forest of northern Borneo. Ph.D. thesis, University of Cambridge.

Dolhinow, P., McKenna, J.J. & vonder Haar Laws, J. (1979). Rank and reproduction among female langur monkeys: Aging and improvement (They're not just getting older, they're getting better). *Aggressive Behavior*, **5**, 19–30.

Dunbar, R.I.M. (1980). Determinants and evolutionary consequences of dominance among female gelada baboons. *Behavioural Ecology and Sociobiology*, **7**, 253–65.

Dunbar, R.I.M. (1988). *Primate Social Systems*. Croom Helm, Beckenham.

Dunbar, R.I.M. & Dunbar E.P. (1976). Contrasts in social structure among black-and-white colobus groups. *Animal Behaviour*, **24**, 84–92.

Emlen, S.T. & Oring. I.W. (1977). Ecology, sexual selection, and the evolution of mating systems. *Science*, **197**, 215–23.

Goodall, J. (1985). *The Chimpanzees of Gombe, Patterns of Behavior*. Harvard University Press, Cambridge, Massachusetts.

Gouzoules, H., Gouzoules, S. & Fedigan, L. (1982). Behavioural dominance and reproductive success in female Japanese monkeys (*Macaca fuscata*). *Animal Behaviour*, **30**, 1138–50.

Hamilton W.D. (1971). Geometry for the selfish herd. *Journal of Theoretical Biology*, **31**, 295–311.

Harcourt, A.H. (1979). Social relationships among adult female mountain gorillas. *Animal Behaviour*, **27**, 251–64.

Herzog, M.O. & Hahmann, G.M. (1984). Male loud calls in *Macaca silenus* and *Presbytis johnii*; a comparison. *Folia primatologica*, **43**, 189–97.

Hinde, R.A. (1983). *Primate Social Relationships, an Integrated Approach*. Blackwell Scientific Publications, Oxford.

Hrdy, S.B. (1977). The Langurs of Abu. Harvard University Press, Cambridge, Massachusetts.

Janson, C.H. (1985). Aggressive competition and individual food consumption in wild brown capuchin monkeys (*Cebus apella*). *Behavioral Ecology and Sociobiology*, **18**, 125–38.

Janson, C.H. (1986). The mating system as a determinant of social evolution in capuchin monkeys (*Cebus*). *Primate Ecology and Conservation* (Ed. by J.R. Else & P. Lee), pp. 169–79. Cambridge University Press, Cambridge.

Janson, C.H. & Schaik, C.P van (1988). Recognizing the many faces of primate food competition in primates: methods. *Behaviour*, **105**, 165–86.

Jay, P.C. (1965). The common langur of north India. *Primate Behavior* (Ed. by I. DeVore), pp. 197–249. Holt, Rinehart & Winston, New York.

Jones, C.B. (1980). The functions of status in the mantled howler monkey, *Alouatta palliata* Grav: Intraspecific competition for group membership in a folivorous neotropical primate, *Primates*, **21**, 389–405.

MacKinnon, J.R. MacKinnon, K.S. & Chivers, D.J (1979). The use of forest space by a community of six species in peninsular Malaysia and of one in North Sulawesi. Paper presented at VIIth congress of International Primatological Society, Bangalore, India.

McFarland Symington, M. (1987). *Ecological and social correlates of party size in the black spider monkey (Ateles paniscus chamek)*. Ph.D. thesis, Princeton University.

McFarland Symington, M. (1988). Food competition and foraging party size in the black spider monkey, *Ateles paniscus chamek. Behaviour*, **105**, 117–34.

Milton, K. (1982). Dietary quality and demographic regulation in a howler monkey population. *The Ecology of a Tropical Forest* (Ed. by E.G. Leigh, Jr. A.S. Rand, & D.M. Windsor), pp. 273–89. Smithsonian Institution Press, Washington D.C.

Moore, J. (1978). Dominance relations among free-ranging female baboons in Gombe National Park, Tanzania, *Recent advances in primatology, Vol. 1* (Ed. by D.J. Chivers & J. Herbert), pp. 67–70. Academic Press, London.

Moore, J. (1984). Female transfer in primates. *International Journal of Primatology*, **5**, 537–89.

Mori, A. (1979). Analysis of population changes by measurement of body weight in the Koshima troop of Japanese monkeys. *Primates*, **20**, 371–9.

Nicholson, A.J. (1967). Self-adjustment of populations to change. *Cold Spring Harbor Symposia in Quantitative Biology*, **22**, 153–73.

Noordwijk, M.A. van & Schaik, C.P. van (1987). Competition among adult female long-tailed macaques. *Animal Behaviour*, **35**, 577–89.

Oates, J.F. (1977). The social life of the black-and-white colobus monkey, *Colobus guereza. Zeitschrift für Tierpsychologie*, **45**, 1–60.

Parker, G.A. (1974). Assessment strategy and the evolution of fighting behaviour. *Journal of Theoretical Biology*, **47**, 223–43.

Post, D.G. Hausfater, G. McCusky. S.A. (1980). Feeding behavior of yellow baboons (*Papio cynocephalus*): relationship to age, gender and dominance rank. *Folia primatologica*, **34**, 170–95.

Pusey, A.F. & Packer, C. (1987). Dispersal and philopatry. *Primate Societies* (Ed. by B.B. Smuts, D.L. Cheney, R.M. Seyfarth, R.W. Wrangham & T.T. Struhsaker), pp. 250–66. Chicago University Press, Chicago, Illinois.

Rasmussen, D.R. (1981). Communities of baboon troops (*Papio cynocephalus*) in Mikumi National Park, Tanzania. A preliminary report. *Folia Primatologica*, **36**, 232–42.

Robinson, J.G. (1981). Spatial structure in foraging groups of wedge-capped capuchin monkeys *Cebus nigrivittatus. Animal Behaviour*, **29**, 1036–56.

Rodman, P.S. (1984). Foraging and social systems of orangutans and chimpanzees. *Adaptations for Foraging in Nonhuman Primates* (Ed. by P.S. Rodman & J.G.H. Cant), pp. 134–60. Columbia University Press, New York.

Schaik, C.P. van (1983). Why are diurnal primates living in groups? *Behaviour*, **37**, 120–44.

Schaik, C.P. van & Hooff, J.A.R.A.M. van (1983). On the ultimate causes of primate social systems. *Behaviour*, **85**, 91–117.

Schaik, C.P. van & Noordwijk, M.A. van (1985). Evolutionary effect of the absence of felids on the social organization of the macaques on the island of Simeulue (*Macaca fasicularis fusca*, Miller 1903). *Folia Primatologica*, **44**, 138–47.

Sigg, H. (1980). Differentiation of female positions in hamadryas one-male units. *Zeitschrift für Tierpsychologie*, **53**, 265–302.

Silk, J.B. (1987). Social behaviour in evolutionary perspective. *Primate Societies* (Ed. by B.B. Smuts, D.L. Cheney, R.M. Seyfarth, R.W. Wrangham & T.T. Struhsaker), pp. 318–29. Chicago University Press, Chicago, Illinois.

Smuts, B.B (1987). Gender, aggression, and influence. *Primate Societies* (Ed. by B.B. Smuts, D.L. Cheney, R.M. Seyfarth, R.W. Wrangham & T.T. Struhsaker), pp. 400–12. Chicago University Press, Chicago, Illinois.

Sondaar, P.Y. (1977). Insularity and its effect on mammal evolution. *Major Patterns in Vertebrate Evolution* (Ed. by M.K. Hecht, P.O. Goody, & B.M. Hecht), pp. 671–707. Plenum Press, New York.

Srikosamatara, S. & Robinson, J.G. (1986). Group size and use of space in wedge-capped capuchin monkeys. *Primate Report*, **14**, 67.

Suglyama, Y. (1967). Social organization of hanuman langurs. *Social Communication among Primates* (Ed. by S.A. Altmann), pp. 221–36. Chicago University Press, Chicago, Illinois.

Suglyama, Y. & Ohsawa, H. (1982). Population dynamics of Japanese monkeys with special reference to the effect of artificial feeding. *Folia Primatologica*, **39**, 238–63.

Taylor, L. & Sussman, R.W. (1985). A preliminary study of kinship and social organization in a semi-free-ranging group of *Lemur catta*. *International Journal of Primatology*, **6**, 601–14.

Terborgh, J. & Janson, C.H. (1986). The socioecology of primate groups. *Annual Review of Ecology and Systematics*, **17**, 11–135.

Thierry, B. (1985). Patterns of agonistic interactions in three species of macaque (*Macaca mulatta, M. fascicularis, M. tonkeana*). *Aggressive Behavior*, **11**, 223–33.

Vehrencamp, S.L. (1983). A model for the evolution of despotic versus egalitarian societies. *Animal Behaviour*, **31**, 667–82.

Waser, P. (1976). *Cercocebus albigena*: site attachment, avoidance, and intergroup spacing. *American Naturalist*, **110**, 911–35.

Waser, P. & Jones, W.T. (1983). Natal philopatry among solitary mammals. *Quarterly Review of Biology*, **58**, 355–90.

Watanabe, K. & Brotoisworo, E. (1982). Field observations of Sulawesi macaques. Kyoto University Overseas Research Report of Studies on Asian Non-Human Primates, **2**, 3–9.

Whitten, A.J. & Whitten, J.E.J. (1982). Preliminary observations of the Mentawai macaque on Siberut island. Indonesia. *International Journal of Primatology*, **3**, 445–59.

Whitten, P.L. (1983). Diet and dominance among female vervet monkeys (*Cercopithecus aethiops*). *American Journal of Primatology*, **5**, 139–59.

Wrangham, R.W. (1979). On the evolution of ape social systems. *Social Science Information*, **18**, 335–68.

Wrangham, R.W. (1980). An ecological model of female-bonded primate groups. *Behaviour*, **75**, 262–300.

Wrangham, R.W. (1981). Drinking competition in vervet monkeys. *Animal Behaviour*, **29**, 904–10.

Wrangham, R.W. (1987). The evolution of social structure. *Primate Societies* (Ed. by B.B. Smuts, D.L. Cheney, R.M. Seyfarth, R.W. Wrangham & T.T. Struhsaker), pp. 282–96. Chicago University Press, Chicago, Illinois.

An Ecological Model of Female-Bonded Primate Groups

_____ Richard W. Wrangham[1] _____

INTRODUCTION

Most multi-female groups of primates have a similar and remarkably uniform pattern of membership. Females spend their lives in the group where they are born, so that different mothers and their offspring tend to be closely related. Breeding males, on the other hand, are normally immigrants who were born elsewhere (Packer, 1979). This paper proposes a model to explain why in these species groups are based on a core of resident females.

Previous analyses of the evolution of primate groups have typically examined the problem in a different way, focussing on both sexes together rather than on females. The classical approach has been to search for correlations of group size with ecological variables such as habitat or diet type (reviewed by Clutton-Brock & Harvey, 1977b). Such correlations are then used to infer the ultimate causes of group life. For example, since larger groups tend to be found in open habitats, where primates are vulnerable to predation, groups are sometimes considered to have arisen in response to predators (Crook & Gartlan, 1966). Extensive analyses now show that there are many exceptions to correlations such as this, and clear insights on the adaptive significance of groups have therefore not yet emerged. Furthermore there is no explanation of species differences in which sex tends to transfer from its natal group before breeding (Clutton-Brock & Harvey, 1976; Harcourt, 1978; Packer, 1979). As a result Clutton-Brock & Harvey (1977b) suggested that a more useful approach might be to examine the species distribution of individual, rather than group, characteristics.

This is attempted here, using the principle that it is selection pressures on female behaviour which ultimately determine the effect of ecological variables on social systems (Bradbury & Vehrencamp, 1977; Emlen & Oring, 1977; Wrangham, 1979b).

'An Ecological Model of Female-Bonded Primate Groups" by Richard W. Wrangham, _Behavior_ 75: 262–300, 1980. Reprinted with permission of E.J. Brill, Leiden.
1) Barbara Smuts helped throughout the preparation of this paper with suggestions, advice and support. Earlier drafts were improved by comments from J. Altmann, D. Bygott, T. Clutton-Brock, N. Davies, R. Dunbar, J. Hanby, P. Harvey, S. Blaffer-Hrdy, D. Rubenstein, M. Simpson, D. Stein and B. Zimmerman. I am grateful to Bernard Chapais for translating the summary.

In a few primates the system of group membership contrasts strikingly with the commoner pattern of female residence (Harcourt, 1978; Marsh, 1979). In the rarer form, groups consist of distantly related mothers who are themselves immigrants. No attempt is made here to explain the evolution of this latter system, but it is compared with the commoner pattern as a test of the ecological model.

Groups composed of resident females are often termed "matrilocal", but here the term "female-bonded" (FB) is preferred. It has the advantage of avoiding confusion with established anthropological concepts, and it conforms to a classification of primate social systems in terms of social relationships within sexes (Wrangham, in prep.). It also draws attention to an important feature of female-residence systems, which is that females have highly differentiated networks of social relationships within groups, based on grooming, aggression and other interactions. These networks are not found in the other group-living primates and their origin is therefore discussed.

A MODEL OF THE EVOLUTION OF FB GROUPS

1. Conceptual Framework.

The model is based on the principle that evolutionary pressures on social systems can be ordered with respect to the importance of their effects. This follows from considering social systems to be descriptions of sets of social relationships, and social relationships to be the result of innumerable behavioural decisions. These decisions, whether unconscious or conscious, are considered to be taken according to particular strategies. If some strategies influence the selective advantage of other strategies, the nature and direction of this influence is of critical importance.

A strategy is used here to mean a set of decisions which produce behaviour patterns with a particular result: namely, the ultimate probable outcome is to increase the behaver's access to a given resource specific to the strategy. Strategies are assumed to have evolved because they led to maximization of possible inclusive fitness. Clearly a variety of different resources are important in this process. Not all of them are equally important, however, because different resources have different levels of cost-effectiveness in increasing inclusive fitness. (Inclusive fitness is defined as Ego's reproductive value plus the reproductive value of relatives, each devalued by the coefficient of relatedness).

For example, important resources for males include food, safety and mates. For adult males who are ready to breed, however, mates are normally uniquely valuable because effort put into acquiring them yields more babies than effort put into acquiring food or safety. As a result, fertile females are classically considered to be a key resource for breeding males, and strategies for mating and guarding them are thought to be uniquely important in determining the social relationships of males (Darwin, 1871; Williams, 1966; Trivers, 1972).

A similar argument can be applied to females. If breeding females have a uniquely cost-effective resource, a strategy adapted to acquiring it will have uniquely large effects of increasing female reproductive success. It is assumed here that females do have a key resource of this kind, and that their social relationships therefore reflect the strategy for obtaining it. The social system, consequently, is viewed as the ultimate outcome of the interaction of two key strategies, of breeding females and breeding males respectively (Bradbury & Vehrencamp, 1977; Emlen & Oring, 1977; Wrangham, 1979b).

Whatever the key strategy is for females, it is clear that it will normally involve an environmental resource in the first instance; their ability to breed is not usually limited by the availability of mates. The key strategy for males, on the other hand, is access to fertile females. This means that the interaction of female and male strategies must begin by an analysis of the adaptive significance of female strategies. In this paper, following Wrangham (1979b), the key resource for females is assumed to be the amount of food absorbed. Their key strategy, consequently, is their feeding strategy.

2. Characteristics of FB Species.

FB species are defined as those in which females maintain affiliative bonds with other females in their group and normally spend their lives in the group where they are born (or, if the group divides, with females who were born in the same group). This leads to three criteria for defining FB groups. (A group is defined as a set of individuals in a closed social network (Struhsaker, 1969).

First, do females typically breed in their natal groups? Long-term field studies are required to find out whether female residence is the normal pattern, and it has been confirmed by direct observation in only four species (Table 1). Second, since female residence is closely associated with inter-group transfer by males (Packer, 1979), systematic movement of males between groups, together with restricted movement of females, is taken as an adequate criterion of an FB species. This has been confirmed in at least 23 species (Table 1). Third, in species where nothing is known of inter-group transfer or residence patterns, differentiated and consistent female relationships based on grooming, aiding, huddling or dominance interactions are used as evidence of FB groups. Table 1 lists a total of 26 FB species for which field data are available.

In FB primates where known individuals have been studied over many years, a proportion of individuals transferring between groups are females. These are normally uncommon cases against the general trend (Packer, 1979; Jones (in press); Rasmussen, 1979; Rudran, 1979; Hausfater, 1975). However, in at least four species females transfer between groups more commonly than males do and these are therefore classified as "non-female-bonded" (non-FB) (Table 2). In non-FB species transferring females show no tendency to join groups containing familiar females, and successive offspring are not necessarily reared in the same group.

412

Table 1

Species	Common name	FB species		Differentiated female relationships
		Females breed in natal group	Males transfer between groups	
Lemur catta	Ringtailed lemur	?	BUDNITZ & DAINIS, 1975	JOLLY, 1966
Propithecus verreauxi	White sifaka	?	RICHARD, 1974	RICHARD, 1974
Alouatta villosa (palliata)	Mantled howler	?	SCOTT et al., 1978	JONES, in press
Alouatta seniculus	Red howler	?	RUDRAN, 1979	NEVILLE, 1972
Cebus capucinus	White-throated capuchin	?	OPPENHEIMER, 1968	OPPENHEIMER, 1968
Saimiri sciureus	Squirrel monkey	?	BAILEY, pers. comm.	COE & ROSENBLUM, 1974
Cercopithecus aethiops	Vervet monkey	LEE, in prep.	CHENEY, in press	STRUHSAKER, 1967
Cercopithecus ascanius	Redtail monkey	?	STRUHSAKER, 1977	STRUHSAKER & LELAND, 1979
Cercopithecus mitis	Blue monkey	?	RUDRAN, 1978	RUDRAN, 1978
Cercocebus albigena	Gray-cheeked mangabey	?	STRUHSAKER & LELAND, 1979	CHALMERS, 1968
Erythrocebus patas	Patas	?	HALL, 1965	HALL, 1965
Papio anubis	Olive baboon	MOORE, 1978	PACKER, 1979	SMUTS, in prep.
Papio cynocephalus	Yellow baboon	?	HAUSFATER, 1975	HAUSFATER, 1975
Papio ursinus	Chacma baboon	?	?	SEYFARTH, 1976
Theropithecus gelada	Gelada	?	DUNBAR & DUNBAR, 1975	DUNBAR & DUNBAR, 1975
Macaca fuscata	Japanese monkey	ITANI, 1975	SUGIYAMA, 1976a	MORI, 1975
Macaca mulatta	Rhesus monkey	CHEPKO-SADE & SADE 1979	SADE, 1972; LINDBURG, 1969	SADE, 1967
Macaca radiata	Bonnet macaque	?	SIMONDS, 1973	SIMONDS, 1974
Macaca sinica	Toque macaque	?	DITTUS, 1977	?
Macaca sylvanus	Barbary macaque	?	?	TAUB, 1978
Macaca fascicularis	Crab-eating monkey	?	ANGST, 1975	CHANCE et al., 1977
Presbytis entellus	Hanuman langur	?	HRDY, 1977a	HRDY, 1977a
Presbytis johnii	Nilgiri langur	?	POIRIER, 1969	POIRIER, 1969
Presbytis senex	Purple-faced leaf monkey	?	RUDRAN, 1973	?
Colobus guereza	Black-and-white colobus	?	OATES, 1977a	OATES, 1977a

FB species are those in which at least two breeding females travel and forage in the same group, and which meet at least one of the criteria shown. Species for which there are no relevant field data are not included. Females are presumed to breed in their natal groups in all FB species, but they have been observed from birth to motherhood only in the species indicated.

413

TABLE 2

Non-FB species

Species	Common name	Males breed in natal group	Females transfer between groups	Undifferentiated female relationships
Colobus badius	Red colobus	?	Marsh, 1978	Struhsaker & Leland, 1979
Papio hamadryas	Hamadryas baboon	?	Kummer, 1968	Kummer, 1968
Pan gorilla berengei	Mountain gorilla	?	Harcourt, 1978	Harcourt, 1979
Pan troglodytes	Chimpanzee	Pusey, 1979	Nishida, 1979	Goodall, 1968, Nishida, 1979

Non-FB species are those in which at least two breeding females live in the same group without forming long-term affiliative relationships with particular other females. See Table 1.

3. FB Groups as a Paradox.

Given the problem of explaining the adaptive significance of FB relationships in terms of female foraging strategies, the form of FB groups presents a paradox. The fact that FB females travel and feed together implies that the effects of feeding competition should be unimportant, since otherwise females would disperse. Yet group foraging appears to increase energy expenditure (Milton & May, 1976), and aggressive competition over food or feeding sites occurs commonly (*Lemur catta, Propithecus verreauxi,* Sussman & Richard, 1974; *Cebus capucinus,* Klein, 1974; *Cercopithecus aethiops,* Wrangham, in prep.; *Cercopithecus ascanius, Cercopithecus mitis,* Struhsaker & Leland, 1979; *Cercocebus albigena,* Chalmers, 1968; *Erythrocebus patas,* Hall, 1965; *Papio anubis,* Smuts, in prep.; *Macaca sinica,* Dittus, 1977). Furthermore, females in many of these species tend to have stable dominance hierarchies, indicating that low-ranking females feed less well than those of higher rank (Dittus, 1977). Why, then, do lower-ranking females not leave?

The problem is heightened by the fact that females in FB groups are closely related to each other. If group-foraging leads females to compete for food, inclusive fitness theory suggests that relatives should disperse in order to avoid imposing costs on their kin (Hamilton, 1964). In fact, however, the pattern of female dispersion shows clumping of close relatives even within groups (Kurland, 1977).

These facts suggest that FB females face a peculiar set of ecological conditions in which the acceptance of significant levels of feeding competition, imposed on or by close kin, is a necessary part of an optimal foraging strategy.

4. The Advantage of Cooperation.

The proposed solution to the paradox is that the costs of intra-group feeding competition are outweighed by the benefits of cooperating against females in other groups (Fig. 1). Cooperation is defined as behaviour which raises the inclusive fitness of each of the cooperating individuals (who may or may not be related to each other) (Wrangham, in press). According to the model, it is favoured because it grants increased access to the best feeding sites, which are distributed in discrete, defensible patches. Access is achieved by the members of one "group" (*i.e.* set of cooperators) helping each other to supplant other individuals or groups from the preferred food patch. Competition within the group is then a disadvantageous side-effect.

The principle is shown in Fig. 1, where the advantages to two, initially solitary, females of forming an alliance are illustrated. The same process forces all females to find allies in order not to be supplanted by those of lower competitive ability. At food patches containing more than two feeding sites larger alliances are favoured.

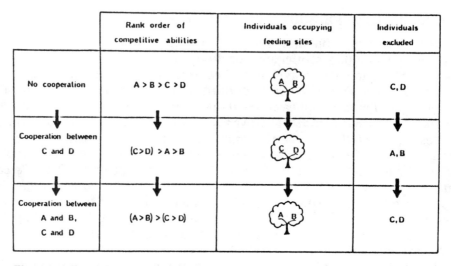

	Rank order of competitive abilities	Individuals occupying feeding sites	Individuals excluded
No cooperation	A > B > C > D		C, D
Cooperation between C and D	(C > D) > A > B		A, B
Cooperation between A and B, C and D	(A > B) > (C > D)		C, D

Figure 1. The advantage of cooperation at a food patch containing a limited number of feeding sites. Four individuals are considered to compete for the only two feeding sites at a discrete food patch. If no-one cooperates the excluded individuals are C and D, who have the lowest intrinsic competitive ability (POPP & DEVORE, 1979) (equivalent to resource-holding power, or RHP, PARKER, 1974). Cooperation between C and D leads to the exclusion of A and B. Consequently A and B are forced to cooperate also.

Their expected size is difficult to predict, however. If new alliances were formed between females at every food patch visited, their size would be related in a simple way to the size of the patch. However, individuals who arrive in the company of their established allies will clearly be able to compete more effectively than those who arrive as solitaries and must form alliances from those they happen to meet at the patch. Selection is therefore considered to favour those who maintain permanent bonds and travel with their established allies. The size of these permanent alliances, or groups, is consequently a complex function of the size of food patches, the disadvantages of intra-group competition, and the historical processes involved in the maintenance of bonds among a set of familiar females. No attempt is made here to model group size.

The choice of individuals as preferred allies depends on which partners will raise inclusive fitness by the greatest amount. Other things being equal, individuals should cooperate with the closest available kin; by doing so, they avoid excluding them from the food patch (which would lead to a fall in inclusive fitness) (Wrangham, in press). However, if the available kin have a low competitive ability this strategy may not be optimal, since the kin may not be an effective ally. This means that individuals are expected to cooperate with their kin in some, but not in all circumstances. In practice, the fact that cooperation with kin is often beneficial means that the group tends to be composed of close relatives, so that there are few opportunities for cooperating with others.

5. Ecological Conditions for Cooperation to be Effective.

The model depends on two ecological conditions. First, the best feeding sites must be found in discrete defensible patches. This is not a sufficient condition however, because the effects of variation in food patch size must be considered. Patch size is defined as the number of feeding sites, *i.e.* the number of animals that can feed simultaneously. If food patches contain too few feeding sites to satisfy all members, groups are expected to fragment.

Food patches must therefore be large enough to satisfy all group members. For animals living in stable groups this is a demanding requirement, since intermittent periods of food scarcity occur; unless there is a change in diet the size of food patches will then normally be expected to fall, leading to increased intensity of feeding competition. There are two circumstances, however, in which food patches need not shrink during periods of food scarcity.

First, food patches may have a constant size, and change only in number. However, since it is clear that food patches such as fruiting trees vary in size this does not apply to most primates.

Second, the diet may change between periods of food abundance and food scarcity. If the result of the change is that the diet comes from larger food patches during periods of food scarcity, intra-group competition is thereby avoided. Of course, these large patches must contain relatively low-quality food, since otherwise they would be preferred at all times. The second condition for the model, therefore, is that during periods of food scarcity the species should switch from a diet of high-quality food (occurring in discrete patches) to a diet of low-quality food found in large, uniform patches.

The ecological conditions are summarised in Fig. 2. The overall diet of a given species is considered to be divisible into two classes, "growth diet" and "subsistence diet". The growth diet consists of food items eaten during periods of food abundance, when population biomass is increasing; the subsistence diet is eaten during periods of food scarcity, when population biomass is falling. Although these definitions imply a clear distinction in time between the two diets, the distinction will normally in fact be blurred: even during periods of extreme food scarcity occasional high-quality food patches can be expected. As a result it is expected that groups should remain as coherent foraging units during periods of food scarcity, in order to compete for the few high-quality patches that will still be found. Nevertheless, the division into growth diet and subsistence diet is considered useful because it indicates that different levels of food abundance may present animals with quite different types of food distribution. Furthermore, it allows a review of field data to test the prediction that the quality and distribution of the diet change when food is scarce.

6. Males in FB Groups.

If FB groups have evolved as alliances to protect access to optimal food patches, the significance of males to females depends on the way groups defend resources.

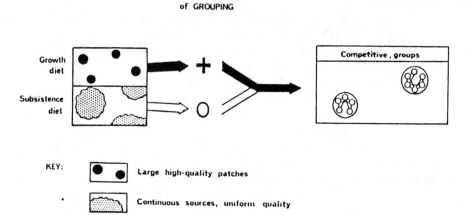

FOOD SOURCES   BENEFIT/COST   FEMALE RELATIONSHIPS
of GROUPING

Growth diet

Subsistence diet

Competitive, groups

KEY:

Large high-quality patches

Continuous sources, uniform quality

Figure 2. Ecological conditions favouring FB groups. The influence of food distribution is considered to differ between periods of food abundance ("Growth diet") and food scarcity ("Subsistence diet"). Growth diets in large high-quality patches, where there is a finite number of feeding sites, favour groups by the principles shown in Fig. 1. Subsistence diets in uniform, continuous patches, in which there is effectively an unlimited number of feeding sites, neither favour nor disrupt group-living. Females therefore sort themselves into groups competing against other groups, as described in the text.

Some groups defend a territory. Theory suggests that this occurs because food density is sufficiently high that effective defence of the home range is possible (Brown, 1964; Schoener, 1971; Crook, 1972). Field data support this by showing that species with long day-ranges in relation to the size of the home range tend to be territorial (Mitani & Rodman, 1979). Furthermore, in species in which the degree of territoriality varies, groups are more territorial where home ranges are smaller and population densities higher (Hamilton *et al.*, 1976). The implication, therefore, is that in habitats where group territoriality is possible there is selection against the tendency to form groups too large to be capable of effective range defence. This appears to explain why group size varies little in territorial species (Oates, 1977b).

This means that the maximum group size is set by the nature of the habitat, and therefore that there is competition for membership as a result of births and immigration attempts. Compared to natal females immigrant males are at a disadvantage in this competition because they have no dependable allies: females can capitalise on competition between males by supporting one male against others, as happens (Hrdy, 1977a). Territorial groups are therefore expected to have only a single male (Fig. 3).

The same might be expected in non-territorial groups, but the latter are not restricted in size by the economics of range defence. Instead, the ultimate constraint on group size is the increased intensity of feeding competition as groups grow. Unlike the constraint on territorial groups, this effect does not impose a

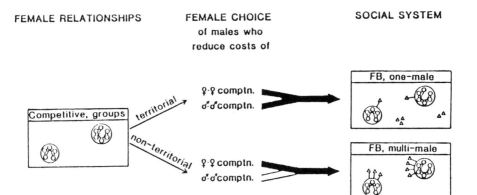

Figure 3. Consequences of range defensibility. Groups of females are considered to have developed as in Fig. 2. Where food density is sufficiently high, groups defend their home ranges as territories. This means that extra males would reduce range defensibility by increasing the area required for foraging; hence only one male is accepted into the group (top row). Non-territorial groups attract extra males to aid in competitive interactions against neighbouring groups (bottom row).

single upper limit on size, however; the difference occurs because the feeding success of non-territorial groups depends on the size of neighbouring groups.

Consider, for example, two adjacent groups of savannah baboons living at equilibrium with each other and a stable food supply. 'A' group contains 40 animals and 'B' group contains 50. Their home ranges overlap extensively and A avoids B when they meet. What would happen if B now divided into two groups, C (30) and D (20), sharing B's former range? When A meets C or D it no longer retreats since its greater size gives it dominance. Consequently A has priority at high-equality patches, and the resulting increase in food intake allows the group to grow to a new equilibrium point. C and D groups would shrink accordingly, with D shrinking faster than C.

The example shows that if individual reproductive success depends on the relative size of groups, there is variable relationship between home range size and maximum group size. Consequently there will be selection for ways of manipulating group size appropriately. Females can use males to do this. For instance, if two adjacent, equal-sized groups of female baboons occupy home ranges of equal quality, the group which attracts more males to compete on its behalf will grow at the expense of the other. Groups are therefore expected to compete by attempting to manipulate the number of males to their own advantage (Fig. 3).

Groups, of course, do not make decisions. Whether or not males join or leave groups depends both on their own strategies and the interests of individual group members: these vary among females according to differences in age, rank, oestrus state, *etc.* (Packer, 1979), so the ideal number of males will vary from female to female. Nevertheless, the model suggests that there will be an intermittent or continuous pressure for all groups except the largest to attract males in the hope of raising their inter-group dominance. Male interests, of course, differ from female interests, and the actual distribution of males in groups of different size should reflect the outcome of this conflict.

An inverse relationship is therefore expected between the number of males in the group and the degree of territoriality.

TESTING THE MODEL: FOOD DISTRIBUTION

1. Diets of FB Species during Periods of Food Abundance.

The model expects that during periods of food abundance FB primates select items found in high-quality patches having a limited number of feeding sites. This undoubtedly occurs in the majority of cases because for most species the principal food is fruit, eaten for more than 40% of feeding time (*Lemur, Propithecus, Cebus, Alouatta, Presbytis, Cercopithecus, Cercocebus, Papio, Macaca*; see studies in Clutton-Brock, 1977 and Chivers & Herbert, 1978). Individual fruiting trees contain a limited number of feeding sites; if too many animals attempt to feed, fighting breaks out and some animals leave the tree (Klein, 1974), and in a fully occupied tree a change of position by one animal leads to changes by others (Ripley, 1970). There is clear evidence also that even when many trees are in fruit there is significant variation in the quality of particular patches (which can be either groves or individual trees). In particular, primates tend to focus their food choice on relatively few species at any one time of year, and ranging behaviour is directed to exploiting a few particularly productive patches, the best being visited earliest in the day (*e.g.* Lindburg, 1977; Waser, 1977; Sugiyama, 1976b).

For seven of the FB species listed in Table I there is at least one field study in which fleshy fruits were found not to provide the major part of the growth diet. Five of these occupy savannah areas and eat fruits when they are available. At other times they turn to reproductive or seasonal parts such as seeds, seed-pods, flowers, young leaves or mushrooms (*Cercopithecus aethiops*, Gartlan & Brain, 1968; *Erythrocebus patas*, Hall, 1965; *Papio anubis*, Rowell, 1966; Nagel, 1973; *P. ursinus*, Hall, 1963; Hamilton *et al.*, 1976). As with fleshy fruits these items tend to be available for short periods at restricted locations, where aggressive competition occurs for access to feeding sites. Thus the majority of FB species exploit high-quality patches having a limited number of feeding sites for a significant proportion of their growth foods.

The two other cases run contrary to expectation. First, *Theropithecus gelada* actually avoids forest strips (where fruits are available) adjacent to its grassland habitat (Dunbar, 1977). Food availability varies markedly between wet and dry seasons, and during the lush wet season the preferred food is grass leaf (Dunbar, 1977; Iwamoto, 1979), which is distributed continuously over wide areas and thus occurs in patches with effectively unlimited feeding sites.

Second, *Colobus guereza* lives in evergreen or deciduous forests where ripe fruits are seasonally available, but they eat few fruits (14% of feeding time, Oates 1977b). Oates (1977b) suggested that young leaves were the preferred food since, unlike fruit, they were eaten in proportion to their availability. Fruit appeared not to be a preferred item since it was eaten most in months when immature leaves were not available. In *C. guereza* habitats food trees are abundant and there was no evidence of competition for individual trees or feeding sites. The growth diet of *C. guereza* is therefore best classified as occurring in uniform rather than high-quality patches.

2. Diets of FB Species during Periods of Food Scarcity.

All FB species continue to forage as groups when food is scarce, though individuals may disperse widely and sub-groups may form. Almost by definition, therefore, they must have access to foods which allow a relatively low level of feeding competition. Subsistence diets vary between species, however, and five principal classes occur.

First, during periods of food scarcity most primates find and eat isolated items of high-quality food types which would be growth foods if they occurred in large sources. For example langurs whose ranging patterns are oriented to sources of mature leaves find and eat occasional ripe fruits (Ripley, 1970).

Second, mature leaves are clearly the principal subsistence food of the colobines (*e.g.* Oates, 1977b; Oppenheimer, 1978). Mature leaves are also known to be eaten by other partly folivorous species and in some cases it is clear that this occurs most when young leaves are not available (*Propithecus verreauxi*, Richard, 1977; *Alouatta villosa*, Glander, 1978; *Cercopithecus mitis*, Rudran, 1978). Mature leaves are invariably a superabundant food source inducing little or no feeding competition.

Third, a principal subsistence food of *Papio* spp. is grass (leaf, root, fruit: *e.g.* Altmann & Altmann, 1970; DeVore & Hall, 1965; Lieberman *et al.*, 1979). Though competition for the best feeding sites may occur, grass meadows undoubtedly qualify as uniform patches.

Fourth, there is evidence that food items containing significant levels of plant secondary compounds are accepted by certain species when food is scarce. In a few cases food types have been analyzed and found to contain significant amounts of toxins or tannins (*Alouatta villosa*, Glander, 1978; *Colobus guereza*, Oates *et al.*, 1977). Other species have been observed making systematic use of foods which to humans taste bitter, astringent or hot, or are thought for other reasons to be protected chemically (*e.g.* unripe fruit) (*Alouatta seniculus*, Klein & Klein, 1975; *Cebus capucinus*, Oppenheimer, 1968; *Cercopithecus ascanius*, Waser, 1977; Sugiyama, 1968; *C. mitis*, Waser, 1977; Sugiyama, 1968; *C. aethiops*, Wrangham & Waterman, in prep.; Whitten, pers. comm.; *Cercocebus albigena*, Waser, 1977; *Macaca radiata*, Rahaman & Parthasarathy, 1969; *Macaca sylvanus*, Taub, 1977; *Papio ursinus*, Hamilton *et al.*, 1978; *P. anubis*, Lieberman *et al.*, 1979; Lock, 1972; *Theropithecus gelada*, Iwamoto, 1979). The fact that some primates will eat foods unpleasant to man suggests they may be partially 'blind' to certain compounds which they are able to detoxify: preliminary data suggest that species differences in taste abilities indeed occur (Glaser, 1972). Competition for feeding sites is expected to be reduced for two reasons. Other species should select toxic items only to a small extent, and individual animals may be limited in their ability to digest more than a certain amount of toxic items at one time (Freeland & Janzen, 1974).

Fifth, some of the smaller social primates spend considerable time foraging for insects when food is scarce (*Saimiri sciureus*, Bailey, pers. comm., *Cebus capucinus*, Oppenheimer, 1968; *Macaca sinica*, Hladik, 1975; Dittus, 1977). The patch type of insect foods depends on the type of insect eaten. *Saimiri* forages through the canopy for small mobile insects which are clearly a uniform source; *Cebus* eats larger, sedentary insects and animals may compete for feeding sites at dead trees (Klein, 1974), so these qualify as small high-quality patches.

The data thus suggests that a variety of species whose principal growth foods are fruits have diverse specialisations for an alternative diet during subsistence periods. The occurrence of species differences in subsistence diets has important implications for niche differentiation. Here, however, the important point is that the way diets change between periods of food abundance and scarcity leads to a reduced intensity of feeding competition.

3. Diets of Non-FB Species.

A corollary of the model is that in non-FB species diets are not expected to be distributed in the same way as in FB species (Fig. 2). This is because if they were distributed as in Fig. 2, the species would be expected to form FB groups. With respect to their diets the non-FB species fall into two categories.

First, *Colobus badius*, *Papio hamadryas* and *Pan gorilla berengei* live in groups which forage as coherent units. This means that females have the opportunity to cooperate against those in other groups, but in fact they do not take it (below). Consequently the model expects that these species do not select foods occurring in high-quality patches.

For *Colobus badius* this is a surprising prediction since the species is confined to evergreen or semi-deciduous forests with much fruit available (Struhsaker, 1975). Like *Colobus guereza*, however, though unlike other colobines, *C. badius* appear not to use ripe fruits as a growth food. First, ripe fruit are eaten for a small proportion of feeding time (annual percentages: <4.2% Struhsaker, 1978; <11.4% Clutton-Brock, 1972; <2.7% Marsh, 1978; 0.0% Gatinot, 1978). Second, *C. badius* eat more unripe than ripe fruit (*loc. cit*). Third, the total per cent time eating fruit is greatest in habitats where tree species diversity is lowest, suggesting that it is eaten because other foods are not available. Fourth, *C. badius* have been observed selecting unripe in preference to ripe fruits (Marsh, 1978; Struhsaker, pers. comm.).

Instead of ripe fruits the growth foods of *C. badius* appear to be young leaves and flowers, which are selected in proportion to their availability and make up a major part of the diet (42%—59%, *loc. cit.*). These are apparently distributed in uniform patches as they are for *C. guereza*, since the crowns of synchronously leafing forest trees contain a large number of feeding sites.

Papio hamadryas was studied in Ethiopia at the western edge of their distribution, where they are replaced by *Papio anubis* (Nagel, 1973). Nagel's study allows a direct comparison of *P. hamadryas* and *P. anubis* habitats. In both species groups had home ranges which included a river strip as well as larger area of thornscrub and savannah away from the river. There was little difference in the savannah vegetation occupied by each species: food sources were evenly distributed, bushes and small trees conforming to overdispersed secondary sources. The single major difference between *P. anubis* and *P. hamadryas* habitats was the amount of forest in the river strip. In *P. anubis* ranges it was abundant and contained fruiting figs and other trees: in *P. hamadryas* ranges the forest was thin and disappeared altogether in places, and it provided no fleshy fruits. *P. hamadryas* thus appear to be unique among *Papio* spp. in being adapted to living in areas so arid that high-quality patches provide an insignificant proportion of their growth foods.

Finally, the diet of *Pan gorilla berengei* consists almost solely of leaves and stems, which are distributed evenly throughout the habitat (Fossey & Harcourt, 1977). Fruits are rare and contribute less than 2% to the feeding time. Thus both their growth diet and their subsistence diet undoubtedly come from uniform patches.

Second, *Pan troglodytes* groups (or "communities", Goodall, *et al.*, 1979) are normally dispersed into small parties or solitaires. Mothers spend the majority of their time alone except for their juvenile offspring, and there is therefore little opportunity for cooperation between females (Wrangham & Smuts, in press). Nevertheless ripe fruits constitute the major part of the diet (Hladik, 1977; Wrangham, 1977). The fact that females do not cooperate to gain access to fruit trees therefore suggests that the nature of their subsistence diet forces females to forage alone.

Relevant data come from comparisons with other primates living in the same habitats. Compared to sympatric species (*Cercopithecus* spp., *Cercocebus albigena, Papio anubis*), *P. troglodytes* has been found to be unusual in the strength of its preference for ripe fruit, and they also avoid bitter leaves and seeds eaten by other species (Sugiyama, 1968; Waser, 1977; Hladik, 1977; Wrangham & Waterman, in prep.). Though leaves are eaten, mature leaves make up only a small proportion, and the time spent eating leaves (10%-50% during food scarcity) is lower than expected on the basis of body weight (>60%, Clutton-Brock & Harvey, 1977a).

These observations suggest that for physiological reasons *P. troglodytes* is relatively restricted in its diet choice even during food scarcity. They imply that as a result the subsistence diet is distributed not in large uniform patches, as in FB species, but in small high-quality patches where competition for feeding sites is intense. This view is supported by data showing that party size in *P. troglodytes* fell during a period of food scarcity, and individuals spent most of their time foraging alone (Wrangham, 1977). Thus the subsistence diet of *P. troglodytes* appears responsible for preventing females from travelling together in

423

permanent groups. An exactly parallel relationship seems to apply in the spider monkey *Ateles belzebuth*, which eats ripe fruit for 80% of its feeding time and appears to be "limited in its ability to utilise substances other than ripe fruit", compared to the sympatric *Cebus, Saimiri* and *Alouatta* (Klein & Klein, 1977). Like *P. troglodytes, A. belzebuth* communities forage in small parties in which females are often alone, but little is known of female relationships.

SOCIAL BEHAVIOUR

1. Relationships Between FB Groups.

The growth and subsistence diets of most FB species conform to the expectations of the model. This section therefore tests a third prediction, that intergroup competition occurs for access to high-quality patches. Relationships between groups vary widely both between and within species, but four principal patterns can be distinguished with respect of competition over food.

First, in some species aggressive interactions occur when groups meet at fruiting trees or other high-quality patches (*e.g. Propithecus verreauxi*, Sussman & Richard, 1974; *Cercopithecus mitis*, Rudran, 1978; *Macaca radiata*, Rahaman & Parthasarathy, 1969; *Macaca mulatta*, Lindburg, 1977; *Presbytis johnii*, Poirier, 1968; *Presbytis entellus*, Ripley, 1970). Interactions tend to occur in the border areas of neighbouring territories and clearly manifest competition for rich patches.

Second, in many species aggressive interactions occur without being related to the location of particular food patches (*e.g. Lemur catta*, Sussman & Richard, 1974; *Cebus capucinus*, Oppenheimer, 1968; *Alouatta* spp., Klein, 1974; *Cercopithecus aethiops*, Struhsaker, 1967; *Cercopithecus mitis*, *C. ascanius*, Struhsaker & Leland, 1979; *Presbytis* spp., Poirier, 1974; *Colobus guereza*, Oates, 1977a). Species showing this pattern maintain defended territories and therefore compete with neighbouring groups for all the resources within the territory. To the extent that these species use high-quality patches inter-group competition occurs over them indirectly.

Third, in most species not showing territorial defence there is extensive overlap of home ranges and groups meet rarely, tending to avoid each other at long distances (Bates, 1970; *e.g. Saimiri sciureus*, Bailey, pers. comm.; *Cercocebus albigena*, Waser & Homewood, 1979; *Papio anubis*, Harding, 1976; *Papio cynocephalus*, Rasmussen, 1979; *Papio ursinus*, DeVore & Hall, 1965; *Macaca fuscata*, Kawanaka, 1973; *Macaca mulatta*, Southwick et al., 1965; *Macaca radiata*, Rahaman & Parthasarathy, 1969; *Macaca fascicularis*, Angst, 1975). This might appear to suggest that inter-group competition does not occur. A more plausible interpretation, however, is that intergroup competition does occur and is mediated by inter-group dominance relationships. On this basis the reason why aggressive interactions are rare is that subordinate groups avoid dominant groups. If so, individuals in dominant groups gain competitive advantage by having access to preferred food patches.

Several lines of evidence support this view. First, neighbouring groups tend to have stable dominance relationships. In some cases the relationship is independent of location, while in others a group which usually dominates another may become subordinate near the center of the other's home range (*Saimiri sciureus*, Bailey, pers. comm.; *Papio ursinus*, Hamilton *et al.*, 1976; *Macaca fuscata*, Kawanaka, 1973; *M. mulatta*, Southwick *et al.*, 1965; Vandenburgh, 1967; Hausfater, 1972; Gabow, 1973; Drickamer, 1975; *M. sinica*, Dittus, 1977; *M. fascicularis*, Angst, 1975; *M. radiata*, Rahaman & Parthasarathy, 1969). Second, the basis for inter-group dominance is normally the relative size of groups or the number and fighting abilities of adult males (*loc. cit.*, Deag, 1973). This shows that dominance depends on competitive ability. Third, occasional intense aggressive interactions may occur, indicating that dominance relationships can be reversed due to changes in the competitive abilities of one or other group (*Papio anubis*, Smuts, pers. comm.). Fourth, neighbouring groups rarely seek each other out. They seem principally to meet by chance, as expected if dominance is important only in giving access to preferred food patches (Deag, 1973; Kawanaka, 1973).

The fourth major system of inter-group relationships is peaceful association, which is found as the normal pattern only in *Theropithecus gelada* (Dunbar & Dunbar, 1975). *T. gelada* groups commonly feed, travel and rest in the company of one or several other groups, and there is no evidence that inter-group competition for food affects their relationships. Other FB species sometimes have peaceful interactions but they rarely travel together (*Papio cynocephalus*, Rasmussen, pers. comm.; *Macaca mulatta*, Hausfater, 1972; *Macaca sylvanus*, Deag, 1973).

Except for *T. gelada* therefore, inter-group relationships of FB species tend to be uniformly competitive (Bates, 1970). In some cases it is clear that the object of competition is a high-quality food patch. In most, however, the function of aggressive relationships must be inferred. The idea that high-quality food patches are the most important resource is supported by the fact that *T. gelada*, whose food is found in uniform patches, show no inter-group competition. Furthermore in other species the frequency of inter-group aggression falls during periods when no high-quality food patches occur (Marsden, 1972; Ripley, 1970). Conversely, the appearance of a high-quality food patch can evoke inter-group aggression (Maxim & Buettner-Janusch, 1963). A number of the cases of groups meeting without showing aggression or avoidance are at resources such as water-holes or superabundant food patches where aggressive competition would be useless; even here, however, groups tend not to intermingle (DeVore & Hall, 1965; Oates, 1977a; Kawanaka, 1973). These points support the concept that a major determinant of the pattern of inter-group relationships among FB groups is the limited availability of high-quality food patches; hence they support the model.

2. Relationships between Non-FB Groups.

Non-FB groups also have regular inter-group interactions. The model expects that competition for high-quality patches is not the function of these interactions since if it were, these species should form FB groups.

Colobus badius, Papio hamadryas and *Pan gorilla berengei* do not exploit high-quality patches; competition for patches is therefore not expected. Observations of inter-group interactions confirm this (Struhsaker, 1975; Kummer, 1968; Harcourt, 1978). First, there is no evidence that interactions occur in relation to the location of particular food patches. Second, none of these species is territorial. Third, interactions tend not to be brief avoidance encounters; instead, they are relatively prolonged and commonly occur as a result of stalking, chasing, following or searching for other groups. Observers concluded that the significance of inter-group interactions lies in male-male competition for females. This is supported by data showing that females tend to join new groups during, or shortly after, inter-group interactions (Marsh, 1979; Kummer, 1968; Harcourt, 1978).

In *Pan troglodytes* inter-group interactions are not related to the defence of specific food patches, but adult males defend the community range against incursions by neighbouring males (Goodall *et al.*, 1979, Nishida, 1979). Defence of food resources is therefore a possible function; for instance, a dominant community regularly supplanted a subordinate community when abundant fruit appeared in the subordinate's range (Nishida, 1979). However the shifting of a community range into a new area does not necessarily benefit females, since when this happens some mothers remain in their original areas and associate with the "new" males (Nishida, 1979; Wrangham, 1979a). Inter-community interactions involve severe aggression towards males, leading sometimes to deaths, and are thought ultimately to be related to male-male competition for females (Wrangham, 1979a, 1979b; Goodall, 1979, Goodall *et al.*, 1979). It is striking, by contrast, that in the only case known where inter-group interactions led to deaths in FB species, those who died were females (Dittus, 1977). This happened when a small group of *Macaca sinica* were dominated by a larger group during a period of extreme food scarcity.

3. Female Participation in Group Behaviour.

In addition to suggesting that competition for high-quality patches is the principal determinant of inter-group relationships, the model expects that female behaviour is ultimately responsible. Female participation in group behaviour is seen in two relevant contexts.

First, in several species females typically take an active role in aggressive inter-group interactions, including making threat gestures, chases and aggressive vocalisations (*Lumer catta, Propithecus verreauxi*, Sussman & Richard, 1974; *Saimiri sciureus*, Castell, 1969; *Cebus capucinus*, Oppenheimer, 1968; *Cercopithecus aethiops*, Cheney, in press; *Cercopithecus ascanius, C. mitis*, Struhsaker & Leland, 1979; *Macaca radiata*, Rahaman & Parthasarathy, 1969;

Presbytis entellus, Ripley, 1967). In others female participation occurs only occasionally (*Presbytis* spp., Poirier, 1974; *Colobus guereza*, Oates, 1977a). Female involvement is difficult to evaluate in species whose groups normally avoid each other at long distance; however on the rare occasions when such groups fight, females take an active role and are seen lining up in opposing ranks (*Papio anubis*, Smuts, pers. comm.; *Macaca mulatta*, Hausfater, 1972).

Second, females play a part in deciding the direction and timing of group movements, and thereby presumably influence whether or not an inter-group interaction occurs. Though males often attempt to initiate movements female involvement appears normally to be the deciding factor (*Lemur catta*, Sussman, 1977; *Alouatta villosa*, Carpenter, 1965; *Cercopithecus aethiops*, Struhsaker, 1967; *Papio anubis*, Rowell, 1966; *Theropithecus gelada*, Dunbar & Dunbar, 1975; *Macaca mulatta*, Drickamer, 1975; *Colobus guereza*, Oates, 1977a).

In both contexts female participation in FB species differs markedly from non-FB species. In the four non-FB species females are uninvolved in inter-group interactions except for the times when they are the objects of male aggression (Struhsaker & Leland, 1979; Kummer, 1968; Harcourt, 1978; Goodall et al., 1979). Group leadership has been studied in *Papio hamadryas* and *Pan gorilla berengei*, and both the direction and timing of movements are decided completely by males (Schaller, 1965; Kummer, 1968). Movements of *Colobus badius* groups are initiated by specific calls given by males, and there are no reports of female involvement. In mixed-sex parties of *Pan troglodytes* females are also passive followers (Goodall, 1968) unless they are in oestrus; in this case a female can lead a party but even then she may be forced by a male's aggressive behaviour to follow him against her will (McGinnis, 1979).

Thus females exert more influence in FB species than in non-FB species both in the outcome of inter-group interactions, and in the ranging patterns of the group.

4. Male Participation in Group Behaviour.

The model expects that territorial species have few males, while non-territorial species should have many males (Fig. 3).

There is indeed a strong tendency for one-male groups to be territorial and for multi-male groups not to be territorial. Thus *Cebus capucinus*, *Cercopithecus mitis*, *C. ascanius*, *Colobus guereza*, *Presbytis johnii* and *P. senex* tend to have one-male groups which defend territories (Struhsaker & Leland, 1979; Oppenheimer, 1968; Poirier, 1974), while non-territorial multi-male groups occur in species of *Lemur*, *Saimiri*, *Alouatta*, *Macaca*, *Cercocebus*, *Papio* (Hamilton et al., 1976; Waser & Floody, 1974; Deag, 1973; Klein, 1974; Sussman & Richard, 1974; Baldwin & Baldwin, 1972). Some species do not fit the pattern: *Cercopithecus aethiops* has territorial multi-male groups (Struhsaker, 1967, *Erythrocebus patas* has non-territorial one-male groups (Hall, 1965), and territorial defence has been recorded in some multi-male groups of *Papio ursinus* and *Lemur catta* (Hamilton et al., 1976; Jolly, 1972b). Where the degree of territoriality varies, however, there is a tendency for less territorial groups to contain more males (*Presbytis entellus*, Yoshiba, 1968; *Colobus guereza*, Oates, 1977a), though the number of males does not necessarily increase (*Propithecus verreauxi*, Sussman & Richard, 1974). Thus though exceptions occur one-male groups tend to be found in species which are territorial. This relationship has apparently not been noted previously, perhaps because it is obscured if one-male groups of non-FB species are included: *Papio hamadryas* and *Pan gorilla berengei* have non-territorial one-male groups (Kummer, 1968; Fossey, 1974), and *Pan troglodytes* has territorial multi-male groups (Goodall *et al.*, 1979).

If females indeed recruit males who serve their own interests by increasing the competitive ability of the group, male participation in inter-group interactions is to be expected, and it occurs in all species. Of course males are also expected to serve their own interests directly, by resisting the attempts both of strange males to join the group and of females to recruit new males. This is seen, for example, in inter-group interactions of *Papio anubis* and *P. ursinus*; males actively herd females of their group away from strangers (Hamilton *et al.*, 1975; Cheney & Seyfarth, 1977; Packer, 1979). Three points suggest, nevertheless, that the behaviour of males is commonly influenced by female interests. First, females may support their males in inter-group interactions (above). Second, even in the absence of males FB groups may have aggressive inter-group interactions (*Cebus capucinus*, Oppenheimer 1968; *Presbytis entellus*, Hrdy, 1977a). Third, inter-group interactions in which males play the major role may be initiated by females (*Cercopithecus aethiops*, pers. obs.). In non-FB groups, by contrast, females neither initiate interactions nor participate actively.

5. Female Relationships Within Groups.

By definition female-female relationships differ in their characteristics between FB and non-FB groups (Table I, 2). In FB groups networks are highly differentiated; grooming, coalitionary, spatial and/or dominance relationships influence significantly the probability of occurrence of social interactions as well as their outcome (Kurland, 1977; Seyfarth, 1976; Hrdy, 1977a; Struhsaker & Leland, 1979, Chapais & Schulman, 1980). In non-FB groups, by contrast, social relationships among different females are uniformly unimportant and undifferentiated; there is very little female-female grooming, rates of aggression are low, coalitionary alliances are rare and dominance relationships are unstable and difficult to detect (Struhsaker, 1975; Struhsaker & Leland, 1979; Kummer, 1968; Harcourt, 1979; Bygott, 1979). Such a marked difference deserves explanation.

The focus on feeding competition in the present model suggests a reason for the differentiation of relationships with FB groups. If FB groups are effectively permanent alliances maintained to compete for food, intra-group competition is expected whenever food patches contain feeding sites of variable quality. Females should therefore attempt to establish dominance over other females as a means of gaining access to prime feeding sites. Other social relationships can emerge from this attempt. Coalitions help in establishing or maintaining dominance status (Chance *et al.*, 1977; De Wall, 1977; Missakian, 1972; Sade, 1965;

Chapais & Schulman, 1980); grooming tends to be given to dominant animals and may help maintain relationships in which dominants aid subordinates (Seyfarth *et al.*, 1978). Dominance status appears to have important effects. Dominant females occupy preferred feeding areas and eat better foods than subordinates (Kurland, 1977; Dittus, 1977; Wrangham, in prep.), and they appear to have higher reproductive rates (Mori, 1975; Smuts, pers. comm.; Drickamer, 1974; Chepko-Sade & Sade, 1979; Chapais & Schulman, 1980). When groups undergo fission, the larger of the 'daughter' groups contains the higher-ranking individuals, and retains the home range of the original group (Furuya, 1969; Chepko-Sade & Sade, 1979). Such long-term effects of dominance status can account for the importance of maintaining effective relationships.

The suggested significance of competition for feeding sites is supported by a comparison of Cercopithecine and Colobine female networks. McKenna (1979) showed that dominance relationships are more enduring and have greater effects in Cercopithecines than Colobines, and argued that this is because of the greater importance of feeding competition in Cercopithecines. More competition is expected in the Cercopithecines because their subsistence diets, though inducing less competition than their growth diets, are distributed less uniformly than the mature leaves eaten by Colobines.

By contrast with FB groups, intra-group competition for feeding sites is not expected in non-FB species (except in *P. troglodytes*, where it leads to females avoiding each other). In the absence of competition for feeding sites females have little reason to develop either friendly or aggressive relationships with each other, and they do not.

The absence of strongly differentiated networks suggests that female-female competition for resources is not an important influence in non-FB species. Wrangham (1979b) suggested that the principal function of group-living for females of *Pan gorilla berengei* is protection from harassment by adult males; females were considered to develop affiliative bonds with whichever males were most effective at protecting them from other males, and association between females was viewed merely as a result of several females sharing the same male. Given the similarities between the social systems of *Pan gorilla*, *Colobus badius* and *Papio hamadryas*, the same concept may well apply to the latter two species. If so, it explains why females in these species take a passive role in group movements and inter-group interactions, and why they occasionally transfer to a new group (cf. Marsh, 1979).

6. Male Relationships Within Groups.

The model provides no specific expectations about the nature of male relationships. Two aspects are mentioned here to show a difference between FB and non-FB species, and to demonstrate the potential importance of female strategies. Only multi-male groups are discussed.

First, in many FB species for which data are available intrasexual grooming is substantially less frequent among males than among females (*Alouatta senicu-*

lus, Neville, 1972; *Cercopithecus aethiops*, Seyfarth, in press; *Cercocebus albigena*, Struhsaker & Leland, 1979; *Papio anubis, P. ursinus*, Hall & DeVore, 1965; *Macaca fuscata*, Mori, 1975; *M. mulatta*, Lindburg, 1973; Drickamer, 1976; review by Sparks, 1967). Trivial exceptions are *Alouatta villosa* (Smith, 1977) and *Saimiri sciureus* in which neither sex grooms; but in the latter a laboratory study showed that huddling, which is an equivalent behaviour, also occurs significantly less among males than females (Coe & Rosenblum, 1974). Interestingly, frequent male-male grooming occurs in both the Prosimian FB species (*Lemur catta, Propithecus verreauxi*, Jolly, 1966); their behaviour differs from most primates in that grooming is almost always mutual. The only other species in which the frequency of grooming among adult males is commonly high in natural groups is *Macaca radiata* (Simonds, 1974); but this was not true in all groups studied.

By contrast, the sex difference is reversed in the two non-FB species with multi-male groups; grooming is more common among males than among females (*Colobus badius*, Struhsaker & Leland, 1979; *Pan troglodytes*, Goodall, 1968). This indicates that affiliative relationships can develop among males in appropriate circumstances. In *C. badius* and *P. troglodytes* males form cooperative relationships and compete jointly against males both within their own group and against those in other groups (Struhsaker & Leland, 1979; Bygott, 1979). Hence in both FB and non-FB groups grooming is associated with alliances, among females and males respectively. Furthermore in both cases grooming tends to flow from subordinates to dominants, as expected if grooming aids in the maintenance of coalitions (Sparks, 1967; Seyfarth, 1977; Simpson, 1973). The form of intra-group relationships thus appears to depend on the significance of inter-group relationships.

Second, high levels of intra-group aggression between males occur in all species having multi-male groups, especially in competition for oestrous females (Hausfater, 1975). A surprising feature is that in many multi-male groups females have sexual swellings or other signals of oestrus (Clutton-Brock & Harvey, 1976). This means that a female characteristic is responsible for increasing the intensity of male-male competition, which they might be expected to attempt to reduce. Sexual signals have been interpreted as mechanisms to enable females to attract the male with the fittest genotype (Clutton-Brock & Harvey, 1976); but if females can choose a male who increases their reproductive success directly, they should be expected to do so (Howard, 1978). The model of FB groups suggests one way sexual signals may achieve this. Sexual signals are associated with promiscuity, and hence increase the number of possible fathers of any infant. Two benefits thereby accrue to females. First, if all males in the group achieve regular matings they all share in the reproductive interests of females; hence, they should prove more reliable allies to females in inter-group interactions (cf. Wrangham, 1979b; Stacey, 1979). The second benefit is unrelated to the model. If males are unsure which infants they have fathered they cannot use infanticide as a safe strategy in male-male competition (Hrdy, 1979); infanticide is indeed rare in multi-male groups compared to one-male groups (Hrdy, 1977b). Whichever of these consequences is more important, it seems clear that the nature of male-male relationships may depend partly on the key strategy of females. Until female strategies have been understood, therefore, it will be difficult to explain fully the complexities of male relationships with females or with each other.

DISCUSSION

Caution is appropriate in interpreting the tests of the model. Given the qualitative nature of the comparisons, the small number of non-FB species and the lack of competing hypotheses the fit between theory and data may be more apparent than real. Further and more exacting tests are therefore required. Nevertheless, the review of ecological and behavioural data shows that many FB species conform to the expectations of the model. High-quality food patches are an important focus of ranging patterns and inter-group interactions, and females are actively involved in group travel decisions and encounters with other groups (Table 3). Furthermore non-FB species differ as expected; high-quality food patches are less important in the diets and inter-group interactions of some species, while in *Pan troglodytes* a peculiar subsistence diet makes feeding competition important during periods of food scarcity. Females are also less involved in group leadership and interactions in non-FB than in FB species. It should be noted that the non-FB species are independent cases. Thus *Papio hamadryas* and *Pan gorilla berengei* have each become adapted to habitats without fruiting trees; *Colobus badius* occupies habitats containing fruiting trees but uses them little; and *Pan troglodytes* has adapted to tropical forest without exploiting uniform patches.

Exceptions to the model's expectations fall into three main classes. First, *Theropithecus gelada* shows no evidence of using high-quality food patches with limited feeding sites, and also has peaceful inter-group interactions. It is clear that in its present form the model does not apply to this species, and a different explanation for its grouping pattern will be required.

Second, *Colobus guereza* is similar in not using high-quality food patches, but unlike *T. gelada* it has aggressive inter-group interactions. Group territoriality in *C. guereza* has been explained previously as a mechanism to minimise locomotion costs, by restricting foraging activity to a small area with a predictable food supply (Clutton-Brock, 1974; Oates, 1977b). It seems possible that minimisation of locomotion costs may have become an important function because high-quality food patches are not used. Some other folivorous primates (*e.g. Alouatta* spp.) may prove to be similar to *C. guereza* in this respect.

Third, there are species in which the general trends of FB groups are seen relatively weakly. *Macaca sylvanus*, for example, has a higher frequency of peaceful inter-group interactions than most species (Deag, 1973); it also appears to have fewer high-quality food patches and a lower rate of male transfer between groups than most *Macaca* spp., though more data are needed (Taub, 1977, 1978). A similar tendency is found among *Papio cynocephalus* in Am-

TABLE 3

Behavioural differences between FB and non-FB species		
	FB species	**Non-FB species**
Importance of food patches in inter-group interactions	High	Low
Frequency of female participation in inter-group interactions	High	Low
Female role in group movements	Active	Passive
Frequency of female-female grooming	High	Low
Frequency of male-male grooming in multi-male groups	Low	High

The table shows trends in the differences between FB and non-FB species. Exceptions are discussed in the text.

boseli, Kenya (Hausfater, 1975; Altmann & Altmann, 1970). Exceptions as these may prove to support the principles of the model if they show that a loss of high-quality food patches leads to modification of social behaviour away from the FB type.

With the exceptions of *T. gelada* and *C. guereza*, therefore, the model is adequately supported. Female-female competition for food can consequently be argued to be a key variable in the evolution of many primate groups; and the significance of most FB groups appears to lie in the importance of females cooperating to dominate other groups. This proposal has not been examined previously for most primates (but see Kurland, 1977). The possible importance of inter-group dominance in the evolution of groups had been emphasized, however, for birds (Emlen, 1978), carnivores (MacDonald, 1979), male chimpanzees (Wrangham, 1979b) and man (Alexander, 1974; Bigelow, 1969); and Davies & Houston (in press) have shown by a quantitative test that temporary alliances of wagtails (*Motacilla alba*) benefit both members of the alliance.

If FB groups have evolved as modelled, they support the view that male strategies are ultimately a result of female distribution, *i.e.* males compete for access to given clumps of females in a system of "female defense polygyny" (Emlen & Oring, 1977; Greenwood, in press). Consequently the number of females per group and the number of males per female are considered to depend ultimately on the strategies of females, rather than on the ability of males to dominate each other in competition for females, as is sometimes implied (Clutton-Brock & Harvey, 1977b). Males have been the traditional focus of attention in primate studies, partly because of the male-biassed structured of sexual selection theory. If male strategies depend on the distribution of females, however, increased attention to female relationships should prove rewarding in the analysis of diverse social structures.

Other Influences of Food Distribution.

The model differs in two major respects from most previous ecological explanations of why primates live in groups. First, the primary focus of attention is on females; groups are therefore categorised according to female relationships rather than by the number of males or group size, as is normally done. Second, feeding competition is considered to be the driving force behind group-life. Although the distribution and abundance of food have often been considered important influences on primate grouping patterns, the nature of the influence has been interpreted in other ways.

First, several studies have argued that a patchy food distribution favours groups. The proposed mechanisms invoke foraging efficiency but not competition for food patches; they argue that patches may be discovered more rapidly (Eisenberg et al., 1972), reached by shorter paths (Wilson, 1975) or cropped more efficiently (Clutton-Brock, 1974) by animals in groups than alone. No data are available to test these ideas. At present, however, there is no evidence that group size or structure is associated with the degree of difficulty of finding food; and most primates appear to know their home ranges well. The fact that patches may be shared with other groups (and species) shows that regulation of the time of return to a previously visited patch is an unlikely function of grouping. Thus there is no empirical support for the supposed importance of foraging efficiency.

Second, food distribution has been suggested to influence grouping patterns where groups defend territories (Denham, 1971; Crook, 1972; Goss-Custard et al., 1972; Altmann, 1974; Clutton-Brock & Harvey, 1977b). However the relationship proposed by these studies is not that feeding competition favors groups, but only that it imposes an upper limit on group size. While this is doubtless correct, it leaves the question of why groups occur at all to be answered in terms of factors other than food. The value of previous hypotheses concerned with food distribution therefore depends on the importance of these other factors.

Ecological Influences Other than Food

The overwhelming consensus in theories of primate sociality is that defence against predators is one of the major benefits of group-living, and it is commonly viewed as the driving force in the evolution of groups (Chance, 1955; Crook & Gartlan, 1966; Crook, 1970, 1972; Denham, 1971; Altmann, 1974; Hladik, 1975; Eisenberg et al., 1972; Wilson, 1975; Alexander, 1974). Nevertheless improved predator defence may be only an incidental effect if groups have evolved for some other reason. No models of the effects of predator pressure have indicated why they should lead to stable groups, or why females should be resident in some species but not in others, and it thus has less explanatory value at present than the model of feeding competition. There are only three sets of data supporting the predation hypothesis, and all have alternative explanations.

First, terrestrial species, which are presumably more exposed to the dangers of predation, tend to have larger groups than arboreal species (Clutton-Brock & Harvey, 1977b); larger groups may provide more effective defence (Bertram, 1978). Alternatively, though, the feeding competition model suggests that this occurs because terrestrial species travel longer distances than arboreal species (Clutton-Brock & Harvey, 1977b); as a result the richest food patches can attract more individuals, and larger groups will be favoured.

Second, multi-male groups are commoner in terrestrial than arboreal species, suggesting that more vulnerable groups retain or attract males to defend against predators (Crook, 1972). An alternative explanation given here is that extra males aid in inter-group competition between non-territorial groups. This fits the data since non-territorial groups are commoner in terrestrial than in arboreal species (Clutton-Brock & Harvey, 1977b) and it explains why in the few non-territorial arboreal species groups are multi-male *(Saimiri sciureus, Cercocebus albigena)*.

Third, males in terrestrial species have relatively larger canines than in arboreal species, suggesting a selection pressure in favour of better weapons for use against predators (Harvey *et al.*, 1978). However, this may be a result of intra-specific competition. If opponents are more easily confronted on the ground than in trees, escalated fights will occur more often; increased canine length could therefore be a result of selection for improved fighting ability in competition between males.

Thus the predation hypothesis is at present supported only weakly. Predator defence is doubtless an important influence on intra-group spacing patterns and possibly on inter-species associations (Altmann, 1979; Gartlan & Struhsaker, 1972), but its importance for the evolution of groups has yet to be established (see also Wrangham, 1979b).

Parasite pressure has also been proposed as a factor which might lead to group-living, but there is little evidence that it can explain species differences in grouping patterns (Freeland, 1976). The same is true of competition for sleeping sites (Kummer, 1968). Previous ideas on the evolution of groups thus rely on ecological factors whose significance is still unproved. Possibly predation or parasite pressure will be shown by further data to be responsible for modifying group sizes or sex ratios away from those expected on other models, but on present evidence the feeding competition model appears preferable for explaining the evolution of groups.

Cooperative Behaviour

The model suggests that cooperative behaviour arises ultimately because it pays two subordinate animals to form an alliance at the expense of a dominant. This has several implications.

First, it emphasizes that groups do not necessarily benefit the species. Instead they are viewed as developing solely because cooperative behaviour is an evolutionary stable strategy unbeatable by any alternative (Maynard Smith, 1976a). The implication is that species advantages which arise from grouping (such as increased avoidance of predators or increased ability to dominate other species) develop as an incidental consequence (cf. Lamprecht, 1978; Robertson *et al.*, 1976).

Second, the optimal size of non-territorial groups may depend on the size of neighbouring groups, rather than merely on the nature of the environment, as is normally considered (Schoener, 1971). This complicates the modelling of optimal group size, and means that it is unclear whether the distribution of group sizes in a given habitat can be understood without reference to historical processes. Since group size can fluctuate by losses or gains in the migratory sex it can change rapidly (*e.g.* Marsh, 1979).

Third, the model draws attention to the selective effects of inter-group competition without invoking inter-group selection. It is sometimes argued that cooperative behaviour is selected against at the individual level but spreads as a consequence of the differential competitive ability of closed groups: for instance, this has been suggested to occur in man (Alexander, 1974; Bigelow, 1969). By contrast, the present model suggests that alliances are formed because cooperative behaviour benefits all members. Migration by one or the other sex means that selection does not act systematically at the level of the group, since group characteristics are dispersed in each generation (Maynard Smith, 1976b). Hence group competition has effects without involving group selection.

Fourth, it raises the question of why cooperating animals should be kin. The classical formulation of inclusive fitness theory suggests that animals should be altruistic to close kin (Hamilton, 1964), but the evolution of cooperative relationships, in which two or more animals gain simultaneous benefits, has rarely been discussed. Wrangham (in press) suggests that if relationships are based on the benefits of cooperating against others of the same sex, close relatives will often be the preferred allies. This is because individuals are expected to avoid imposing costs on their kin, as they would be forced to do if they cooperated against them; inclusive fitness is therefore maximised, other things being equal, by those who cooperate with kin against non-kin (*e.g.* Bygott *et al.*, 1979). Ecological pressures thus favour cooperation, while genetic considerations favour kin as partners.

The hypothesis that FB groups have evolved as a result of the benefits of cooperation, between allies competing against others of the same species, thus has several interesting implications. To test it properly, quantitative models using field data are required. A difficult but important task is to describe food abundance and distribution in appropriate terms. When this is done it will be possible to make a rigorous test of the importance of cooperative behaviour.

SUMMARY

1. Multi-female groups of primates fall into two main classes, (a) female-bonded (FB) and (b) non-female-bonded (non-FB). A model is presented to account for the evolution of FB groups in terms of ecological pressures on female relationships.
2. The model suggests that FB groups have evolved as a result of competition for high-quality food patches containing a limited number of feeding sites. Groups are viewed as being based on cooperative relationships among females. These relationships are beneficial because cooperators act together to supplant others from preferred food patches.
3. Ecological data support the model for most FB species, but not for *Theropithecus gelada* or *Colobus guereza*, whose foods are not found in high-quality patches with limited feeding sites. Non-FB species conform to expectation, either because they do not use high-quality patches, or because feeding competition has disruptive effects during periods of food scarcity.
4. The behaviour of females differs as expected between FB and non-FB species in group movements and in inter-group interactions; in both contexts females are move involved in FB species.
5. Multi-male groups tend to be found in non-territorial FB species. The presence of several males per group is suggested to benefit females by raising the competitive ability of the group in inter-group interactions.
6. Competitive relationships among females are more strongly marked in FB groups than in non-FB groups. The model suggests that relationships in most FB groups are ultimately related to feeding competition.

REFERENCES

Alexander, R.D. (1974). The evolution of social behaviour. —Ann. Rev. Ecol. Systemat. 5, p. 325–383.
Altmann, S.A. (1974). Baboons, space, time and energy. —Amer. Zool. 14, p. 221–248.
_____ (1979). Baboon progressions: order or chaos? A study of one-dimensional group geometry. —Anim. Behav. 27, p. 46–80.
_____ & Altmann, J. (1970). Baboon ecology. —University of Chicago Press, Chicago.
Angst, W. (1975). Basic data and concepts on the social organisation of *Macaca fascicularis*. —In: Primate behaviour, (L.A. Rosenblum, Ed.), Vol. 4, p. 325–388.
Baldwin, J.D. & Baldwin, J. (1972). The ecology and behaviour of squirrel monkeys (*Saimiri oerstedi*) in a natural forest in Western Panama. —Folia primat 18, p. 161–184.
Bates, B. (1970). Territorial behaviour in primates: a review of recent field studies. —Primates 11, p. 271–284.

Bertram, B.C.R. (1978). Living in groups: predators and prey.—In: Behavioural ecology, (J.R. Krebs & N.B. Davis, Eds) p. 64–96. Blackwell Scientific Publications, Oxford.

Bigelow, R. (1969). The dawn warriors: man's evolution towards peace.—Atlantic-Little, Brown, Boston.

Bradbury, J.W. & Vehrencamp, S.L. (1977). Social organisation and foraging in emballonurid bats.—Behav. Ecol. Sociobiol. 2, p. 1–17.

Brown, J.L. (1964). The evolution of diversity in avian territorial systems.—Wilson Bull. 76, p. 160–168.

Budnitz, N. & Dainis, K. (1975). *Lemur catta*, ecology and behaviour.—In: Lemur biology I. (Tattersall & R.W. Sussman, Eds) Plenum Press, New York.

Bygott, J.D. (1979). Agonistic behaviour, dominance, and social structure in wild chimpanzees of the Gombe National Park. —In: The great apes (D.A. Hamburg & E.R. McCown, Eds) Benjamin/Cummings, Menlo Park.

_____, Bertram, B.C.R. & Hanby, J.P. (1979). Male lions in large coalitions gain reproductive advantage. —Nature 282, p. 839–841.

Carpenter, C.R., (1965). The howlers of Barro Colorado Island.—In: Primate behaviour: field studies of monkeys and apes. (I. DeVore, Ed). Holt, Rinehart and Winston, New York.

Castell, R. (1969). Communication during initial contact: a comparison of squirrel and rhesus monkeys.—Folia primat. 11, p. 206–214.

Chalmers, N.R. (1968). The social behaviour of free-living monkeys in Uganda.—Folia primat, 8, p. 263–281.

Chance, M.R.A. (1955). The sociability of monkeys.— Man, 55, p. 162–165.

_____, Emory, G.R. & Payne, R.G. (1977). Status referents in long-tailed macaques (*Macaca fascicularis*): precursors and effects of a female rebellion.—Primates 18, p. 611–632.

Chapais, B. & Schulman, S.R. (1980). An evolutionary model of female dominance relations in primates.—J. theor. Biol. 82, p. 47–89.

Cheney, D.L. (in press). Intergroup encounters among free-ranging vervet monkeys.—Folia primat.

_____ & Seyfarth, R.M. (1977). Behaviour of adult and immature male baboons during inter-group encounters.— Nature 269, p. 404–406.

Chepko-Sade, B.D. & Sade, D.S. (1979). Patterns of group splitting within matrilineal kinship groups: a study of social group structure in *Macaca mulatta.*—Behav. Ecol. Sociobiol. 5, p. 67–86.

Chivers, D.H.J. & Herbert, J. (1978) (Eds). Recent advances in primatology, Vol. I: Behaviour.—Academic Press, London.

Clutton-Brock, T.H. (1972). Feeding and ranging behaviour in the red colobus monkey.—Ph. D. thesis, University of Cambridge.

_____, (1974). Primate social organization and ecology.—Nature 250, p. 539–542.

_____, (Ed.) (1977). Primate Ecology— Academic Press, London.

_____ & Harvey, P.H. (1976). Evolutionary rules and primate societies.—In: Growing points in ethology (P.P.G. Bateson & R.A. Hinde, Eds). Cambridge University Press.

_____ & _____. (1977a). Species differences in feeding and ranging behaviour in primates.— In: Primate ecology (T.H. Clutton-Brock, Ed), Academic Press, London.

_____ & _____. (1977b). Primate ecology and social organisation.—J. Zool., Lond. 183, p. 1–39.

Coe, C.L. & Rosenblum, L.A. (1974). Sexual segregation and its ontogeny in squirrel monkey social structure.—J. Hum. Evolution 3, p. 551–561.

Crook, J.H. (1970). The socio-ecology of primates.— In: Social behaviour in birds and mammals (J.H. Crook, Ed.). Academic Press, London.

_____ (1972). Sexual selection, dimorphism and social organisation in the primates.—In: Sexual selection and the descent of man (B. Campbell, Ed.). Aldine, Chicago.

_____ & Gartlan, J.S. (1966). Evolution of primate societies.—Nature 210, p. 1200–1203.

Darwin, C. (1871). The descent of man, and selection in relation to sex.—John Murray, London.

Deag, J.M. (1973). Intergroup encounters in the wild barbary macaque *Macaca sylvanus*.—In: Comparative ecology and behaviour of primates. (R.P. Michael & J.H. Crook, Eds).—Academic Press, London.

Denham, W.W. (1971). Energy relations and some basic properties of primate social organisation.—Amer. Anthrop. 73, p. 77–95.

DeVore, I. & Hall, K.R.L. (1965). Baboon ecology. —In: Primate behaviour (I. DeVore, Ed.). Holt, Rinehart and Winston, New York.

Dittus, W.P.J. (1977). The social regulation of population density and age-sex distribution in the toque monkey. —Behaviour 63, p. 281–322.

Drickamer, L.C. (1974). A ten-year summary of reproductive data for free-ranging *Macaca mulatta*.— Folia primat. 21, p. 61–80.

_____ (1975). Patterns of space utilisation and group interactions among free-ranging *Macaca mulatta*. —Primates 16, p. 23–33.

_____ (1976). Quantitative observations of grooming behaviour in free-ranging *Macaca mulatta*. —Primates 17, p. 323–355.

Dunbar, R.I.M. (1977). Feeding ecology of gelada baboons: a preliminary report.—In: Primate ecology (T.H. Clutton-Brock, Ed.). Academic Press, London.

_____ & Dunbar, E.P. (1975). Social dynamics of gelada baboons.—Contrib. primatol. 6, S. Karger, Basel.

Eisenberg, J.F., Muckenhirn, N.A. & Rudran, R. (1972). The relation between ecology and social structure in primates. —Science 176, p. 863–874.

Emlen, S.T. (1978). The evolution of cooperative breeding in birds.—In: Behavioural ecology (J.R. Krebs & N.B. Davies, Eds), p. 245–281. Blackwell Scientific Publications, Oxford.

_____ & Oring, L.W. (1977). Ecology, sexual selection and the evolution of mating systems.—Science 197, p. 215–223.

Fossey, D. (1974). Observations on the home range of one group of mountain gorillas (*Gorilla gorilla berengei*). —Anim. Behav. 22, p. 568–581.

_____ & Harcourt, A.H. (1977). Feeding ecology of free-ranging mountain gorilla (*Gorilla gorilla berengei*). —In: Primate ecology (T.H. Clutton-Brock, Ed.). Academic Press, London.

Freeland, W.J. (1976). Pathogens and the evolution of primate sociality.—Biotropica 8, p. 12–24.

_____ & Janzen, D.H. (1974). Strategies of herbivory in mammals: the role of plant secondary compounds. —Am. Nat. 108, p. 269–289.

Furuya, Y. (1969). On the fission of troops of Japanese monkeys. II. General view of troop fission of Japanese monkeys. —Primates 10, p. 47–69.

Gartlan, J.S. & Brain, C.K. (1968). Ecology and social variability in *Cercopithecus aethiops* and *C. mitis*. —In: Primates: studies in adaptation and variability. (P.C. Jay, Ed.). Holt, Rinehart and Winston, New York.

_____ & Struhsaker, T.T. (1972). Polyspecific associations and niche separation of rain-forest anthropoids in Cameroon, West Africa.—J. Zool. 168, p. 221–266.

Gabow, S.L. (1973). Dominance order reversal between two groups of free-ranging rhesus monkeys.—Primates 14, p. 215–223.

Gatinot, B.L. (1978). Characteristics of the diet of West African red colobus.—In: Recent advances in primatology, Vol. I: Behaviour (D.J. Chivers & J. Herbert, Eds). Academic Press, London.

Glander, K.E. (1978). Drinking from arboreal water sources by mantled howling monkeys (*Alouatta palliata* Gray).—Folia primat. 29, p. 206–217.

Glaser, D. (1972). Vergleichende Untersuchungen über den Geschmackssin der Primates.—Folia primate. 17, p. 267–274.

Goodall, J. (1968). The behaviour of free-living chimpanzees in the Gombe Stream Reserve.—Anim. Behav. Monogr. 1, p. 161–311.

_____ (1979), Life and death at Gombe.— National Geographic Magazine 155(5), p. 592–621.

_____ Bandora, A., Bergmann, E., Busse, C., Matama, H., Mpongo, E., Pierce, A. & Riss, D. (1979). Intercommunity interactions in the chimpanzee population of the Gombe National Park.—In: The great apes (D.A. Hamburg & E.R. McCown, Eds). Benjamin/Cummings, Menlo Park.

Goss-Custard, J.D., Dunbar, R.I.M. & Aldrich-Blake, F.P.G. (1972). Survival, mating and rearing strategies in the evolution of primate social structure.—Folia primat. 17, p. 1–19.

Greenwood, P.J. (in press). Mating systems, philopatry and dispersal in birds and mammals.—Anim. Behav.

Hall, K.R.L. (1963). Variations in the ecology of the chacma baboon (*Papio ursinus*).—Symp. Zool. Soc. Lond. 10, p. 1–28.

_____ (1965). Behaviour and ecology of the wild patas monkey, *Erythrocebus patas*, in Uganda.—J. Zool. 148, p. 15–87.

_____ & DeVore, I. (1965). Baboon social behaviour. —In: Primate behaviour (I. DeVore, Ed). Holt, Rinehart and Winston, New York.

Hamilton, W.D. (1964). The genetical evolution of social behaviour.—J. Theoret. Biol. 7, p. 1–52.

Hamilton, W.J., Buskirk, R.E. & Buskirk, W.H. (1975). Chacma baboon tactics during intertroop encounters.—J. Mammal. 56, p. 857–870.

_____, _____ & _____ (1976). Defence of space and resources by chacma (*Papio ursinus*) baboons in an African desert and swamp.—Ecology 57, p. 1264–1272.

_____, _____ & _____ (1978). Omnivory and utilisation of food resources by chacma baboons, *Papio ursinus*.—Am. Nat. 112, p. 911–924.

Harcourt, A.H. (1978). Strategies of emigration and transfer by primates, with particular reference to gorillas. —Z. Tierpsychol. 48, p. 401–420.

_____ (1979). Social relationships among adult female mountain gorillas.—Anim. Behav. 27, p. 251–264.

Harding, R.S.O. (1976). Ranging patterns in a troop of baboons (*Papio anubis*) in Kenya.—Folia primat. 25, p. 143–185.

Harvey, P.H., Kavanagh, M. & Clutton-Brock, T.H. (1978). Sexual dimorphism in primate teeth.—J. Zool. London. 186, p. 475–485.

Hausfater, G. (1972). Intergroup behavior of free-ranging rhesus monkeys (*Macaca mulatta*).—Folia primat. 18, p. 78–107.

_____ (1975). Dominance and reproduction in baboons (*Papio cynocephalus*): a quantitative analysis. —Contrib. Primat. 7. S. Karger, Basel.

Hladik, C.M. (1975). Ecology, diet and social patterning in Old and New World primates.—In: Socioecology and psychology of primates (R.H. Tuttle, Ed.). Mouton, The Hague.

_____ (1977). Chimpanzees of Gombe and chimpanzees of Gabon: some comparative data on the diet.—In: Primate ecology (T.H. Clutton-Brock, Ed.). Academic Press, London.

Howard, R.D. (1978). The evolution of mating strategies in bullfrogs, *Rana catesbeiana*—Evolution 32, p. 850–871.

Hrdy, S.B. (1977a). The langurs of Abu.—Harvard University Press.

_____ (1977b). Infanticide as a primate reproductive strategy.—American Scientist 65, p. 40–49.

_____ (1979). Infanticide among animals: a review, classification, and examination of the implications for the reproductive strategies of females.—Ethology and Sociobiol. 1, p. 13–40.

Itani, J. (1975). Twenty years with Mount Takasaki monkeys.—In: Primate utilization and conservation (G. Dermont & D. Lindburg, Eds). Wiley and Sons.

Iwamoto, T. (1979). Feeding ecology.—In: Ecological and sociological studies of gelada baboons, Contributions to primatology, Vol. 16, (M. Kawai, Ed.). S. Karger, Basel.

Jolly, A. (1966). Lemur behaviour.—University of Chicago Press, Chicago.

_____ (1972). Troop continuity and troop spacing in *Propithecus verreauxi* and *Lemur catta* at Berenty (Madagascar).—Folia primat. 17, p. 335–362.

Jones, C.B. (in press). The functions of status in the mantled howler monkey, *Alouatta palliata* Gray: intraspecific competition for group membership in a folivorous Neotropical primate.—Primates.

Kawanaka, K. (1973). Intertroop relationships among Japanese monkeys.—Primates 14, p. 113–159.

Klein, L.L. (1974). Agonistic behaviour in neotropical primates.—In: Primate aggression, territoriality and xenophobia (R.L. Holloway, Ed.). Academic Press, New York.

_____ & Klein, D.J. (1975). Social and ecological contrasts between four taxa of Neotropical primates.—In: Socioecology and psychology of primates (R.H. Tuttle, Ed.). Mouton, The Hague.

_____ & _____ (1977). Feeding behaviour of the Colombian spider monkey.—In: Primate ecology (T.H. Clutton-Brock, Ed.). Academic Press, London.

Kummer, H. (1968). Social organisation of hamadryas baboons.—University of Chicago Press, Chicago.

Kurland, J.A. (1977). Kin selection in the Japanese monkey.—Contrib. primat. 12, S. Karger, Basel.

Lamprecht, J. (1978). The relationship between food competition and foraging group size in some larger carnivores. A hypothesis.—Z. Tierpsychol. 46, p. 337–343.

Social Grooming in Primates

C. Goosen
*Primate Center, REP — Institutes of the
Division for Health Research. The Netherlands*

INTRODUCTION

Grooming is an activity that is widespread among the taxa of the animal kingdom. In prosimians, grooming consists of tooth combing and licking of hairs: in anthropoid primates, it involves manual brushing and picking at the hairs. An animal can direct this behavior to its own fur (auto- or self-grooming) or to that of another individual (allo- or social grooming). Grooming behavior leads to cleaning of the pelage and preservation of its insulating capacity. Social grooming is a very conspicuous activity in many species: characteristically, amounts of time spent in social grooming can be great, often in excess of that necessary for cleaning purposes. The animals show a definite preference for certain grooming partners on certain occasions. These characteristics lead to the assumption that social grooming serves some important function in the social life of the animals.

Data on social grooming are widely scattered over many articles on various aspects of behavior. The reported data differ greatly in both quantity and detail among the taxa. This review is meant to give both a cross section and an introduction to the available data. The first part briefly presents morphological and social aspects of grooming in the different taxa. The somewhat informally arranged information facilitates recognition of possibly more general rules among taxa rather than establishing such rules. The second part briefly considers different functional aspects. In the latter section, literature reference is less extensive than in the first so as not to affect adversely the readability of the text. The end of the chapter speculates on comparative aspects of grooming in nonhuman primates and humans.

GROOMING IN THE DIFFERENT TAXA

Prosimians

Tupaiidae. Grooming in *Tupaia glis* consists of rubbing the fur with the fore-paws, scratching, licking, and combing or raking the fur with the lower incisors [for a detailed description, see Kaufmann, 1965]. Combing is mostly directed to the tail, which is long-haired in this species; the other body parts are licked. Most grooming is self-directed and occurs shortly before leaving the nest box or between feeding bouts. Social grooming is a rare event: eg, there were two brief licks on the crown of a partner in 45 h of observation [Vandenbergh, 1963; Kaufmann, 1965]. Social grooming is not reported by Kawamichi and Kawamichi [1981]. In other species of the family (*Tupaia minor, T. gracilis, T. chinensis, T. longpipes,* and *Tana tana*), social grooming occurs at a rate no more than 12 bouts per 100 h of observation [Sorenson and Conaway, 1966]. Female/male grooming is always associated with copulation: the licking by the male changes to a bite to hold the female during mounting. Grooming between females is directed to the throat and abdomen, which sometimes seems to stimulate the recipient to lie down as if nursing young. Social grooming is rarely reciprocal: ie, it is not generally returned simultaneously or shortly after receipt.

Grooming invitation behavior has not been observed. After a bout of aggression, an aggressor was once seen to lick the exposed genital area of the partner. Although social grooming is rare, other social interactions such as heterosexual behavior, aggression between animals of the same sex, and sitting in contact together are not uncommon. There are no observations on females with young [Sorenson and Conaway, 1966].

Tarsiidae. In *Tarsius,* grooming is performed with the fingers and lips [Doyle, 1974]. Social grooming does not normally seem to be very prominent (as it was not mentioned by Niemitz [1979]). But precopulatory displays including chasing, vocalizations, and spreading of legs are interrupted by prolonged bouts of grooming [Van Horn and Eaton, 1979].

Daubentoniidae. In the single nocturnal and solitary representative of this family, self-grooming is performed with the mouth and the elongated third finger [Doyle, 1974]. Little is known about social interactions of the animals, and no data on allo-grooming are available.

Lorisidae. In this nocturnal family, grooming consists of muzzling, licking, stroking, and scraping with the lower incisors as well as licking of the hands, which are then rubbed over the ears and eyebrows. Social grooming consists mainly of licking [Pinto et al, 1974; Charles-Dominique, 1977].

In *Loris,* social grooming is often by mother to infant; grooming by the infant first appears at 2–3 weeks of age [Charles-Dominique, 1977; Ehrlich and

Musicant, 1977]. Adult group members groom each other often while hanging down by their feet, concentrating mainly on the trunk and head and other parts not readily accessible for self-grooming. Grooming is also invited, mostly by bending the head down but also by dangling from the feet or lifting an arm [Ehrlich and Musicant, 1977]. Mutual grooming between the male and female while suspended may be a prelude to mating [Charles-Dominique, 1977]. The adult male of a group is often involved in grooming interactions either as groomer or as groomee [Ehrlich and Musicant, 1977].

In *Perodicticus potto*, most grooming contacts are between male and female. Animals familiar with each other show prolonged reciprocal grooming that can be followed by grappling, probably as a prelude copulation [Epps, 1976; Doyle, 1974].

Galago senegalensis shows extensive self-grooming after waking; self-grooming is evenly distributed over time and alternates with feeding. The amount of time spent in social grooming is less than that spent in self-grooming; the distribution over the night is the same [Doyle et al, 1967; Pinto et al, 1974; Doyle, 1976]. Social grooming between adults takes place in a variety of situations, including courtship. The groomer holds the groomee with one hand. An adult male may hold a female with two hands when grooming her back [Doyle, 1976]. In a group of four individuals, the occurrence rate of grooming was 5–13 times per hour as determined by the focal animal technique during a nocturnal activity period [Nash and Flinn, 1978]. Intensive self-grooming and grooming of nest box partners is reported for a female shortly before parturition. Mothers also groom their infants [Doyle et al, 1967].

In *G. demidovii*, grooming is less frequent in the wild than in captivity. It is concentrated shortly before and after sleep. Adult males rarely groom each other [Charles-Dominique and Martin, 1972].

In *G. crassicaudatus*, the time adults spend in self-grooming shows a peak at the beginning of the night; the amount of self-grooming is more than that of social grooming [Pinto et al, 1974]. Mothers groom their infants, during which the mothers may also lick urine [Buettner-Janusch, 1969]. The infant grooms its mother from the age of 1–2 months onward [Rosenson, 1972]. Social grooming by adults is observed between opposite-sex pairs and between females but not between males [Doyle, 1974; Van Horn and Eaton, 1979].

Aggressive interactions are reported between animals of the same sex; females frequently show dominance reversals, but the males do not [Roberts, 1971]. Social grooming may be invited [Ehrlich, 1977]. Females seem tense when being groomed by the male. Males and females self-groom between copulations [Ehrlich, 1977]. Shortly after formation of a group, grooming as well as rejection of grooming is frequent; at later times, fights are frequent [Drews, 1973; Rosenson, 1973]. In new groups, social grooming seems to be stressful, as the groomee presents and "spat-calls." Amounts of grooming increase over time, perhaps indicating "closer social bonds" between colony members [Tandy, 1976].

Lemuridae. Grooming in this family is by licking and combing with the lower incisors which have long, even spaces between them and thus form a comb [Buettner-Janusch and Andrew, 1962; see also Szalay and Seligsohn, 1977].

In *Lemur catta*, self- and social grooming take place during quiet periods of the day [Jolly, 1966]. Mothers often groom their infants; juveniles may join in if they are not too vigorous. The adult male initially avoids contact with mother and infant and joins in grooming only later [Klopfer and Boskoff, 1979].

L. fulvus mothers groom their infants. The male consort is occasionally also allowed to groom the infant, but other females are rebuked by the mother [Klopfer and Boskoff, 1979].

L. macaco mothers spend a great deal of time grooming their infants, especially their heads and anogenital regions. Infants regularly groom mothers and themselves by the fifth week of age [Harrington, 1978].

In *L. variegatus*, social grooming is mostly between mother and infant and much less between adult males and females [Kress et al, 1978]. Males and juveniles also participate in grooming of infants [Klopfer and Boskoff, 1979].

In *Microcebus murinus*, self-grooming shows a peak at the beginning of the night; social grooming is less frequent and does not change over time [Pinto et al, 1974]. Males are more active in social grooming than females [Glatston, 1979].

Allogrooming is frequently a part of male/female interactions of *M. coquereli* [Pages, 1980].

Indriidae. In *Propithecus verreauxi*, the mother licks the infant shortly after birth and also her own genital area. The mother tolerates being groomed by nonadults, but their attempts to groom her baby provoke defense by slapping [Richard, 1976]. Grooming of the infant by the mother is directed primarily to parts difficult to reach by the infant itself—ie. the craniofacial area (52%), the anogenital area (25%), and the dorsal trunk (10%.) [Eaglen and Boskoff, 1978]. During the first 2 months after the birth of the infant, the father directs most grooming attention to the mother; later on, he grooms the infant and mother for similar amounts of time [Eaglen and Boskoff, 1978]. The infant shows self-grooming from the age of 4 weeks and social grooming from the age of 5 weeks [Jolly, 1966].

Social grooming is the most commonly observed nonaggressive social interaction between adults. It occurs during periods of rest and is performed mostly by animals lowest in the feeding hierarchy, probably as a response to persistent aggression [Richard, 1974, 1978]. Social grooming can be invited by moving the chin up or lifting an arm in front of the prospective groomer. The groomer often holds the area groomed with one hand [Jolly, 1966]. Social grooming is mostly directed to the head, and most bouts (70%) are unidirectional or (26%) simultaneous by both partners, but only rarely (4%) alternatingly reciprocal [Richard, 1978]. Adult male grooming is most prominent in the dry season. In the wet season, eating and fighting are prominent [Richard, 1978].

In *Indri indri*, groups consist of an adult pair with 1–3 offspring. All social activities together comprise only 2% of the observation time (occurrence rate of 0.76 events per hour). The consequently rare social grooming is performed by use of the tooth comb and is usually directed to the face, neck, ears, and back. Reversal of groomer and groomee roles during a bout of social grooming is common. Social grooming by adult and subadult males mostly concerns the youngest infant. Sometimes, animals seem to briefly groom in order to invite grooming through role reversal [Pollock, 1979].

In *Phaner furcifer*, which lives in monogamous or digamous groups, social grooming by males, females, and juveniles is common [Charles-Dominique and Petter, 1980].

Summary on Prosimians. In most species (*Tarsius* expected) grooming is done with the mouth rather than manually and involves licking with the tongue and combing with the lower incisors. Self- and social grooming are seen in all species; social grooming is less prominent than self-grooming. The various species vary widely with respect to group life and ecological characteristics. Some species are nest builders, whereas others are not; some are solitary, whereas others live in groups; and some are territorial, but others are not. However, the average amount of social grooming is not clearly related to these traits. The occurrence of social grooming seems to be prominent in certain situations such as maternal care giving, copulation, and resting and appears to be related to submissiveness in group-living species.

Propithecus verreauxi is exceptional, as the members often groom each other simultaneously rather than alternatingly (which is the more common pattern).

Anthropoidea

Callitrichidae. Social grooming is reported for a variety of species: *Callimico goeldii* [Epple, 1967; Pook and Pook, 1981]; *Callithrix jacchus* [Rothe, 1973; Box, 1975a.b; Wookcock, 1982]; *Cebuella pygmaea* [Christen, 1974]; *Leontideus rosalia* [Epple, 1967; Rathbun, 1979]; *Saguinus fuscicollis* [Epple, 1975, Moody and Menzel, 1976; Vogt, 1978]; *S. nigricollis* [Izawa, 1978]; *S. mystax* [Box and Morris, 1980]; *S. oedipus* [Hampton et al, 1966; Epple, 1967]; *S. spixi* [Epple, 1967]; and *S. tamarin* [Christen, 1974].

Grooming is more similar in appearance to that of higher primates than to that of prosimians [Hampton et al, 1966; Epple, 1967; Izawa, 1978]. It consists mainly of manual combing through the fur and parting of the hairs. Hairs sticking together are separated by the teeth; small particles are picked up with the tongue and then chewed [Epple, 1967; Izawa, 1978]. Self-grooming is directed mainly to the tail and the legs [Hampton et al, 1966]. In social grooming, the groomer and groomee change roles [Box, 1975a]. Social grooming also involves the opening and licking of the inside of the groomee's mouth [Hampton et al, 1966; Epple, 1967; Box and Morris, 1980].

Inviting social grooming is done by lying prone in a relaxed manner with the legs extended [Epple, 1966; Rothe, 1973] or by sitting with the head down in front of the groomer [Rothe, 1973; Pook and Pook, 1981]. In *S. fuscicollis*, grooming invitation is accomplished by a particular, infantile call. Invitations are not seen in *Cebuella pygmaea* [Christen, 1974]. The amounts of time spent in self-grooming and in social grooming are considerable [Hampton et al, 1966;

Pook and Pook, 1981]. Both activities occur at the beginning of a resting period; self-grooming is also interspersed between bouts of feeding activity.

The mother licks and grooms the infant shortly after birth (*Callithrix jacchus* [Rothe, 1973], *Cebuella pygmaea* [Christen, 1974], *Saguinus fuscicollis* [Epple, 1975], and *Tamarin tamarin* [Christen, 1974]). Infants self-groom from 2–3 weeks of age; social grooming from 7 weeks of age occurs in a brief, "informal" manner [Box, 1975b].

Social grooming is an important activity which mostly involves adults (which, however, have few ectoparasites [Box, 1975b; Izawa, 1978; Vogt, 1978]). There are no sex differences with regard to the amounts of self- or social grooming; social grooming is directed mostly to the head of the receiver [Box, 1975a]. In *Cebuella pygmaea* and *Tamarin tamarin*, most social grooming takes place at between 0900 and 1500 h. Dominant females are groomed more by submissive females than the reverse. Adult males groom dominant and submissive females equally often [Christen, 1974].

In newly formed pairs, male-grooms-female is always more frequent than female-grooms-male. Very little self-grooming is shown during periods of sexual activity [Woodcock, 1982]. In *Saguinus labiatus*, males groom more than females, and those that most actively solicit also receive most of the grooming [Coates and Poole, 1983].

In summary, Callitrichidae are a fairly homogeneous family in many respects, having small body size, territoriality, monogamous social life, delivery of twins or triplets, and paternal participation in infant rearing as usual characteristics.

Grooming is mostly manual. Mothers groom their infants shortly after birth. Both self- and social grooming are prominent in adults. Social grooming is frequently invited, and the animals often change roles of groomer and groomee in a single grooming bout. Self- and social grooming show a peak at the beginning of a resting period. Social grooming seems to be related to resting together, to dominance relations between the animals, and to pair formation.

Cebidae. In *Alouatta palliata*, social grooming occurs at a rate of less than one bout per hour; most grooming is by the dominant toward the subordinate [Jones, 1979]. Grooming is not mentioned in a detailed report on interactions between adult females and their infants; this suggests that it only rarely occurs [Baldwin and Baldwin, 1973].

Social grooming appears to be rare in *A. seniculus*; Carpenter [1934, 1935, 1965] did not mention grooming, and Bernstein [1965] saw only five brief bouts. But in other populations, social grooming is observed more frequently [Neville, 1972]. As the animals have no thumb, grooming is rather clumsy in appearance. Most social grooming is by adults, the male being a frequent recipient. Infants also receive grooming from adult females and from subadults and juveniles of either sex [Neville, 1972].

Allogromming in *A. villosa* is mentioned by Richard [1970].

In the nocturnal *Aotus trivirgatus*, self- and social grooming take place mostly during the night. Captive individuals from one region are more active in grooming and also cleaner than those from another region [Jones and Simpson, 1982].

In *Ateles*, the amount of time spent in grooming is about 3% of the observation time.

Social grooming is shown between females that rest together. Females also groom males, though they do not rest with them. Grooming is presumed to reduce tension [Rondinelli and Klein, 1976]. Grooming is not seen after copulation [Klein, 1971]. Mothers groom their infants [Carpenter, 1935].

Allogrooming in *Cacajao* is mentioned by Abordo et al [1975].

In *Callicebus moloch*, the monogamous, territorial pair members remain close to each other and show social grooming rather often [Mason, 1974]. In *C. torquatus*, amounts of social grooming are very great, especially during midday rest and at the beginning and end of the day when the adult pair remains on its sleeping bough. The less the pairs groom during the day, the more they do at the end of that day. Grooming is not increased during periods of sexual activity [Kinzey and Wright, 1982].

In newly formed groups of *Cebus capucinus*, social grooming is observed from the second day after group formation. Grooming consumes 3.6% of observation time; huddling and aggressive contacts amount to about 32%. An old wound does not elicit grooming. Grooming is not mentioned as a maternal activity [Bernstein, 1965].

In *C. nigrivitatus*, social interactions consist mainly of play and allogrooming. Most bouts are initiated by invitation, in the form of sitting with the chest turned to the partner to be. Most grooming is by the adult females directed to juveniles and adult males [Oppenheimer and Oppenheimer, 1973].

In *C. albifrons*, social grooming is solicited by approach and lying down on the abdomen; grooming bouts last only a few seconds. The top-ranking male is exclusively groomed by adult females. Most grooming is probably performed by adult females toward juveniles. Self- and social grooming occurs less often than in macaques [Defler, 1979].

C. apella mothers groom infants, which may then fall asleep [Nolte and Dücker, 1959].

In *Saimiri sciureus*, grooming occurs rather rarely [Ploog et al, 1963]. It is not even mentioned in various reports on social behavior [Alvarez,1975; Anschel and Talmage-Riggs, 1977; Mendoza et al, 1978; Candland et al, 1978], nor is it mentioned for *S. oerstedii* [Baldwin and Baldwin, 1972]. But in captive pairs of adult males, grooming accounts for up to 10% of the observation time [Francois et al, 1970]. In captive groups of *S. sciureus*, social grooming between top- and second-ranking males leads to intense relaxation in the groomee. Social grooming appears at an earlier age than self-grooming [Ploog et al, 1963].

In *Lagothrix*, social grooming is a common activity [Williams, 1969].

In summary, grooming is observed in all species, and it is largely manually performed. Social grooming may be invited. The amounts of social grooming vary greatly between species. Species also vary widely in their life-styles. However, the amount of social grooming is not clearly correlated with a single ecological or life-style characteristic. For instance, the amounts of grooming may be great or small in territorial species (compare *Callicebus* to *Alouatta*) and also in nomadic species (compare *Cebus* to *Saimiri*). The amount of social grooming varies between groups in the wild (*Alouatta seniculus*) and in captivity (*Saimiri*). In group living species (*Alouatta, Ateles,* and *Cebus*), social grooming is mostly performed by adult females, often directed to the adult male and the infants.

Cercopithecidae

Cercocebus. In *Cercocebus albigena*, grooming is one of the most time-consuming social activities, with a peak at around 1500 hr [Chalmers, 1986a]. Social grooming is alternatingly reciprocal [Chalmers and Rowell, 1971]. It may be invited by presenting or by standing squarely in front of the groomer to be, sometimes for a long period of time [Chalmers and Rowell, 1971; Wallis, 1981]. Most grooming is by adult females and is directed toward adult males and infants [Chalmers, 1986b]. Grooming interaction between adult males and females occurs mostly during the ovulatory stage of the menstrual cycle, during which time the perineum is inflated [Chalmers and Rowell, 1971]. A postreproductive female (who is treated with deference by adult female and juvenile group members) has grooming interaction only with adults [Waser, 1978].

In *C. atys* groups, the amount of time spent in grooming varies between 7% and 17%, also peaking during the midafternoon. It drops to very low rates during rainy weather. Introduction of newcomers typically leads to high levels of social interaction: at first aggression, then sex and later (after 1 hr) grooming and play. Initially, grooming takes place mostly among resident members, later on involving newcomers. Introduction of a newcomer leads to increased grooming in one group but not in another [Bernstein, 1971].

Cercopithecus. In *C. aethiops*, mothers groom their infants. The mother of a newborn baby receives grooming interest from adult and juvenile females who also make contact with the baby [Lancaster, 1971; Struhsaker, 1971]. Among adults, most social grooming is directed to animals higher in rank; the top-ranking animals groom and are groomed most. Grooming may be invited, and about half of the invitations are successful. The most active inviters also receive the most grooming [Rowell, 1971; Seyfarth, 1980]. Females are attracted by and groom the dominant male; unlike kin, however, the dominant male does not always support those females in disputes with others [Fairbanks, 1980]. Females also compete for the opportunity to groom high-ranking individuals [Seyfarth, 1980]. Termination of grooming by aggression is only done by the highest-ranking animal of the grooming pair. During encounters between groups, intergroup grooming contacts are few and are seen only between the lowest-ranking females [Cheney, 1981].

In *C. sabaeus*, grooming and leisure feeding are most likely to take place at around noon. [Poirier, 1972]. A fourfold increase in spatial density leads to a threefold increase in huddling, embracing, and grooming, but aggressive behavior does not increase [McGuire et al, 1978].

A detailed description of self- and social grooming and of the areas groomed had been given for *C. diana* in Mörike [1973].

In *C. campbelli*, social grooming occurs mainly in adult male/female and in female pairs [Heinkeler, 1972].

The amounts of social grooming in *C. neglectus* vary greatly, between 0% and 83% of the observation time [Mörike, 1976].

In *C. (Miopithecus) talapoin*, social grooming is shown by all age and sex classes. Social grooming is often solicited. Grooming may be rough at the beginning of a bout; otherwise it is relaxed [Woltheim and Rowell, 1972]. Grooming interaction between males and females takes place during the breeding season. Adult males do not groom infants. Grooming between juveniles is likely to be interrupted by play [Gautier-Hion, 1970]. In captive individuals, the total amount of grooming varies between 0% and 5% of the observation time. Most grooming bouts are unidirectional. There is a negative correlation between the amount of grooming given and received. The amount of grooming is not correlated with social rank. However, within a grooming pair, most grooming is done by the higher-ranking animal. Grooming is mostly between females; male/female grooming accounts for only 25% of all grooming interactions [Wolfheim, 1977a,b]. Strangers that enter an established group are subject to aggression by same-sex residents especially and therefore have few grooming contacts. Upon introduction of a stranger, grooming between residents can increase as well as decrease [Scruton and Herbert, 1972].

Colobus. In *C. angolensis*, self-grooming is seen under the slight tension of becoming aware of the observer; social grooming is rare [Groves, 1973].

In *C. badius*, the amounts of self- and social grooming each involve about 2% of the observation time. Most of the grooming is performed by females, although the male also actively participates [Struhsaker and Oates, 1979; Marsh, 1981].

Social grooming is seen in *C. polykomos*, but apparently only rarely [Sharon, 1973].

In *C. guereza*, self-grooming is directed mainly to the hind legs and tail, and social grooming is directed toward the cheeks, head, back, and flanks. The bout duration varies widely; longer bouts concern the more infrequently groomed body parts.

Social grooming is an important activity. It can be invited, and the groomee often lies down. Amounts of social grooming seem to vary during the menstrual cycle. The amount of adult female grooming peaks from between 1 week before and 3 weeks after the birth of an infant [Horwich and Wurman, 1978]. Mothers with infants are groomed by other females, which are then permitted to hold the baby [Woodridge, 1971]. Adult females are involved in 86% of all grooming interactions; they groom other females, their infants, or the male. Subadult females are involved in 45% of all grooming; they groom and may also hold young infants for some time. The male rarely grooms other individuals [Horwich and Wurman, 1978; Oates, 1977; Struhsaker and Oates, 1979].

449

Erythrocebus. In *E. patas*, prolonged and frequent social grooming takes place in the early morning and at around noon, when the animals are relaxed and sleepy [Hall and Mayer, 1967; Hall, 1968]. Newborn infants are licked shortly after birth. Later on, grooming of the infant by the mother occurs in the ventroventral position [Hall et al, 1965]. Most grooming interactions are between adults, often involving the male. In male/female pairs, grooming by the male takes place mostly during the preovulatory phase of the menstrual cycle. The male grooms briefly and in a perfunctory way that seems to reduce tension in timid females [Hall and Mayer, 1967]. Invitations, mostly by the male, occur through the use of different postures such as turning a cheek and lying down (which presumably indicates that there is no intention to attack); invitations are sometimes simultaneous by both partners. Grooming may be initiated by grabbing the top knot of hair and pulling the groomee's head down. Lack of tension is often evident between habitual friends. But subordinate monkeys do not lie down; indeed, they sometimes show clear signs of flight. Social grooming is accompanied by an alternation between slight opening and closing of the mouth [Hall, 1968; Hall et al, 1965]. Females shift grooming interest at the end of the mating season from adult females to juveniles and infants. Among females, most grooming is between animals of similar social rank; an interaction is equally likely to be started by either partner, but the highest-ranking individual is groomed for the longest periods of time [Kaplan and Zucker, 1980; Hall and Mayer, 1967].

Macaca. In *M. arctoides*, grooming is described as the examination of the hair and skin of another animal using the hands, sometimes assisted by mouth movements [Bertrand, 1969; Estrada et al, 1977; Weisbard and Goy, 1976]. The amount of social grooming varies between 6% and 25% of the observation time [Rhine and Kronenwetter, 1972; Bernstein, 1980]. Social grooming occurs most in the late afternoon and least at midday and during cold weather [Bernstein, 1980]. In some groups the amounts of grooming given are negatively correlated with the social ranks of the individuals, and the amounts received are positively correlated with rank; in other groups, however, there is no correlation with rank [Bertrand, 1969; Estrada et al, 1977]. Grooming may be solicited [Bertrand, 1969; Blurton-Jones and Trollope, 1968]. Most social grooming is shown by the least aggressive females. Grooming between females is mostly done by only one of the partners. In male/female pairs, the roles of groomee and groomer switch [Blurton-Jones and Trollope, 1968]. Most grooming is shown by adults and more by females than males [Bertrand, 1969; Estrada and Estrada, 1978]. Grooming takes place mostly between individuals of similar rank. Within a grooming pair, most of the grooming is administered by the member of the lower rank.

Grooming is used as an appeasement gesture to establish, maintain, and renew contacts and to somehow strengthen social bonds, but it can also be alternated with bullying of the groomee [Bertrand, 1969; Rhine, 1973]. Young infants are groomed by their mothers and by other adult females [Bertrand, 1969; Rhine and Hendy-Neely, 1978a,b]. The infants' first fragmentary grooming movements appear at 3–5 weeks of age and are well coordinated at 4–6 months [Chevalier-Skolnikoff, 1974]. The arrival of newcomers in a group causes a temporary increase in all social interactions—especially in antagonism, but also in social grooming [Estrada and Estrada, 1978]. In male/ female pairs, the female remains for a longer time in close proximity to the male when grooming is possible, but she does not remain close by after a period of grooming [Goosen, 1974a, 1980]. Grooming reduces the probability of self-directed aggression [Goosen and Ribbens, 1980; Goosen and Metz, 1980]. In adults, self-grooming is induced by proximity to a partner if social grooming is experimentally prevented [Goosen, 1974b].

In *M. cyclopis*, self-grooming duration varies from 6% to 16% and social grooming from 3% to 12% of observation time. There is no consistent pattern in the distribution of grooming over the day [Kawai and Mito, 1973].

In *M. fascicularis*, social grooming accounts for most of the social activity; social grooming is twice as frequent as self-grooming (which occurs at a rate of 1 bout per hour). Groomer and groomee may exchange roles [Sussman and Tattersall, 1981]. Infants are groomed by their mothers. Young infants are also groomed when abducted by the highest-ranking female [Welker et al, 1980]. Adult females groom much more than subadults and adult males [Soczka, 1974]. Grooming is mainly directed to close relatives, who also provide support in agonistic episodes [Angst, 1975]. The sequence of activities upon introduction into a group is first agonistic behavior, then sexual interaction, and finally social grooming [Welker et al, 1980]. A newly introduced, sexually active male receives much grooming interest from females, especially from those that are also sexually active [Jones et al, 1982].

In *Macaca fuscata*, social grooming is much more frequent than self-grooming. Just before and during a social grooming interaction, the animals make use of complex utterances [Mori, 1975]. The groomer is often excited and has a reduced sensitivity to surroundings; the groomee relaxes and assumes a defenseless posture [Oki and Maeda, 1973]. Social grooming is often reciprocal and mostly directed to the groomee's back. Possibly, flakes of dandruff or ectoparasites are removed. Grooming in parties of several individuals takes place mostly around midday [Furuya, 1965]. Grooming is most frequent between females and offspring; it is less frequent between adult male and adult female and very rare between other partners [Mori, 1977; see also Furuya, 1965; Oki and Maeda, 1973; Hasegawa and Hiraiwa, 1980; Grewal, 1980b]. Under captive conditions, the amounts of grooming are greater [Oki and Maeda, 1973; Tartabini, 1978]. Some mothers groom infants while holding a stone as a way to distract the baby [Weinberg and Candland, 1981].

The amount of grooming is not correlated with social rank [Alexander, 1970]. Sometimes, a dominant reacts aggressively to grooming invitations from submissive animals. If a groomer is socially submissive, it may be startled by small movements of the groomee [Oki and Maeda, 1973].

Dominant males associate with and groom females during the birth season; submissive males groom females in the mating season [Alexander, 1970]. During the mating season, adult females shown an increase in the amount of grooming with males as well as with females [d'Amato et al, 1982; Furuya, 1965]. The male grooms his genitals after ejaculation; the female also self-grooms or just sits after copulation [Hanby et al, 1971].

Grooming between males is performed mostly unilaterally by the low-ranking individual, presumably to dissolve tension [Furuya, 1965]. So-called central males groom more than other males and have grooming relations with a number of different kinship groups; they have little grooming contact with their own kin [Grenwal, 1980a].

M. mulatta. Social grooming is an important social activity of adults; it takes place throughout the day, with a peak in the midmorning or midday rest [Seay, 1966; Post and Baulu, 1978]. There is often a brief bout of grooming when an animal awakes from napping. Grooming is often solicited and reciprocated [Sade, 1965]. Mothers groom their infants; the amount of grooming in primiparous mothers is not different from that of multiparous mothers [Seay, 1966]. Mothers with babies attract interest from other females and are groomed by them [Lindburg, 1973; Hinde and Proctor, 1977]. Mothers of young infants groom less than other adult females; they also show less support to nonkindred [Small, 1982]. A high infant mortality rate may be related to a relatively low level of infant grooming by the mother [Teas et al, 1980].

Most grooming is between adult females [Lindburg, 1973; Teas et al, 1980]. Social grooming is the first-ranking social activity of adult females. Adult males receive more grooming from adult females than they give. Among females, the amount of social grooming in which an individual is involved correlates with its social rank and the number of relatives it has [Post and Baulu, 1978]. Most grooming is between animals of similar rank; in some groups, slightly more than half of the grooming is by the higher-ranking member of the pair [Lindburg, 1973]; in other groups, however, the reverse holds true [Kaufmann, 1970]. Submissive animals may make vigorous movements when grooming high-ranking individuals [Lindburg, 1973]. Most (76%) of all social grooming interactions are between relatives which are frequently in each others' vicinity. From three to six years of the offspring's age, mothers and daughters groom each other more than do mothers and sons. Parents receive more grooming from their older offspring then they give [Sade, 1965; Missakian, 1974].

The movements in social grooming and the sites groomed are not predictable by those evident in self-grooming [Boccia, 1983]. Body sites groomed depend on the rank, sex, and gestures of the groomee [Boccia et al, 1982]; different body sites (head versus posterior) may indicate different tendencies to discontinue the grooming [Boccia, 1984] or any other interaction [Boccia et al, 1982]. Wounded animals solicit grooming; this is more successful in higher- than in lower-ranking individuals. In males, the amount of self-grooming is inversely related to rank and to the amount of social grooming [Post and Baulu, 1978], which suggests that self-grooming can be a substitute for social grooming.

During the mating season, males prefer nonrelated females as partners. Females prefer male grooming partners of high rank [Kaufmann, 1970; see also Wade, 1976]. Strange females introduced during the mating season are groomed by males, but the same females can be attacked during the nonmating season [Bernstein et al, 1977; Wade, 1976]. Female grooming of the male takes place in alternation with copulations. Estrous females often groom with the consort male but also with other males and juvenile females [Carpenter, 1942; Sade, 1965; Southwick et al, 1965; Drickamer, 1976]. During estrus, females and consorts are often aggressive to third parties [Lindburg, 1973]. In males, castration leads to a decrease in sexual behavior and grooming; subsequent gonadotropin administration leads to an increase in sexual behavior as well as in grooming [Gordon et al, 1979]. Castrates have grooming contact almost exclusively with each other [Wilson and Vessey, 1968; Boelkins and Wilson 1972]. An agonadal adult male with a juvenile testosterone level showed normal grooming and consort relations with adult females, although there was no copulation [Bernstein et al, 1979].

The relationship between aggression and grooming is complex. Former groomers may renew conflict, but there are also instances in which the groomer seems somehow to placate an aggressor. An aggressed animal also seems to be comforted by being groomed by a third party [Lindburg, 1973; DeWaal and Yoshihara, 1983]; an aggressor is likely to groom a third party after the conflict [DeWaal and Yoshihara, 1983]. Individuals crowd and fight in a feeding area but do not groom there [Baulu and Redmond, 1980]. Social contacts between different groups consist mainly of aggressive and sexual interactions. Exceptional grooming contacts occur between relatives [Vessey, 1968; Marsden, 1968; Hausfater, 1972]. When new males are introduced into a group of established males, the newcomers are initially aggressed and later groomed [Bernstein and Gordon, 1980]. Newly introduced individuals show a gradual increase in social grooming interaction with resident group members [Bernstein, 1964].

M. nemestrina. In the field, grooming is rather rare [Bernstein, 1967a,b] compared with in captivity [Bernstein, 1970]. During grooming, the groomee often adopts a relaxed posture. Wounds are groomed even when painful to the groomee [Rosenblum et al, 1966]. The amount of self-grooming is negatively correlated with the amount of social grooming received [Rosenblum et al, 1966], which suggests that animals revert to self-grooming if for some reason social grooming is not possible. The amounts of self-grooming are not different for males and females [Kaufmann and Rosenblum, 1966; Defler, 1978].

Social grooming is most prominent at around noon and in cold weather [Bernstein, 1972]. It is shown primarily by adults; females groom more than males [Rosenblum et al, 1966; Defler, 1978]. Mothers groom their infants at a fairly constant rate during the first 3 months of infant life [Jensen et al, 1973]. The amount of grooming by an adult male after temporary removal from the group is initially small and gradually increases after a week [Bernstein, 1972]. Bouts of social grooming last for longer on the average than those of self-grooming [Rosenblum et al, 1966]. Male copulatory behavior may be interrupted by brief grooming of the female, and the female may groom the male after copulation [Rosenblum et al, 1966; Goosen and Kortmulder, 1979].

M. nigra. Grooming is usually reciprocal but not simultaneous [Nickelson and Lockard, 1978].

M. radiata. Grooming is mainly manual, rarely with the mouth; self-grooming is only a small percentage of all grooming [Simonds, 1965; Rosenblum et al, 1966; Koyama, 1973]. Negative correlations between amounts of self-grooming and initiation as well as receipt of social grooming [Rosenblum et al, 1966] suggest that the animals revert to self-grooming when they do not engage in social grooming.

The amount of time spent in grooming varies among troops; the greatest amounts of social grooming are at around noon after the morning eating period [Simonds, 1965; Rahaman and Parthasarathy, 1969]. Most social grooming is performed by adults, and females groom more than males [Rosenblum et al, 1966; Defler, 1978]. Most grooming is directed to same-sex partners [Simonds, 1965]. In some groups, females are groomed especially by their own daughters and daughters of lower-ranking mothers [Silk et al, 1981]. Females groom relatives and higher-ranking individuals, and they also support them against lower-ranking opponents. There is no consistent preferential support for the most favored grooming partner. Group members rarely attack their own groomer or the groomer of higher-ranking individuals [Silk, 1982; Koyama, 1973]. However, differences in amounts of grooming between males and females and grooming preferences according to rank or kinship are not present in all groups [Simonds, 1965; Sugiyama, 1971; Defler, 1978]. Mothers with infants are groomed more than females without infants. Mothers also groom their babies [Sugiyama, 1971]. Wounds on adults elicit grooming [Rosenblum et al, 1966].

M. silenus. A mother with a baby is reported to be groomed by subadult and juvenile females, who occasionally also groom the baby [Kumar and Kurup, 1981].

M. sylvana. Mothers groom their babies [Whiten and Rumsey, 1973] often during nursing [Deag and Crook, 1971]. Mothers with babies are groomed by females and juveniles; the latter do this apparently in order to get a look at the baby [Deag and Crook, 1971]. Adult males interact with [Whiten and Ramsey, 1973] and groom [Lahiri and Southwick, 1966] infants [Deag and Crook, 1971], which serve as a "buffer" against male-male aggression. The males then proceed to groom each other while abandoning their "buffer." Occasionally, a dead infant may be groomed [Merz, 1978].

Mandrillus. In *M. sphinx,* most grooming is done by females to their infants. The male is little involved in social grooming [Mellen et al, 1981].

Papio. In *P. anubis,* the highest-ranking member receives on the average the longest grooming bouts in a social grooming pair. Social grooming can also be invited—eg, by grasping the hindquarters of the groomer to be [Buirski et al, 1973]. Females show little social grooming during the last phase of pregnancy, but they receive much interest and grooming from female group members after the infant's birth. The amount of grooming given or received by mothers is not related to social rank. Mothers cannot relax when groomed, however, because the baby may be taken away for some time by a group member [Altmann, 1980]. Infants receive the greatest amounts of grooming by group members when they start to leave their mothers; at this age, the infant is often approached and groomed by adults. The infant grooms its mother often when the mother starts to reject it and tolerates having it nearby only when it is grooming [Nash, 1978; Anthoney, 1968]. In a social group, a stepwise decrease in cage size leads to increases in aggression and sexual behavior; grooming first increases and then decreases with decreasing cage size [Elton and Anderson, 1977].

In *P. hamadryas*, social grooming consumes a large proportion of the time. The species lives mainly in one-male units; grooming is mostly a female activity directed toward the male or her infants [Kummer and Kurt, 1963; Kummer, 1968; Nagel, 1973]. Grooming movements of the female are often more frantic after the receipt of a neck bite by the male [Kummer, 1968]. Females compete for the opportunity to groom the male. Frequent grooming between the young male and juvenile female may be a first step in the formation of a one-male unit [Kummer, 1968].

Infants start to groom briefly at the age of 6–8 weeks; they submit to being groomed only at 16–20 weeks of age [Bowden, 1966]. In juvenile play, wrestling can be alternated with aggression and submission or with grooming [Le Resche, 1976].

Females prefer to groom a dominant individual when housed in a group, but they avoid dominant individuals when housed in pairs. In the group, the amount of grooming between two partners depends on the groomee's general willingness to submit to grooming; in pairs the amount of grooming depends on the groomers general likelihood to groom [Stammbach and Kummer, 1982].

In *P. cynocephalus*, grooming is a very prominent activity, especially in the early morning and at the midday [Hall and DeVore, 1965]. Grooming may be invited by turning the flank to the groomer. Females compete to be near high-ranking females [Seyfarth, 1978b], which are groomed more than submissive ones [Hall and DeVore, 1965].

Adult males and females groom each other when they are close together as consorts [Saayman, 1970, 1971]. Postcopulatory grooming occurs, especially by the female in the ovulatory phase of the menstrual cycle [Saayman, 1970; Seyfarth, 1978a]. Females groom males more than males groom females, except during the "swollen" stage of the menstrual cycle, for which the reverse holds true [Saayman, 1970]. A lactating female grooms a male when another, swollen female presents to him. Immature males groom and attempt to copulate with lower-ranking females; immature females groom and attempt to interact with infants of higher-ranking members [Cheney, 1978]. Females with young infants receive much interest and grooming from other group members [Hall and DeVore, 1965].

Theropithecus. In *T. gelada*, social grooming is a prominent activity; it is reciprocal though not simultaneous. Grooming is the most frequent social contact [Bramblett, 1970; Bernstein, 1975; Alvarez and Consul, 1978]. The grooming scores are low during the early morning and in hot weather, and are highest in the afternoon and during cold weather [Fedigan, 1972; Bernstein, 1975]. Members of the one-male units groom only each other; the bachelor males do like-wise [Bernstein, 1975].

Grooming behavior of females is directed mainly to relatives [Dunbar, 1983]. The unit's male is preferred only be females without close relatives. Amounts of male/female grooming do not differ between periods with and without mating. Mothers groom their infants as early as from 2 h after birth. Mothers with young infants are approached by other group members, who may groom her but are allowed to groom the infant only at a later age [Dunbar and Dunbar, 1974].

Pygathrix. P. *nemaeus* social behavior, grooming included, is similar to that of *Colobus*; only the eyelid display and copulation are different [Kavanagh, 1978].

Presbytis. P. *entellus* mothers groom their infants at 30 min after birth, when the infant is on the nipple [Oppenheimer, 1976]. Social grooming is a prominent adult interaction, especially between females. Grooming interactions may include invitations to groom, mutual grooming, refusal of grooming, ignoring or turning away, termination of grooming, and self-grooming. Grooming involves quick manual brushing aside of hairs and picking between them [Jay, 1965; Dolhinow, 1978; McKenna, 1978]. Most social grooming takes place under relaxed conditions; 35% of all social grooming follows a bout of aggression and is therefore regarded as tension-reducing. Relaxed grooming is directed mostly to the groomer's ventrum, and tension-reducing grooming mostly to the back. The adult male tolerates female proximity to subadult males when the female grooms the subadult but not when she solicits sexually [McKenna, 1978]. Licking of the hand and wiping over the face is also reported as a form of self-grooming [Lorenz, 1966].

In *P. cristalus*, social grooming is often reciprocal. Grooming is shown by all age and sex classes, and it often involves mother/infant pairs. Self-grooming is rare [Bernstein, 1968].

P. johnii grooming is performed manually, but particles are removed with the mouth. Social grooming is directed mainly to body parts that are difficult to reach and is mainly between females; this may be enhanced by the nearby presence of a male. Being groomed seems to be a relaxing experience. Most grooming is on warm days at around noon. About half of all grooming bouts are initiated in agonistic situations. Most grooming is performed by the submissive member of the pair [Poirier, 1970].

Summary on Cercopithecidae. Cercopithecidae are the most extensively studied primate family. Grooming is performed manually, and it may be accompanied by opening and closing the mouth or by lip smacking as if the animal were ingesting a small particle. Grooming behavior is conspicuous in all species, but more so in some (*Macaca* and *Papio*) than in others (*Colobus*).

The Cercopithecidae are rather diverse in their habitat choice, nutritional requirements, and type of social organization. Some species (*Cercocebus, Cer-*

456

copithecus, except for *C. aethiops*) live high up in the primary or secondary forest (*Colobus, Presbytis, Miopithecus*) or on the forest floor (*Mandrillus, Macaca arctoides*). Other species may live in open woodland (*Cercopithecus aethiops, Macaca mulatta*), in savanna (*Papio cynocephus*), or in near desert (*Presbytis entellus, Papio hamadryas, Theropithecus*). Some species like *Colobus* and *Presbytis* can be characterized as largely folivorous; others, like *Macaca* and *Papio*, are rather much less specialized and exploit a variety of food resources. Many species live in small groups usually composed of one adult male and a few breeding females and offspring. But in other genera (*Macaca, Papio*), there can be a great variation from small single male groups to large multimale groups with a distinct structure. The amount of time spent in grooming varies between groups within one species almost as much as it varies between groups of different species of a genus. Differences in the amounts of grooming between species are not clearly correlated with specific ecological or life-style characteristics.

From the reviewed data, it is clear that grooming is intricately related to the social life of the animals, which may be very complex, especially in *Macaca* and *Papio*. A number of social aspects of grooming are given in the general summary below.

Hylobatidae

Symphalangus (Hylobates) syndactylus. Being engaged in social grooming is the most frequent adult social activity; the time of peak activity during the day differs between groups. Male-grooms-female is the main direction during the breeding season; the reverse holds true for the nonbreeding season [Fox, 1972; Chivers, 1979]. Grooming of the male by the female is seen after approach by the male and as a prelude to copulation [Koyama, 1971]. Infants are groomed by their mothers.

Hylobates. In captive *H. lar*, amounts of grooming are rather small [Bernstein and Schusterman, 1964]. Grooming is invited by lying down. It is most frequent at about 11 a.m. or between morning naps. In a different population, the peak occurred at around 3 p.m. Social grooming is directed mostly to the head and shoulders, legs, arms, and back [Fox, 1972; Carpenter, 1940]. Grooming also takes place in the early morning prior to the calling session [Ellefson, 1968]. Most grooming is directed toward the adult male, who reciprocates little [Fox, 1972; Chivers, 1979]. Grooming between male and female may alternate with mating [Carpenter, 1940]. One socially isolated individual that attempted to groom or to receive grooming was aggressively rebuffed [Fox, 1972].

Summary on Hylobatidae. The family Hylobatidae is an arboreal family of brachiators living in the canopy of secondary forests. The typical group structure is a male/female pair with young offspring. Social grooming is seen in all species, but more in *Symphalanglus* than in *Hylobates* [Chivers, 1979].

457

Pongidae

Pongo pygmaeus. In wild orangs, self-grooming takes place only occasionally and not very thoroughly. Social grooming between adults is seen only briefly during consorting; otherwise, it is rare in this rather solitary species [Mackinnon, 1974; Horr, 1975]. Mothers occasionally groom their infants [Mackinnon, 1974].

In captive groups, adults groom each other but juveniles do not participate in grooming [Edwards, 1982]. In experimental encounters between two females with infants, the socially dominant female reaches out to the subordinate, examines the infant, and then grooms or hits and bites the subordinate [Nadler and Tilford, 1977].

Pan. Grooming is performed with the fingers, and small particles may be picked up with the lower lip [Nishida, 1983]. Self-grooming is more frequent in old animals than in young [Goodall, 1965; Van Lawick-Goodall, 1968]. Social grooming is directed to parts difficult to reach in self-grooming [Van Lawick-Goodall, 1968]. The animals frequently groom themselves as well as each other when heavily infested with ticks [Wilson and Elicker, 1976]. Social grooming is often accompanied by an exaggerated lip smacking—ie, loud noises resulting from pressing air through firmly compressed lips [Van Lawick-Goodall, 1968; "splutter," Van Hooff, 1971].

Social grooming is a time-consuming activity, often taking place over long periods of time in parties of up to six individuals of any age [Goodall, 1965; Van Lawick-Goodall, 1968]. The greatest amounts are shown by adults, particularly during the morning hours [King et al, 1980; Kraemer et al, 1982]. During rest, chimpanzees often indulge in grooming for long periods of time [Nishida, 1970], but frequent grooming partners do not sleep together [Riss and Goodall, 1976]. Grooming is increased shortly after rainy weather [Sugiyama, 1969]. Grooming is brief when used as a form of greeting and when used after copulation [Goodall, 1965]. Rapid and ineffective self- or social grooming movements are made when chimpanzees are waiting for food. Grooming redirected to dry leaves is used to attract attention from other nearby individuals [Van Lawick-Goodall, 1968]. An adult male spends a rather constant 10% of its time in social grooming [Riss and Busse, 1977].

In captivity, the amount of grooming is sometimes less than that seen in wild chimpanzees [King et al, 1980]. Male/female grooming is increased during estrous [Reynolds and Reynolds, 1965]. An estrous female may alternate between grooming with one male partner and copulation with another [Sugiyama, 1971]. Fully adult males copulate quite openly with receptive females. Grooming between males may be shown as an appeasement gesture; it may even be a prelude to a new coalition [DeWaal, 1982].

Most grooming among adults is between males, which are the tight nucleus of the group important with regard to foraging and territory defense [Nishida, 1979; Van Lawick-Goodall, 1968b; Bygott, 1979; Goodall et al, 1979; Kuroda,

458

1980]. Among adult males, the highest-ranking animals are most likely to participate in grooming interactions [Simpson, 1971; Bygott, 1979]. Grooming is equally often initiated by high- and low-ranking partners, but the highest-ranking partner is groomed longer [Simpson, 1971]. High-ranking males may "force" a submissive animal to continue grooming by threatening him. Males often groom each other's genitals, which seems to be a way of releasing tension [Sugiyama, 1971]. High-ranking individuals that display aggressively have more brief grooming contacts than nondisplaying males. In the food provision area, displaying males are more likely to be groomed than they are outside the area [Bauer, 1979]. Grooming activity is relatively high during periods when conflicts are frequent [DeWaal, 1982]. A dramatic decrease in housing space leads to a moderate increase in aggression and a somewhat greater increase in grooming [Nieuwenhuijsen and DeWaal, 1982]. Grooming between allies may be performed prior to starting conflict with a third party [DeWaal, 1982]. The lower-ranking partner in a male coalition may extensively groom the dominant prior to copulating with a receptive female; such grooming is regarded as a way of "negotiating" access to the female [DeWaal, 1982]. An adult male joining a meat-eating party is groomed by the top-ranking male, after which the adult male does not join the party again [Kawanaka, 1982].

Mothers with infants often groom each other [Van Lawick-Goodall, 1968]. In captivity, mothers sometimes groom their own infants [Savage and Malick, 1977; Horvat and Kraemer, 1981] so persistently that it becomes uncomfortable to the infants [Savage et al, 1973]. In the wild, very young infants are groomed very little by their mothers and often remain soiled for several days. Mothers sometimes seem to distract their infants by grooming them. Infants over 2 years of age are often groomed by siblings [Van Lawick-Goodall, 1968 a and b]. Mothers with infants also receive interest from and are groomed by adult males and nulliparous females. This may be followed by transfer and alloparental holding of the infant [Nishida, 1983]. Mothers also groom subadult offspring [Van Lawick-Goodall, 1968 a and b]. Being groomed by a person enables a young animal to stay close to that person; having the opportunity to groom the person may [Falk, 1958] or may not [Mason, 1965] be rewarding in this respect.

P. paniscus uses its lips while searching between the hairs during grooming. Grooming is not solicited [Patterson, 1979; Kuroda, 1980]. Grooming is most prominent after rain. Grooming bouts between adults last longer than those between subadults. Grooming occurs more often between males and females than between females [Kuroda, 1980].

Gorilla. Self-grooming, which may be intense, is performed by females twice as often as it is by males [Schaller, 1965]. Social grooming has been seen between the adult male and females, but, in general, adult social grooming is rare [Schaller, 1964; 1965; Elliot, 1976; Fischer and Nalder, 1977; Hoff et al, 1982; Maple and Hoff, 1982]. It is not seen in alternation with mating [Schaller, 1964; Maple and Hoff, 1982].

Females groom their infants [Reynolds, 1979]; during suckling, grooming is casual. At 12 months, the infants more readily submit to being groomed by their mothers and initiate grooming themselves. From 2–3 years of age, social grooming may be directed to the mother, siblings, and peers as well as to the silver-backed male [Fossey, 1979]. Juveniles seem to use grooming to make contact with females with infants [Schaller, 1969]. Grooming is more frequent in captivity than in the wild [Carpenter, 1937]. Captive mothers inspect and poke at the infants, but grooming of the infant is rare [Hess, 1981; Maple and Hoff, 1982].

Summary on Pongidae. Self- and social grooming have been observed in all pongids. There seems to be a relationship between grooming and the type of social life of the species. Grooming is rare in the rather solitary *Pongo* and in *Gorilla*, which live in small groups of stable composition; it is quite prominent in *Pan troglodytes*, which lives in small groups varying in membership, a larger community.

Summary of the Distribution of Grooming Across Families

All primates show self- and social grooming, but the type and quantities very among the taxa. In all prosimians, grooming is mainly oral. With the possible exception of the mother/infant relationship, self-grooming is much more prevalent than social grooming. In all Anthropoidea, grooming consists mainly of manual separation of hairs, visual inspection of the skin, and removal of small particles with the thumb and index finger and sometimes with the lips and tongue. Social grooming in Old World monkeys is often accompanied by opening and closing of the lips (as in *Cercopithecus*) or by more extensive and conspicuous lip smacking (as in *Macaca*). In *Pan*, social grooming is often accompanied by rather loud noises which come from the pressing of air through the compressed lips. In anthropoids, social grooming is often invited by the animal adopting a posture as if it were already being groomed. Social grooming in anthropoids is seldom mutual and simultaneous, but is often reciprocated; ie, groomer and groomee often exchange roles during one uninterrupted grooming interaction. Social grooming may be either cursory or extensive, depending on the social relation between the participants. It is often directed to body parts difficult to reach for self-grooming.

There is no simple correlation between the amount of grooming and a single life-style characteristic. There seems to be a tendency for folivorous species to groom less than frugivorous ones (compare *Presbytis* to *Macaca*, *Alouatta* to *Ateles*, *Colobus badius* to *Colobus guereza*, *Gorilla* to *Pan*). This might relate to the fact that these folivorous species must spend more time in foraging (and therefore have less time available for social interaction) than the more opportunistic, frugivorous species. In this regard, it is of interest that the frugivorous *Hylobates* travels more than the folivorous *Symphalangus*, which is the more active groomer. However, it seems likely that the amount of grooming is constrained also by factors other than foraging, such as demands imposed by avoidance of predation. For instance, the savanna-dwelling *Papio cynocephalus* is a less active groomer than is *Papio hamadryas* [Nagel, 1973], which lives in near desert, where carnivores are rare. To live in large, highly nomadic bands leaves *Saimiri* less time to spend in grooming than the relatively sedentary life-style allows the other Cebidae.

Social grooming, however, is not evenly distributed over the members of a species. It varies greatly with the social situation of the individuals. Among the various socially living species, there is a certain consistency in the characteristics of social grooming, which can be summarized as follows.

1) Social grooming is mostly between adults rather than between subadults or juveniles.
2) It is prevalent during periods of resting by the group.
3) Social grooming between adults often constitutes a major part of all the time spent in social interaction.
4) It takes place more often between animals of similar social rank than between those of distant rank.
5) It is increased after episodes of agonism.
6) It is performed more by the submissive than by the dominant member of a grooming pair.
7) It is shown more by females than by males, with the notable exception of the chimpanzee, in which it is most often between dominant males.
8) It is increased during the mating season, especially between members of the opposite sex.
9) Male grooming of the female is increased during the ovulatory phase of the female's menstrual cycle when she consorts with a male.
10) Mothers groom their offspring.
11) Grooming is directed to a female with a newborn baby by other group members that are interested in the baby.
12) It occurs most between close relatives, at least in the nonmating season.
13) It is usually not directed to members of another group.
14) Arrival of newcomers in a group affects grooming between resident members.

FUNCTIONAL ASPECTS OF GROOMING

There can be little doubt that grooming behavior has a function in removing ectoparasites from the skin. Primates are natural hosts of lice and ticks [Kuhn, 1967; Dunn, 1968], parasites that can transmit dangerous diseases. That the animals often appear to be relatively free of ectoparasites is a result of the grooming efforts and of social grooming being directed to body parts of difficult access to the groomee.

Grooming probably also keeps the pelage in good condition by the removal of dirt and separation of hairs sticking together. In fact, the type of grooming shown by a species seems to be adapted to the structure of the pelage; Tupaii-dae lick and rub normal body hair but rake the long, coarse tail hairs with the lower incisors. Most prosimians have a toothcomb to groom their fine and rather dense fur, but anthropoids, with their much coarser hairs, mostly groom manually. The cleaning function of grooming clearly explains why an animal submits to being groomed. Since grooming the coat of another individual does not increase the cleanliness of the groomer's own coat, the reason animals groom socially is less straightforward. There is no indication that social grooming yields any nutrients to the groomer. The functional significance of social grooming to the groomer must be explained in terms of altruism, either through inclusive fitness [Hamilton, 1964] or reciprocal altruism [Trivers, 1971].

However, there are a number of indications that cleaning is not a major function of social grooming. Most animals are almost free of parasites and yet eagerly participate in lengthy grooming sessions. The coordination, sequence, and orientation of movements during social grooming are often rather perfunctory instead of being a careful and thorough searching and picking up of particles. Moreover, the state of the pelage of an animal does not determine the amount of grooming it receives; most animals are already quite clean, but soiled animals obviously in need of grooming do not elicit more grooming than do others [see Bertrand, 1969].

The idea that grooming served some important social function was early expressed by Watson [1908], who considered "flea catching" the most fundamental form of social intercourse between rhesus monkeys. Carpenter [1942] later suggested that grooming strengthens social bonds. Sade [1965] considered grooming useful for establishing, maintaining, and renewing peaceful relations. Terry [1970] regarded grooming as a way to reduce tension. Since then, similar views have been expressed by many authors [see Sparks, 1967]. The present review further supports the close relation between grooming and many aspects of social life ranging from simple and relaxed situations (such as a single pair resting together) to complex and tense (such as alliance formation against a third party). The nature of this complicated relation is still poorly understood. A tentative hypothesis is as follows [see also Goosen, 1981].

By grooming another individual, the groomer actively indicates merely that under the given circumstances it wishes to remain close to the groomee. This message cannot be interpreted otherwise as long as the groomee's coat is hardly in need of any cleaning. It is also clear to whom it is directed and for how long because groomer and groomee are in close tactile contact. The degree to which the given message is informative depends entirely on the situation, in which third parties may or may not be involved. By submitting to being groomed, the groomee gives essentially the same message to the groomer as the groomer gives to the groomee; the only difference is that the effort by the groomer is greater than that of the groomee. The frequency at which the animals indulge in grooming depends on the likelihood of misunderstanding between the grooming partners. The duration of the grooming interaction depends on whether in the given situation either or both individuals have more urgent things to attend to, such as napping or allying against a third party. Under this hypothesis, social grooming can lead to a reduction of tension but probably also to the building up of tension. This is supported by the fact that a groomee sometimes attacks its partner. The observation that a dominant male in a party of chimpanzees can make a submissive male stay away from that party simply by grooming him [Kawanaka, 1982] also suggests that building up of tension. In this instance, the cause of the tension might be that the low-ranking animal's relationship to the dominant male calls for agonistic competition from other, intermediate-ranked males.

SUGGESTIONS FOR FURTHER RESEARCH

The above review shows that some taxa have been studied less than others; further research could therefore fill some of the gaps. In the literature, there is general agreement that the functions served by social grooming are largely the same in related species. The previous section tentatively explains grooming as emphasizing that the performer wished to be near the groomee in the given situation. A logical next step, therefore, is to investigate how the animals perceive the various situations and why the emphasis is worth the effort. In such an approach, the present hypothesis can be used to formulate concrete questions and new hypotheses. In this regard, the relationship between social grooming and dominance rank has been frequently considered. But rank is only a relative measure usually based on the ratio of winning and losing disputes; it includes no information about the nature and frequency of the disputes. For instance, how can a subdominant adult male chimpanzee, by prolonged grooming, "negotiate" access to an estrous female from a dominant male [DeWaal, 1982]? A possible answer is that, by prolonged grooming, the subdominant stresses that he wished to remain close to the dominant in that situation (of a nearby estrous female). This informs the dominant that by courting the female, he risks a dispute with the subdominant which jeopardizes his good relation with his aide-decamp. Since the dominant needs this good relation in order to dominate the other males in the group, he must occasionally grant the subdominant access to a female. Another example: Why do pair members of the rather sedentary, monogomous *Callicebus* spend large amounts of time in grooming each other [Kinzey and Wright, 1982]? A possible explanation could be that, since the animals are territorial and communicate vocally with neighboring pairs [Mason, 1968], coordination of activities between pair members is not a matter of course, because of the possibilities of separation, recoupling, and territory takeovers. Further investigations aimed at testing the hypotheses can lead to better insightinto each situation with regard to the survival resources and risks it involves. Further research could also be extended to the morphology of grooming—ie, the type and speed of the movements and the body parts addressed that are likely to be of communicative significance [Boccia, 1984]. Up to now, however, this aspect has received little attention.

MAN

A review on grooming in primates is hardly complete without some words on the human primate (*Homo sapiens*). Grooming behavior in humans is special in many ways. Humans are virtually naked; they grow long hairs only on the skull and course hairs only on eyebrows, eyelashes, armpits, genital areas, and, in adult males, on the lower face. Grooming behavior similar to that of Old World monkeys, therefore, is seen only when it is directed to these hairy body parts. When we consider the functional aspect of grooming, maintaining the "pelage" in good condition, then humans achieve this by a large number of techniques including combing, brushing, and washing hairs. As cover for the naked parts of the body, humans dress themselves in disposable coats for either mechanical protection, thermal insulation, or social display purposes. These coats are prepared and kept in good condition by a variety of dressmaking and cleaning activities. As in Old World monkeys, humans also solicit grooming from other individuals, often doing this in preparation for certain social occasions or gatherings. Such soliciting is usually directed to certain professional groomers (hairdressers, dressmakers, etc) who, if they are nonrelatives, normally demand additional rewards (money) for their efforts. In these cases, there is usually no role reversal between groomer and groomee.

The social function of these grooming activities in humans, however, is primarily related to the display of being thoroughly and stylishly groomed. So far, we have no indication that a similar phenomenon exists in nonhuman primates. In monkeys, well-groomed subjects frequently look different from poorly groomed ones, but we have no indication that monkeys make use of looking well groomed as a social display.

An important aspect of social grooming in monkeys, however, is that it is a time-consuming activity that in itself is socially informative to the partners. An analogous activity in humans would be conversation, comprising lip-smacking movements accompanied by mostly low, gruntlike vocalizations with semantic value (possibly similar to the signals seen during grooming in *Macaca fuscata* [Mori, 1975]. Like social grooming in Old World monkeys, the activity itself has little intrinsic survival value, it is time-consuming, and the partners often alternate the roles of giver and receiver within an interaction. I am not aware of a list of the situations in which conversation takes place, but it is likely that such a list would be strikingly similar to that for social grooming in monkeys. It would probably also include groups of dominant males involved in food seeking and territorial defense (as in chimpanzees) and diverse contacts of more politically oriented "central" males (as in *Macaca fuscata*).

The analogy between conversation and social grooming is also supported by the fact that the communicative significance of the utterances (words) depends strongly on the situation in which they are spoken. The major difference between human conversation and social grooming in monkeys is that human speech permits a more detailed symbolic reference to environmental conditions. These comparisons between human and nonhuman primates show that the manual social grooming of Old World monkeys is relatively rare in man. However, man makes use of a number of more highly developed activities for the various functions grooming serves in monkeys. Comparative study of social grooming in monkeys and human conversation might therefore increase our basic understanding of human communication and social behavior.

ACKNOWLEDGMENTS

The author is grateful to Dr. H. Dienske and Dr. A.C. Ford for their valuable comments and to Ms. D. van der Velden for typing the manuscript.

REFERENCES

Abordo, E.J.; Mittermeier, R.A.; Lee, J.; and Mason, P. Social grooming between squirrel monkeys and uakaris in a seminatural environment. PRIMATES 16:217–221, 1975.

Alexander, B.K. Parental behavior of adult male Japanese monkeys. BEHAVIOUR 34:270–285, 1970.

Altmann, J. BABOON MOTHERS AND INFANTS. Cambridge, MA. Harvard University Press, 1980.

Alvarez, F. Social hierarchy under different criteria in groups of squirrel monkeys. *Saimiri sciureus*. PRIMATES 16:437–445, 1975.

Alvarez, F.; Consul, C. The structure of social behaviour in *Theropithecus gelada*. PRIMATES 19:45–59, 1978.

Angst, W. Basic data and concepts on the social organization of *Macaca fascicularis*. Pp. 325–388 PRIMATES BEHAVIOR, DEVELOPMENTS IN FIELD AND LABORATORY RESEARCH, L.A. Rosenblum, ed., New York, Academic Press, 1975.

Anschel, S.; Talmage-Riggs, G. Social organization of captive nonandrous squirrel monkey groups (*Saimiri sciureus*). FOLIA PRIMATOLOGICA 28:203–215, 1977.

Anthoney, T.R. The ontogeny of greeting, grooming and sexual motor patterns in captive baboons (super-species *Papio cynocephalus*). BEHAVIOUR 31:358–372, 1968.

Baldwin, J.D.; Baldwin, J.I. The ecology and behavior of squirrel monkeys (*Saimiri oerstedi*) in a natural forest in western Panama. FOLIA PRIMATOLOGICA 18:161–184, 1972.

Baldwin, J.D.; Baldwin, J.I. Interactions between adult female and infant howling monkeys (*Alouatta palliata*). FOLIA PRIMATOLOGICA 20:27–71, 1973.

Bauer, H.R. Agonistic and grooming behavior in the reunion context of Gombe Stream chimpanzees. Pp. 395–404 in THE GREAT APES. D.A. Hamburg, E.R. McCown, eds. Benjamin Cummings, Menlo Park, 1979.

Bauiu, J.; Redmond, D.E. Social and nonsocial behaviours of sex- and age-matched enclosed and free-ranging rhesus monkeys (*Macaca mulatta*). FOLIA PRIMATOLOGICA 34:239–258, 1980.

Bernstein, I.S. The integration of rhesus monkeys introduced to a group. FOLIA PRIMATOLOGICA 2:50–63, 1964.

Bernstein, I.S. Activity patterns in a cebus monkey group. FOLIA PRIMATOLOGICA 3:211–224, 1965.

Bernstein, I.S. A field study of the pigtail monkey (*Macaca nemestrina*). PRIMATES 8:217–288, 1967a.

Bernstein, I.S. Intertaxa interactions in a Malayan primate community. FOLIA PRIMATOLOGICA 3:198–207, 1967b.

Bernstein, I.S. The lutong of Kuala Selangor. BEHAVIOUR 32:1–17, 1968.

Bernstein, I.S. Activity patterns in a pigtail monkey group. FOLIA PRIMATOLOGICA 12:187–198, 1970.

Bernstein, I.S. The influence of introductory techniques on the formation of captive mangabey groups. PRIMATES 12:33–44, 1971.

Bernstein, I.S. Daily activity cycles and weather influences on a pigtail monkey group. FOLIA PRIMATOLOGICA 18:390–415, 1972.

Bernstein, I.S. Activity patterns in a gelada monkey group. FOLIA PRIMATOLOGICA 23:50–71, 1975.

Bernstein, I.S. Activity patterns in a sooty mangabey group. FOLIA PRIMATOLOGICA 26:185–206, 1976.

Bernstein, I.S. Activity patterns in a stumptail macaque group. (Macaca arctoides). FOLIA PRIMATOLOGICA 33:20–45, 1980.

Bernstein, I.S.; Gordon, T.P. The social component of dominance relationships in rhesus monkeys (Macaca mulatta). ANIMAL BEHAVIOUR 28:1033–1039, 1980.

Bernstein, I.S. and Schusterman, R.J. The activity of gibbons in a social group. FOLIA PRIMATOLOGICA 2:161–170, 1964.

Bernstein, I.S.; Rose, R.M.; Gordon, T.P. Behavioral and hormonal responses of male rhesus monkeys introduced to females in the breeding and non-breeding season. ANIMAL BEHAVIOUR 25:609–614, 1977.

Bernstein, I.S.; Gordon, T.P.; Peterson, M. Role behavior of an agonadal alpha-male rhesus monkey in a heterosexual group. FOLIA PRIMATOLOGICA 32:263–267, 1979.

Bertrand, M. The behavioral repertoire of the stumptail macaque. BIBLIOTHECA PRIMATOLOGICA II. H. Hoter, A.H. Schultz, D. Starck eds., Basel, Karger, 1969.

Blurton-Jones, N.G.; Trollope, J. Social behaviour of stumptailed macaques in captivity. PRIMATES 9:365–394, 1968.

Boccia, M. A functional analysis of social grooming patterns through direct comparison with self-grooming in rhesus monkeys. INTERNATIONAL JOURNAL OF PRIMATOLOGY 4:399–418, 1983.

Boccia, M.L. Grooming site preferences as a form of tactile communication and their role in the social relations of rhesus monkeys. In SELECTED PROCEEDINGS OF THE NINTH INTERNATIONAL CONGRESS OF PRIMATOLOGY. D.M. Taub; E.A. King, et al, eds. New York, Van Nostrand Reinhold, 1986.

Boccia, M.L.; Rockwood, B.; Novak, N.A. The influence of behavioral context and social characteristics on the physical aspect of social grooming in rhesus monkeys. INTERNATIONAL JOURNAL OF PRIMATOLOGY 3:91–108, 1982.

Boelkins, R.C.; Wilson, A.P. Intergroup social dynamics of the Cayo Santiago rhesus (Macaca mulatta) with special reference to changes in group membership by males. PRIMATES 13:125–140, 1972.

Bowden, D. Primate behavioral research in the USSR, the Sukhumi medico-biological station. FOLIA PRIMATOLOGICA 4:346–360, 1966.

Box, H.O. Quantitative studies of behavior within captive groups of marmoset monkeys. (Callithrix jacchus). PRIMATES 16:155–174, 1975a.

Box, H.O. A social development study of young monkeys (Callithrix jacchus) within a captive family group. PRIMATES 16:419–435, 1975b.

Box, H.O.; Morris, J.M. Behavioural observation on captive pairs of wild caught tamarins (Saguinus mystax). PRIMATES 21:53–65, 1980.

466

Bramblett, C.A. Coalitions among gelada baboons. PRIMATES 11:327–333, 1970.

Buettner-Janusch, J. The breeding of galagos in captivity and some notes on their behavior. FOLIA PRIMATOLOGICA 2:93–110, 1969.

Buettner-Janusch, J.; Andrew, R.K. Use of the incisors by primates in grooming. AMERICAN JOURNAL OF PHYSICAL ANTHROPOLOGY 29:129–132, 1962.

Buirski, P.; Kellerman, H.; Plutchnik, R.; Weiniger, R.; Buirski, N. A field study of emotions, dominance and social behavior in a group of baboons. (*Papio anubis*). PRIMATES 14:67–78, 1973.

Bygott, J.D. Agonistic behavior, dominance and social structure in wild chimpanzees of the Gombe National Park. Pp. 408–428 in THE GREAT APES. D.A. Hamburg; E.R. McCown, eds. Benjamin Cummings, Menlo Park, 1979.

Candland, D.K.; O'Connor, K.; Dresdale, L.; Leshner, A.; Cahill, B.; Eberhart, J. Behavior of unacquainted *Saimiri* troops upon encounter: A suggestive case study. PRIMATES 19:643–655, 1978.

Carpenter, L.R. A field study of the behavior and social relations of howling monkeys, 1934. Pp. 3–92 in NATURALISTIC BEHAVIOR OF NON-HUMAN PRIMATES. C.R. Carpenter, ed., University Park, Pennsylvania State University Press, 1964.

Carpenter, L.R. Behavior of red spider monkeys in Panama, 1935. Pp. 93–105 in NATURALISTIC BEHAVIOUR OF NON-HUMAN PRIMATES. C.R. Carpenter, ed., University Park, Pennsylvania State University Press, 1964.

Carpenter, L.R. An observational study of two captive mountain gorillas, 1937. Pp. 106–121 in NATURALISTIC BEHAVIOR OF NON-HUMAN PRIMATES. C.R. Carpenter, ed., University Park, Pennsylvania State University Press, 1964.

Carpenter, L.R. A field study in Siam of the behavior and social relations of the gibbon (*Hylobates lar*), 1940. Pp. 145–271 in NATURALISTIC BEHAVIOR OF NON-HUMAN PRIMATES. C.R. Carpenter, ed., University Park, Pennsylvania State University Press, 1964.

Carpenter, L.R. Sexual behavior of free ranging rhesus monkeys (*Macaca mulatta*). JOURNAL OF COMPARATIVE PSYCHOLOGY 33:113–142, 1942.

Carpenter, L.A. The howlers of Barro Colorado Island. Pp. 250–291 in PRIMATE BEHAVIOR: FIELD STUDIES OF MONKEYS AND APES. I. de Vore, ed., New York, Holt, Rinehart and Winston, 1965.

Chalmers, N.R. Group competition, ecology and daily activities of free living mangabeys in Uganda. FOLIA PRIMATOLOGICA 8:247–262, 1968a.

Chalmers, N.R. The social behavior of free living mangabeys in Uganda. FOLIA PRIMATOLOGICA 8:262–281, 1968b.

Chalmers, N.R.: Rowell, T.E. Behaviour and female reproductive cycles in a captive group of mangabeys. FOLIA PRIMATOLOGICA 14:1–14, 1971.

Charles-Dominique, P. ECOLOGY AND BEHAVIOUR OF NOCTURNAL PRIMATES. London, Duckworth, 1977.

Charles-Dominique, P.; Martin, R.D. Ecologie et vie sociale de *Galago demidovii* (Fisher 1808, Prosimin). ZEITSCHRIFT FUR TIERPSYCHOLOGIE SUPPLEMENTUM 9:7–41, 1972.

Charles-Dominique, P.; Petter, J.J. Ecology and social of *Phaner furcifier*, Pp. 75–96 in NOCTURNAL MALAGASY PRIMATES; ECOLOGY, PHYSIOLOGY AND BEHAVIOUR. P. Charles-Dominique, ed., London, Duckworth, 1980.

Cheney, D.L. Interactions of immature male and female baboons with adult females. ANIMAL BEHAVIOUR 26:389–408, 1978.

Cheney, D.L. Intergroup encounters among free-ranging vervet monkeys. FOLIA PRIMATOLOGICA 35:124–126, 1981.

Chevalier-Skolnikoff, S. The ontogeny of communication in the stumptail macaque (*Macaca arctoides*). CONTRIBUTIONS TO PRIMATOLOGY 2. F.S. Szalay, ed., Basel, Karger, 1974.

Chivers, D.J. The stamang and the gibbon in the Malay Peninsula. Pp. 205–315 In PRIMATE ECOLOGY: PROBLEM-ORIENTED FIELD STUDIES. R.W. Sussman, ed., New York, Wiley, 1979.

Christen, A. FORTPFLANZUNGSBIOLOGIE UND VERHALTEN BEI *CEBUELLA PYGMAEA* UND *TAMARIN TAMARIN*. Berlin, Parey, 1974.

Coates, A.: Poole, T.B. The behavior of the callithricid monkey *Saguinus labiatus labiatus* in the laboratory. INTERNATIONAL JOURNAL OF PRIMATOLOGY 4:339–371, 1983.

d'Amato, F.R.; Troisi, A.; Scucchi, S.; and Fucillo, R. Mating season influence on allogrooming in a confined group of Japanese macaques: A quantitative analysis. PRIMATES 23:220–232, 1982.

Deag, J.M.; Crook, J.H. Social behaviour and "agonistic buffering" in the wild Barbary macaque *Macaca sylvana* L. FOLIA PRIMATOLOGICA 15:183–200, 1971.

Defler, T.R. Allogrooming in two species of macaque (*Macaca nemestrina* and *Macaca radiata*). PRIMATES 19:153–167, 1978.

Defler, T.R. On the ecology and behavior of *Cebus albifrons* in eastern Colombia. II. Behavior. PRIMATES 20:491–502. 1979.

DeWaal, F. CHIMPANZEE-POLITICS. London, Jonathan Cape, 1982.

DeWaal, F.B.M.; and Yoshihara, D. Reconciliation and redirected affection in rhesus monkeys. BEHAVIOUR 85:224–241, 1983.

Dolhinow, P. A behavior repertoire for the Indian lagur monkey (*Presbytis entellus*). PRIMATES 19:449–472, 1978.

Dolhinow, P. An experimental study of mother loss in the Indian langur monkey (*Presbytis entellus*). FOLIA PRIMATOLOGICA 33:77–128, 1980.

Doyle, G.A. Behavior of prosimians. Pp. 155–353 in BEHAVIOUR OF NONHUMAN PRIMATES. MODERN RESEARCH TRENDS. Vol. 5. A.M. Schrier; F. Stollnitz, eds. New York, Academic Pres, 1974.

Doyle. G.A. The behaviour of the lesser bushbaby. Pp. 213–232 in PROSIMIAN BEHAVIOUR. R.D. Martin; G.A. Doyle; A.C. Walker, eds. London, Duckworth, 1976.

Doyle, G.A. Development of behavior in prosimians with special reference to the lesser Bushbaby. *Galago senegalensis moholi*. Pp. 158–206 in THE STUDY OF PROSIMIAN BEHAVIOUR. G.A. Doyle; R.D. Martin, eds. London, Duckworth, 1979.

Doyle, G.A.; Pelletier, A.; Bekker, T. Courtship, mating and parturition in the lesser Bushbaby (*Galago senegalensis moholi*) under semi-natural conditions. FOLIA PRIMATOLOGICA 7:169–197, 1967.

Drews, D.R. Group formation in captive *Galago crassicaudatus*: Notes on the dominance concept. ZEITSCHRIFT FUR TIERPSYCHOLOGIE 32:425–535, 1973.

Drickamer, L.C. Quantitative observations of grooming behavior in free-ranging *Macaca mulatta*. PRIMATES 17:323–335, 1976.

Dunbar, R.I.M. Structure of gelada baboon reproductive units, III. The male's relationship with his partner. ANIMAL BEHAVIOUR 31:565–575, 1983.

Dunbar, R.I.M.; Dunbar, P. Behaviour related to birth in wild gelada baboons (*Theropithecus gelada*). BEHAVIOUR 50:185–191, 1974.

Dunn, L.F. The parasites of *Saimiri*: In the context of platyrrhine parasition. Pp. 31–68 in THE SQUIRREL MONKEY. L.A. Rosenblum; R.W. Cooper, ed., New York, Academic Press, 1968.

Eaglen, R.H; Boskoff, K.J. The birth and early development of a captive sifaka. *Propithecus verreauxi coquereli.* FOLIA PRIMATOLOGICA 30:206–219, 1978.

Edwards, S.D. Social potential expressed in captive, group-living orangutans. Pp. 249–256 In THE ORANG UTAN, ITS BIOLOGY AND CONSERVATION. L.E.M. de Boer, ed., The Hague, Junk, 1982.

Ehrlich, A. Social and individual behaviour in captive greater galagos. BEHAVIOUR 63:192–214, 1977.

Ehrlich, A.; Musicant, A. Social and individual behaviour in captive greater galagos. BEHAVIOUR 63:192–214, 1977.

Ehrlich, A.; Musicant, A. Social and individual behaviours in captive slow lorises. BEHAVIOUR 60:195–220, 1977.

Ellefson, J.O. Territorial behaviour in the common white-handed gibbon. *Hylobates lar.* Pp. 180–199 in PRIMATES, STUDIES IN ADAPTATION AND VARIABILITY. P.C. Jay, ed., New York, Holt, Rinehart and Winston, 1968.

Elliott, R.C. Observations on a small group of mountain gorillas (*Gorilla gorilla beringei*). *FOLIA PRIMATOLOGICA 25:12–24, 1976.*

Elton, R.H.; Anderson, B.V. The social behavior of a group of baboons (*Papio anubis*) under artificial crowding. PRIMATES 18:225–234, 1977.

Epple, G. Vergleichende Untersuchungen über sexual- und sozialverhalten der Krallenaffen (*Hapalidae*). FOLIA PRIMATOLOGICA 7:37–65, 1967.

Epple, G. Parental behavior in *Saguinus fuscicollis* ssp. (Callithricidae). FOLIA PRIMATOLOGICA 24:221–238, 1975.

Epps, J. Social interactions of *Perodicticus potto* kept in captivity in Kampala, Uganda. Pp. 233–244 in PROSIMIAN BEHAVIOUR. R.D. Martin; G.A. Doyle; A.C. Walker eds. London, Duckworth, 1976.

Estrada, A.; Estrada, R. Changes in social structure and interactions after the introduction of a second group in a free-ranging troop of stumptail macaques (*Macaca arctoides*). Social relations II. PRIMATES 19:665–680, 1978.

Estrada, A.; Estrada, R.; Ervin, F. Establishment of a free-ranging colony of stumptail macaques (*Macaca arctoides*). Social relations I. PRIMATES 18:647–676, 1977.

Fairbanks, L.A. Relationships among adult females in captive vervet monkeys: Testing a model of rank-related attractiveness. ANIMAL BEHAVIOUR 28:853–859, 1980.

Falk, J.L. The grooming behavior of the chimpanzee as a reinforcer. JOURNAL OF EXPERIMENTAL ANALYSIS OF BEHAVIOUR 1:83–85, 1958.

Fedigan, L.M. Roles and activities of male geladas (*Theropithecus gelada*). BEHAVIOUR 49:82–90, 1972.

Fisher, R.B.; Nadler, R.D. Status interactions of captive female lowland gorillas. FOLIA PRIMATOLOGICA 28:122–133, 1977.

Fossey, D. Development of the mountain gorilla (*Gorilla gorilla beringei*), the first six months. Pp. 139–187 in THE GREAT APES. D.A. Hamburg; E.R. McCown, eds. Benjamin Cummings, Menlo Park, 1979.

Fox, J.F. Some comparisons between siamang and gibbon behavior. FOLIA PRIMATOLOGICA 18:122–139, 1972.

Francois, G.R.; Barratt, E.S.; Harris, C.S. Assessing the spontaneous cage behaviour of the squirrel monkey (*Saimiri sciureus*). PRIMATES 11:89–92, 1970.

Furuya, Y. Grooming behavior in wild Japanese monkeys. Pp. 1–30 in JAPANESE MONKEYS: A COLLECTION OF TRANSLATIONS. K. Imanishi, ed. Atlanta, Yerkes Regional Primate Center, 1965.

Gautier-Hion, A. L'organization sociale d'une bande de talapoins (*Miopithecus talapoin*) dans le nord-ouest du Gabon. FOLIA PRIMATOLOGICA 12:116–141, 1970.

Goodall, J. Chimpanzees of the Gombe Stream Reserve. Pp. 425–473 in PRIMATE BEHAVIOUR: FIELD STUDIES OF MONKEYS AND APES. I. DeVore, ed., New York, Holt, Rinehart and Winston, 1965.

Goodall, J.; Bundorn, A.; Bergmann, E.; Busse, C.; Matama, H.; Mpongo, E.; Pierce, A.; Riss, D. Intercommunity interactions in the chimpanzee population of the Gombe Park. Pp. 12–54 in THE GREAT APES. D.A. Hamburg; E.R. McCown, eds. Benjamin Cummings, 1979.

Goosen, C. Immediate effects of allogrooming in adult stumptailed macaques (*Macaca arctoides*). BEHAVIOUR 48:75–88, 1974a.

Goosen, C. Some causal factors in autogrooming behaviour of adult stumptailed macaques (*Macaca arctoides*). BEHAVIOUR 49:111–129, 1974b.

Goosen, C. Aftereffects of allogrooming on proximity and locomotion in pairs of stumptailed macaques (*Macaca arctoides*). BEHAVIOUR 74:1–21, 1980.

Goosen, C. On the function of allogrooming in Old World monkeys. Pp. 110–120 in BEHAVIOUR AND SOCIOBIOLOGY. A.B. Chiarelli; R.S. Corruccini, eds. Berlin, Springer-Verlag, 1981.

Goosen, C.; Kortmulder, K. Relationships between faces and body motor patterns in a group of captive pigtailed macaques (*Macaca nemestrina*). PRIMATES 20:221–236, 1979.

Goosen, C.; Metz, J.A.J. Dissecting behaviour: Relations between autoaggression, grooming and walking in a macaque. BEHAVIOUR 75:97–132, 1980.

Goosen, C.; Ribbens, L.G. Autoaggression and tactile communication in pairs of adult stumptailed macaques. BEHAVIOUR 73:165–174, 1980.

Gordon, T.P., Rose, R.M., Grady, C.L., and Bernstein, I.S. Effects of increased testosterone secretion on the behavior of adult male rhesus monkeys living in a social group. FOLIA PRIMATOLOGICA 32:149–160, 1979.

Grewal, B.S. Social relationships between adult central males and kinship groups of Japanese monkeys at Arashiyama with some aspects of troop organization. PRIMATES 21:161–180, 1980a.

Grewal, B.S. Changes in relationships of multiparous and parous females of Japanese monkeys at Arashiyama with some aspects of troop organization. PRIMATES 21:330–339, 1980b.

Groves, C.P. Notes on the ecology and behaviour of the Angola colobus (*Colobus angolensis* R.L. Sclater, 1860) in N.E. Tanzania. FOLIA PRIMATOLOGICA 20:12–26, 1973.

Hall, K.R.L. Behaviour and ecology of the wild patas monkey. *Erythrocebus patas*, in Uganda. Pp. 32–119 in PRIMATES, STUDIES IN ADAPTATION AND VARIABILITY. Jay, P.C. ed. New York, Holt, Rinehart and Winston, 1968.

Hall, K.R.L.; DeVore, I. Baboon social behavior Pp. 52–110 in PRIMATE BEHAVIOR, FIELD STUDIES OF MONKEYS AND APES, I. DeVore, ed. New York, Holt, Rinehart and Winston, 1965.

Hall, K.R.L.; Mayer, B. Social interactions in a group of captive patas monkeys (*Erythrocebus patas*). FOLIA PRIMATOLOGICA 5:213–236, 1967.

Hall, K.R.L.; Boelkins, R.C.; Goswell, M.J. Behavior of patas monkeys. *Erythrocebus patas*, in captivity, with notes on the natural habitat. FOLIA PRIMATOLOGICA 3:22–49, 1965.

Hamilton, W.D. The genetical evolution of social behaviour. JOURNAL FOR THEORETICAL BIOLOGY 7:1–15, 1964.

Hampton, J.K.; Hampton, S.H.; Landwehr, B.T. Observations on a successful breeding colony of the marmoset. *Oedipomidas oedipus*. FOLIA PRIMATOLOGICA 4:265–287, 1966.

Hanby, J.P.; Robertson, L.T.; Phoenix, C.M. The sexual behavior of a confined troop of Japanese macaques. FOLIA PRIMATOLOGICA 16:123–143, 1971.

Harrington, J.E. Development of behavior in *Lemur macaco* in the first nineteen weeks. FOLIA PRIMATOLOGICA 29:107–128, 1978.

Hasegawa, T.; Hiraiwa, M. Social interactions of orphans observed in a free-ranging troop of Japanese monkeys. FOLIA PRIMATOLOGICA 33:129–158, 1980.

Hausfater, G. Intergroup behavior of free-ranging rhesus monkeys (*Macaca mulatta*). FOLIA PRIMATOLOGICA 18:78–107, 1972.

Hess, J.P. Some observations on the sexual behaviour of captive lowland gorillas. *Gorilla g. gorilla* (Savage and Wyman) Pp. 507–581 in COMPARATIVE ECOLOGY AND BEHAVIOUR OF PRIMATES. J.H. Crook, R.P. Michael, eds., Academic Press, London, 1971.

Hinde, R.A.; Proctor, L.P. Changes in the relationships of captive rhesus monkeys on giving birth. BEHAVIOUR 61:304–321, 1977.

Hoff, M.P.; Nadler, R.D.; Maple, T.L. Control role of an adult male in a captive group of lowland gorillas. FOLIA PRIMATOLOGICA 38:72–85, 1982.

Horr, D.A. The Borneo orang utan: Population structure and dynamics in relationship to ecology and reproductive strategy. Pp. 307–324 in PRIMATE BEHAVIOUR, DEVELOPMENTS IN FIELD AND LABORATORY RESEARCH. L.A. Rosenblum, ed. New York, Academic Press, 1975.

Horvat, J.R.; Kraemer, H.C. Infant socialization and maternal influence in chimpanzees. FOLIA PRIMATOLOGICA 36:99–110, 1981.

Horwich, R.H. Development of behaviors in a male spectacled langur. PRIMATES 15:151–178, 1974.

Hunkeler, C.; Bourliere, F.; Bertrand, M. Le comportement social de la mone de Lowe (*Cercopithecus campbelli lowei*). FOLIA PRIMATOLOGICA 17:218–236, 1972.

Izawa, K. A field study of the ecology and behavior of the blackmantle tamarin (*Saguinus nigricollis*). PRIMATES 19:241–274, 1978.

Jay, P. The common langur of North India. Pp. 197–249 in PRIMATES BEHAVIOR: FIELD STUDIES OF MONKEYS AND APES. I. DeVore, ed. New York, Holt, Rinehart and Winston, 1965.

Jensen, G.D.; Bobbitt, R.A.; Gordon, B.N. Mothers' and infants' roles in the development of independence of *Macaca nemestrina*. PRIMATES 14:79–88, 1973.

Jolly, A. LEMUR BEHAVIOR, A MADAGASCAR FIELD STUDY. Chicago, University of Chicago Press, 1966.

Jones, A.C.; Simpson, J.S. Comparison of behaviour between two subspecies of owl monkey (*Aotus trivirgatus*) in a laboratory environment. LABORATORY ANIMALS 16:274–277, 1982.

Jones, C.B. Grooming in the mantled howler monkey. *Alouatta palliata* Gray. PRIMATES 20:289–292, 1979.

Jones, E.; Byrne, B.; Chance, M.R.A. Influence of a novel male on the social behaviour of a captive group of mature female long-tailed macaques (*Macaca fascicularis*). LABORATORY ANIMALS 16:208–214, 1982.

Kaplan, J.R.; Zucker, E. Social organization in a group of free-ranging patas monkeys. FOLIA PRIMATOLOGICA 34:196–213, 1980.

Kaufmann, I.C.; Rosenblum, L.A. A behavioral taxonomy for *Macaca nemestrina* and *radiata*: Based on longitudinal observation of family groups in the laboratory. PRIMATES 7:206–258, 1966.

Kaufmann, J.H. Studies on the behavior of captive tree shrews (*Tupaia glis*). FOLIA PRIMATOLOGICA 3:50–74, 1965.

Kaufmann, J.H. Social relations of adult males in a free-ranging band of rhesus monkeys. Pp. 73–98 in SOCIAL COMMUNICATION AMONG PRIMATES. S.A. Altmann, ed., Chicago, University of Chicago Press, 1967.

Kavanagh, M. The social behaviour of doucs (*Pygathrix nemaeus nemaeus*) at San Diego Zoo. PRIMATES 19:101–114, 1978.

Kawai, M.; Mito, N. Quantitative study of activity patterns and postures of Formosan monkeys by the cradiotelemetrical technique. PRIMATES 14:179–194, 1973.

Kawamichi, T.; Kawamichi, M. Social organization of tree shrews (*Tupaia glis*). Pp. 1–17 in PRIMATES BEHAVIOUR AND SOCIOBIOLOGY. A.B. Chiarelli; R.S. Corruccini, eds., Berlin. Springer-Verlag, 1981.

Kawanaka, K. Further studies on predation by chimpanzees of the Mahale Mountains. PRIMATES 23:364–384, 1982.

King, N.E.; Stevens, V.J.; Mellen, J.D. Social behavior in a captive chimpanzee (*Pan troglodytes*) group. PRIMATES 21:198–210, 1980.

Kinzey, W.G.; Wright, P.C. Grooming behavior in the titi monkey (*Callicebus torquatus*). AMERICAN JOURNAL OF PRIMATOLOGY 3:267–275, 1982.

Klein, L.L. Observations on copulation and seasonal reproduction of two species of spider monkeys. *Ateles belzebuth* and *A. geoffroyi*. FOLIA PRIMATOLOGICA, 15:233–248, 1971.

Klopfer, P.H.; Boskof, K.J. Pp. 123–154 in THE STUDY OF PROSIMIAN BEHAVIOUR. G.A. Doyle; R.D. Martin eds. New York, Academic Press, 1979.

Koyama, N. Observations on mating behavior of wild siamang gibbons at Fraser's Hill, Malaysia. PRIMATES 12:183–189, 1971.

Koyama, N. Dominance, grooming and clasped-sleeping relationships among bonnet monkeys in India. PRIMATES 14:255–244, 1973.

Kraemer, H.C.; Horvat, J.R.; Doering, Cl; McGinnis, P.R. Male chimpanzee development focusing on adolescence: Integration of behavioral with physiological changes. PRIMATES 23:393–405, 1982.

Kress, J.H.; Conley, K.M.; Eaglen, R.A.; Ibanez, A.E. The behavior of *Lemur variegatus*. ZEITSCHRIFT FUR TIERPSYCHOLOGIE 48:87–99, 1978.

Kuhn, H.J. Parasites and the phylogeny of the catarrhine monkeys. Pp. 187–195 in TAXONOMY AND PHYLOGENY OF OLD WORLD PRIMATES WITH REFERENCES TO THE ORIGIN OF MAN. B. Chiarelli, ed. Torino, Rosenberg and Sellier, 1967.

Kumar, A.; Kurup, G.U. Infant development in the lion-tailed macaque. *Macaca silenus* (Linnaeus): The first eight weeks. PRIMATES 22:512–522, 1981.

Kummer, H.; Kurt, F. Social units of a free living population of hamadyras baboons. FOLIA PRIMATOLOGICA 1:4–19, 1963.

Kummer, H. Social organization of hamadryas baboons. In BIBLIOTHECA PRIMATOLOGIA, No. 6. H. Hofer, A.H. Schultz, D. Starck eds. Basel, S. Karger, 1968.

Kuroda, S. Social behavior of the pygmy chimpanzees. PRIMATES 21:181–197, 1980.

Lahiri, R.K.; Southwick, C.H. Parental care in *Macaca sylvana*. FOLIA PRIMATOLOGICA 4:257–264, 1966.

Lancaster, J.B. Play-mothering: The relations between juvenile females and young infants among free-ranging vervet monkeys (*Cercopithecus aethiops*). FOLIA PRIMATOLOGICA 15:161–182, 1971.

Le Resche, L.A. Dyadic play in hamadryas baboons. BEHAVIOUR 57:190–205, 1976.

Lindburg, D.G. Grooming behavior as a regulator of social interactions in rhesus monkeys. Pp. 124–148 in BEHAVIORAL REGULATORS OF BEHAVIOR IN PRIMATES. L.R. Carpenter, ed. Lewisburg, PA. Bucknell University Press, 1973.

Lorenz, R. Waschen bei zwei Arten der Gattung *Presbytis* (Cercopithecoidea, Primates). FOLIA PRIMATOLOGICA 4:191–193, 1966.

Mackinnon, J. The behaviour and ecology of wild orangutans (*Pongo pygmaeus*). ANIMAL BEHAVIOUR 22:3–74, 1974.

Maple, T.L.; Hoff, M.P. GORILLA BEHAVIOR. New York, Van Nostrand Reinhold, 1982.

Marsden, H.M. Behavior between two social groups of rhesus monkeys within two tunnel-connected enclosures. FOLIA PRIMATOLOGICA 8:240–246, 1968.

Marsh, C.W. Time budget of Tana River red colobus. FOLIA PRIMATOLOGICA 35:30–50, 1981.

Mason, W.A. Use of space of *Callicebus* groups. Pp. 180–199 in PRIMATES, STUDIES IN ADAPTATION AND VARIABILITY, P. C. Jay. ed. New York, Holt, Rinehart and Winston, 1968.

Mason, W.A. Determinants of social behavior in young chimpanzees. Pp. 335–364 in BEHAVIOR OF NONHUMAN PRIMATES, MODERN RESEARCH TRENDS. Vol. II. A.M. Schrier; H.F. Harlow; F. Stolnitz, eds. New York Academic Press, 1965.

Mason, W.A. Comparative studies of social behavior in *Callicebus* and *Saimiri*: Behavior of male-female pairs. FOLIA PRIMATOLOGICA 22:1–8, 1974.

McGinnis, P.R. Sexual behavior in free-living chimpanzees: Consort relationships. In THE GREAT APES. D.A. Hamburg; F.R. McCown, eds. Benjamin Cummings, Menlo Park, 1979.

McGuire, M.T., Cole, S.R.; Crookshank, C. Effects of social and spatial density changes in *Cercopithecus aethiops sabaeus*. PRIMATES 19:615–631, 1978.

McKenna, J.J. Biosocial functions of grooming behavior among the common Indian langur monkey (*Presbytis entellus*). AMERICAN JOURNAL OF PHYSICAL ANTHROPOLOGY 48:503–510, 1978.

Mellen, J.D.; Littlewood, A. P.; Barrow, B. C.; Stevens, V. J. Individual and social behavior in a captive troop of mandrills (*Mandrillus sphinx*). PRIMATES 22:206–220, 1981.

Mendoza, S.P.; Lowe, E.L.; Levine, S. Social organization and social behavior in two subspecies of squirrel monkeys (*Saimiri sciureus*. FOLIA PRIMATOLOGICA 30:126–144, 1978.

Merz, E. Male-male interactions with dead infants in *Macaca sylvanus*. PRIMATES 19:749–754, 1978.

Missakian, E.A. Mother-offspring grooming relations in rhesus monkeys. ARCHIVES OF SEXUAL BEHAVIOR 3:135–141, 1974.

Moody, M.I.; Menzel, E.W. Vocalizations and their behavioral contexts in the tamarin *Saguinus fuscicollis*. FOLIA PRIMATOLOGICA 25:73–94, 1976.

Mori, A. Signals found in the grooming interactions of wild Japanese monkeys of the Koshima troop. PRIMATES 16:107–140, 1975.

Mori, A. Intra-troop spacing mechanism of the wild Japanese monkeys of the Koshima troop. PRIMATES 18:331–357, 1977.

Mörike, D. Verhlaten einer Gruppe von Diana Meerkaken im Frankfurter Zoo. PRIMATES 14:263–300, 1973.

Mörike, D. Verhalten einer Gruppe von Brazza meerkatzen (*Cercopithecus neglectus*) im Heidelberger Zoo. PRIMATES 17:475–512, 1976.

Nadler, R.D.; Tilford, B.L. Agonistic interactions of captive female orang-utans with infants. FOLIA PRIMATOLOGICA 28:298–305, 1977.

Nagel, U. A comparison of *Anubis* baboons. *Hamadryas* baboons and their hybrids at a species border in Ethiopia. FOLIA PRIMATOLOGICA 19:104–165, 1973.

473

Nash, L.T.; Flinn, L. Group formation in captive lesser galagos. PRIMATES 19:493–503, 1978.

Nash, T. The development of the mother-infant relations in wild baboons (*Papio anubis*). ANIMAL BEHAVIOUR 26:746, 1978.

Neville, M.K. Social relations within troops of red howler monkeys (*Alouatta seniculus*). FOLIA PRIMATOLOGICA 18:47–77, 1972.

Nickelson, S.A.; Lockard, J.S. Ethogram of Celebes monkeys (*Macaca nigra*) in two captive habitats. PRIMATES 19:437–447, 1978.

Niemitz, C. Outline of the behaviour of *Tarsius bancanus*. Pp. 631–660 in THE STUDY OF PROSIMIAN BEHAVIOR. Doyle, G.A., R.D. Martin, eds. New York, Academic Press, 1979.

Nieuwenhuijsen, K.; DeWaal, F.B.M. Effects of spatial crowding on social behavior in a chimpanzee colony. ZOO BIOLOGY 1:1–8, 1982.

Nishida, T. The social structure of chimpanzees of the Mahale Mountains. Pp. 73–122 in THE GREAT APES. D.A. Hamburg; E.R. McCown, eds. Benjamin Cummings, 1979.

Nishida, T. Alloparental behaviour in wild chimpanzees of the Mahale Mountains, Tanzania. FOLIA PRIMATOLOGICA 41:1–33, 1983.

Nishida, T. Social behavior and relationships among wild chimpanzees of the Mahale Mountains. PRIMATES 11:47–87, 1970.

Nolte, A.; Dücker, G. Jugendentwicklung eines Kapuzineraffen (*Cebus apella*) mit besonderer berücksichtigung des wechselseitigen Verhaltens vor Mutter und Kind. BEHAVIOUR 14:335–373, 1959.

Oates, J.F. The social life of a black-and-white colobus monkey. *Colobus guereza.* ZEITSCHRIFT FUR TIERPSYCHOLOGIE 45:1–60, 1977.

Oki, J.; Maeda, Y. Grooming as a regulator of behavior in Japanese macaques. Pp. 149–163 in BEHAVIORAL REGULATORS OF BEHAVIOR IN PRIMATES. C.R. Carpenter, ed. Lewisburg, PA. Bucknell University Press. 1973.

Oppenheimer, J.R. *Presbytis entellus*: Birth in a free-ranging primate troop. PRIMATES 17:541–542, 1976.

Oppenheimer, J.R.; Oppenheimer, E.C. Preliminary observations of *Cebus nigrivittatus* (Primates: Cebidae) on the Venezuelan llanos. FOLIA PRIMATOLOGICA 19:409–436, 1973.

Packer, C. Male care and exploitation of infants in *Papio ursinus*. ANIMAL BEHAVIOUR 28:512–520, 1980.

Pages, E. Ethoecology of *Microcebus conquereli* during the dry season. Pp. 97–116 in NOCTURNAL MALAGASY PRIMATES: ECOLOGY, PHYSIOLOGY AND BEHAVIOUR. P. Charles-Dominique et al, eds. New York, Academic Press, 1980.

Patterson, T. The behavior of a group of captive pygmy chimpanzees (*Pan paniscus*). PRIMATES 20:341–354, 1979.

Pinto, D.; Doyle, G.A.; Bearder, S.K. Patterns of activity in three nocturnal prosimian species. *Galago senegalensis, G. crassicaudatus umbrosus* and *Microcebus murinus murinus* under seminatural conditions. FOLIA PRIMATOLOGICA 21:135–147, 1974.

Ploog, D.W.; Blitz, J.; Ploog, F. Studies on social and sexual behavior of the squirrel monkeys (*Saimiri sciureus*). FOLIA PRIMATOLOGICA 1:29–66, 1963.

Poirier, F.E. The Nilgiri Langur (*Presbytis johnii*) of South India. In PRIMATE BEHAVIOR, DEVELOPMENTS IN FIELD AND LABORATORY RESEARCH. Rosenblum, L.A., ed. New York, Academic Press, 254–383, 1970.

Poirier, F.E. The St. Kitts green monkey (*Cercopithecus aethiops sabaeus*): Ecology, population dynamics and selected behavioral traits. FOLIA PRIMATOLOGICA 17:20–55, 1972.

Pollock, J.I. Female dominance in *Indri indri*. FOLIA PRIMATOLOGICA 31:143–164, 1979.

Pook, A.G., Pook, G. A field study of the socio-ecology of the Goeldi's monkey (*Callimico goeldii*) in northern Bolivia. FOLIA PRIMATOLOGICA 35:288–312, 1981.

Post, W.; Baulu, J. Time budgets of *Macaca mulatta*. PRIMATES 19:125–140, 1978.

Rahaman, H.; Parthasarathy, M.D. The expressive movements of the bonnet macaque. PRIMATES 9:259–272, 1968.

Rahaman, H.; Parthasarathy, M.D. Studies on the social behaviour of bonnet monkeys. PRIMATES 10:149–162, 1969.

Rathbun, C.D. Description and analysis of the arch display in the golden lion tamarin *Leontopithecus rosalia rosalia*. FOLIA PRIMATOLOGICA 32:125–148, 1979.

Reynolds, V. Some behavioural comparisons between the chimpanzee and the mountain gorilla in the wild. Pp. 323–340 in PRIMATE ECOLOGY: PROBLEM-ORIENTED FIELD STUDIES. R.W. Sussman, ed. New York, Wiley, 1979.

Reynolds, V.; Reynolds, F. Chimpanzees of the Budongo Forest. Pp. 368–424 in PRIMATE BEHAVIOR: FIELD STUDIES OF MONKEYS AND APES. I. DeVore, ed., New York, Holt, Rinehart and Winston, 1965.

Rhine, R.J. Variation and consistency in the social behavior of two groups of stumptail macaques (*Macaca arctoides*). PRIMATES 14:21–35, 1973.

Rhine, R.J.; Hendy-Neely, H. Social development of stumptail macaques (*Macaca arctoides*): Momentary touching, play and other interactions with aunts and immatures during infants' first 60 days of life. PRIMATES 19:115–122, 1978a.

Rhine, R.J.; Hendy-Neely, H. Social development of stumptail macaques (*Macaca arctoides*): Synchrony of changes in mother-infant interactions and individual behaviors during the first 60 days of life. PRIMATES 19:681–692, 1978b.

Rhine, R.J.; Kronenwetter, C. Interaction patterns of two newly formed groups of stumptail macaques (*Macaca artoides*). PRIMATES 13:19–33, 1972.

Richard, A. A comparative study of the activity patterns and behavior of *Alouatta villosa* and *Ateles goeffroyi*. FOLIA PRIMATOLOGICA 12:241–263, 1970.

Richard, A. Intraspecific variation in the social organization and ecology of *Propithecus verreauxi*. FOLIA PRIMATOLOGICA 22:178–207, 1974.

Richard, A. Preliminary observations on the birth and development of *Propithecus verreauxi* to the age of six months. PRIMATES 17:357–366, 1976.

Richard, A.F. BEHAVIORAL VARIATION: CASE STUDY OF A MALAGASY LEMUR. Lewisburg, PA. Bucknell University Press, 1978.

Riss, D.C.; Busse, C.D. Fifty-day observation of a free-ranging adult male chimpanzee. FOLIA PRIMATOLOGICA 28:283–307, 1977.

Riss, D.C.; Goodall, J. Sleeping behavior and association in a group of captive chimpanzees. FOLIA PRIMATOLOGICA 25:1–11, 1976.

Roberts, P. Social interactions of *Galago crassicaudatus*. FOLIA PRIMATOLOGICA 14:171–181, 1971.

Rondinelli, R.; Klein, L.L. An analysis of adult social spacing tendencies and related social interaction in a colony of spider monkeys (*Ateles goeffroyi*) at the San Francisco Zoo. FOLIA PRIMATOLOGICA 25:122–142, 1976.

Rosenblum, L.A.; Kaufmann, I.C.; Stynes, A.J. Some characteristics of adult social and autogrooming patterns in two species of macaque. FOLIA PRIMATOLOGICA 4:438–451, 1966.

Rosenson, L.W. Observations of the maternal behaviour of two captive greater bush babies (*Galago crassicaudatus argentatus*). ANIMAL BEHAVIOUR 24:677–688, 1972.

Rosenson, L.M. Group formation in the captive greater bush baby (*Galago crassicaudatus crassicaudatus*). ANIMAL BEHAVIOUR 21:67–77, 1973.

Rothe, N. Beobactungen zur Geburt beim Weisbüscheläffchen (*Callithrix jacchus*, Erxleben, 1777). FOLIA PRIMATOLOGICA 4:438–451, 1973.

Rowell, T.E. Organization of caged groups of *Cercopithecus* monkeys. ANIMAL BEHAVIOUR 19:625–645, 1971.

Saayman, G.S. The menstrual cycle and sexual behaviour in a troop of free ranging chacma baboons (*Papio ursinus*). FOLIA PRIMATOLOGICA 12:81–110, 1970.

Saayman, G.S. Behaviour of the adult males in a troop of free-ranging chacma baboons (*Papio ursinus*). FOLIA PRIMATOLOGICA 15:36–57, 1971.

Sade, D.S. Some aspects of parent-offspring and sibling relations in a group of rhesus monkeys, with a discussion of grooming. AMERICAN JOURNAL OF PHYSICAL ANTHROPOLOGY 23:1–8, 1965.

Savage, E.S.; Temerlin, J.W.; Lemmon, W.B. Group formation among captive mother-infant chimpanzees (*Pan troglodytes*. FOLIA PRIMATOLOGICA 20:453–473, 1973.

Savage, F.S.; Malick, C. Play and sociosexual behaviour in a captive chimpanzee (*Pan troglodytes*) groups. BEHAVIOUR 60:179, 1977.

Schaller, G.B. THE YEAR OF THE GORILLA. Chicago, University of Chicago Press, 1964.

Schaller, G.B. The behavior of the mountain gorilla. Pp. 324–367 in PRIMATE BEHAVIOR: FIELD STUDIES OF MONKEYS AND APES. I. DeVore, ed. Holt, Rinehart and Winston, 1965.

Scruton, D.M.; Herbert, J. The reaction of groups of captive talapoin monkeys to the introduction of male and female strangers of the same species. ANIMAL BEHAVIOUR 20:463–473, 1972.

Seay, B. Maternal behavior in primparous and multiparous rhesus monkeys. FOLIA PRIMATOLOGICA 4:146–168, 1966.

Seyfarth, R.M. Social relationships among adult male and female baboons. I. Behaviour during sexual consortship. BEHAVIOUR 64:204–226, 1978a.

Seyfarth, R.M. Social relationships among adult male and female baboons. II. Behaviour throughout the female reproduction cycle. BEHAVIOUR 64:226–247, 1978b.

Seyfarth, R.M. The distribution of grooming and related behaviours among adult female vervet monkeys. ANIMAL BEHAVIOUR 28:798–813, 1980.

Sharon, B.F. Observations on infant sharing in captive *Colobus polykomos*. PRIMATES 14:93–100. 1973.

Silk, J.B. Altruism among female *Macaca radiata*: Explanations and analyses of patterns of grooming and coalition formation. BEHAVIOUR 79:162–188, 1982.

Silk, J.B.; Samuels, A.; Rodman, P.S. The influence of kinship, rank and sex on affiliation and aggression between adult female and immature bonnet macaques (*Macaca radiata*). BEHAVIOUR 78:111–137, 1981.

Simonds, P.E. The bonnet macaque in South India. Pp. 175–196 in PRIMATE BEHAVIOR: FIELD STUDIES OF MONKEYS AND APES. I. DeVore, ed. New York, Holt, Rinehart and Winston, 1965.

Simpson, M.J.A. The social grooming of male chimpanzees. Pp. 411–505 in COMPARATIVE ECOLOGY AND BEHAVIOUR OF PRIMATES. R.P. Michael; J.H. Crook, eds. London, Academic Press, 1971.

Small, M.F. A comparison of mother and nonmother behaviors during birth season in two species of captive macaques. FOLIA PRIMATOLOGICA 38:99–107, 1982.

Soczka, L. Ethologie sociale et sociometrie: Analyse de la structure d'un group de singe crabier (*Macaca fascicularis*) en captivite. BEHAVIOUR 50:254–269, 1974.

Sorenson, M.W.; Conaway, C.H. Observations on the social behavior of tree shrews in captivity. FOLIA PRIMATOLOGICA 4:124–145, 1966.

Southwick, C.H.; Beg, M.A.; Siddiqui, M.R. Rhesus monkeys in North India. In PRIMATE BEHAVIOUR: FIELD STUDIES OF MONKEYS AND APES. I. DeVore, ed. New York, Holt, Rinehart and Winston, 111–159, 1965.

Sparks, J. Allogrooming in primates: A review. Pp. 148–175 in PRIMATE ETHOLOGY, D. Morris, ed. London, Weidenfeld and Nicholson, 1967.

Stammbach, E.; Kummer, H. Individual contributions to a dyadic interaction: An analysis of baboon grooming. ANIMAL BEHAVIOUR 30:964–971, 1982.

Struhsaker, T.T. Social behaviour of mother and infant vervet monkeys (*Cercopithecus aethiops*). ANIMAL BEHAVIOUR 19:233–250, 1971.

Struhsaker, T.; Oates, J.F. Comparison of the behavior and ecology of red colobus and black-and-white colobus monkeys in Uganda: A summary. Pp. 165–186 in PRIMATE ECOLOGY: PROBLEM-ORIENTED FIELD STUDIES. R.W. Sussman ed. New York, 1979.

Sugiyama, Y. Social behaviour of chimpanzees in the Budongo Forest, Uganda. PRIMATES 10:196–225, 1969.

Sugiyama, Y. The social structure of wild chimpanzees: A review of field studies. Pp. 375–410 in COMPARATIVE ECOLOGY AND BEHAVIOUR OF PRIMATES. R.P. Michael; J.H. Crook eds. London, Academic Press, 1971.

Sugiyama, Y. Characteristics of the social life of bonnet macaques (*Macaca radiata*). PRIMATES 12:247–266, 1971.

Sussman, R.W.; Tattersall, I. Behavior and ecology of *Macaca fascicularis* in Mauritius: A Preliminary study. PRIMATES 22:192–205, 1981.

Szalay, F.S.; Seligsohn, D. Why did the strepsirhine toothcomb evolve. FOLIA PRIMATOLOGICA 27:75–82, 1977.

Tandy, J.M. Behaviour and social structure of a laboratory colony of *Galago crassicaudatus*. Pp. 245–259 in PROSIMIAN BEHAVIOUR. R.D. Martin; G.A. Doyle; A.C. Walker, eds. London, Duckworth, 1976.

Tartabini, A. An analysis of dyadic interactions of male Japanese monkeys (*Macaca fuscata fuscata*) in a cage room observation. PRIMATES 19:423–436, 1978.

Teas, J.; Richie, T.; Taylor, H.; Southwick, C. Population patterns and behavioral ecology of rhesus monkeys (*Macaca mulatta*) in Nepal. In THE MACAQUES, STUDIES IN ECOLOGY, BEHAVIOUR AND EVOLUTION. D.G. Lindburg, ed. New York Van Nostrand Rheinhold, 1980.

Trivers, R.L. The evolution of reciprocal altruism QUARTERLY REVIEW OF BIOLOGY 46:35–57, 1971.

Vandenbergh, J.G. Feeding, activity and social behaviour of the tree shrew. *Tupaia glis*, in a large outdoor enclosure. FOLIA PRIMATOLOGICA 1:199–207, 1963.

Van Hooff, J.A.R.A.M. Aspects of the social behaviour and communication in human and higher non-human primates. Dissertation. State University, Utrecht, The Netherlands, 1971.

Van Horn, R.N.; Eaton, G.G. Reproductive physiology and behavior in prosimians. Pp. 79–123, in THE STUDY OF PROSIMIAN BEHAVIOUR. D.G. Doyle; R.D. Martin, eds. New York, Academic Press, 1979.

Van Lawick-Goodall, J. A preliminary report on expressive movement and communication in the Gombe Stream chimpanzees. Pp. 313–374 in PRIMATES, STUDIES IN ADAPTATION AND VARIABILITY. P.C. Jay, ed. New York, Holt, Rhinehart and Winston, 1968a.

477

Van Lawick-Goodall, J. The behaviour of free-living chimpanzees in the Gombe Stream Reserve. ANIMAL BEHAVIOUR MONOGRAPH 8, 1968b.

Vessey, S.H. Interactions between free-ranging groups of rhesus monkeys. FOLIA PRIMATOLOGICA 8:228–239, 1968.

Vogt, J.L. The social behavior of a marmoset (*Saguinus fuscicollis*) group. II. Behavior patterns and social interaction. PRIMATES 19:287–300, 1978.

Wade, T.D. The effect of strangers on rhesus monkey groups. BEHAVIOUR 66:194–214, 1976.

Wallis, S.J. The behavioural repertoire of the grey-cheeked mangabey *Cercocebus albigena johnstoni*. PRIMATES 22:523–532, 1981.

Waser, P.M. Postreproductive survival and behavior in a free-ranging female mangabey. FOLIA PRIMATOLOGICA 29:142–160, 1978.

Watson, J.B. Imitation in monkeys. PSYCHOLOGICAL BULLETIN 5:169–178, 1908.

Weinberg, S.M.; Candland, D.K. "Stone-grooOming" In *Macaca fuscata*. AMERICAN JOURNAL OF PRIMATOLOGY 1:465–468, 1981.

Weisbard, C.; Goy, R.W. Effect of parturition and group composition on competitive drinking order in stumptail macaques (*Macaca arctoides*). FOLIA PRIMATOLOGICA 25:95–121, 1976.

Welker, C., Lührmann, B.; Meinel, W. Behavioral sequences and strategies of female crab-eating monkeys, *Macaca fascicularis*. Raffles 1821, during group formation studies. BEHAVIOUR 73:219–237, 1980.

Whiten, A.; Rumsey, T.J. Agonistic buffering in the wild barbary macaque (*Macaca sylvana*). PRIMATES 14:421–425, 1973.

Williams, L. MAN AND MONKEYS. London, Panther, Science, Panther Books, 1969.

Wilson, A.P.; Vessey, S.H. Behavior of free-ranging castrated rhesus monkeys. FOLIA PRIMATOLOGICA 9:1–14, 1968.

Wilson, M.L.; Elicker, J.G. Establishment, maintenance and behavior of free-ranging chimpanzees on Ossaban Island, Georgia, U.S.A. PRIMATES 17:451–473, 1976.

Wolfheim, J. Sex differences in behavior in a group of captive juvenile talapoin monkeys (*Miopithecus talapoin*). BEHAVIOR 63:110–128, 1977a.

Wolfheim, J.H. A quantitative analysis of the organization of a group of captive talapoin monkeys (*Miopithecus talapoin*. FOLIA PRIMATOLOGICA 27:1–27, 1977b.

Wolfheim, J.H., Rowell, T.E. Communication among captive talapoin monkeys (*Miopithecus talapoin*). FOLIA PRIMATOLOGICA 18:224–255, 1972.

Woodridge, F.L. *Colobus guereza*: Birth and infant development in captivity. ANIMAL BEHAVIOUR 19:481–485, 1971.

Woodcock, A.J. The first weeks of cohabitation of newly-formed heterosexual pairs of common marmosets. FOLIA PRIMATOLOGICA 37:228–254, 1982.

Zuckerman, S. THE SOCIAL LIFE OF MONKEYS AND APES. London Kegan Paul, Trench, Trubner, and Co., 1932.

Female Choice in Nonhuman Primates

Meredith F. Small

Abstract: As outlined by Darwin, sexual selection is composed of two parts, within-sex competition for mates, and mate choice. The fact that males compete for fertile females has been well established. More equivocal is the notion that females have preferences for certain males, and that those preferences have an evolutionary effect ("female choice"). We now have an evolutionary framework and sophisticated mathematical models to evaluate female choice. A review of the literature on primate species reveals that 20 species have exhibited some sort of preference. Females most often choose males based on familiarity, novelty, or status. But there is no evidence that selection for particular males affects conception or fitness, or male characteristics. Female sexual assertiveness is not necessarily female choice.

Key Words: Sexual selection, Female mating strategies

. . . it is improbable that the unions of quadrupeds in a state of nature should be left to mere chance. It is much more probable that the females are allured or excited by particular males, who possess certain characters in a higher degree than other males: but what these characters are, we can seldom or never discover with certainty.—C. Darwin, 1871
Estrous females cannot be considered as passive resources like water and peanuts.—L. Fedigan, 1983
If it's not forced copulation, is it female choice?—D. Winkler, 1988

Nonhuman primates are studied by anthropologists to gain some understanding of the evolution of human behavior. This approach is employed because 1) humans are members of the order Primates, and thus we share a close genetic relationship with extant nonhuman primates in comparison to other mammals; 2) broad behavioral patterns have a genetic basis and they are assumed to be under similar evolutionary pressures for nonhuman and human primates; and 3) the living primates presumably reflect stages of our own primate ancestry. It follows that nonhuman primates, and their patterns of behavior, may be windows to the evolution of hominid behavior. In other words, the reproductive, ecological and social pressures that molded extant nonhuman primate behavior are probably similar, in a broad sense, to those that constrained our hominid forbears.

Since W. D. Hamilton's description of kin selection in 1964, and Wilson's (1975) presentation of a sociobiological framework, anthropologists who study primates have readily applied evolutionary theory to patterns of primate behavior. Mating strategies have received a good deal of attention because they directly affect reproductive success. Sexual selection theory, as outlined by Darwin, has formed the structure for these studies.

This review focuses on one aspect of sexual selection theory, female choice. For most anthropologists, knowing that female nonhuman primates might exhibit mate choice is not enough. We evaluate mating strategies with a larger question in mind: what were the mating strategies of our female hominid ancestors and how did they shape the evolution of mating systems in *Homo sapiens?* To this end, we use our primate cousins as informants to the past.

THE CONCEPT OF SEXUAL SELECTION IN EVOLUTIONARY THEORY

Darwin and the Development of Sexual Selection Theory

Charles Darwin first introduced the concept of sexual selection on two pages in *The Origin of Species* (1859). Darwin addressed a paradox in nature. If all individuals of a species are under the same selective pressures, why are there morphological and behavioral differences between the sexes? In response, he suggested that certain characteristics could be selected for because they enhanced mating success, regardless of survival value. The ability to win mates, attract mates, or choose mates would directly affect copulations and conceptions, and thus mating behavior could directly alter differential reproductive success.

At that time, Darwin believed that sexual selection only affected males because they were more apt to compete for mates than were females.

> This depends, not on a struggle for existence, but on a struggle between males for possession for females: the result is not death to the unsuccessful competitor, but few or no offspring. (1859:136.)

He added that sexual selection would not necessarily favor male vigor. It would, instead, favor those characteristics that aided in winning females, or attracting females. Females were mentioned briefly as perpetrators of unusual male attributes. When females consistently prefer males with certain characteristics and those males thereby leave more offspring than other males, the preferred traits will be passed on to future generations.

Darwin delivered a more precise explanation for differences between males and females 12 years later in *The Descent of Man, and Selection in Relation to Sex* (1871). In this volume, Darwin was concerned with two major themes: 1) the evolution of human racial variation, and 2) differences in behavior and morphology between males and females.

Fourteen chapters were devoted to an explanation of sexual selection, and following the style of *Origin*, Darwin supported his theories with examples from an extensive array of taxa. He began by reiterating that there were obvious differences in morphology between males and females in the primary sex organs and that these differences were directly involved in reproduction. He reasoned further that some of these differences could be explained by the functional needs of mating and rearing offspring. For example, females require mammary glands for lactation, or males might require a particular kind of forelimb morphology to hold a female during copulation.

> So again the primary sexual organs, and those for nourishing or protecting the young, come under this same head; for those individuals which generated or nourished their offspring best, would leave, *caeteris paribus*, the greatest number to inherit their superiority; whilst those which generated or nourished their offspring badly, would leave but few to inherit their weaker powers. (1871:256.)

He also commented that in most cases it was impossible to determine if some of these primary traits had evolved by natural or sexual selection.

It was more clear, he suggested, that sexual selection was responsible for many secondary sexual characteristics. These were traits that either allowed males to compete with other males for access to females, or traits that differentially attracted females. He found the evolution of these characteristics more intriguing ". . . as they are in many respects interesting, but more especially as they depend on the will, choice, and rivalry of the individuals of each sex." (1871:258.) Here then were animals involved in action and interaction, dynamic individuals affecting the evolution of traits. Darwin was setting up, or perhaps acknowledging, the battle of the sexes, both between males and females, and within each sex.

Darwin divided sexual selection theory into two components, competition within one sex for access to the other sex (usually manifest as male-male competition), and choice of one sex by the other (usually female choice of certain males). This difference in mating strategy is the result of differences in gamete production between the sexes. Males produce large numbers of sperm and are potentially able to fertilize many females in rapid succession. Thus males should be expected to compete with each other for reproductive opportunities. Females, on the other hand, produce fewer gametes at intervals, and they should be more cautious about their mating partners. Females should be choosey.

Darwin was very clear on his position regarding male-male competition. This was, he felt, the driving force of sexual selection. He also suggested that physical combat, rather than attractiveness to females, ruled which males gained reproductive access to females.

> With mammals the male appears to win the female much more through the law of battle than through the display of his charms. The most timid animals, not provided with any special weapons for fighting, engage in desperate conflicts during the season of love. (1871:239.)

His ideas were born out by the observations of naturalists. There were countless examples of males fighting and then moving directly to fertile females. More than a hundred years later, this portion of sexual selection theory (male-male competition) remains intact.

Female choice, however, has had a more checkered history. Whereas Darwin had essentially ignored the importance of female choice in *Origin*, he emphasized it in the latter volume. But he strongly stated that the only effect females had, in terms of sexual selection, was choosing males. There is no mention of the possibility that females might compete among themselves for preferred males. At the same time, Darwin did consider the possibility that males might have the opportunity to make choices, and that they would choose the most vigorous and attractive females. In any case, he considered female choice a secondary consequence of male-male competition.

By suggesting that individuals make mate choices, Darwin implied that animals had powers of discrimination. Darwin also felt that mate choice would be most likely among animals with advanced neurophysiology. Since primates have advanced cognitive abilities, discrimination among possible mates is a reasonable assumption. Along the same line, females, for whom mate choice is critical, should be especially equipped with the ability to differentiate among males, evaluate their abilities and appearance, and make discriminating choices. However, there is no evidence of a sex difference in cognitive abilities for primates or any other animals.

It is difficult to separate Darwin's attitude about female animals from the prevailing Victorian attitude about women and female sexuality. For example, he stated:

> The female, on the other hand, with the rarest exception, is less eager [to engage in sex] than the male. As the illustrious Hunter long ago observed, she generally 'requires to be courted'; she is coy, and may often be seen endeavoring for a long time to escape from the male. (1871:273.)

Darwin even suggested that females made choices not based on the best male, but on the one "least distasteful." (1871:273.) At the same time, he repeatedly noted that males were eager to mate with just about any female. Thus Darwin rendered scientific support for the myth of the shy, passive, coy female (Blaffer Hrdy, 1981). It has taken generations of animal behaviorists to dispel this myth and establish that females, regardless of mate choice per se, are always active sexual partners.

Fisher, Huxley, and the Obfuscation of Female Choice

The development of the theory of evolution by natural selection, and controversies over its acceptance for some 60 years, cast a shadow over consideration of the importance of sexual selection (Maynard Smith, 1987). It was not until the publication of R. A. Fisher's *The Genetical Theory of Natural Selection* in 1930 that sexual selection theory was revived as a viable force in evolution. Fisher pointed out that Darwin grouped male-male competition and female choice together because they involved competition, and usually competition confined to one sex. He also pointed out that biologists of the day were more concerned with the dichotomy between male-male competition and female choice rather than their commonalities as aspects of sexual selection. Most of the problems with the acceptance of sexual selection centered on female choice, and Fisher suggested that the concept of "choice" baffled most biologists. Fisher was also the first to clearly state conditions for mate choice to operate: 1) preference must occur in at least one sex, and 2) this preference must confer a reproductive advantage. In other words, choice must have an evolutionary effect.

Interestingly, Fisher's passage on sexual selection focused on mate choice, specifically female choice, rather than competition. He noted that preferences would be driven by selection only as long as 1) the sons of the chosen males were more successful than other sons, 2) natural selection did not quickly override sexual selection and eliminate the advantage of a preferred trait, and 3) there was a continuing advantage to the preferred trait. More important, he pointed out, the evolutionary effect of mate choice is decided by the action of both males and females. It occurs in tandem.

Here Fisher also introduced the concept of runaway selection. Initially male traits are selected because they confer some advantage to males independent of female choice. But if females consistently choose males with particular traits, and those males pass that trait on to sons, who are also preferred, it is possible that the trait will be driven to extreme proportions if there is no counterselection. Apparently Fisher viewed mate choice, specifically female choice, as a powerful evolutionary force.

In 1938, Julian Huxley revised (or in his words, amended) and tried to clarify sexual selection in two important papers (Huxley, 1938a,b). Huxley was dissatisfied with Darwin's definition of sexual selection. He noted that many of the characteristics that Darwin attributed to sexual selection, such as displays, actually occurred after pairing and had little or nothing to do with attracting mates. Huxley suggested that these characteristics, or behaviors, were really aimed at priming a mate and thus had evolved through natural selection rather than sexual selection. He also noted that competition for mates and mate choice were limited to those species that mated polygamously. These were not as common as Darwin had suggested. Huxley extensively discussed male-male competition and essentially dismissed female choice as an important aspect of mating behavior. In addition he proffered new terms for sexual selection: *epigamic* and *all-esthetic selection* for traits that promote the union of gametes (i.e., mate choice), and intra-sexual selection for competition within one sex. Huxley specifically divided mate choice into two levels: epigamic selection refers to adaptations that promote the union of gametes (including primary sex organs), and all-esthetic selection refers to display characters (secondary sexual characteristics). The term *epigamic selection* is occasionally used in the modern literature (and used incorrectly), and thus most authors prefer the term *inter-sexual selection* in reference to mate choice. Although Huxley felt he was clarifying sexual selection, in fact he added little to the development of the concept of female choice. His reevaluation of sexual selection has been criticized by O'Donald

(1980) as "hopelessly confused." Nevertheless, his papers were responsible for placing sexual selection back into the spotlight. Simultaneously, they obscured the importance of female choice for several decades.

During the 1940s and 1950s, a number of geneticists conducted experiments with fruit flies (*Drosophila*) in an attempt to verify or discount the importance of the general theory of sexual selection (e.g., Merrell, 1949; Rendel, 1945; Tan, 1946). The two most influential works were conducted ten years apart. First, Bateman (1948) used a series of mating experiments to prove that the variance in male reproductive success was much greater than the variance in female reproductive success. This was an important point; Darwin had suggested that males would compete for access to females, and Bateman's work demonstrated that females (with their fewer gametes) were indeed a limiting resource. But Bateman continued to dismiss the effect of female choice. According to Bateman, females were always able to conceive, and they exhibited "discriminating passivity" in their choice of mates. It is Bateman's framework that has influenced the language of sexual selection theory today. Males are usually described as competitive for access to mates, and females are described as "passive" but choosey.

The second *Drosophila* study that is important to the development of female choice theory in particular was conducted by Maynard Smith in 1955. Although this article has received little attention, it is the first to concentrate on female choice rather than male-male competition. Maynard Smith found that female *Drosophila* had the ability to discriminate among males. Females favored males who performed the appropriate courtship behavior, and these behaviors were best performed by males who were noninbred. These outbred males also had higher sperm counts than inbred males (Maynard Smith, 1955, 1958). When they obtained an adequate supply of sperm, females discouraged males. In other words, females apparently chose males based on fertilizing ability as reflected by courtship behavior. Maynard Smith also anticipated Robert Trivers by 20 years when he stated that individuals must also be fit parents (either more fertile or as better caregivers) to be considered preferred mates.

Robert Trivers and the Resurrection of Female Choice

Prior to the 1970s, sexual selection theory claimed that males compete for access to females because females produce few gametes and are the limiting resource. Furthermore, females are choosey, but passively so. However, in the 1970s behavioral biology experienced a revolution. Several converging events produced a new framework for analysis of animal behavior. First, field and laboratory studies of a number of animal species had reached a critical mass. Second, a century of development of the theory of evolution by natural selection had refined the concepts that sought to explain behavioral patterns. For example, W. D. Hamilton's (1964) response to Wynne-Edward's (1962) description of group selection was a key element in this process. Wynne-Edwards had suggested that altruism could be explained only if it aided the group as a whole. Hamilton argued that since related individuals share genes in common, much of what appears to be altruistic, can actually be explained through kin selection. This theoretical framework for the study of behavior was set out in detail by Wilson in 1975 under the title "sociobiology," the study of the biological basis of behavior. It became standard for animal behaviorists to test hypotheses based on evolutionary theory in an attempt to understand the evolution of particular behavioral patterns.

Lastly, as in Darwin's day, social attitudes played a role in the development of sexual selection theory during the 1970s. Along with radical changes in the expected role of women in society and the emancipation of female sexuality came a new perspective on female animal behavior (see also Andersson and Bradbury, 1987). Female animals were no longer considered as just "mothers," but as individual strategists with improved reproductive success as their goal.

During this period, sexual selection resurfaced as a controversial issue. Bernard Campbell's edited anniversary volume *Sexual Selection and the Descent of Man*, published in 1972, commemorated the 100th anniversary of Darwin's volume on sexual selection. It also contained one of the most influential papers on contemporary sexual selection theory. In that paper, Robert Trivers pointed out that differences in male and female mating strategies were not just relevant to the differential production of gametes. Because parents have only a limited amount of energy and resources to expend on offspring, the sex that invests more per offspring will be the limiting resource for the opposite sex. Thus, members of the sex that invests less per offspring will compete among themselves for the sex that invests more. "What governs the operation of sexual selection is the relative parental investment of the sexes in their offspring" (Trivers, 1972:141). Trivers observed that female choice had been heretofore restricted to the female's ability to choose the right species, the right sex, and the right age male. He then stated:

> While the adaptive value of such choices is obvious, the adaptive value of subtler discriminations among broadly appropriate males is much more difficult to visualize or document. (Trivers, 1972:165.)

The problems of female choice were clear to Trivers. Theoretical support was required for assuming that certain variables had adaptive value to females, and female choice had to be documented.

Trivers was the first to outline what might constitute important variables to investigate when considering the issue of females choice. He listed 1) sexual competence, 2) potential male parental investment in offspring, 3) good genes, and 4) males with good territories or resources. The importance of Triver's article was its instigation of a new phase of research on female choice.

Contemporary Theory of Female Choice

The concept of female choice is now developing along three lines of inquiry: one is theoretical, another provides mathematical models of mate choice, and the third is observational. The evolutionary framework that supports the notion of mate choice has become theoretically sophisticated. As a result, sexual selection theory has developed rapidly, and thus incites "divergent views and outspoken disputes (Andersson and Bradbury, 1987:1). A state-of-the-art explanation of female choice is best provided by Heisler et al. (1987). These authors divide the theoretical models for mate selection into two types. The first set, subsumed into a "Fisherian model," includes those models by Boak (1986), O'Donald (1980), Lande (1981), Kirkpatrick (1982), and Seger (1985) in which female choice for male traits can evolve regardless of the effect of those traits on infant viability. Following Fisher's concept of runaway selection, male traits are initially selected by females and then exaggerated by the male-expression/female-choice feedback loop. Eventually, the male traits no longer have any fitness value, they are selectively neutral (Boak, 1986). The second group of models, outlined by Zahavi (1975), Kordic-Brown and Brown (1984), Hamilton and Zuk (1982), and Andersson (1986) consider the possibility that females choose male traits that reflect survivorship and vigor ("truth in advertising"). Many secondary sexual characteristics or male traits might indicate male condition to a female regardless of their effect on mating. Zahavi (1975) suggested that males with extreme characteristics are demonstrating to females that even with a "handicap" they can survive, and thus would make the best mates. Females then choose these males because of their overall vigor, and are rewarded with high fitness for both their male and female offspring. While none of these theorists have presented a clear picture of the evolution of mate choice, the end result is that female choice has been dissected into components that can be explored.

Evolutionary biologists have also provided various mathematical models for understanding the potential options and effects of alternate mate choices (e.g., Janetos, 1980; O'Donald, 1980). While these models do not tell us what females really do, they do provide testable hypotheses. They also often explain patterns of behavior that cannot be understood in the short term, but make sense only when they are projected onto a life-history pattern, something that is rarely observed in the field. Janetos's model in particular has illuminated several constraints that presumably define female choice. He demonstrated mathematically that random mating yields the worst outcome to females in terms of fitness, and choice for the "best" possible male returns the highest fitness. In between those options, females do best when they are able to make two-by-two decisions among a restricted number of males. The model has also demonstrated that females only have limited time and energy to expend on making choices, and that eventually a long search does them more harm than good (see also Halliday, 1983). However, none of these models have been applied directly to primates.

The observational exploration of the issue of female choice is illustrated by the works of a multitude of behaviorists in the 1970s and 1980s that have focused on the females themselves to determine what females really do during the mating process (see, for example, the volume by Bateson, 1983, Searcy, 1982; and below). Behaviorists have increasingly documented examples of female preference for certain males in fish, insects, birds, and mammals. Armed with a basic theoretical framework, some researchers are beginning to make strong arguments for female choice as a significant factor in the determination of individual reproductive success.

Although there has been an intense focus on sexual selection over the last decade, the problems with female choice are curiously similar to those of Darwin's time. Theoretical constructs and models aside, we still rarely understand the how or why of female mate preference or choice. The problems include a difficulty in separating female choice from male-male competition, the inability to determine or to understand exactly what females of any species interpret as preferable, and the almost impossible task of determining if female preference has an evolutionary effect. Put more succinctly, 1) What do females want? 2) Why do they want it? 3) If they have a preference are they able to execute it? 4) Are the traits they prefer heritable? 5) Is the process of selection heritable?, and 6) Does this preference result in higher fitness? These questions remain essentially unanswered.

DO FEMALE PRIMATES CHOOSE THEIR MATES?

The Art of Choice

The verb *choose* is defined in Webster's dictionary as "to take as a choice; pick out by preference from all available; select." When the word *choice* is used to describe human behavior, we assume it always includes some sort of decision-making process. The individual is presented with a number of options, evaluates those alternatives, and then makes the selection known. Westerners like to believe that all our choices are conscious; we firmly believe in the concept of free will, and the thought that some decisions in life are unconscious often implies a lack of freedom. But humans make both conscious and unconscious choices. It is reasonable to suggest that choice for a certain sandwich at lunch is a conscious choice, whereas choice for a particular mate is probably more unconscious.

When the word *choice* is applied to animal behavior, we are at a loss to describe exactly what is meant. In most studies of female mate choice authors provide a qualifying statement to the effect that their subjects are not making "real choices," but that natural selection has operated to favor those females who prefer mates with certain qualities. The choice then is presumably unconscious. Only Robin Dunbar, in his volume on *Theropithecus gelada*, is straightforward in his opinion that the animals are making conscious decisions about their social interactions:

> . . . I shall make frequent use of the language of conscious decision-making . . . I do so partly because this is much the easiest way to discuss the animals' behavior, but also partly because fifteen years of field work have made it abundantly clear to me that strategy evaluation is precisely what the animals are doing. (Dunbar, 1984:4.)

It is, perhaps, useful to avoid the semantic machinations involved in deciding if mate choice is conscious or unconscious. After all, we will probably never know how animals think or how they make decision (Griffin, 1984). We can, however, proceed with an objective evaluation of their actions, regardless of the motivation and its level of consciousness.

The same argument should be applied to use of the word *preference*. While *choice* indicates an action that could presumably be observed and measured, *preference* denotes desires that may or may not result in choice (Heisler et al., 1987). If we have difficulty determining the active behavior of *choice*, how can we evaluate *preference*?

Preference aside, the use of the word *choice* by evolutionary biologists has a precise meaning; it implies an evolutionary effect. Female choice is not just a mere desire or an action, but a desire and action that affects a female's fitness and the fitness of her partner. In the end, reproduction is all that counts. The task at hand, then, is to determine who conceives with whom, and what role female actions play in the conception of offspring with particular males. How powerful are female primates in expressing their mating preferences, what exactly are those preferences, and do their preferences have an evolutionary effect?

Decades of field and laboratory observation on primate matings have provided extensive data on female mating patterns. Although early research focused on males as the more assertive sex, it soon became clear that females were intensely involved in the determination of who mates with whom (Blaffer Hrdy, 1981). Even more recently, it has also become clear that in situations where females are assertive sexual partners, their preferences are sometimes unrequited because of male-male competition or because the preferred males are not available (Small, 1988). Females may prefer a particular male (desire or motivation), but be unable to gain access to that male (the choice itself). The most realistic description of mating might be that of a compromise between male and female interests. This presents a major problem in the determination of how important female choice is to sexual selection. The separation of male mating behavior from female mating behavior is an artificial division of an interpersonal dyadic behavior pattern. But to understand female choice and its impact, it is necessary to observe females alone to determine their mating behavior independent of the activity undertaken by males. With that caveat in mind, we can survey the primate order for any evidence of female action that suggests that females are making choices for mates.

What "Should" Females Want?

Primate females have limited reproductive potential. Primates tend to reach sexual maturity late (compared to other mammals), they usually produce singleton births, and have long intervals between births. On a scale of r- and K-selected species, primates tend toward production of fewer offspring that require higher investment; they are K-selected. Since females have a limited amount of energy to expend on the production of infants, they should be careful to select a mate who will enhance the survival of the offspring and hence the survival of the offspring's genes. Female choice, when it occurs, should reflect the reproductive interests of females.

From an evolutionary standpoint, certain male characteristics should be critical to female choice (Halliday, 1983). The importance of each variable will vary with the phylogenetic, ecological, and social makeup of each species. However, it is possible to proffer several attributes of males that we assume could be important.

Good Genes The argument for good genes is confusing because we define "good genes" as those that are passed on, and at the same time, suggest that good genes are *why* an individual is reproductively successful in the first place. Yet there has been little consideration of exactly what is meant by "good genes," except that they must be responsible for high reproductive success.

The most important choice a female should make is for a male of the same species. The basic set of "good genes" is one that combines with one's own to make a viable offspring.

Beyond that, fertile and fecund males should be preferred. Females might then be at least expected to choose mature over sexually immature male partners. "Good genes" might also include a good immune system that resists diseases and the genes that fight endo- and exo-parasites (Hamilton and Zuk, 1982). Given a genetic basis of behavior, there might also be genes that accompany behaviors that are more desirable than others.

Status Most of the studies that evaluate female choice in nonhuman primates have concentrated on male status. We assume that females prefer males of high status (rank) because high status is generally correlated with access to resources. In addition, high-status males are often older and more powerful than low-status males. These males might afford some protection from predators, or during inter-individual interactions among troop mates.

Under special circumstances, however, lower-ranking males might be preferred partners. For example, maintenance of high rank usually means extensive attention to male-male status interactions by those males involved in conflicts. These males then have less time to spend with females, or with their offspring.

Novelty Females are presumably interested in these males because they attract attention. This selection for novel males may have evolved to avoid inbreeding depression. Along the same lines, females might gain by choice for genetic variability among their offspring.

Familiarity Some researchers have suggested that females place themselves at risk when interacting with males, especially where male-male competition is intense. For some females, familiarity, or past social relationships with particular males, might guide female choice during mating. This would be possible in groups where males hold tenure for long periods, or do not emigrate.

Resources Female primates could trade matings for scarce resources. These resources might include immediate food or shelter, or more long-term benefits such as a friendship that protects a female.

Parental Care On the altricial-precocial continuum, primates produce relatively altricial young. Although females are usually capable of nursing and rearing a single offspring at intervals, male care is often important to infant survival. If paternal care is advantageous, then females might choose for paternal characteristics.

Assessment of Female "Wants"

These six types of female choice represent only those variables that have been evaluated in the extensive insect, avian, and mammalian literature on female choice. Although these variables are presented as discrete entities, many are clearly interrelated. For example, high-status males are usually also older than lower-status males, and they might also be privy to better resources. These interrelationships, therefore, further confuse our evaluations of male attributes that might be important to females.

The importance of each to nonhuman primates will be considered below in a review of mating behavior and the evidence for female choice among primates. A primate focus on female choice is rather recent, and thus we should keep an open mind about the variables outlined above and their relative importance to each species. There is a real possibility that there are variables yet to be revealed as important to female primates.

How Might Females Evaluate Males?

Primate females cannot count sperm, do health checks, or predict male vigor. Nor can they evaluate their own future fitness. They can only make choices (if they do so) on proximate cues provided by males. These cues are both physiological and behavioral. As suggested by Kordic-Brown and Brown (1984), some male traits, usually exaggerated ones, are presumably indicators of good health and high fitness. Primate males tend not to have exaggerated secondary sexual characteristics that attract females (the large mane of Hamadryas males or the turquoise testicles of male vervets might be exceptions). However, some individuals survive longer because they have relatively better immune systems that fight diseases and parasites. In addition, older males have proven that they can find food resources and escape predators and survive. In this case, age alone might be an indicator of a male with high vigor, and the "good genes" that a female might want to pass on to her male and female offspring.

There is certainly a genetic component to morphological traits such as size and weight. These traits might be important to female choice if they aid in the survival of an offspring that carries genes for those traits, or if they later allow an offspring to win in reproductive competition.

Hamilton and Zuk (1982) have considered the relationship between blood parasite load and male condition. According to these authors, females should choose males with good skin and coat condition. Since most primates engage in extensive grooming bouts, females could readily assess these parameters in potential mates.

If familiarity or paternal behavior are important to females, male behavior is an indicator of male social abilities. Females could choose males who demonstrate caring interactions with present infants, or who support the female during aggressive interactions. This assumes that females are "socially intelligent" (Byrne and Whiten, 1988). They must have the ability to discriminate among males, repeatedly interact with the same males, and possess a large memory for sorting social information and understanding a social network. Since primates are known for just this type of mental processing (Cheney et al., 1986), this suggestion seems reasonable.

Humans base many of their mate decisions on "attractiveness." The components of beauty are distinctly different from culture to culture, and they change with time. We cannot, however, dismiss the possibility that nonhuman primates also have some concept of attractiveness, or beauty. In fact, many of the choices made by nonhuman primate females that seem unexplainable to human observers might fall into this category.

How Might Females Exert Choice?

There are at least five behavioral and physiological means by which female primates can potentially exert choice. During her receptive phase, a female can simply approach a male and make sure she is in close proximity. Taub (1980a) used this definition for female choice in Barbary macaques (*Macaca sylvanus*) by suggesting that once a female entered a male's "sphere of influence," she had freely placed herself in a position for mating with that male. In addition, a female can more assertively walk up to a male, present her hindquarters and effectively "choose" him for a mounting, assuming that he is interested. Females can also avoid certain males. Any female could be truculent, that is run away, sit down when an unwanted male approaches her, or otherwise refuse to cooperate. A female might also fight for a certain male. Although sexual selection theory suggests that males rather than females should be expected to fight over mates, limited access to especially preferred males could also result in female-female competition (Robinson, 1982; Small, 1988). And finally, a female could, perhaps affect sperm transport internally, although there is as yet no evidence of a physiological mechanism that would allow such an influence, conscious or otherwise, by females.

Female Primate Sexual Behavior

Blaffer Hrdy and Whitten (1986) have provided an excellent review of primate female sexual behavior. As their paper describes, nonhuman primates display a wide variety of reproductive biological features. All female primates experience sexual cycles that include periods of attractivity when males are attracted to females, proceptivity when females become interested in males, and receptivity during which females facilitate copulation by their behavior. Cycle length varies: The average for 11 prosimian species is 39.2 days (range 24–51.5 days), for 13 species of new world monkeys 19.5 days (range 16–25.5 days), for 27 species of old world monkeys 31.6 days (range 27–40 days), and for 6 species of apes cycle length is also 31.6 days (range 30–37 days) (taken from Blaffer Hrdy and Whitten, 1986). Some apes and some monkeys also have a visible menstruation at the end of the cycle.

Some nonhuman primates breed only seasonally (Lindburg, 1987), although the length of the breeding season can vary widely. For example, patas monkeys (*Erythrocebus patas*) (Chism et al., 1984) and vervet monkeys (*Cercopithecus aethiops*) (Andelman, 1987) have a relatively brief breeding season of (two months while rhesus macaques (*Macaca mulatta*) have a breeding season that can last as long as 6 months (Lindburg, 1987; Small and Smith, 1986). Presumably, seasonal breeding is tied into ecological adaptations for producing infants, or timing lactation, to periods of resource abundance (Lindburg, 1987). Other species breed throughout the year (e.g., baboons *Papio*; chimpanzees *Pan troglodytes*), or show birth "peaks" (e.g., longtail macaques *Macaca fascicularis*).

Infants are produced at varying intervals from yearly (most macaques) to a number of years (chimpanzees). Interbirth interval is, of course, associated with infant dependency and time to weaning.

Nonhuman primate females use morphological, behavioral, olfactory, and visual cues to signal their receptivity. Females in some species, such as chimpanzees, savannah baboons, and Barbary macaques display large pink perineal swellings that are a result of hormonal changes during ovulation. These swellings have an ascending phase to maximum turgescence, and then deflate after ovulation (see Scott, 1984 or Wallis, 1983 for charts of perineal swellings). Male primates often monitor female cycle states by smelling and tasting vaginal secretions (bonnet macaques, Kangawa et al., 1977) or urine (slender loris, Izard and Rasmussen, 1985). There are also behavioral sequences that occur only during breeding that signal to males that a female is ready to mate. These include female approaches to males, sexual solicitation in which a female presents her hindquarters to a male for inspection, or facial expressions that catch the attention of males. For example, female Hanuman langurs (*Presbytis entellus*), (Blaffer Hrdy, 1977) and patas monkeys (*Erythrocebus patas*) (Chism et al., 1984; Loy, 1981) have a distinct behavioral sequence that is exclusively reserved for soliciting copulations from males. These displays include an approach, head bobbing, the presentation of the hindquarters, and sometimes a vocalization. Blaffer Hrdy and Whitten (1986) estimate that of the 78 primate species on which they reported, females in 44 species exhibit some sort of initiation of sexual interaction. These initiations include elaborate ritual displays (9 species), sexual presentation (26 species), face-to-face solicitation (6 species), rubbing or touching the male (3 species), and mere approach (2 species). Females of some species, of course, exhibit more than one of these proceptive behaviors. While these behaviors are most easily quantified, they do not necessarily define the more subtle instances of female choice, let alone female preference. They do, however, allow for an examination of behaviors that can be observed and understood by human observers.

SURVEY OF FEMALE CHOICE IN NONHUMAN PRIMATES

Survey of the Primate Order

Table 1 presents a survey of research relevant to female choice among captive and free-ranging primates. This list reflects those studies of female mating behavior that indicate some sort of consistent preference, or actual choice. Many other sources were consulted (approximately 200), but these studies either did not mention female mating behavior, or if they did, there was no indication of female preference or choice. Some studies designed specifically to address issues of mating only analyzed male-male competition and male reproductive success. Others were not concerned with female mate selection, or more likely, they were unable to determine consistent mate selection by females that could be interpreted as choice (for an example, see Cords, 1984). It may also be that no mention was made of female selectivity because the females of those species did not exhibit any behaviors that indicated to observers that choice was part of the mating system. In addition, for choice to appear as part of a female's mating strategy, she must first have the possibility of selecting among more than one male. Thus a number of species, which breed monogamously (e.g., gibbons, marmosets) or in one-male harems (e.g., gelada baboons), would be less likely to have a clear picture of female preference since any effect of mate choice occurs early in the establishment of the breeding pair. There are a number of species for which we have no information on female mating at all. This is a result of a combination of factors: 1) primates are long-lived and require long-term observation to gain any sense of mating behavior, let alone an understanding of female preference; 2) many species are difficult to observe, especially arboreal animals, and a consistent record of mating behavior by identified individuals is almost impossible to obtain; 3) females do not mate that often; they often conceive after one or a few cycles, and spend most of their adult lives pregnant or lactating. It is therefore difficult to make statements about female choice with so few data. The vagaries of the subjects, rather than the abilities of researchers, make this task so difficult.

Table 1 is arranged by variables that might indicate preference for males by rank, age, size, familiarity, paternal care, resources, and novelty. Some species appear in more than one variable because they show preference for both variables, or different researchers have observed differences in the importance of the these variables for that species.

Studies Specifically Addressing Female Choice

Squirrel monkeys (Saimiri oerstedii) Boinski (1987) conducted the first field study of squirrel monkeys in which individual animals were recognized. Squirrel monkeys live in medium to large multi-male/multi-female groups (approximately 35 individuals in Boinski's study), and they are exclusively arboreal. Boinski was able to determine that females, not males, transfer between groups, that there is little male-male aggression and no discernible male hierarchy. Females are seasonally receptive and each estrus lasts only 6–8 days. Male squirrel monkeys increase in size by 20% during the breeding season. More significantly, Boinski determined that the largest male is responsible for 70% of the observed copulations. Females actively and assertively solicit copulations. They engage in mutual olfactory investigations with males and place their hindquarters up to the nose of males. Females apparently prefer the largest male, but when he was occupied, or did not respond, they copulated with other males. When the largest males were out of sight, estrous females would "wander through the forest calling vigorously" (Boinski, 1987:16). Although females might choose the largest males so that their male offspring would also be larger and the next generation of females would therefore select their sons ("Fisherian selection"), Boinski felt that female choice for large size is actually in anticipation of future paternal care. Large males exhibit vigilance behavior against a variety of predators in the Costa Rican forest, and this behavior might be selected because these males are protecting their own offspring. In any case, squirrel monkey females, who have no male status to evaluate, apparently choose males by size.

Brown Capuchins (Cebus apella) Janson (1984) observed brown capuchins in Manu National Park, Peru, for several years. Observation of these arboreal primates was extremely difficult but he was able to describe sexual behavior, especially that of females. Capuchin groups consist of 1 to 4 males and 1 to 4 sexually mature females. Although this species does not restrict breeding to a defined season, there is a period during which several females might be in estrus simultaneously (a breeding "peak"). During estrus, females are skittish, they grimace frequently, and produce a distinct vocalization. This vocalization begins as a soft whistle and then turns into a whine and can last for up to 3 hours at a time. The estrous female also becomes a "gadfly" in the true sense of the word (see Blaffer Hrdy, 1981). Whistling and whining, she pesters the dominant male by repeated approaches, grimaces, and the constant presentation of a submissive posture in his direction. She might also try to engage him in a game of sexual tag; she runs up to the dominant male, touches and pushes him and then runs away. She even fails to eat during this time. For 4 of her 6 days of estrus, the female unrelentingly solicits the dominant male. But he is not necessarily the most responsive partner: Males on average only copulate once a day. Janson also discovered that the attraction was not the personality or morphology of a male, but the fact that he was highest ranking. Females would ignore a certain male if he were low ranking, but if that same male achieved highest

Table 1. Female choice among nonhuman primates

Species	Comment	Reference
Rank		
Galago senegalensis	Although the dominant male sequesters females, there is some indication that females would reject lower-ranking males	Doyle et al., 1967
Propithecus verrecuzi	Females prefer dominant males	Richard, 1974
Cebus apella	Females actively choose the dominant male	Janson, 1984
Miopithecus talapoin	Given a choice of two males in the laboratory, females choose the more dominant male	Scruton and Herbert, 1970
Cercopithecus aethiops	Choice for high rank in captivity and the field	Keddy, 1986 Struhsaker, 1975 Andelman, 1987
Macaca mulatta	For highest-ranking available male	Altmann, 1962 Kaufmann, 1965 Lindburg, 1983
Macaca fascicularis	For highest-ranking male	van Noordwijk. 1985
Papio anubis	For highest-ranking males	Packer, 1979
Papio cynocephalus	For highest-ranking available male	Hausfater, 1975 Seyfarth, 1978
Age		
Varecia variegata	Females choose older, "stronger" males	Foerg, 1982
Cercocebus albigena	Female initiates most copulations and directs initiation more toward adult than subadult males	Wallis, 1983
Macaca fuscata	Adult females tend to copulate with older rather then immature males	Takahata, 1980
Papio ursinus	Females present to adult males more often than to subadult males	Saayman, 1970
Pongo pygmaeus	Females most often resist subadult nonresident males	Mitani, 1985
Size		
Saimiri oerstedii	Females assertively seek large males	Boinski, 1987
Familiarity		
Macaca mulatta	Personality can overshadow the effects of age or rank	Loy, 1971
Macaca fuscata	Consortships reestablish year after year	Fedigan and Gouzoules, 1978
Papio anubis	"Friends" form more successful consortships	Packer, 1979 Smuts, 1985
Papio cynocephalus	Consortships formed by "friends" are more coordinated	Rasmussen, 1983
Pongo pygmaeus	Females most often resist nonresident males	Mitani, 1985
Pan troglodytes	Females choose familiar males and long-term friends	Goodall, 1986 McGinnis, 1979 Tutin, 1979 Brereton, 1981
Novelty		
Saimiri oerstedii	Females seek extra-troop males	Boinski, 1987
Alouatta pigra	Females seek extra-troop males	Horwich, 1983
Cercopithecus mitis	Females seek extra-troop males and not the harem leader	Tsingalia and Rowell, 1984
Presbytis entellus	Females mate with recent immigrant males to avoid infanticide	Blaffer Hrdy, 1977
Macaca mulatta	Females mate with extra-troop males	Lindburg, 1983 Brereton, 1981
Macaca fuscata	Females mate with extra-troop males and will transfer to new groups during breeding season	Burton and Fukada, 1981 Wolfe, 1986

(continued)

Table 1. Female choice among nonhuman primates *(continued)*

Species	Comment	Reference
Macaca fascicularis	Females ocasionally copulate with "visiting males"	van Noordwijk, 1985
Pan troglodytes	Females will mate with extra-group males and return to their natal group	Goodall, 1986
Erythrocebus patas	Females seek out extra-troop males in the area, but these males may be familiar	Olson, 1985
Resources		
Pan troglodytes	Males who share food are preferred consort partners	Tutin, 1979
Paternity		
Macaca sylvanus	Females mate with multiple males to confuse paternity and gain male care	Taub, 1980
Other		
Lemur catta	Females choose winners of "stink fights"	Jolly, 1966
Colobus badius	Females transfer among groups to avoid potentially infanticidal males	Marsh, 1979
Macaca mulatta	Females conceive with males who maintain the genetic integrity of the matriline	Silk and Boyd, 1983 Smith and Small, 1987
Macaca fuscata	Females choose males who perform courtship displays	Modahl and Eaton, 1977

rank, he suddenly became attractive. If the dominant male did not readily respond, a female might solicit and copulate with lower-ranking males. She will also copulate with these less attractive males at the beginning and end of the 6 day estrus, when she is less likely to conceive. Cebus females rival Barbary macaques (see chart) in their rate of sexual activity and the number of different partners involved. Janson recorded data on one female who copulated with four different males in 10 minutes. In any case, these highly assertive females are clearly choosing partners based on rank. But when that male is inadequate, she becomes, as Small (1988) suggested, more concerned with conception itself than conception with a preferred male.

Vervet monkeys (Cercopithecus aethiops) African vervets live in small groups and mate polygynously. Females do not exhibit signs of estrus (Andelman, 1987), and breeding is restricted to 2 months a year. Keddy (1986) conducted a series of experiments on captive vervets to determine if females made mate choices based on male dominance status when both male-male and female-female competition were eliminated. Matings were observed both in the normal group setting, and as isolated dyads matched for various combinations of dominant and subordinate animals. All females preferred dominant males when placed in dyads; females rarely showed aggression toward dominant males who attempted to mate. Females placed in dyads with subordinate males, however, usually rejected them, but only dominant females were able to prevent these lower ranking males from repeated attempts. Subordinate females only approached dominant males when in dyads, suggesting that female-female competition prevents subordinate females from expressing their preference for dominant males. Subordinate males only mated when they were placed in dyads and they were free from domination from other males. In this study, females exerted choice through approaches, and by rejecting undesirable males. In addition, there was clear choice and preference for dominant males. These data should be viewed with caution, however, because female mating behavior was constrained by the artificial nature of the experimental procedure.

Andelman (1987) reported that vervet females in the wild rebuff most copulation attempts by males. Females either sit down or walk away, and sometimes these rejections escalate into attacks by the females. Females bite and chase males, and often they mount coalitions against a male. Only 42% of copulation attempts by males were successful. As in the captive study, high-ranking males were more successful in completing copulations than were low-ranking males. Recently, Cheney et al. (1988) evaluated the long-term relationship between rank and reproductive success, and determined that dominance had an effect only in some groups, and only during certain years.

Macaques (Macaca spp.) There are approximately 19 species of macaques (Fooden, 1980) and a number have been studied intensively in the field and the laboratory. Rhesus macaques, for example, have been used for decades in biomedical research, and much of our knowledge of their behavior comes from colony breeding programs. Some species of macaques are also reasonably accessible in the field, especially those species that are terrestrial. Rhesus and Japanese macaques have a long history of living close to human populations and they have been the subjects of long-term research and demographic monitoring. Macaques exhibit wide-range species-specific behavioral differences (See Lindburg, 1980), but in general they share a multi-male/multi-female social organization. Group size varies from small (*M. fascicularis*) to as large as 100 individuals (*M. mulatta*). All macaques are omnivorous, and their evolutionary radiation across the Old World is presumably linked to their ability to adapt to ecological changes, including climate and food availability.

Females undergo estrous periods of approximately 25–35 days. Females usually experience more than one cycle during estrus, and they frequently have postconception cycles. Some species breed seasonally, such as rhesus, while others breed throughout the year, like longtails (*M. fascicularis*) (Lindburg, 1987). Seasonality is related to the ecological constraints of food availability and annual rainfall cycle (Lindburg, 1987; Small and Smith, 1986). There are marked physiological changes at estrus for some species. For example, Barbary macaques (*M. sylvanus*) and pigtail macaques (*M. nemestrina*) display large perineal swellings, like baboons, that correspond with ovulation (Kuester and Paul, 1984; Michael and Zumpe, 1971), while bonnet (*M. radiata*) and stumptail (*M. arctoides*) macaques experience no overt changes in the sexual skin (Michael and Zumpe, 1971). Only adolescent rhesus females exhibit large edemous swellings (Kaufmann, 1965; Loy, 1971, Lindburg, 1983). Adult rhesus and Japanese macaque females show some swelling, but their major physiological changes are deep redness of both the perineal area and the face (Kaufmann, 1965; Loy, 1971; Lindburg, 1983; Tokuda, 1961). While these perineal and facial changes are considered signals to males of female fertility, olfaction is also important to males in determining which females are near ovulation (Michael and Zumpe, 1970). Female macaques also change behaviorally during estrus.

In general, most macaques females do not have close relationships with males. Female "friendships" are usually with other females, most often members of the same matriline: They are a "female-bonded" genus (Wrangham, 1980). Once in estrus, females begin interacting with males. They solicit copulations, may spend time in consortships, and groom males. This change in behavior is most noticeable in seasonally breeding species, in which social interactions among adult animals is markedly different as soon as females come into estrus (Small, 1983, in press, a, b). Reproduction and mating behavior have been studied in detail in rhesus macaques (*M. mulatta*), Japanese macaques (*M. fuscata*), and Barbary macaques (*M. sylvanus*), and are summarized below.

(1) Rhesus macaques (M. mulatta) The behavior of rhesus macaque (*M. mulatta*) females is best known from laboratory research, including studies of breeding colonies such as Cayo Santiago, La Parguera, and the California Primate Research Center, and from field work in India. Rhesus breed seasonally in the fall during a 5 month period (Lindburg, 1987); Loy, 1971; Kaufmann, 1965; Small and Smith, 1986). Carpenter (1934) first defined a consortship as an exclusive relationship that included mating, but the term has been used inaccurately for decades to include male-female associations of only a few hours, and relationships that are not exclusive. Rhesus females engage in what has been called "consortships" that last from a few hours to several days, but these consortships are not necessarily exclusive for either the male or the female (Small, in press, a). A number of studies have found a correlation between male dominance and mating in rhesus, although this correlation is not always strong or straightforward, (Altmann, 1962; Carpenter, 1942; Chapais, 1983; Conaway and Koford, 1964; Kaufmann, 1965; Lindburg, 1983). The relationship between male dominance and reproductive success has been better substantiated by paternity exclusion studies (Smith, 1981). This information is important because the association between copulation frequency, or timing, and actual conception has been questioned (Curie-Cohen et al., 1983; Stern and Smith, 1984). Apparently high-ranking males consistently father more infants than low-ranking males (Curie-Cohen et al., 1983; Shivley and Smith, 1985; Smith, 1981), but high-ranking males do not conceive disproportionately with high- or low-ranking females (Small and Smith, 1982). Thus, regardless of female choice, the end result is that higher-ranking rhesus males, on average, produce the most offspring.

The extent of female choice among rhesus can be determined by the sexual solicitations and their cooperation in consortships. Sexual solicitations of males include the presentation of the hindquarters, cautious grooming, rubbing the male, reaching out, and head bobbing (Lindburg, 1983; Michael and Zumpe, 1970). Females are also often responsible for maintaining proximity to preferred males (Kaufmann, 1965). Brereton (1981) cited a case of one female who transferred temporarily to a non-natal group and consorted with several males during estrus. Lindburg (1983) asserted that male-male competition has the stronger

498

role in determining mating because in this species males are so much larger than females. He may be correct since male rhesus frequently push an unwilling female into mounting position, often roughly, and try to herd females into consorts (Carpenter, 1942; Lindburg, 1983). Lindburg (1983) also described the following: An estrous female tried to move away from her alpha consort toward a lower-ranking male. Each time she moved, she was attacked by the alpha male, and she eventually died from the wounds. Outside of consortships with the powerful alpha males, female rhesus display mate preference, but they direct most of their solicitations toward the highest-ranking males. Females have as many as four different male partners during estrus (Loy, 1971; Small, in press, a), and rhesus females have been known to move from male to male in rapid succession (Carpenter, 1942; Lindburg, 1983). Small (1983) also discovered that females altered their sexual behavior according to their reproductive status. Females who had not produced a viable infant the previous breeding season were more sexually assertive than females with 6-month-old infants. Silk and Boyd (1983) suggested that when matriline size and relatedness is important to females, they might choose to conceive with males who would increase or maintain, the relatedness of their offspring within the matriline. Smith and Small (1987) supported this hypothesis through paternity analysis of rhesus matrilines, which documented preferential mating with particular patrilines by females of the same matriline.

In general, given the chance, female rhesus do chose males other than alpha and they will mate with multiple males regardless of rank. And they sometimes choose males who will increase the genetic relatedness within their matriline. Regardless of what females might want, high-ranking males can monopolize females though consortships, and they father the most infants.

(2) Japanese macaques (M. fuscata)

Studies of mating in Japanese macaques have been conducted on provisioned animals in Japan, and captive colonies. Japanese macaques are unusual among macaques in that females frequently solicit males by mounting them (Takahata, 1980; Wolfe, 1979). In addition, males often use courtship displays to attract mates, and males who display most often, mate most often (Modahl and Eaton, 1977), but females choose to respond or ignore these displays (Enomoto, 1974). There is an equivocal relationship between male rank and mating success, ranging from none to slight in some groups (Eaton, 1978; Enomoto, 1974; Hanby et al., 1971; Stephenson, 1974; Takahata, 1980); but there is some indication that adults prefer to mate with partners of the same rank (Stephenson, 1974; Takahata, 1980; Wolfe, 1979). Enomoto (1974) and Hanby et al. (1971) found that, like rhesus (Small, 1983), female Japanese macaques with 6-month-old infants are not as sexually active as females who did not conceive the previous year. Females are highly sexually assertive; in fact, they will mount other females if there are few available males for sexual interactions (Takahata, 1980; Wolfe, 1979, 1984, 1986). Females will also transfer to new groups during breeding season, mate with extra-troop males (Burton and Fukada, 1981; Wolfe, 1986), and are eager in general to exchange partners (Hanby et al., 1971; Tokuda,

1961). Fedigan and Gouzoules (1978) suggested that consortships were never based on affiliative bonds established outside of the breeding season. Takahata (1982) and Entomoto (1978) reinforced this notion when they discovered that "friends" tended to avoid mating; males appear interested, but females reject them. However, consort pairs do seem to reestablish their relationship year after year, and thus familiarity, albeit only in a sexual context, is an important variable to Japanese macaque females (Fedigan and Gouzoules, 1978).

(3) Barbary macaques (M. sylvanus) Barbary macaques have been of special interest to primatologists because of two interesting features. Females mate with almost all available males in the group, and yet males interact extensively with infants. In other words, males interact with infants that may not be their own. Based on observations of two separate colonies of provisioned animals, Kuester and Paul (1984) and Small (in press, b) have provided detailed descriptions of the mating patterns of female Barbary macaques. Females breed in the fall and undergo an average of 2 cycles. They exhibit extreme swelling and color changes of the perineal area that can last several weeks. Detumescence is rapid, and is followed by visible menstruation 14 days later. The second cycle is often less physiologically intense, although it may not be so behaviorally. In addition, females have a second or third estrus even if they are pregnant and solicit males at the usual rate. The most remarkable feature of Barbary macaque mating is the frequency of copulations and the number of partners. Small (in press, b) calculated an average of 2.23 copulations per hour with an average of 7 different partners during each estrus (range 1–14). Small also observed one female who copulated with 3 different males in 6 minutes. Taub (1980a) used the euphemism "consociation" in an attempt to gain some respectability for female Barbary macaque "promiscuity." In fact, females rarely stay more than a few minutes with any male, and move from partner to partner while the males seem unable to stop them (Small, in press, b). In captivity and in the field, these are the most sexually assertive of female macaques, and they seem to play the major role in determining mates with whom, and when.

Taub (1980b) and Blaffer Hrdy (1981) have suggested that female Barbary macaques are attempting to confuse paternity by mating with all possible males. Under this scenario, females would be choosing for male care. However, males primarily use infants as social "buffers" in hierarchical interactions (Deag and Crook, 1971; Kuester and Paul, 1986) and most male-infant interactions are time-limited (6 months or so). Small (in press, c) has suggested that alloparental care among Barbary macaques of all age-sex categories might be related to socialization, and that males have their own agenda for infants: They are solely for use in status games. And finally, no one has demonstrated that male-infant interactions in Barbary macaques are advantageous to infants in terms of survival or later reproductive success.

Female Barbary macaques do not appear to be making choices at all. Small (in press, b) found slight female mate favoritism (in sexual solicitations and copulations) for 1 male out of a possible 24, but this preference was not significant. It may be simply that males are not interested in expending the energy to stop female promiscuity. Males may be somewhat related, and they also are not extensively dimorphic in size from females. Thus they have little to gain from trying to sequester females. Females might move indiscriminately from male to male simply because they are not constrained by male-male competition (Small, in press, b).

Savannah baboons (Papio spp.) The most detailed and longest-term information on primate mating comes from several studies of savannah baboons. This wealth of information has been facilitated by two factors: 1) savannah baboons live in large multi-male, multi-female groups on open plains and thus are easily observed, and 2) baboon females are distinguished by large colorful perineal swellings that appear during estrus and track the hormonal changes that occur with ovulation. While the various species of savannah baboon, olive (*P. anubis*), chacma (*P. ursinus*), and yellow (*P. cynocephalus*), differ in important ways, both ecologically and behaviorally, their mating patterns are very similar.

Female baboons exhibit estrous cycles that last approximately 35–40 days (Scott, 1984). The perineal area is initially flat, then it begins to redden and swell in a systematic manner. It reaches "maximum tumescence" in about 2 weeks and remains swollen at this stage for about a week. Suddenly, the swelling begins to deflate, marking the end of the cycle, and providing a post hoc marker for ovulation. Laboratory research has determined that ovulation occurs about 1–4 days before the detumescence (Hendrickx and Kraemer, 1969; Wildt et al., 1977). Most researchers familiar with individual females, can easily chart the start, middle, and end of an estrous cycle and, given mating information, can make a reasonable guess about which males might be likely fathers (see Scott, 1984; Smuts, 1985, for examples). Savannah baboons are not seasonal breeders and at any given time, there might be one or more female in estrus in the group.

Inflating females frequently present to males (Saayman, 1970). However, during maximum swelling, females are most often involved in consortships, over which they seem to have little control. For that reason, studies of female baboon mating have been unable to clearly determine if females have, or can exert, a preference for particular males. They do not move among males and solicit one after another (except adolescent females who are less favored by males [Scott, 1984]), nor do they seem to discourage certain males (Smuts, 1985). However, a female may have a subtle effect on the ability of one male to oust her current consort partner. In reference to Hamadryas baboons (*P. hamadryas*), Kummer has suggested that a consort pair can present a "pair gestalt" that discourages other males from interfering (Bachman and Kummer, 1980; Kummer et al., 1974). This attitude is read by competing male baboons, is not challenged, and the consortship remains intact. On the other hand, the female can signal that she would rather be out of the consortship. She might break from the male and run away a short distance, be unresponsive to the male's movements, or avoid sexual interactions with him. Since baboons live in large groups where interindividual distance is close, any interested male can read these signals. In addition, baboons are known for their socially cognitive abilities (Cheney et al.,

1986) and it is reasonable to suggest that "attitudes" and "desires" are conveyed among groups members whose communication skills are highly refined. Females are unable to exert more overt choices because males are twice their size, and are often aggressive to females who are unwilling partners (Smuts, 1985). In support, Smuts (1985) found that 82% of consort turnovers in olive baboons occurred immediately after a female ran away from her current consort. Yellow baboon females also determine which consortships will be free of harassment by other males. Rasmussen writes: "Females who strongly prefer their male consorts actively facilitated both social and sexual interactions with their partners" (Rasmussen, 1983, p. 120). Thus female choice among savannah baboons may be subtle to human eyes, but have a significant effect.

Sexual solicitation (sexual presents, and the "eye-face" of chacma baboons [Saayman, 1970]) and cooperation during consortships have been used to evaluate female choice of mates. Two variables appear to be important to female savannah baboons, dominance rank and familiarity. High-ranking males are consistently successful in initiating and maintaining consortships, and they are also more successful than low-ranking males in participating in consortships during the time of maximum female fertility (Hausfater, 1975; Packer, 1979; Seyfarth, 1978). At the same time, females are most often cooperative with males with whom they spend the most time outside of consortships (Packer, 1979; Rasmussen, 1983; Smuts, 1985). Smuts has termed these relationships "friendships," and feels that prior friendship has a significant effect of the reproductive opportunities of male baboons.

While not overt, female choice nonetheless has an important place in mating patterns of savannah baboons. It is not enough to be dominant and capable of sequestering a fertile female. Female cooperation, and a previously established relationship with her, best predict paternity. Seyfarth has even suggested that female preference has such a strong effect that it negates male-male competition. While this may be an overstatement, female preference certainly influences male access.

Chimpanzees (Pan troglodytes) Over 20 years of research on the Gombe Stream chimpanzees has provided us with detailed accounts of this long-lived primate, our closest living relative. This work is summarized eloquently by Goodall in her recent volume (Goodall, 1986). Female chimpanzees exhibit an estrous cycle of about 36 days. Like savannah baboons, these cycles are typified by changes in the perineum. The perineal area swells into a large protuberance that appears to interfere with sitting, and the skin is vulnerable to wounding. This cycle also tracks the hormonal changes that accompany ovulation, although anovulatory cycles are common. Swellings also signal changes in female and male behavior. Chimpanzees live in a society that undergoes frequent fissions and fusions, and females spend much of their time alone. Once in estrus, a female becomes the center of attention for males in her area. She will then travel with a party of males, copulate with them, and interact socially with them.

Males do not overtly compete for females. Instead, a male will sit in a posture that exposes his erect penis, the "male-invite" posture, and flick the penis in the direction of an estrous female. The male might also gaze at the female, shake branches, move about, or reach out to her. These displays are intended to lure the female in his direction and reassure her that the display is sexual in nature and not aggressive. At that point a female can choose to ignore this display, or approach the male and present her rump to him (Goodall, 1986; Tutin and McGinnis, 1981).

Three patterns of mating have been outlined for chimpanzees: 1) opportunistic, when a female mates with all available males; 2) possessive, when a male forms a short-term exclusive relationship with a female; and 3) consortships that are mutually exclusive and isolated from the rest of the group (Tutin, 1979). Most of the copulations occur promiscuously. Based on 14 conceptions, Tutin suggested that most of the conceptions occur during exclusive consortships (Tutin, 1979), but a reanalysis by Goodall (1986) shows that only half of the consortships recorded at Gombe over 17 years of data collection (N = 258) could have resulted in conception. In all situations, females exhibit choice. First of all, females decide which males to mate with in the group situation. Although involved in a "flurry of sexual activity," a fertile female surrounded by males still decides if she will respond to a male invitation (Goodall, 1986). In addition, consortships are formed only with female cooperation. Males initiate consorts by a sexual display directed toward a female, and when she responds, he moves away expecting her to follow. If she does not, he repeats the display over and over. In some cases he will resort to violence if the female does not cooperate. Females are often reluctant to move away from the other males, and they will stall or vocalize to gain attention. As she moves away, she can also become distracted by the vocalizations of the remaining males, and return to the group. Sometimes females remain with male parties because no male is interested in forming a consortship, no male is able to entice her away, or a male is unable to deal with the group level of sexual excitement that has developed over a particular female.

There is some correlation between male mating success and dominance. The most dominant male, if his position is clearly demarcated, sometimes has the most success mating in group situations. While Tutin (1979) found no correlation between rank, age, or antagonism and successes in 14 consortships, the reanalysis by Goodall of the 258 consortships shows that only well-established dominant males have an advantage. This correlation is not, however, particularly strong in either the group or consort situation. Goodall (1986), Tutin (1975, 1979), and McGinnis (1979) all feel that "personality" is the major variable that determines which males will be preferred by females, and rank is only one aspect of personality. Chimpanzee females have the intellect to distinguish males as individuals and retain long-term personality profiles for each male. Chimpanzees in general are known for their complex social interactions, and it is not unreasonable to suggest that personality plays a major role in determining mate choice. Because of a lack of intense male-male competition, female chimpanzees also have numerous opportunities to exert choice (de Waal, 1982),

503

and they apparently choose based on past social interactions with males. Interestingly, Goodall (1986) found that out of 1,475 sexual invitations by adult males recorded over a 5-year period, only 4.1% were ignored by females. One might conclude from these data that female chimpanzees are not particularly choosey, but when they are, they base their choices most often on familiarity and individual personality.

DISCUSSION

Does Female Choice Have an Evolutionary Effect?

As Table 1 reveals, indications of female preference have only been observed in 20 species. Given the nature of primate lives, and the difficulty in observing most species, this is not surprising. There is an additional important consideration in the paucity of data on primate female mating; female choice operates in tandem with male mating strategies. Thus the expression, or the very existence, of female choice can be obscured by behavioral patterns of males. In addition, females who breed synchronously must compete with the preferences of other females in the group. This is especially important since female choice can only have an evolutionary effect when females consistently chose males with similar characteristics, and this may not always be possible when females breed synchronously (Small, 1988). This notion also highlights the difficulty of observing female preference when it is not consistently translated into female choice. What female primates want and what they actually do can be two different things.

The variation among species in the strength of apparent female preference or choice is unexpected. Females in some species are highly assertive, such as Barbary macaques and brown capuchins, and they appear to guide the direction of most copulations. Females of other species, such as savannah baboons, seemingly have much less influence on mate selection. However, we do not have the data to determine if female assertiveness, when it occurs, directly effects conception with particular males. In other words, just because females present to particular males, or initiate copulations with particular males, does not necessarily mean that they conceive with those males, or that the offspring of those matings are more fit than other infants.

Table 1 also demonstrates an interesting distribution in the possible variables that could be important to female primates. Of the 20 species in which some sort of preference was noted, females of 9 species often choose unfamiliar males over known males, and this is sometimes a risky venture. But it does not mean that choice for unknown males is the only pattern that these females exhibit. Sometimes choice for unfamiliar males is part of a pattern of indiscriminate mating with many males. Females of 7 species choose in the opposite direction: Often they have preestablished relationships with preferred sexual partners. Presumably, these males have demonstrated some sort of social ability with the female, or her infant, and he has become a "friend" outside of breeding. Dominance is an important feature for mate choice among 9 species. Since age and dominance are sometimes correlated, selection for age can also be for the most dominant males. In addition, dominant males are often the largest, the ones holding tenure for the longest time, and those with access to preferred resources. Status often represents an entire "personality" that females can evaluate.

CONCLUSIONS

Evolutionary theorists have only recently begun to consider the impact of female choice on male morphology and the evolution of mating strategies. Perhaps the most significant, and unexpected, finding of this review is the lack of any conclusive evidence for female choice among primates. Although there is clear evidence of female mate preference, there is no unambiguous information about the effects of that assertiveness on individual fitness or the evolution of male characteristics.

Why are we still unsure of the evolutionary impact of female choice? In some cases it may be that researchers have not observed, or are not attuned to, the subtleties of female mating behavior. More reasonable is the suggestion that primatologists have not completed enough observation hours to unravel the tangled patterns of male and female mating behavior. Research directed specifically at female choice is a relatively recent phenomenon, and the lack of support for a strong evolutionary effect of female choice among primates may be just the result of small data sets. For example, no study cited in this review was initially designed to support or refute the importance of female choice. In fact, only one study of primates has specifically tested the hypothesis that female choice might have an effect on male characteristics (see Mitani, 1985), and in that study, male-male competition, rather than female choice, was deemed responsible for the evolution of male orang-utan long calls. It is also possible that, as Darwin first thought, female choice, at least among primates, may be not as important to individual reproductive success as male-male competition. But since the study of female choice among primates is so recent, this possibility cannot be substantiated or discounted.

We do know that in many cases, female primates are assertive sexual partners, but when they are, they seem to be less discriminating than might be expected. It may be that in an attempt to substantiate female choice, we have confused sexual assertiveness with real evidence for the evolutionary effect of female choice. Future studies of female choice should therefore concentrate not on female sexual behavior alone, but on the effect of that behavior on conception, individual reproductive success, and the evolution of male characteristics.

ACKNOWLEDGMENTS

I thank Lynne Isbell, William Kimbel, Ryne Palombit and two anonymous reviewers for helpful comments on the manuscript.

LITERATURE CITED

Altmann S (1962) A field study of the sociobiology of rhesus monkeys *Macaca mulatta.* Ann. N.Y. Acad. Sci. *102:*338–435.

Andelman SJ (1987) Evolution of concealed ovulation in vervet monkeys. Amer. Nat. *129:*785–799.

Andersson M (1986) Evolution of condition-dependent sex ornaments and mating preferences: sexual selection based on viability difference. Evolution *40:*804–816.

Andersson M, and Bradbury JW (1987) Introduction. In JW Bradbury and MB Andersson (eds.): Sexual Selection: Testing the Alternatives. New York: John Wiley and Sons, pp. 1–8.

Bachmann C, and Kummer H (1980) Male assessment of female choice in hamadryas baboons. Behav. Ecol. Sociobiol. *6:*315–321.

Bateman AJ (1948) Intra-sexual selection in *Drosophila.* Heredity *2:*349–368.

Bateson P (1983) Mate Choice. Cambridge: Cambridge University Press.

Blaffer Hrdy S (1977) The Langurs of Abu. Cambridge: Harvard University Press.

Blaffer Hrdy S (1981) The Woman That Never Evolved. Cambridge: Harvard University Press.

Blaffer Hrdy S, and Whitten PL (1986) Patterning of sexual behavior. In B Smuts, D Cheney, R Seyfarth, R Wrangham, and TT Struhsaker (eds.): Primate Societies. Chicago: University of Chicago Press, pp. 370–384.

Boak CR (1986) A method for testing adaptive hypotheses of mate choice. Am. Nat. *127:*654–666.

Boinski S (1987) Mating patterns in squirrel monkeys (*Saimiri oerstedii*). Behav. Ecol. and Sociobiol. *21:*13–21.

Bradbury JW, and Andersson MB (1987) Sexual Selection: Testing the Alternatives. New York: John Wiley and Sons.

Brereton AR (1981) Inter-group consorting by a free-ranging female rhesus monkey (*Macaca mulatta*). Primates *22:*417–423.

Bryne R, and Whiten A (1988) Machiavellian Intelligence. Oxford: Clarendon Press.

Burton FD, and Fukuda F (1981) On female mobility: The case of the Yugawara-T group of *Macaca fuscata.* J. Human Evol. *10:*381–386.

Campbell B (1972) Sexual Selection and the Descent of Man. Chicago: Aldine.

Carpenter CR (1934) A field study of the behavior and social relationships of howling monkeys (*Alouatta palliata*). Comp. Psyche. Monog. *10:*1–168.

Carpenter CR (1942) Sexual behavior of free-ranging rhesus monkeys (*Macaca mutlatta*) Specimens, procedures and behavioral characteristics of estrus. J. Comp. Psychol. *33:*113–142.

Chapais B (1983) Reproductive activity in relation to male dominance and the likelihood of ovulation in rhesus monkeys. Behav. Ecol. and Sociobiol. *12:*215–228.

Cheney DL, Seyfarth R, and Smuts BB (1986) The evolution of social cognition in nonhuman primates. Science *243:*1361–1366.

Cheney DL, Seyfarth RM, Andelman SJ, and Lee PC (1988) Reproductive success in vervet monkeys. In TH Clutton-Brock (ed.): Reproductive Success. Chicago: University of Chicago Press. pp. 384–402.

Chism J, Rowell T, and Olson D (1984) Life history patterns of female patas monkeys. In MF Small (ed.): Female Primates. Studies by Women Primatologists. New York: Alan R. Liss, Inc., pp. 175–190.

Conaway CH and Koford CB (1964) Estrous cycles and mating behavior in a free-ranging band of rhesus monkeys. J. Mammol. *45:*577–588.

Cords M (1984) Mating patterns and social structure in redtail monkeys (*Cercopithecus ascanius*). Zet. Tierpsychol. *64*:313–329.

Curie-Cohen M, Yoshihara D, Luttrell L, Benforado K, MacCluer JW, and Stone WH (1983) The effects of dominance on mating behavior and paternity in a captive group of rhesus monkeys. Am. J. Primatol. *5*:127–138.

Darwin C (1859) The Origin of Species by Means of Natural Selection. New York: 1979 Avenel edition.

Darwin C (1871) The Descent of Man, and Selection in Relation to Sex. 1981 Princeton University Press edition, photoreproduction of 1871 edition published by J. Murry, London.

Deag JM, and Crook JH (1971) Social behavior and "agonistic buffering" in the wild Barbary macaque, *Macaca sylvanus*. Folia Primatol. *15*:183–200.

Doyle GA, Pelletier A, and Bekker T (1967) Courtship, mating and parturition in the lesser bushbaby (*Galago senegalensis moholi*) under seminatural conditions. Folia Primatol. *7*:169–197.

Dunbar RIM (1984) Reproductive Decisions. Princeton: Princeton University Press.

Eaton GG (1978) Longitudinal studies of sexual behavior of the Oregon troop of Japanese macaques. In TE McGill, DA Dewsbury, and BD Sachs (eds): Sex and Behavior. New York: Plenum Publishing. pp 35–59.

Enomoto T (1974) The sexual behavior of Japanese monkeys. J Hum. Evol. *3*:351–372.

Enomoto T (1978) On social preference in sexual behavior of Japanese monkeys (*Macaca fuscata*). J. Hum. Evol. *7*:283–293.

Fedigan L (1983) Dominance and reproductive success in primates. Yrbk. Physical Anthropol. *26*:91–129.

Fedigan L, and Gouzoules H (1978) The consort relationship in a troop of Japanese monkeys. In DJ Chivers and J Herbert (eds.): Recent Advances in Primatology, Vol 1. New York: Academic Press, pp. 493–495.

Fisher RA (1930) The Genetical Theory of Natural Selection. 1958 Dover Edition, original published by Oxford University Press.

Foerg R (1982) Reproductive behavior in *Varecia variegata*. Folia Primatol. *38*:108–121.

Fooden J (1980) Classification and distribution of living macaques (*Macaca Lacepede*). In DL Lindburg (ed.): The Macaques. New York: Van Nostrand Reinhold, pp. 1–9.

Goodall J (1986) The Chimpanzees of Gombe. Cambridge: Harvard University Press.

Griffin DR (1984) Animal Thinking. Cambridge: Harvard University Press.

Halliday TR (1983) The study of mate choice. In P Bateson (ed): Mate Choice. Cambridge: Cambridge University Press, pp. 3–32.

Hamilton WD (1964) The genetical evolution of social behavior. J. Theor. Biol. *7*:1–51.

Hamilton WD and Zuk M (1982) Heritable true fitness and bright birds: A role for parasites? Science *218*:384–387.

Hanby JP, Robertson, LT, and Phoenix CH (1971) The sexual behavior of a confined troop of Japanese macaques. Folia Primatol. *16*:123–143.

Hausfater G (1975) Dominance and reproduction in baboons (*Papio cynocephalus*). Contrib. Primatol. *7*:1–150.

Heisler L, Andersson MB, Arnold SJ, Boake, CR, Borgia G, Hausfater G, Kirkpatrick M, Lande R, Maynard Smith J, O'Donald P, Thornhill AR, and Weissing FJ (1987) The evolution of mating preferences and sexually selected traits. In JW Bradbury and MB Andersson (eds.): Sexual Selection: Testing the Alternatives. London: John Wiley and Sons, pp. 97–118.

507

Hendrickx AG, and Kraemer DG (1969) Observation on the menstrual cycle, optimal mating time and pre-implantation embryos of the baboon, Papio anubis and Papio cynocephalus. J. Repro. Fert. [Suppl.] 6:119–128.

Horwich RH (1983) Breeding behaviors in the black howler monkey (Alouatta pigra) of Belize. Primates 24:222–230.

Huxley JS (1938a) The present standing of the theory of sexual selection. In GR deBeer (ed.): Evolution: Essays on Aspects of Evolutionary Biology. Oxford: Clarendon Press, pp. 11–42.

Huxley JS (1938b) Darwin's theory of sexual selection and the data subsumed by it, in the light of recent research. Am. Nat. 72:416–433.

Izard MK, and Rasmussen DT (1985) Reproduction in the slow loris (Loris tardigradus mulabaricus) Am. J. Primatol. 8:153–165.

Janetos AC (1980) Strategies of female mate choice: A theoretical analysis. Behav. Ecol. Sociobiol. 7:107–112.

Janson CH (1984) Female choice and mating system of the brown capuchin monkey Cebus apella Z. Tierp 65:177–200.

Jolly A (1966) Lemur Behavior. Chicago: University of Chicago Press.

Kangawa H, Hafez ESE, Mori J. Kurosawa T, and Kothari L (1977) Cyclic changes in cervical mucus and LH levels in the bonnet macaque (Macaca radiata). Primates 19:208–217.

Kaufmann JH (1965) A three-year study of the mating behavior in a free-ranging band of rhesus monkeys. Ecology 46:500–512.

Keddy AC (1986) Female mate choice in vervet monkeys (Cerropithecus aethiops) Am. J. Primatol. 10:125–143.

Kirkpatrick M (1982) Sexual selection and the evolution of female choice. Evolution 39:370–386.

Kodric-Brown A, and Brown JH (1984) Truth in advertising: The kinds of traits favored by sexual selection. Am. Nat. 124:309–323.

Kuester J, and Paul A (1984) Female reproductive characteristics in semi-free ranging Barbary macaques (Macaca sylvanus) Folia Primatol. 43:69–83.

Kuester J, and Paul A (1986) Male-infant relationships in semifree-ranging Barbary macaques (Macaca sylvanus) of Affernber Salem FRG: Testing the "male care" hypothesis. Am. J. Primatol. 10:315–327.

Kummer H, Gotz W, and Angst W (1974) Triadic differentiation: An inhibitory process protecting pair bonds in baboons. Behaviour 49:62–87.

Lande R (1981) Models of speciation by sexual selection on polygenic traits. Proc. Natl. Acad. Sci. 78:3721–3725.

Lindburg DL (1980) The Macaques. New York: Van Nostrand Reinhold.

Lindburg DL (1983) Mating behavior in the Indian rhesus monkey. In PK Seth (ed.): Perspectives in Primate Biology. New Delhi: Today and Tomorrow's Printers and Publishers, pp. 45–61.

Lindburg DL (1987) Seasonality of reproduction in primates. Comp. Primate Biol. 2:167–218.

Loy, J (1971) Estrous behavior of free-ranging rhesus monkeys (Macaca mulatta). Primates 12:1–31.

Loy J (1981) The reproductive and heterosexual behavior of adult patas monkeys in captivity. Anim. Behav. 29:714–726.

Marsh CW (1979) Female transference and mate choice among Tana River red colobus. Nature 281:568–569.

Maynard Smith J (1955) Fertility, mating behavior and sexual selection in *Drosophila subobscura*. Genetics *54:*261–279.

Maynard Smith J (1958) Sexual selection. In SA Bennett (ed.): A Century of Darwin. London: Heineman, pp. 231–244.

Maynard Smith J (1987) Sexual selection—A classification of models. In JW Bradbury and MB Andersson (eds.): Sexual Selection: Testing the Alternatives. New York: John Wiley and Sons, pp. 9–20.

McGinnis PR (1979) Sexual behavior in free-living chimpanzees: Consort relationships. In DA Hamburg and ER McCown (eds.): The Great Apes. Menlo Park: Benjamin Cummings, pp. 429–439.

Merrell DJ (1949) Selective mating in *Drosophila melanogaster*. Genetics *34:*370–389.

Michael RP, and Zumpe D (1970) Sexual initiating behavior by female rhesus monkeys (*Macaca mulatta*) under laboratory conditions. Behaviour *36:*168–187.

Michael RP, and Zumpe D (1971) Patterns of reproductive behavior. In ESE Hafez (ed.): Comparative Reproduction of Nonhuman Primates. Springfield: Charles C. Thomas. pp. 205–242.

Mitani JC (1985) Mating behavior of male orang-utans in the Kutai Reserve. East Kalimantan, Indonesia Anim. Behav. *33:*392–402.

Modahl KB, and Eaton GG (1977) Display behavior in a confined troop of Japanese macaques (*Macaca fuscata*). Anim. Behav. *25:*525–535.

O'Donald P (1980) Genetic Models of Sexual Selection. Cambridge: Cambridge University Press.

Olson D (1985) The importance of female choice in the mating system of wild patas monkeys. Am. J. Physical Anthropol. *66:*211 (abstract).

Packer C (1979) Male dominance and reproductive activity in *Papio anubis*. Anim. Behav. *27:*37–45.

Rasmussen KL (1983) Influence of affiliative preferences upon behavior of male and female baboons during sexual consortships. In RA Hinde (ed.): Primate Social Relationships. Sunderland: Sinauer Assoc., pp. 116–120.

Rendel JM (1945) The genetics and cytology of *Drosophila subobscura*. II. Normal and selective matings in *Drosophila subobscura*. J. Genet. *48:*287–302.

Richard A (1974) Mating in Propithecus verreauxi verreauxi. In RD Martin, GA Doyle, and AC Walker (eds.) Prosimian Biology. Pittsburg: University of Pittsburg Press, pp. 49–79.

Robinson JG (1982) Intrasexual competition and male choice in primates. Am. J. Primatol. [Suppl.] *1:*131–144.

Saayman GS (1970) The menstrual cycle and sexual behavior in a troop of free-ranging chacma baboons. Folia Primatol. *12:*81–110.

Scott LM (1984) Reproductive behavior of adolescent female baboons (*Papio anubis*) in Kenya. In MF Small (ed.): Female Primates: Studies by Women Primatologists New York: Alan R. Liss, Inc., pp. 77–100.

Scruton DM, and Herbert T (1970) The menstrual cycle and its effect on behavior in the talapoin monkey (*Miopithecus talapoin*) Proc. Zool. Soc. Lond. *162:*419–436.

Searcy WA (1982) The evolutionary effects of mate selection. Annu. Rev. Exol. Syst. *13:*57–85.

Seger J (1985) Unifying genetic models for the evolution of female choice. Evolution *39:*1185–1193.

Seyfarth RM (1978) Special relationships among adult male and female baboons. I. Behaviour during sexual consortship. Behaviour *64:*204–226.

Shivley C, and Smith DG (1985) Social status and reproductive success of male *Macaca fascicularis*. Am. J. Primatol. *9*:129–135.

Silk JB, and Boyd R (1983) Cooperation, competition, and mate choice in matrilineal macaque groups. In SK Wasser (ed.): Social Behavior of Female Vertebrates. New York: Academic Press, pp. 315–347.

Small MF (1983) Females without infants: Mating strategies in two species of captive macaques. Folia Primatol. *40*:125–133.

Small MF (1988) Female primate sexual behavior and conception: Are there really sperm to spare? Curr. Anthropol. *29*:81–100.

Small MF (in press, a) Consortships and conceptions in captive *Macaca mulatta*. Primates.

Small MF (in press, b) Promiscuity in Barbary macaques (*Macaca sylvanus*) Am. J. Primatol.

Small MF (in press, c) Alloparental behavior in Barbary macaques (*Macaca sylvanus*) Anim. Behav.

Small MF, and Smith DG (1982) The relationship between maternal and paternal rank in rhesus macaques (*Macaca mulatta*) Anim. Behav. *30*:626–627.

Small MF and Smith DG (1986) The influence of birth timing upon infant growth and survival in captive rhesus macaques (*Macaca mulatta*) Int. J. Primatol. *7*:289–304.

Smith DG (1981) The association between rank and reproductive success of male rhesus monkeys. Am. J. Primatol. *1*:83–90.

Smith DG, and Small MF (1987) Mate choice by lineage in three captive groups of rhesus macaques (*Macaca mulatta*) Am. J. Physical Anthropol. *73*:185–191.

Smuts BB (1985) Sex and Friendship in Baboons. New York: Aldine.

Stern B, and Smith DG (1984) Sexual behavior and paternity in three captive groups of rhesus monkeys (*Macaca mulatta*). Anim. Behav. *32*:23–32.

Stephenson GR (1974) Social structure of mating activity in Japanese macaques. Symp. 5th Cont. Int. Prim. Soc., pp. 63–115.

Struhsaker TT (1975) The Red Colobus Monkey. Chicago: University of Chicago Press.

Takahata Y (1980) The reproductive biology of a free ranging troop of Japanese monkeys. Primates *21*:303–329.

Takahata Y (1982) The socio-sexual behavior of Japanese monkeys. Zet. Tierpsychol. *59*:89–108.

Tan CC (1946) Genetics of sexual isolation between *Drosophila pseudobscura* and *Drosophila persimilis*. Genetics *31*:558–573.

Taub DM (1980a) Female choice and mating strategies among wild Barbary macaques (*Macaca sylvanus*). In D Lindburg (ed.): The Macaques: New York: Van Nostrand Reinhold, pp. 287–344.

Taub DM (1980b) Testing the "agonistic buffering" hypothesis. Behav. Ecol. and Sociobiol. *6*:187–197.

Tokuda K (1961) A study on the sexual behavior in the Japanese monkey troop. Primates *3*:1–40.

Trivers RL (1972) Parental investment and sexual selection. In B Campbell (ed.): Sexual Selection and the Descent of Man. Chicago: Aldine, pp. 1136–179.

Taingalia HM, and Rowell TE (1984) The behavior of adult male blue monkeys. Z. Tierp. *64*:253–268.

Tutin C (1975) Exceptions to promiscuity in a feral chimpanzee community. Contemp. Primatol. pp. 445–449.

Tutin C (1979) Mating patterns and reproductive strategies in a community of wild chimpanzees (*Pan troglodytes schweinfurthii*). Behav. Ecol. Sociobiol. *6*:29–38.

Tutin C, and McGinnis P (1981) Chimpanzee reproduction in the wild. In C.E. Graham (ed.): Reproductive Biology of the Great Apes. New York: Academic Press, pp. 239–264.

van Noordwijk MA (1985) Sexual behaviour of Sumatran long-tailed macaques (*Macaca fascicularis*). Z. Tierp. 70:277–296.

de Waal F (1982) Chimpanzee Politics Power and Sex Among Apes. New York: Harper and Row.

Wallis JS (1983) Sexual behavior and reproduction of *Cercocebus albigena johnstonii* in Kibale Forest. Uganda. Int. J. Primatol. 4:153–166.

Wildt DE, Doyle LL, Stone SC, and Harrison RM (1977) Correlation of perineal swelling with serum ovarian hormone levels, vaginal cytology, and ovarian follicular development during the baboon reproductive cycle. Primates. *18*:261–270.

Wilson EO (1975) Sociobiology: The New Syntheses. Cambridge: Harvard University Press.

Winkler D (1988) Personal communication.

Wolfe L (1979) Behavioral patterns of estrous females of the Arashiyama West troop of Japanese macaques (*Macaca fuscata*) Primates 20:525–534.

Wolfe L (1984) Japanese macaque female sexual behavior: A comparison of Arashiyama East and West. In MF Small (ed.): Female Primates: Studies by Women Primatologists. New York: Alan R. Liss, Inc., pp. 141–158.

Wolfe L (1986) Sexual strategies of female Japanese macaques (*Macaca fuscata*). Hum. Evol. *1*:267–275.

Wrangham RW (1980) An ecological model of female-bonded primate groups. Behaviour 75:262–300.

Wynne-Edwards VC (1962) Animal Disperson in Relation to Social Behavior. Edinburgh: Oliver and Boyd.

Zahavi A (1975) Mate selection—A selection for a handicap. J. Theor. Biol. *53*:205–214.

Gallup's Mirrors—More than an Operationalization of Self-Awareness in Primates?[1]

———————— Alain Morin and Sandra DeBlois ————————

Summary: This speculative article comments on Gallup's work on self-recognition and self-awareness in primates. It exposes Gallup's position on the social origin of the self-concept and proposes the existence of "self representational" processes capable of reproducing internally the social phenomena implicated in the acquisition of self-information. On that basis, the possibility is raised that allowing primates to see themselves in a mirror might provide them with such a process, with which introspection, and consequently, the formation of a more sophisticated self-concept, would be possible.

Gordon G. Gallup, Jr., through the use of a series of well-designed experiments, has shown that as far as we actually know only chimpanzees and orangutans, besides humans, are capable of self-recognition in front of a mirror (for reviews, see Gallup, 1982, 1983, 1985, 1986). This ability seems to represent a fairly straightforward way of objectifying self-awareness (and, by the same token, the existence of a self-concept) in any visually competent organism, for self-recognition presupposes that one can become the object of one's own attention, and because one has to know at least partially who one is to infer correctly the identity of the reflection in the mirror as being oneself.

Of course, this rationale has been criticized (see, for example, Jaynes, 1978; Epstein, *et al.*, 1981; Goustard, 1983; Kummer, cited by Vauclair, 1985); for the present purpose, however, it will be assumed that Gallup's reasoning is correct.

Since for Gallup, the ability to become the object of one's own attention and the subsequent emergence of a self-concept from the acquisition of information about the self are *social* in origin, it is unlikely that chimpanzees' and orangutans' sense of identity emerges out of experience with a mirror. "A mirror simply represents a means of mapping what the chimpanzee already knows, and it provides him with a new and more explicit dimension of knowing about himself, in the sense that he now has the opportunity to see himself as he is seen

1. We acknowledge M. C. Dumas and F. Tournier for their comments on the first draft of this paper. We also thank Gordon G. Gallup for providing us with the Thompson and Calhoun reference. Address requests for reprints to Ecole de Psychologie, Université Laval, Cité Universitaire, Québec, Canada G1K 7P4.

by other chimpanzees. In other words, chimpanzees may already have a self-concept, and the mirror may merely represent a means of objectifying its existence" (Gallup, 1977, p. 335).

Gallup frequently cites Mead (1934) and Cooley (1912) in support of his view, according to whom the opportunity to see oneself as one is seen by others is required for the self to emerge as an object to conscious inspection and where the primary information we have about ourselves is represented in terms of reflected appraisals we obtain from other people.

We do definitely agree with this but that does not prevent us from proposing that Gallup might nevertheless have underestimated the impact of the very special experience his primates had with mirrors, on the formation of a self-concept. The goal of the present comment is to raise the possibility that allowing primates to see themselves in a mirror, thereby giving them access to their body-images as a whole, as well as their facial features, might increase their capacity to introspect, giving them the opportunity to acquire more information about themselves, all of this possibly resulting in a more sophisticated self-concept.

Since the acquisition of any new information about the self is likely to enhance self-knowledge, we must admit from the start (as Gallup does) that the very fact of confronting a primate with its own image enriches his self-concept. But if, in addition, we consider the possibility that the primate might not only mentally retain but *use* this new information about himself, the problem takes a quite different route.

Let us start with the reiteration that the primary source of information an organism has about itself is his social milieu. That is, a potentially self-aware organism first learns things about itself by being confronted by others' perspectives and ways of behaving [Mead], and by "being told" (verbally, or in the case of primates, probably by considering others' reactions to one's behavior) how it is [Cooley]. Now, if such an organism depended on this unique source of information, it could not be self-aware (i.e., it could not introspect and build a self-concept) *outside social situations*. In humans, at least, this is prevented by the existence of what might be called "self-representational" processes, capable of reproducing *internally* the social phenomena of examining one's self from another point of view and of learning what we are from the direct feedback we have from others.

Take inner speech as a point in case. Mead himself (1934) postulated that talking to oneself could give rise to a fictional dialogue, where verbalization of an objective, and so a different, point of view about ourselves could be possible. In addition, asking ourselves self-directed questions about how we act, think, and feel, and identifying verbally the content of our subjective experience while living it, would allow us to develop a self-concept and to become explicitly aware of mental states as they are experienced, much in the same way that people around us can observe and notice for us some aspects of ourselves, as well as infer from the way we behave, at a given point, the way we feel.

Imagery too, among other possible self-representational processes, can be conceived as fulfilling the same function that inner speech (although it is probably less effective). In effect, mental images empower us to *see* ourselves acting

513

(or having behaved) this or that way as others could see (or have seen) us acting, giving us the opportunity to deduct aspects of our past or present functioning from what is internally seen. This information could then be used to enrich our self-concept.

So, we humans would still be self-aware if deprived of these two and possibly other self-representational processes, *but only when confronted with other persons*, that is, in a social context.

Let us now get back to Gallup's primates. Of course, chimpanzees and orangutans have no inner speech. It might very well be that they nevertheless use other similar modes of self-communication (like propositional, gestural self-communication), but such self-representational processes would still have to be identified. At any rate, we can reasonably assume that primates have images (even pigeons appear to use mental images; cf. Neiworth & Rilling, 1987). This being said, we are now faced with two equally plausible situations: primates have self-representational processes (yet to be discovered) in addition to imagery, or they have only imagery as a means of representation. Let us consider first this latter possibility.

For imagery to be functional as a self-representational process, we would suggest that *it must have in its content a decisive ingredient, that is, the organisms's body-image*. When placing his subjects in front of a mirror, Gallup provided them precisely with such a content: their body-image, which they may thereafter be able to contemplate mentally without the mirror as we humans do and which allows them to see themselves as seen by others in nonsocial situations. Therefore, if this reasoning is correct, it would mean that Gallup's experimental subjects would gain a new and very important content to an already existing representational process (thereby becoming a *self*-representational process), absent in wild primates. Now, since the opportunity to reflect more often on one's self (that is, in *as well as outside* social situations) can logically be correlated with the acquisition of *more* information about the self, it is plausible to evoke a richer self-concept in primates having been confronted with a mirror.

If chimpanzees and orangutans were already equipped with other self-representational processes prior to their confrontation with the mirror, the argument would still hold, for the addition of a new means of introspection would permit the acquisition of more information. In this second case, however, the impact of the mirror experience on the growth of the self-concept would be less important.

Now, it is clear that if Gallup's primates did not retain their body-image after the self-recognition test, our proposal would turn out to be groundless. But consider the following: Thompson and Calhoun (in press) describe an experiment on the retention of self-recognition in chimpanzees. Following initial exposure to a mirror, chimpanzees were then tested a year later without any intervening mirror experience, where they showed evidence of *immediate* self-recognition. Better yet, one of the chimpanzees had lost a front tooth during the retention interval, and when it saw itself in the mirror without the tooth, it got very distressed, vacillated between going up to the mirror and opening the mouth, and then screaming and hiding in a corner of the cage only then to repeat the episode over and over. This definitely suggests that between two independent exposures to mirrors, primates' body-image persists.

One could assert that wild primates might build a "haptic" body-image (by tactually comparing their facial features with those of others) and use it for introspection purposes, in which case the experience with mirrors would probably add little to their self-concept. But if this was the case, why would the chimpanzee described above have any reason to be so upset by the sight of its missing teeth? Surely, it had received considerable prior tactile experience with the effect via the tongue.

Of course, there is no proof that primates having been confronted with a mirror actively use their body-image to introspect or, in other words, that mirrors represent more than merely a means of objectifying the existence of a self-concept in chimpanzees and orangutans. But since knowledge of self provides an intuitive basis for achieving knowledge of others (to be able to infer that a baby chimpanzee is sad and lonely presupposes, from the part of the chimpanzee making such an inference, the knowledge of what it is like to feel sad and lonely [Gallup, 1983]), and since, consequently, the capacity to infer mental states to other organisms is dependent upon one's own self-awareness, we would suggest that Gallup's primates could be observed to make *more frequent*, and *better* inferences about others' mental states than wild primates would. This double hypothesis might be tested using already existing experimental paradigms.

For instance, Woodruff and Premack (1979) have provided evidence to the effect that chimpanzees can engage in deliberate deception by selectively withholding information or even providing misinformation about the location of an incentive. Clearly, deception is based on an intuitive knowledge of others' intentions that implies a knowledge of one's own intentions. In our view, one's natural propension to introspect more or less frequently on one's intentions might shape one's natural propension to infer intentions to others as well. In that perspective, we would predict a more important incidence of deception, as measured for example by behaviors such as pointing with extended limb to an unbaited container to mislead the competitive trainer deliberately, in chimpanzees having been confronted with mirrors compared to controls. Premack and Woodruff (1978) have also presented to chimpanzees videotapes of persons engaged in many different actions (for example, shivering) and asked the subjects to choose photographs providing correct solutions to such problems (among an array of different photographs: a person activating a familiar heater)—which they did. So chimpanzees appear to make attributions and inferences about mental states in humans, an ability that presupposes the awareness of their own mental states. If the extent to which one is self-conscious determines one's ability to infer others' mental states *correctly*, it is plausible then to propose that Gallup's subjects would do better on these tasks than naive chimpanzees.

REFERENCES

Calhoun, S., and Thompson, R. L. (1988) Long-term retention of self-recognition by chimpanzees. *American Journal of Primatology,* 1988, 15, 361–365.

Cooley, C. H. (1912) *Human nature and the social order.* New York: Scribner's.

Epstein, R., Lanza, R. P., and Skinner, B. F. (1981) "Self-awareness" in the pigeon. *Science,* 212, 695–696.

Gallup, G. G., Jr. (1977) Self-recognition in primates: a comparative approach to the bidirectional properties of consciousness. *American Psychologist,* 32, 329–338.

Gallup, G. G., Jr. (1982) Self-awareness and the emergence of mind in primates. *American Journal of Primatology,* 2, 237–248.

Gallup, G. G., Jr. (1983) Toward a comparative psychology of mind. In R. L. Mellgren (Ed.), *Animal cognition and behavior.* New York: North Holland, Pp. 473–510.

Gallup, G. G., Jr. (1985) Do minds exist in species other than our own? *Neuroscience & Biobehavioral Reviews,* 9, 631–641.

Gallup, G. G., Jr., and Suarez, S. D. (1986) Self-awareness and the emergence of mind in humans and other primates. In J. Suls and A. Greenwald (Eds.), *Psychological perspectives on the self.* Vol. 3. Hillsdale, NJ: Erlbaum, Pp. 3–26.

Goustard, M. (1983) A propos des capacités mentales des singes anthropoides. *Journal de Psychologie,* 4, 339–425.

Jaynes, J. (1978) In a matter of speaking. *The Behavioral and Brain Sciences,* 4, 578–579.

Mead, G. H. (1934) *Mind, self and society from the standpoint of a social behaviorist.* Chicago, IL: Univer. of Chicago Press.

Neiworth, J. J., and Rilling, M. E. (1987) A method for studying imagery in animals. *Journal of Experimental Psychology: Animal Behavior Processes,* 13, 203–214.

Premack, D., and Woodruff, G. (1978) Does the chimpanzee have a theory of mind? *The Behavioral and Brain Sciences,* 4, 515–526.

Vauclair, J. (1985) Représentation et intentionalité dans la cognition animale. In M. Siguan (Ed.), *Comportement, cognition, conscience: la psychologie à la recherche de son objet.* Presses Universitaires de France. Pp. 59–87.

Woodruff, G., and Premack, D. (1979) Intentional communication in the chimpanzee: the development of deception. *Cognition,* 7, 333–362.

Political Animal
Social Intelligence and the
Growth of the Primate Brain

——————————————— Meredith F. Small ———————————————

Almost four million years ago hairy creatures with long arms, low brows and jutting faces stood up on two legs and began to stroll across the African savanna. Less than four feet tall at their full bipedal height, these hominids, now called australopithecines (meaning southern apes), actually were more human than ape, but they shared an important feature with their simian ancestors: they had a small brain, measuring scarcely 450 cubic centimeters, a bit smaller than a softball and not quite a third the volume of the modern human brain. Although next to nothing is known of their daily life and social behavior, it is reasonably certain that the australopithecines underwent an adaptive radiation about three million years ago and that eventually several species coexisted.

It was from one of these small-brained groups that our own genus, *Homo*, evolved some two million years ago. The first human species, known as *Homo habilis* (handy man)—a sobriquet conferred in the early 1960s by the English paleontologist Louis S. B. Leakey for the animal's knack of fashioning stone tools—flourished in eastern and southern Africa. Above all else the trait that distinguished the new humans from their forebears was a substantially larger brain.

H. habilis's evolutionary successor was *Homo erectus* (upright man), who made his appearance in the Pleistocene, about 1.5 million years ago. It was *H. erectus*, the fossil record suggests, that radiated north from Africa and made the first forays into Europe and Asia. Though he retained many simian features, he had a much more developed brain than any of his antecedents—perhaps as large as 750 cubic centimeters. This encephalization continued steadily in the next several hundred millennia, until, about 100,000 years ago, *H. erectus* gave way to *Homo sapiens sapiens*—modern man—who had all but shed his apelike appearance and whose brain had burgeoned to its present volume of 1,400 cubic centimeters.

The enormous increase in the growth and sophistication of the hominid brain over a relatively short period in evolution (it doubled in size in roughly a million years) has long intrigued investigators. Human beings have the largest

This article is reprinted by permission of THE SCIENCES and is from the March/April 1990 issue. Foreign individual subscriptions are $23.00 per year. Write to THE SCIENCES, 2 East 63rd Street, New York, NY 10021.

brains, relative to body size. In absolute size the brains of whales, dolphins and elephants are larger than the human brain, but they are far less complex. Clearly the large human brain and the power of reason it confers have been crucial to our survival and success. But why did natural selection favor humans with such a unique mental development?

Until recently the most commonly held view among anthropologists was that the rapid growth of the human brain was a result of some combination of the beginning of tool use, the rise of group hunting and the development of language. And to be sure, it must be more than coincidence that the most dramatic growth of hominid brain tissue took place in the million years or so of evolution from *H. habilis* through *H. erectus*. For it was in that period that tools, a carnivorous diet (instead of a herbivorous one), the consequent need for cooperative tracking of game, and, it is thought, a spoken language became essential features of hominid life.

Nevertheless, there is a competing body of research initiated in the 1960s and greatly intensified in the past several years, suggesting that although the tool-hunting language connection may have accelerated human brain development, it was not the only driving force. Indeed the fossil record indicates that in the matter of brain growth we humans are not unique. Rather we represent the extreme end of a sixty-million-year primate continuum, throughout which our biological order has consistently outstripped our mammalian competitors in intelligence. What is it then about being a primate that has fostered superior mental evolution? Field and laboratory studies conducted on apes, monkeys and lemurs has demonstrated that those animals live remarkably complex social lives: they recognize kinship, form long-term friendships and make strategic social decisions. A growing number of investigators believe that this social acumen, which, after all, provided the foundation for such late hominid refinements as cooperative hunting and language—may be the fundamental selective force behind the evolution of primate intelligence.

In the early 1960s, when Louis and Mary Leakey unearthed stone tools—essentially sharpened flakes of stone—alongside bones of *H. habilis* in Tanzania's (then Tanganyika) Olduvai Gorge, the find provoked enormous scholarly interest in the significance of toolmaking to human evolution. Subsequent discoveries in Africa by the Leakeys and others gave rise to a school of thought according to which the design, manufacture and use of utensils were considered the first milestones in the emergence of mankind. Certainly the capacity to envision a three-dimensional object, to foresee its potential applications, and then to set about creating the tool and putting it to work were far beyond the intellectual endowments of the ape. It thus seemed logical that handy man's time on earth coincided with such a sharp increased in hominid brain development. In particular, scholars noted, one of the regions of the human brain that underwent the greatest growth and sophistication in that period was the sensory–motor cortex, the area charged with controlling our hands.

Although the tool-use theory of human brain development still appears in some textbooks on evolution, it no longer holds sway among most scholars.

Crucial in debunking the theory were long-term studies of African chimpanzees conducted by the English primatologist Jane Goodall, among other investigators. In her 1982 book, *The Chimpanzees of Gombe*, Goodall notes two extracts from a diary she had compiled a quarter-century before. In the entry for November 4, 1960, she described watching a chimpanzee (which she had named Dave Greybeard) hovering around a termite mound. After a few moments, the animal "very deliberately, pulled a thick grass stalk toward him and broke off a piece about 45 centimeters long." Then Greybeard loped out of view. Two days later Goodall encountered two other male chimpanzees at the termite mound, each with his own length of grass—which she refers to as "straw." This time she saw something more:

> It [the straw] was held in the left hand, poked into the mound, and then removed coated with termites. The straw was raised to the mouth and the insects [were] picked off with the lips along the length of the straw, starting in the middle.

More than a decade passed before the idea gained acceptance, but Goodall's observation revealed for the first time that toolmaking and tool use are not uniquely human activities. Admittedly grass dipsticks are crude tools compared with hand axes; nevertheless it is now clear that chimpanzees too have the foresight to craft implements for improving their lives. Although Goodall acknowledged that the invention of progressively intricate and specialized tools marked "a crucial step in our evolution," she maintained that it is not what separates man from the apes.

Other adaptive skills might also account for the human encephalization. Perhaps *H. habilis*'s shift from a preference for vegetable matter to a reliance on meat led to an increase in intellect in that stage of our past. Tracking large, often dangerous herds of game, for example, and cooperating in organized group hunts require sophisticated thought processes. Even more plausible is the possibility that the early hominids were scavengers who had to use their wits to compete with scavenging wolves, hyenas, lions and other social carnivores, or even with the primary predator, for rights to a carcass. But a tie between selection for large brain size and meat eating is equivocal. The complexities of group hunting or scavenging doubtless sped our journey toward reason, but as with tool use these activities are not peculiar to the genus *Homo* or even to the primate order at large. Many other social carnivores both track transient food resources and actively cooperate to fell prey. More likely, many investigators began to believe, the rapid neural expansion in the hominid lineage was prompted by a feedback loop involving toolmaking, hunting and the development of speech.

The increasing complexity of their lives also made it highly advantageous for hominids to develop an effective system of communication—a means of conveying information about how to make tools and weapons, where to find food, how to coordinate hunting expeditions, and other aspects of day-to-day existence. Our ancestors' morphological response to this challenge culminated in a spoken language. Exactly when this transpired is a mysterious and widely debated issue. Concrete proof of any hypothesis seems impossible, since most of the anatomical accessories for human speech, made of muscle and cartilage, have disappeared from the fossil record. Nevertheless, it seems likely that speech evolved relatively late in the evolution of *Homo*.

Although the human ability to articulate abstract ideas with vocal symbols is unique among living things, humans are not the only creatures with a signaling system. A host of other highly social animals—including insects—communicate through noises, body language or chemical secretions. They also have an uncanny ability to keep track of their food resources. A spoken language, to be sure, enhanced the quality of hominid life and may have been an invaluable ally in the harsh natural world. But it was not necessary for survival.

Indisputably then, toolmaking, hunting and speech combined in some way to develop the evolving hominid brain. Manual dexterity, tactical planning, language, learning and memory all point to an increase in cerebral capacity and complexity—and so to enhanced adaptiveness in the hominid environment. This increasing cultural sophistication no doubt helped foster the neural explosion that took place between the time of *H. habilis* and that of *H. sapiens*. But to assume that this late-blooming surge of brain tissue represents the whole of the evolution of human intellect is to take a narrow view. Such a hypothesis ignores the reality that consistent brain growth was nothing new for primates; rather it was a characteristic trait of the primate order tens of millions of years before the hominids' debut on the evolutionary stage.

As far back as the Eocene, sixty million years ago, the brains of the ancestral prosimians were expanding—in relative as well as absolute size—both in the temporal lobe and in the cerebellum. The primate brain became broader and more spherical. The ancestral prosimians were primarily arboreal creatures, and much of the increase in brain size reflects advances in visual acuity that were important for flying through space. Fossil remains indicate that a tarsierlike prosimian—assumed to be the transitional primate between the prosimians and the anthropoids (monkeys and apes)—underwent substantial brain expansion: during the Eocene alone, a span of twenty million years, this ancestral tarsier's brain increased in size by sixty-five percent. The upward trend in brain size and, presumably, intelligence continued throughout the Oligocene (the age of monkeys, which began forty million years ago) and the Miocene (which began twenty-five million years ago, and during which apes were the dominant primates). The monkeys and the apes of the Oligocene and the Miocene probably had color vision, manual dexterity and excellent motor control in order to conduct their arboreal lives.

Taken as a whole, the primate fossil record suggests that the spurt of hominid brain growth is only the steep rise of an already positive slope. The consistent and precipitous increase in brain size among fossil primates represents anatomical and intellectual specialization of the entire order—not merely of its human membership. But what does it mean to have a larger brain? Is there necessarily a direct relation between quantity and quality of brain tissue?

The connection between brain size and intelligence and, indeed, the very definition of intelligence have been points of considerable controversy. To a large extent, modern notions about the parallel growth of the brain and the primate mind are traceable to broad assumptions put forth by Othniel Charles Marsh, a nineteenth-century paleontologist from Yale University who once combed the American West for fossils under the guidance of William F. ("Buffalo Bill") Cody. In 1886 Marsh proposed that brain size increased gradually in relation to body size through geologic time and that the growth was accompanied by an increase in the complexity of cerebral convolutions and connections.

In recent years the influential neuroanatomist Harry Jerison of the University of California at Los Angeles has argued that "gross brain size" is a "natural biological statistic" for estimating the number of neurons and glial cells in the brain. More precisely, Jerison suggests, the mass of a particular area of the brain is a measure of the extent to which an individual can perform the tasks that the region controls. But, as other workers have cautioned, a complete understanding of the brain and intelligence will be possible only when neuroanatomists have detailed the brain's microorganization and local circuitry, features that—contrary to Marsh's durable, century-old theory—may prove to have little or nothing to do with overall brain size. Furthermore, the correlation between brain and intellect awaits a satisfying, quantitative definition of animal intelligence, which has generally been sidestepped by comparative psychologists and animal behaviorists. Does intelligence stop at information processing (attention, learning, memory, concept formation)? Or should the definition also embrace emotion, aggression, motivation and biological rhythms? These are open questions, though most experts would agree that whatever else constitutes intelligence, the brighter creatures among us can reason, remember, strategize and alter their behavior according to novel situations.

Acknowledging the considerable scholarly murkiness about the connection between brain and mind, one is left with the following: some selective pressure has been driving the persistent growth of the primate brain since Eocene times. Increasingly, workers are tracing this trend to one theme that runs consistently through the primate order, from the relatively small-brained prosimians to human beings. In contrast with the vast mammalian majority, most primates live in some kind of group. In contrast with schools of fishes or herds of ungulates, the primate groups are not mere aggregations but true social organizations, involving complicated interactions between members and usually maintaining long-term cohesiveness from generation to generation through a dynamic web of interpersonal intrigue.

The sense of community comes at a price, of course: group members force a competition at all levels for food, mates and comfortable places to sleep. Nevertheless, primate social life has endured, and one can only assume that the benefits, such as protection from predators, sharing parental tasks, and more efficient foraging, far outweigh the inconveniences. It may well be that social intelligence, the ability to exploit relationships within one's own group—whether among a troop of lemurs on Madagascar, or at a cocktail party in Manhattan—

has energized the growth of the primate brain and the expansion of the primate mind.

In 1966 the primatologist Alison Jolly, now at Princeton University, published a paper in the journal *Science,* titled "Lemur social behavior and primate intelligence," which stands as the first study linking sociality to the evolving primate brain. Lemurs, whose brains are smaller than those of most other primates, traditionally fail miserably on standard laboratory tests of animal intelligence. As Jolly pointed out, however, the tests more often than not involve the manipulation of some sort of gadgetry—bells, buttons or the like—for a reward, typically food. She suggested that a more appropriate measure of their mental capacity is their ability to form and sustain intricate social bonds.

Like the monkeys and the apes, which so outclass them on the standard tests, lemurs live in troops made up of a diverse blend of sexes and ages. The troops are organized in female-dominated hierarchies, and they display various cohesive behaviors, including play, mutual grooming, intramural spats and stink fights (during which a male wipes urine on his tail and shakes it at another male), and group response to hostile carnivores, usually expressed by gathering round to mob the predator. This knack for functioning as a social group, day in and day out, is a special kind of intelligence, more subtle than that required to push buttons—a social acumen calling for a good memory, the ability to recognize and categorize others and the capacity to act on that knowledge.

Detailed observations of several primate species in the past two decades have borne out Jolly's contention: primates are indeed socially sophisticated creatures that maintain consistent, tightly reinforced relationships with troopmates. Three of the most thoroughly studied social animals are Old World monkeys—macaques, vervet monkeys and baboons of the savanna. These primates live in female-bonded societies: the males are transients that migrate to other troops on reaching sexual maturity, but the females remain lifelong members of the groups in which they were born.

Serving as the infrastructure of these societies are complex female dominance hierarchies, which tend to be remarkably stable—an entrenched simian caste system perpetuated over the course of generations. From infancy each female learns her place in the scheme by experiencing the interactions between her mother and other females. A baby macaque, for instance, spends its first three months of life riding on its mother's back, where it may find itself swept into the midst of a fight, with a front-row seat from which to view the behavior of the combatants and to see how its mother fares in the altercation. My work on Barbary macaques has demonstrated that the period of infant socialization is crucial to development. Barbary infants are passed among group members like squeaky toys; males, females and juveniles try their best to gain access to the pink and black babies. For infants these interactions form the macaque social web: personalities are shaped, relationships are established and long-term bonds begin to form. In other words, the infant gets a vivid seminar in the fabric of monkey life.

The bonds of blood are strong among Old World monkeys. One of the most apparent expressions of this intimacy is physical closeness: relatives typically travel, feed and sleep together. Mutual grooming, another common gesture of familiarity, most often takes place between mothers and offspring but also is engaged in by more distant relations—aunts and nieces, as well as males who have not yet abandoned the group. In hostile encounters relatives always back up one another. Indeed, in the occasional instances when lower-ranking females mount successful coups against their superiors, they usually do so with the aid of a gang of nearby kin.

Friendships and alliances between monkeys often transcend the bounds of kinship. For example, the primatologist Barbara Smuts of the University of Michigan has shown that among certain baboons, males and females from different lineages carry on chaste friendships—at least in the beginning of a relationship. A female will typically associate with one or two males year round, grooming, feeding and sleeping with them. For most of this time she is either pregnant or lactating and is not sexually receptive. Then, when in estrus, she likely will favor her long-term pals as mates. In general, it is common for Old World monkeys to form alliances with members of other families. This clearly is a case of "you scratch my back, and I'll scratch yours"; alliances are forged and maintained through the principle of reciprocal altruism: a favor, whether it involves grooming in peacetime or defensive assistance in conflict, does not go unreturned.

Whenever friendships, alliances or other such relationships among monkeys were discussed two decades ago, there was the suspicion that the discussant was a wayward primatologist guilty of anthropomorphism, or projecting human social values onto baboons and other simians. These doubts were dispelled, at least in part, by work conducted in Kenya during the late 1970s on the small vervet monkey.

In a series of elegant field experiments Dorothy Cheney and Robert Seyfarth of the University of Pennsylvania asked a basic question: Are monkeys conscious of relationships? Cheney and Seyfarth played audiotape recordings of the screams of an imperiled juvenile vervet through a loudspeaker they had placed in a bush. The young monkey's mother and two female companions were next to the bush, and when the mother heard her offspring's recorded cries, she immediately turned toward the loudspeaker. Her behavior was hardly surprising, since most female mammals respond to the sounds of their offspring in distress. What was intriguing was the reaction of the two companions: on hearing the screams, they turned their heads not toward the loudspeaker but toward the mother. In other words, they could recognize the vocalization of the young vervet, and they could associate that juvenile with its mother.

A similar study by Sarah and Harold Gouzoules of Rockefeller University in New York focused on the rhesus macaques of Cayo Santiago, an island near Puerto Rico. The Gouzouleses discovered that mothers' responses varied with nuances in juveniles' screams. When their offspring were menaced by relatives, mothers responded with little more than indifference. Only when the young were threatened by nonkin macaques were their mothers roused to intervention. The investigators concluded that screams carry specific information about social relationships that macaques process when deciding on a course of action.

Working again with vervets, Cheney and Seyfarth probed further the subtleties of primate social awareness, this time paying attention to patterns of aggression. They noted that if monkey A threatened monkey B, it was likely that A would also threaten a relative of B later in the day. Even more intriguing was that a relative of A would also typically seek out and menace an unsuspecting member of B's troop, hinting that the original skirmish might escalate into a feud reminiscent of the battles between the Hatfields and the McCoys in the Appalachian hills. These observations support the idea that vervets have a concept of affiliation between individuals in their groups. In short, they know one another.

Another study, published in 1988 by Verena Dasser of the University of Zurich, proved that Javanese lion-tailed macaques also recognize relationships between troopmates. Dasser spent one year training her two female subjects to respond to slides depicting the mothers and juveniles in their group. The macaques were then tested on their ability to match slides of each mother with those of their offspring. Dasser's monkeys passed with flying colors: one answered correctly fourteen times in fourteen tries, and the other successfully linked mother and offspring twenty times out of twenty-two.

Discerning these complex social relationships, including kin associations, nonkin alliances, long-term friendships and interfamily grudges, requires intelligence of a reasonably high order. To be sure, just to keep track of it all requires a voluminous memory. These monkeys not only must remember who's who in the group but also must keep daily mental scorecards of their troopmates' actions. A bitter foe one day may be an ally the next, and vice versa. This knack for recognizing and cataloguing relationships, which primatologists call social cognition, seems impressive enough. But what a growing number of investigators believe is that the true distinction of primates is their dark side: an ability to manipulate others for personal gain.

As early as 1967 the Swiss ethologist Hans Kummer outlined what he called tripartite relations in the Hamadryas baboon of Ethiopia. Kummer observed that one Hamadryas, when embroiled in a conflict with another, is apt to use a third baboon—previously uninvolved in the fracas—to deceive the enemy. In other words, one baboon is able to use another for its own benefit.

Recently two psychologists, Andrew Whiten and Richard W. Byrne of the University of Saint Andrews in Fife, Scotland, suggested that social manipulation could be a prominent force in the evolution of primate intelligence. During fieldwork in South Africa Whiten and Byrne noted several expressions of what they describe as Machiavellian deception among baboons. In one instance a juvenile spied an adult female digging for corms, a kind of grass bulb or tuber—and a valued food resource that juveniles normally find hard to get. Although the young baboon was entirely unprovoked, it shrieked as if it were being attacked, prompting its mother to rush to the rescue and chase the feeding adult down the hill. Having duped both its mother and the unwitting feeder, the devious juvenile moved in to feast on the remaining corms.

Other investigators have cited cases of similar primate behavior that, if not quite worthy of the Borgia popes, nonetheless smacks of double-dealing. In a 1985 article Shirley C. Strum of the University of California at San Diego tells a steamy vignette about olive baboons, the plot of which—including the crucial ingredients sex, thievery and a corpse—might have been lifted from a grade-B movie:

> One of the female baboons . . . grew particularly fond of meat, although the males do most of the hunting. A male, one who does not willingly share, caught an antelope. The female edged up to him and groomed him until he lolled back under her attentions. She then snatched the antelope carcass and ran.

Taken together, these and other pieces of experimental and anecdotal evidence support the notion that primates are socially intelligent animals. Macaques, vervet monkeys and baboons recognize and differentiate between troopmates; they adhere to sophisticated hierarchies; they form and maintain relationships that benefit them in daily activities; and on occasion they manipulate others to serve their own desires. Members of the primate order have especially long periods of infant dependency compared with other mammals, because, it is believed, juveniles need the time to learn the ropes of their uniquely intricate social world.

What remains to be seen is whether this knowledge serves them well in the evolutionary sense. Any proposal that the need for these social machinations must have favored large and complex primate brains is equivocal because no one has yet demonstrated a direct relation between social acumen and individual reproductive success. Until this critical information is in our grasp we must tread lightly when suggesting that social intelligence is the sole—or even the major—driving force behind the evolution of the primate brain. Still, it is incontestable that we are social animals and that knowing who we are, where we stand and how to get what we want—even at the expense of others—is key to survival for all primates, monkeys and humans alike.

PART 5

Biological Perspectives on Humans as Primates

Sympatry with Supertramp, Overexploiter (Human) Primates

M. E. Stephens

Homo sapiens sapiens translates into human, the wise, the wise. Surely culture-bearing hominids are different in kind, not merely in degree, from other primates. Or, are they?

This final section considers this question and some related concerns. Is access to nutritional resources still the key limiting factor for the reproductive success of human females? Have culture and technological inventions set humans free from biological constraints?

If our answer to the last question is negative, does it mean that humans should quit striving to improve their lot?

The primate part of me refuses to accept determinism. An understanding of primate nature and the intricate interplay of each primate species with all other species and parts of global ecology should engender a respect for the fragility of each. More than 99.9% of the species which have evolved on earth are now extinct. By understanding the biological nature of our own species we may enhance its probability of survival.

Besides, "primates are neat critters and a course on primates has fewer formulas to memorize than does a course in chemistry." (Anon., 1990?)

Menstrual Synchrony and Suppression

_____ Martha K. McClintock _____

Synchrony and suppression among a group of women living together in a college dormitory suggest that social interaction can have a strong effect on the menstrual cycle.

Studies of the influence of pheromones on the oestrous cycles of mice[1-4], and of crowding on variables such as adrenalin production in mice and other species[5] have suggested that social grouping can influence the balance of the endocrine system. Although there has been little direct investigation with humans, anecdotal and indirect observations have indicated that social groupings influence some aspects of the menstrual cycle. Menstrual synchrony is often reported by all-female living groups and by mothers, daughters and sisters who are living together. For example, the distribution of onsets of seven female lifeguards was scattered at the beginning of the summer, but after 3 months spent together the onset of all seven cycles fell within a 4 day period.

Indirect support is given by the investigation of Collet *et al.*[6] on the effect of age on menstrual cycle patterning. A higher percentage of anovulatory cycles were reported for college age women than for older women. Although Collet *et al.* attributed this to a maturational factor, it is interesting that most of the college aged women attended all female schools. Considering the parallel with the Lee-Boot effect in mice[1] (groups consisting only of females become pseudopregnant or anoestrous), it seems possible that an interpersonal factor is operating together with the maturational factor.

Subjects were 135 females aged 17–22 yr—all residents of a dormitory in a suburban women's college. The dormitory in which they resided has four main corridors each with approximately twenty-five girls living in single and double rooms. Six smaller living areas, separated from the main corridors by at least one door, each house approximately eight girls in single rooms.

Three times during the academic year, each subject was asked when her last and second to last menstrual periods had begun; thus the date of onset was determined for all cycles between late September and early April. The average duration of menstruation and presence of dysmenorrhoea were noted. In addition, subjects estimated how many times each week they were in the company of males and listed by room number the girls (N ≤ 10) with whom they spent the most time, indicating which two of these they saw most often.

The date of menstrual onset was compared for room mates and closest friends, for close friend groups and for living groups. Two people qualified as "closest friends" only if both had indicated that they saw each other most often. While menstrual cycle timing in women using birth control pills is individually invariant, these women were still included in the analysis, because their influence on the menstrual cycles of the others was unknown. For room mates and closest friends, the difference between the date of onset in October for one arbitrarily chosen member of the pair and the closest date of onset for the other was calculated. This difference was compared with a difference for March calculated in a similar way, but with one change: instead of choosing the closest onset dates for the pair, both onsets for March were chosen to follow the initial October onset by an equal number of cycles. For example, if onset 6 occurred on March 10 for the first member of the pair, and onsets 5 and 6 for the other member occurred on March 1 and March 29 respectively, then the March 10 and March 29 dates were used to calculate the difference in onset. This procedure was used to minimize chance coincidences that did not result from a trend towards synchrony.

The Wilcoxon matched-pairs signed-ranks test[7] was used to test for a significant decrease in the difference between onset dates of room mates and closest friends. This test utilizes both the direction and magnitude of change in differences and is therefore a relatively powerful test.

There was a significant increase in synchronization (that is, a decrease in the difference between onset dates) among room mates ($P ≤ 0.0007$), among closest friends ($P ≤ 0.003$) and among room mates and closest friends combined ($P ≤ 0.0003$). The increase in synchrony for room mates did not differ significantly from the increase for closest friends. The increase in synchrony was further substantiated by non-overlapping confidence intervals, calculated for the median difference on onset dates[8] (Table 1).

This synchrony might be due to some factor other than time spent with an individual; Koford[9] has attributed synchrony of the breeding season in *Macaca mulata* on Cayo Santiago to common seasonal changes in available food. The fact that the subjects generally eat as a dormitory group in a common dining room might be a significant factor in creating synchrony. A similar life pattern and common, repeated stress periods might also effect synchrony. Subjects were therefore randomly paired and tested for synchrony within the dormitory as a whole, but no significant trend (N.S., $P ≤ 0.8$) was found, and the confidence intervals for the median difference in onset date overlapped completely.

Group synchrony was also investigated and the data were analysed to verify that the decrease in difference between onset dates was a true measure of synchrony. All subjects were divided into fifteen groups of close friends ($5 ≤ N ≤ 10$), using the lists of close friends made by each subject. During the interview, it was stressed to each subject that her list of "close friends" should include the people she saw most often and with whom she spent the most time, not necessarily those with whom she felt the closest. But because there is usually some

Table 1 Confidence Intervals (> 0.99 in days) for the Median Difference in Onset Date between Members of the Pair

	October	March
Close friends and room mates		
N = 66	7 < M < 10	3 < M < 7
Random pairs		
N = 33	6 < M < 14	5 < M < 15

overlap, the term "close friends" was adopted. Only subjects who mutually listed each other were included in a group.

A mean onset date (μ_1) was determined for each group in October, late November, January, late February and April. As before, the onset dates (X_1) being compared, each followed the October onset (X_1) by an equal number of cycles. The mean individual difference from the group onset mean

$$\frac{\Sigma(X_1 - \mu_1)}{n}$$

was determined for each group and compared across time in two ways. First, a linear rank method, designed by Page[10] to test ordered hypotheses for multiple treatments, showed a significant decrease in individual differences from the group onset mean for close friend groups ($P \leq 0.001$). Second, a graph of this decrease as a function of time indicated that the greatest decrease occurred in the first 4 months with little subsequent change. This asymptotic relation indicated that the decrease in difference between onset dates was indeed an increase in synchrony for close friend groups.

Usually those who considered themselves close friends lived together. Because this was not always the case, however, subjects were divided into thirteen living groups ($5 \leq N \leq 12$), solely on the basis of arrangement of rooms, to test the importance of geographic location. When grouped in this way, there was no significant increase in synchrony within groups.

Dewan[11] has suggested that the menstrual cycles of monkeys around the equator are synchronized because each cycle is locked in phase with the Moon. As the production by the pineal gland of a substance which inhibits the action of luteinizing hormone is suppressed by light, the continuous light of nights with a full Moon would facilitate ovulation across a group of monkeys and induce synchrony. This suggests that the synchrony in close friend groups and among room mates comes from a common light-dark pattern, perhaps with common stress periods in which the subjects may stay up for a large part of the night. It would be expected that if synchrony arose from common light–dark cycles, room mates would exhibit a more significant amount of synchrony than do closest friends. The opposite trend was found, however, although it was not significant (room mates, $P \leq 0.007$; closest friends, $P \leq 0.003$). It does not seem likely therefore that a photoperiodic effect is a significant cause of synchrony.

Table 2. Mean Cycles Lengths and Duration of Menstruation

Estimated exposure to male (days/week)	Length of cycle (days)	Duration (days)
0–2	30.0 ± 3.9	5.0 ± 1.1
N = 56		
3–7	28.5 ± 2.9	4.8 ± 1.2
N = 31		
P	≤ 0.03	N 5 ≤ 0.2

This is further supported by the lack of significant synchrony in random pairings in the dormitory.

Paralleling the Whitten effect in mice[3] (in which suppression of oestrus in groups of females can be released by the introduction of a male pheromone) synchrony may result from a pheromonal interaction of suppression among close friend groups followed by a periodic release due to the presence of males on the weekend. However, this would be insufficient to explain the synchrony which occurred among room mates and close friends, but did not occur throughout the dormitory. Some additional pheromonal effect among individuals of the group of females would be necessary. Perhaps at least one female pheromone affects the timing of other female menstrual cycles.

Another possible source of synchrony might be the awareness of menstrual cycles among friends. A sample taken from the dormitory, however, indicated that 47% were not conscious of their friends menstrual cycles, and, of the 53% who were, 48% (25% of the total) were only vaguely aware.

The significant factor in synchrony, then, is that the individuals of the group spend time together. Whether the mechanism underlying this phenomenon is pheromonal, mediated by awareness or some other process is a question which still remains open for speculation and investigation.

Subjects were divided into two groups: those who estimated that they spent time with males, once, twice or no times per week (N = 42), and those who estimated that they spent time with males three or more times per week (N = 33). Borderline cases and those taking birth control pills were discarded. After testing for homogeneity of variance, the mean cycle length and duration of menstruation was compared using Student's t test. Those who estimated seeing males less than three times per week experienced significantly ($P \geq 0.03$) longer cycles than those of the other group whose mean cycle length corresponded with national norms (approximately 28 days)[12]. There was no significant difference in duration of menstruation itself ($P \geq 0.2$, Table 2).

The possibility that the results were confounded by a maturational factor was tested, as subjects included members of the freshman, sophomore, junior and senior classes. The subjects were regrouped and compared according to class: underclassmen were compared with upperclassmen. There was no significant difference in cycle length (underclassmen 29.6 ± 5.6 days; upperclassmen 29.9 ± 5.7 days).

Exposure to males may not be the significant factor. It may be, for example, that those with longer cycles are less likely to spend time with males. However, many subjects spontaneously indicated that they became more regular and had shorter cycles when they dated more often. For example, one subject reported that she had a cycle length of 6 months until she began to see males more frequently. Her cycle length then shortened to 4.5 weeks. Then, when she stopped seeing males as often, her cycle lengthened again. Whether this is due to a pheromone mechanism similar to the Lee-Boot effect in mice[1] has yet to be determined.

Although this is a preliminary study, the evidence for synchrony and suppression of the menstrual cycle is quite strong, indicating that in humans there is some interpersonal physiological process which affects the menstrual cycle.

I thank Professor Patricia Sampson and Monty Slatkin for help in preparing the manuscript.

1. Van der Lee, S., and Boot, L. M., *Acta Physiol. Pharmacol. Neerl.*, **5**, 231 (1956).
2. Whitten, W. K., *J. Endocrinol.*, **18**, 102 (1959).
3. Whitten, W. K., *Science*, **16**, 584 (1968).
4. Parkes, A. S., and Bruce, H. M., *J. Reprod. Fertil.*, **4**, 303 (1962).
5. Thiessen, D., *Texas Rep. Biol. Med.*, **22**, 266 (1964); Leiderman, P. H., and Shapiro, D., *Psychobiological Approaches to Social Behavior* (Stanford University Press, 1964).
6. Collet, M. E., Wertenberger, G. E., and Fiske, V. M., *Fertil. Steril.*, **5**, 437 (1954).
7. Siegal, S., *Nonparametric Statistics for the Behavioral Sciences*, (McGraw-Hill, New York, 1956).
8. Nair, K. R., *Indian J. Statistics*, **4**, 551 (1940).
9. Koford, C. B., in *Primate Behavior: Field Studies of Monkeys and Apes* (edit. by Devore, 1.) (Holt, Rinehart and Winston, New York, 1965).
10. Page, E. B., *Amer. Stat. Assoc. J.*, **58**, 216 (1963).
11. Dewan, E. M., *Science Tech.*, **20** (1969).
12. Turner, C. D., *General Endocrinology* (Saunders, Philadelphia, 1965).

Fatness and Fertility

_____ Rose E. Frisch _____

Loss of fat from dieting or exercise can lead to infertility that is reversible with fat gain. It is possible that fat tissue exerts a regulatory effect on the reproductive ability of human females.

Ever since the Stone Age, symbols of female fertility have been fat, particularly in the breasts, hips, thighs and buttocks—the places where estrogen, the female sex hormone, promotes fat storage. This historical linking of fatness and fertility actually makes biological sense; in fact, I propose that body fat, or adipose tissue, has a regulatory role in reproduction.

The evidence gathered in the past 15 years is strong. It indicates, for instance, that a female must store at least a threshold, or minimum, amount of body fat in order to begin and maintain normal menstrual cycles and hence have the ability to reproduce. Activities that reduce fat below the threshold, such as serious dieting and intensive exercise, can delay the age of menarche (the first menstrual cycle) to as late as 20 years. Such a loss can also "silently" halt ovulation—the midcycle release of an egg from the ovary—in someone who menstruates every month or cause frank amenorrhea: the absence of menstrual cycles. The resulting infertility is reversible by weight gain or reduction of activity or both.

A woman need not suffer from anorexia nervosa (the psychologically driven syndrome of self-starvation in which as much as a third of the body weight is lost) in order to induce menstrual irregularities. Even a rather moderate loss, in the range of from 10 to 15 percent below the normal weight for height, which is primarily a loss of fat, is sufficient.

Recent work has shown that the menstrual disorders associated with excessive leanness derive from the abnormal activity of the hypothalamus, the part of the brain that regulates reproduction as well as food intake and other basic functions. It has long been known that the hypothalamus receives information from higher centers of the brain. External factors such as temperature and stress can therefore affect the reproductive activity of the hypothalamus. It is now certain that nutrition and physical effort also have an effect.

It is not surprising that the reproductive function of the hypothalamus falters when a woman becomes too lean. Such a response would have given our female ancestors a selective advantage by ensuring that they conceived only when they could complete a pregnancy successfully. Reproduction, after all, requires energy, or calories: some 50,000 to 80,000 calories to produce a viable infant and then from 500 to 1,000 calories a day for lactation. (These figures are over and above the calories needed for other life processes.) In ancient times, when the food supply was scarce or fluctuated seasonally and when breast milk was a newborn's only food, a woman who became pregnant when she lacked an adequate store of body fat—the most readily mobilized fuel in the body—could have endangered both her own life and that of her developing fetus and newborn infant.

Indeed, one can speculate that females who continued to ovulate in spite of being undernourished left no viable offspring or did not survive themselves; they therefore left no descendants. Thus natural selection had its way: today most women have more than a fourth of their weight in fat (about 16 kilograms, or 35 pounds, representing some 144,000 calories) when they reach maturity. The main function of this fat store may be to provide energy for a pregnancy and about three months of lactation. Men, in contrast, have roughly from 12 to 14 percent of their weight in fat at maturity. Studies of very obese women (and animals) show that excessive fatness, like excessive leanness, is also associated with amenorrhea and infertility; the mechanisms are not yet known.

The discovery of a relation between fatness and fertility came about somewhat indirectly. Early in the 1970's I worked with Roger Revelle, who was then at Harvard University, gathering data on the heights, weights and calorie supplies of populations in Latin America and Asia in order to estimate the food needs of the world. In the course of analyzing the growth data I noted that a poor food supply delayed the age at which adolescent girls had their most rapid growth in weight, an event that precedes menarche; abundant calorie supplies advanced the age of the spurt. This was not particularly surprising, but another finding was: within each population the growth spurt, whether it was early or late, came when girls had achieved the same average weight. In other words, weight appeared to be the determining factor.

To explore the implied relation between weight and menarche, we then analyzed the height and weight data for 181 girls who had been followed from birth to age 18 (when growth was completed) in three comparable U.S. studies. We found that both the early and the late maturers had the same average weight (47 kilograms, or 103 pounds) at menarche; in contrast, the average height increased significantly with menarcheal age.

The finding that weight seemed to be important to the timing of menarche helped to explain many puzzling observations. For example, in the past century girls in the U.S. and Europe have attained menarche progressively earlier. On the average, American girls now begin to menstruate when they are 12.6 years old; a century ago the age was 15.5 years. Revelle and I postulate that the earlier menarche is explained by the fact that children now become bigger sooner because they are better nourished and have less disease. The association between average weight at menarche and the timing of menarche in a population also explained why malnutrition delays menarche, why twins (who grow relatively slowly in utero and postnatally and hence take longer to reach the critical weight for menarche) begin to menstruate later than "singletons" in the same population and why high altitude (which slows the rate of growth) also delays menarche.

Knowing the average weights at menarche did not enable us to predict the timing of menarche for individual girls, whose weights at menarche vary considerably. I wondered if there was some weight-related factor that would make such prediction possible. Elegant animal studies by the late Gordon C. Kennedy of the University of Cambridge provided a clue. Kennedy found that puberty in the female rat is more closely related to body weight than to age. He also found that rats given different diets that altered their growth rates ate the same amount of food per unit of body weight at first estrus (the animal equivalent of menarche). He postulated that the feeding signal and the onset of estrus may both be regulated by the amount of fat in the body.

On the basis of Kennedy's findings—as well as those of his associates Elsie Widdowson and Peter A. McCance and work done on the composition of the human body by Francis D. Moore and his co-workers at the Harvard Medical School—I began to suspect that some aspect of body composition, particulary stored fat, in the human female might also influence the timing of the first menstrual cycle in girls. My colleagues and I therefore investigated the changes in body composition in girls during the adolescent growth spurt and at menarche. Specifically, we looked at the amounts of both fat and lean body mass, which together account for one's weight. The lean mass, or the nonfat parts of the body, includes the muscles, the fat-free skin, the viscera (the heart, kidney and other organs) and the skeleton.

The 181 girls in the longitudinal studies had long since grown up, but we had their heights and weights at menarche and throughout the adolescent growth spurt. We could therefore calculate their body composition by inserting this information into standard equations that estimate the total amount of water in the body; this value makes it possible to determine the relative contributions of lean mass and of fat to a person's total weight. The equations are based on direct measurements of body water that had been made on a normal group of girls and women.

One might ask: How could measurements of body water provide information about the composition of the entire body? The answer lies in the fact that after childhood 72 percent of the lean mass of the body is accounted for by water. Knowing the total amount of water in the body, one can determine the weight of the lean mass, which is equal to the amount of water divided by .72. Subtracting the weight of the lean mass from the total body weight yields the weight of the fat. The percentage of water in the entire body is a fatness index. Since fat has little water (from 5 to 10 percent), the more fat one has, the lower will be the percentage of water in the entire body.

We found that the greatest change in estimated body composition during the premenarcheal weight spurt is a large increase in body fat: on the average, both early- and late-maturing girls had a 120 percent increase in body fat (from five to 11 kilograms), whereas they had only a 44 percent increase in the weight of lean mass. Therefore the ratio of lean mass to fat declined from about 5:1 at the initiation of the growth spurt to about 3:1 at menarche. What all the girls had in common at menarche, even though individual weights varied, was a similar ratio of lean mass to fat and a similar amount of water as a percentage of body weight. On the average at menarche 55 percent of the body weight of the girls was water (a "body-water percentage" of 55), which indicated that an average of 24 percent of the weight was accounted for by body fat.

The findings strongly suggested that girls must reach a threshold lean/fat ratio, and hence a certain degree of fatness, in order to menstruate. Still, the average ratio for the population did not predict the threshold for any given individual. Janet W. McArthur of the Massachusetts General Hospital and I tackled this problem by comparing the height, weight and estimated body composition of young girls and women who had menstrual disorders with the same measures for our normal subjects at menarche and at age 18.

We compared the groups by means of charts called nomograms, which indicated the weights for heights that corresponded to the levels of relative fatness observed in the 181 normal girls at menarche and at the completion of growth. The relative-fatness levels were indicated on the chart by percentiles of our fatness index (total water as a percentage of body weight).

Somewhat to our surprise, we discovered that cases of delayed menarche and amenorrhea were each associated with being below a threshold value of relative fatness. Specifically, the comparison showed that in order to have menarche, young girls whose height growth was nearly or fully completed had to gain enough weight for their height to decrease their body-water percentage to 59.8 percent. This would ensure that they had at least 17 percent of their weight in fat (the lower the body-water percentage, the fatter the body). The threshold body-water percentage was the 10th-percentile value of normal girls at menarche. That is, 90 percent of the sample at menarche had a lower value and so were fatter. For a 15-year-old girl whose completed height was 165 centimeters (five feet five inches), the numbers translated into the prediction that she had to weigh at least 44 kilograms (97 pounds) before menarche would be expected.

The comparisons also showed that women who were amenorrheic because of simple weight loss needed to reach a weight that was about 10 percent heavier than the menarche threshold in order to restore and maintain normal ovulatory cycles. They had to have a total body-water percentage of no more than 56.1, indicating that fat accounted for about 22 percent of the body weight. This value was the 10th percentile of the body-water percentage at completion of growth for the normal girls at the age of 18. A woman this age or older whose height was 165 centimeters had to weigh at least 49 kilograms (108 pounds) before her cycles could be expected to resume. (Also, cycles would stop if her weight fell below this threshold.)

We were somewhat puzzled to find that heavier weights and higher fat percentages were necessary for regular, ovulatory cycles in the mature group. Why should one need more fat at age 18 than at menarche? An analysis of the data from the normal sample provided the answer: normal women gain fat during the interval between their first menstrual cycle and age 18. (By 18 they typically have completed the phase of adolescent subfertility, when the ovary, uterus and oviducts are still growing, and there are many anovulatory cycles.) We found that both early- and late-maturing girls gain an average of 4.5 kilograms (10 pounds) of fat between menarche and age 18, when our normal subjects had an average of 28 percent of their body weight in fat. At first we could hardly believe the human female stores such a large amount of fat when she is ready to reproduce, but data in the literature based on postmortem dissections confirmed this value.

Many physicians now rely on the nomograms as a guide to recommending weight increases for underweight women with amenorrhea or anovulatory cycles. (Of course, all pathology must be ruled out.) In many cases a weight increase of merely three to five pounds above the threshold weight for height results in the resumption of menstruation; it is not yet possible, however, to predict the precise amount any given individual has to gain above the threshold. At body weights close to the required minimum, women may still have anovulatory cycles even if they are menstruating. (Ultrasound images of the ovary or measurements of hormone levels would reveal the disorder.) A further weight gain—up to the range indicated by the 25th percentile for body-water percentage—could be necessary to ensure regular, ovulatory cycles. The narrowness of the weight threshold is actually quite surprising: some athletes we studied turned their menstrual cycles on and off at will with just a three-pound weight change.

I must note a few caveats here. Because factors other than weight, such as emotional stress, affect the onset or maintenance of menstruation, cycles that are disrupted by weight loss may not resume in some women even though they reach the minimum weight for their height. Also, the time it takes before the cycles resume with weight gain varies with the length of time a woman was amenorrheic. I should also point out that our nomograms apply as yet only to U.S. or European females and do not apply to extremely muscular women. Because muscles contain a lot of water (80 percent), which is heavy, they are heavy themselves; hence a muscular woman with a normal weight for her height may actually have little fat in relation to her lean mass.

By what mechanism might a modification in the amount of body fat affect fertility? The critical role of the hypothalamus in controlling reproduction was established by measurements of a hypothalamic hormone called gonadotropin-releasing hormone (GnRH). This substance, which is secreted in pulses, controls the chain of events leading to ovulation. In underweight or excessively lean women the pattern of secretion of gonadotropin-releasing hormone is abnormal in amount and timing and is similar to that of prepubertal girls. As a result the cascade of hormonal events that normally leads to ovulation and prepares the uterus to support a pregnancy is disrupted.

In the mature female body GnRH pulses stimulate the pituitary gland to release two other hormones: follicle-stimulating hormone, which controls the growth of an ovarian follicle (specialized cells that encase an egg), and luteinizing hormone, which controls the cyclical release of the egg from the follicle. When these hormone levels are low, ovulation cannot occur.

Estrogen and progesterone secreted by the ovary are also necessary for ovulation and menstruation. These hormones are affected by a decline in the levels of gonadotropin-releasing hormone and the consequent changes in follicle-stimulating hormone and luteinizing hormone. The growing follicle normally releases estrogen, which modulates the hormonal secretions of the pituitary, leading to a midcycle surge of luteinizing hormone and hence to ovulation. Estrogen also stimulates the growth of the breasts and the uterine lining. After ovulation the follicle becomes the corpus luteum ("yellow body") and secretes progesterone, which increases the vascularity of the uterine lining in preparation for implantation of the fertilized egg. If no egg is implanted, the levels of progesterone and estrogen fall and the monthly flow of blood ensues.

Just what signal the hypothalamus responds to when menstruation is disrupted is still not certain. It may receive signals from the abnormal temperature control or the changes in metabolism that are associated with loss of body fat due to undernutrition and a high expenditure of energy. It is also possible that the hypothalamus may receive signals from changes in estrogen that result from fat loss.

How can fat make a difference to estrogen? Adipose tissue was once thought to be inert and to merely insulate and cushion the body. It is now known to be quite active in the turnover of fuels in the body. It also stores steroids (sex hormones) and influences the amount and potency of estrogen circulating in the blood.

Several research groups have delineated the interrelation between body fat and estrogen. Pentti K. Siiteri of the University of California at San Francisco School of Medicine and Paul C. Macdonald of the Cecil H. and Ida Green Center for Reproductive Biology Sciences in Dallas have found that fat tissue converts androgen (male hormones) into estrogen. This conversion accounts for roughly a third of the estrogen that circulates in the blood of premenopausal women and is the main source of estrogen in postmenopausal women. (Men also convert androgen into estrogen in body fat.) The fat of the breast, abdomen, omentum (the apron of fat in the abdomen) and, as my colleagues and I have found, the fatty marrow of the long bones all convert androgen into estrogen.

Jack Fishman, H. Leon Bradlow and their associates at Rockefeller University have shown that whether androgen is converted into a potent or a nonpotent form of estrogen is related to how fat one is. For instance, anorectic lean girls have elevated levels of a relatively inactive form of estrogen, whereas fatter women produce less of this form and have an elevated level of a highly potent type. Siiteri and his colleagues also found that obese women have a relatively low level of a substance known as sex-hormone-binding globulin; as its name suggests, the hormone binds estrogen. Low levels of this binding protein result in a high concentration of free estrogen in the circulation. Leaner girls at menarche have higher amounts of the binding protein and therefore less free estrogen.

538

Several recent studies, including our own, have shown that dieting is not the only way women become lean enough to impair their hypothalamic function and disrupt menstruation. Well-trained athletes of all kinds, such as runners, swimmers and ballet dancers, have a high incidence of delayed menarche, irregular cycles and amenorrhea. This pattern implies that exercise could be the cause—presumably by building muscles and reducing fat, thus raising the ratio of lean mass to fat.

My colleagues and I have been able to establish that regular intensive exercise is indeed the explanation. We found that collegiate swimmers and runners whose training began before menarche first menstruated at an average age of about 15 years; women whose training began later had an average menarcheal age of about 12.7 years—similar to that of both our nonathletic control group and the general population. In our sample each year of premenarcheal training delayed menarche by five months.

Our data also showed that training that begins before menarche is associated with a high incidence of menstrual irregularities. Of our college athletes who had begun training before menarche, only 17 percent had regular cycles; 61 percent had irregularly timed cycles and 22 percent did not menstruate at all. On the other hand, 60 percent of the women who began training after menarche had regular cycles, 40 percent had irregular cycles and none were amenorrheic. During intensive training the incidence of irregular cycles and amenorrhea increased in both groups, in association with loss of body weight and increased leanness.

Measurements of hormones added support for the suggestion that fat loss contributes to menstrual disorders in athletes. The findings indicated that lean athletes with disrupted menstrual cycles or late menarche had low levels of estrogen and low levels of luteinizing hormone. Cessation of exercise because of an injury restored the hormones to normal levels, and the cycles resumed. Recent measurements made by other workers have further shown that well-trained athletes with irregular cycles and amenorrhea had hypothalamic dysfunction: the levels of gonadotropin-releasing hormone were abnormal and were similar to those of underweight women, as would be expected if a loss of fat and an increase of muscle mass were the cause of menstrual disorders.

We have also studied a female body builder who does not run, jog or dance but who concentrates on building her muscles with exercise machines. She becomes amenorrheic when she is in shape for competition. Measurements of her hormones have shown that her levels of estrogen, follicle-stimulating hormone and luteinizing hormone are as low as those of dieting and athletic women.

New findings from former college athletes add a different kind of confirmation that relative fatness has an important effect on the human reproductive system. A group of us in Boston studied data on 5,398 college graduates between 20 and 80 years old, half of them former athletes and half of them not. The former athletes had a significantly lower lifetime occurrence of breast cancer and cancers of the reproductive system than the nonathletes. The analysis took into account possible confounding factors, such as age, family history of cancer and smoking. The likeliest explanation is that the former athletes (who were leaner than the nonathletes in every age group) had lower estrogen levels and a higher proportion of low-potency estrogen. Apparently the same factors that, when extreme, can cause infertility in underweight or athletic women also exert a protective effect against cancers that are sensitive to sex hormones.

For direct evidence of a connection between body composition and fertility one has to turn to animals, which can be dissected to determine the weight of the lean body mass and fat. At present all methods for measuring body fat in the human being are indirect, including underwater weighing. D. Mark Hegsted, Koii Yoshinaga, both then at Harvard, and I have shown that rats given a high-fat diet had first estrus significantly earlier than rats fed a low-fat diet of equal calories. Direct carcass analysis of the tissues showed that both groups had a similar body-water percentage at first estrus and hence a similar lean/fat ratio even though their absolute body weights differed.

Other animals provide more circumstantial but nonetheless interesting data. Consider the case of the so-called double-muscled Charolais cattle, whose particulary lean meat makes them a desirable commodity. Unfortunately for the farmers who breed them, these animals have delayed puberty and difficulty reproducing. The Charolais bulls similarly are relatively infertile.

Another set of findings relates to an unusual phenomenon known as flushing: an increase in the rate of twin births in sheep when they are fed a high-calorie diet for a short time—perhaps a week—before mating. Sheep farmers routinely capitalize on this phenomenon to increase the number of twin births. The effect is so strong that one can calculate the number of twin lambs that will be born to a healthy ewe on the basis of the number of calories she eats.

The well-nourished human female fortunately does not normally superovulate in response to a high-calorie meal (at least as far as we know). Nevertheless, there is evidence for a residual flushing effect. The rate at which women gave birth to fraternal twins (from two eggs) but not to identical twins (from one egg that divides) declined in Holland during World War II when there were food restrictions; the rate of birth of fraternal twins returned to normal after the food supply became more plentiful.

Data from both the animal and the human studies suggest an explanation for the variation in the natural fertility of human populations, both historically and today. The total number of live children born to couples who do not use contraception can vary from as few as four among the hard-living nomadic Bush people of the Kalahari Desert in Africa to an average of 11 children among the well-nourished Hutterites, a prosperous, noncontracepting religious sect in the U.S. I explain these differences in terms of a direct pathway from food intake to fertility.

The idea is not completely new. Charles Darwin described this common-sense relation years ago with several observations: domestic animals (which have a regular and plentiful food supply) are more fertile than their wild relatives; "hard living retards the period at which animals conceive"; the amount of available food affects the fertility of a given animal, and it is difficult to fatten a lactating cow. I have shown that Darwin's dicta apply to human beings and that food supplies can affect fertility throughout the life span.

For instance, data on growth and reproduction of women in Great Britain in the mid-1800's show that poorly nourished females, who grew to maturity relatively slowly (a pattern that results in less fat per unit of lean mass), differed from well-nourished females in each event of the reproductive span. Their menarche was later, adolescent subfecundity lasted longer, their age of peak fertility came later, the number of live births in a given age group was smaller and the number of unsuccessful pregnancies was larger. Moreover, the duration of amenorrhea during breast-feeding was longer and the interval between births was therefore longer, and the age of menopause (when menstrual cycles cease) was earlier. In that British population, as in many other populations of the past, poor couples still living together at the end of their reproductive lives had had only six or seven living births.

Most poor couples in developing countries today also have about that number. This may seem like many offspring, but the number is actually well below the average human capacity. The relative infertility of the women can be explained by the fact that they tend to be undernourished and also to perform hard physical labor. If undernourished women have fewer children than well-nourished ones who do not practice contraception, why is there such rapid population growth in the developing countries? The paradox is explained by the fact that the death rate in these countries has been reduced by modern public-health measures while the birthrate has remained the same.

Whether they live in developing or developed countries, women need to be aware that they can become pregnant even though they are breast-feeding. In developing nations nursing mothers who are ill nourished generally do not resume ovulating and menstruating until a year or more after they give birth. Women who are well nourished, however, can resume ovulatory cycles as soon as three months after delivery, even if they are nursing full time. Having too short an interval between births is potentially dangerous because pregnancy is an energy drain on the mother and can cause the baby she is carrying to have a low birth weight; this would threaten the child's survival and put it at risk for neurological and other problems. Moreover, hormonal changes that accompany a pregnancy reduce the amount of breast milk the mother produces. Particularly in poor countries the health of the already-suckling child would then be jeopardized; in such nations it is important that mothers nurse for as long as possible because infants are often weaned onto diets that are low in protein.

Some investigators have argued that the pattern of suckling is the only factor that affects the length of "lactational amenorrhea." Yet studies in Africa by Peter G. Lunn and Roger G. Whitehead of the University of Cambridge show that nutrition and physical work clearly affect the time to resumption of regular, ovulatory menstrual cycles.

My work has focused on the female, but undernutrition and weight loss also affect the male's ability to procreate. In a classic study of starvation in men Ancel Keys, Josef M. Brozek and their associates at the University of Minnesota found that a decrease in calorie intake and subsequent weight loss first cause a

541

loss of libido. Continued weight loss results in a reduction of prostate fluid and then in lessened motility and longevity of sperm; the production of sperm is reduced when men weigh approximately 25 percent less than the normal weight for their height. Weight gain restores function in the reverse order of the loss.

Recent studies of male marathon runners and other top-ranking lean athletes have shown that many male athletes, like female ones, have hypothalamic dysfunction: the hypothalamus of many subjects secreted too little gonadotropin-releasing hormone, or released it in an abnormal pattern, causing the levels of testosterone (a male hormone) to be lower than normal. Whether such athletes may also have decreased fertility is not yet known.

There is as yet little discussion of the significance of fertility changes related to fatness in men. In contrast, the value of temporary infertility in women who are too thin was recognized a century ago. In 1884, when there were many cases of nutritional amenorrhea, the physician J. Matthews Duncan advised the Royal College of Physicians to treat a so-called sterile woman with an ample diet, such as roast beef and a French wine. "If a seriously undernourished woman could get pregnant," he said, "the chance of her giving birth to a viable infant, or herself surviving the pregnancy, is infinitesimally small."

Does Malnutrition Affect Fecundity?
A Summary of Evidence

John Bongaarts

Summary. Moderate chronic malnutrition has only a minor effect on fecundity (reproductive capacity), and the resulting effect on fertility (actual reproduction) is very small. Among the fecundity components examined here in non-contracepting populations, age at menarche and the duration of lactational amenorrhea appear to be the ones most affected by malnutrition. But from neither of those effects can a difference in fertility of more than a few percent be expected between poorly and well-nourished women in developing countries.

That malnutrition has an effect on human reproductive capability is suggested by several research findings. For example, by the end of their reproductive years well-nourished Hutterite women have given birth, on the average, several more times than relatively poorly nourished women in developing countries or in historical populations. It is also well established that famines cause reductions in birthrates. These facts provide support for the current hypothesis that malnutrition impairs fecundity, the ability to reproduce (*1, 2*). But the strength of this relationship and its demographic significance are controversial issues, which have recently become a focus of a number of investigations (*3*). A strong link between nutrition and fecundity would have important implications, especially for food aid programs for the developing world. If improving nutrition in those countries increased their birthrates, it would exacerbate an already serious population growth problem.

The object of this article is to review existing evidence for the effect of malnutrition on human reproductive capability and to make an assessment, even if a rather crude one, of its demographic impact. Because findings vary with the degree of malnutrition, a distinction will be made between the chronic moderate malnutrition that prevails in the poorer classes of many developing countries and the severe malnutrition resulting from famine and starvation. The discussion will focus on the effects in females; the literature contains relatively little information about the effects in males.

EVIDENCE FROM FERTILITY DIFFERENTIALS

Inferences about the effect of chronic malnutrition on the ability to reproduce are often made from fertility differences among populations which differ with respect to nutrient intake. Such inferences, however, are not reliable, because the ability to reproduce (fecundity) is not necessarily, and in fact is only rarely, reflected in actual reproductive performance (fertility). If one were to collect fertility and nutrition data for a large number of populations from around the world, one would find a strong negative correlation between nutrition and fertility. Nutrient intake is highest in the Western industrialized nations with only about two children per woman at the end of the reproductive years, whereas malnutrition is most prevalent in the poorest underdeveloped countries, where completed fertility is typically six to seven births per woman. One can obviously not conclude from these data that good nutrition impairs fecundity, because the low fertility in the developed countries is the consequence of voluntary fertility control.

In general, the fertility of a population is determined both by its fecundity, which sets an upper limit to fertility, and by a number of fertility-inhibiting behavioral factors, which can reduce actual fertility to a fraction of this upper limit. The most important behavioral factors are (i) late marriage and marital disruption, (ii) deliberate birth control by contraception, abstention, or induced abortion, and (iii) breast-feeding, which can delay the return of ovulation after a birth (4). One or more of these factors reduces fertility to well below its potential level in all known populations. This fact greatly complicates the analysis of the effect of nutrition on fecundity.

In order to circumvent this problem, the analysis of fertility differentials is usually confined to populations in which contraception and induced abortion are virtually absent. However, neglect of the other behavioral factors can still make it difficult to draw conclusions. An example is provided by the often-cited comparison of Hutterite fertility with the fertility of poor populations in underdeveloped countries such as Bangladesh. Hutterite women who reached the end of the child-bearing years in 1950 had an average of 9.5 childbirths (5), women in Bangladesh in the early 1970's only about 7 (6). Since the use of contraception or induced abortion is negligible in both populations, it has been suggested that this fertility difference is due to the high prevalence of malnutrition in Bangladesh (2). While that would appear to be a plausible explanation, there are several counterexamples. In the rich and better-nourished populations of Kuwait and Saudi Arabia, where contraception is virtually absent and marriage is early and universal, fertility is approximately the same as in Bangladesh (6). Particulary instructive is the case of the Amish population, which is culturally very similar to the Hutterites. Both populations consist of descendants of Swiss settlers in the United States, and both enjoy a high standard of living and good nutrition. Most aspects of daily life are under strict social and religious control in both societies, and there is minimum contact with the world outside their agricultural communities. Fertility is natural, that is, without deliberate control, yet Amish fertility is only 6.3 births per woman (7).

The existence of extremely high marital fertility in a few historical populations is also difficult to reconcile with the nutrition hypothesis. There is good evidence of a low level of nutrition in the laboring classes in mid-19th-century England, but the mean birth interval—an inverse indicator of marital fertility—was short, 20 to 24 months, about the same as among the Hutterites (2, 8, 9). Similarly, age-specific marital fertility rates of the 18th-century Canadian population were very close to those of the Hutterites (10), despite a probably substantial difference in nutrition levels.

Clearly, these simple comparisons of the fertility of different populations do not allow the conclusion that there is a substantial effect of nutrition on fecundity. What then explains the high fertility of the Hutterites? To demonstrate that the behavioral factors are responsible for the fertility differentials requires a detailed analysis of the fertility determinants, which is not possible in many populations because of lack of data. The needed data are available, however, for the well-nourished Hutterites and the poorly nourished population of Bangladesh.

Table 1 summarizes these data. The estimates of general fertility indicate that, on the average, Hutterite women have 2.3 more children in their reproductive lifetimes than women in Bangladesh (5, 6). This fertility difference increases if one controls for the Hutterites' later age at marriage. The second column in Table 1 presents fertility rates standardized for age at marriage. The total marital fertility rate given equals the average number of births women in these populations would have if they married at exactly age 20 and remained married throughout the reproductive period. This rate is 39 percent less in Bangladesh than among the Hutterites (10, 11). The mean birth intervals are correspondingly shorter in the Hutterites (8, 9) than in the Bangladeshi (12).

The problem is now reduced to finding the causes of the difference of 13.4 months between the mean birth intervals of the two populations. It is evident from the last column of Table 1 that the primary factor is the difference in the duration of lactational amenorrhea. The difference of 11.9 months (8, 13) accounts for 89 percent of the birth interval difference of 13.4 months. The remaining 11 percent, or 1.5 months, may be due to the seasonal absence of husbands (14), a slightly lower frequency of intercourse, and the use of contraception or abortion by a small number of couples in Bangladesh.

The difference in lactational amenorrhea is not surprising in view of the difference in the breast-feeding practices of the two populations. Among the Hutterites lactation is relatively short and supplemental feeding is introduced early in an infant's life, whereas in Bangladesh most women nurse their infants for a long time—often until the next pregnancy occurs (15). Since the duration and pattern of breast-feeding are the primary determinants of the duration of amenorrhea (as will be shown below), the Bangladeshi women would be expected to have longer amenorrhea and therefore lower marital fertility than the Hutterite women.

For comparison, Table 1 also gives estimates of fertility rates and their determinants for the 18th-century population of Ile-de-France (16, 17). The general

Table 1. Measures of general fertility, marital fertility, and determinants of fertility for the Hutterites (marriages of 1921 to 1930), Bangladeshi (in 1970 to 1975), and three villages of Ile-de-France (18th century). The total general fertility rate is the average number of births per woman at the end of the reproductive years. The total marital fertility rate is the average number of births per woman married at age 20 and remaining married to the end of the reproductive years.

| Population | Total general fertility rate (births per woman) | Marital fertility | | Determinants of fertility | | |
		Total marital fertility rate (births per woman)	Mean birth interval (months)	Median age at marriage	Contra-ceptive practice	Mean duration of lactational amenorrhea (months)
Hutterites	9.5	10.9	24.0	22.0	Absent	6.0
Bangladesh	7.2	6.8	37.4	17.0	Very low	17.9
Ile-de-France	6.1	10.1	26.0	25.5	Very low	8.6*

*Estimated by subtracting the mean duration of the interval between marriage and first birth from the mean duration of the interval between first and second births.

fertility rate of this population is substantially below that of the Hutterites and even slightly lower than in Bangladesh, the apparent cause being the relatively late age of women at marriage (17). The marital fertility rate, as well as the mean birth interval and the duration of lactational amenorrhea, are almost the same as among the Hutterites. Thus the fertility differences between the Hutterites and the populations of Bangladesh and Ile-de-France can be attributed to the various behavioral factors that inhibit fertility. There is consequently no need to hypothesize a substantial difference in fecundity between these populations.

In the evidence reviewed up to this point no direct estimates of fecundity have been available. However, in one recent study fecundity in two groups of populations is estimated with a reproductive model that calculates a fecundity rate. This rate is defined as the average number of times women would give birth over their reproductive lifetimes in the absence of celibacy, contraception, induced abortion, and lactation. It comes to 15.4 in a group of developed countries and 15.2 in a group of poor, less-developed countries (4), a difference that is not statistically significant. Since there is a significant difference in nutritional intake, this study also suggests that moderate chronic malnutrition has little effect on fecundity in the underdeveloped countries.

A more detailed understanding of the link between malnutrition and fecundity can be gained from an examination of the various biological factors that determine fecundity. The following factors can be identified: (i) age at menarche, (ii) age at menopause, (iii) prevalence of permanent (primary) sterility, (iv) ovulation-inhibiting effect of breast-feeding, (v) regularity of ovulation (among menstruating women) and the quality and quantity of sperm, and (vi) probability of intrauterine death. A population or group of women can be considered to have relatively high fecundity if the values of factors (ii) and (v) are relatively high and the values of the other factors are relatively low. Evidence for an effect of chronic malnutrition on each of these factors will now be reviewed briefly and, where appropriate, the impact on fertility will be discussed.

MENARCHE

In the contemporary Western world the average age at menarche is about 13 years (16, 18–21). Averages in developing countries are typically higher and vary substantially—for example, 12.4 in Cuba (22), 13 to 14 in India (20, 23), 13.4 in Sri Lanka (24), 15.0 among the South African Bantus (25), 15.7 in Bangladesh (26), and 18.8 among the Bundi in New Guinea (22). Estimates for 19th-century European populations are also high—around 16 years (21). Much effort has been devoted to analyzing the determinants of menarche, but there is still substantial disagreement about the relative importance of various biological, environmental, and socioeconomic factors (18, 19).

Most investigators believe, however, that nutrition has a substantial effect. The conclusion is based on four types of direct and indirect evidence. First, a direct link between nutritional intake and age at menarche was found in a U.S. study in which well-nourished girls reached menarche 2 years earlier than undernourished girls (27). Similarly, an Indian study concluded that girls whose diets were higher in calories and proteins had earlier menarche (28). Second, nutritional status as measured by anthropometric indicators is correlated with age at menarche. A number of reports from different societies has established that the probability of reaching menarche by a given age is positively related to body size and weight (21, 26, 27, 29-31). On the basis of this evidence, Frisch has developed a procedure for estimating a minimum weight for height necessary for the onset of menarche (30), but this method has been questioned (32, 33). Third, in Western societies where there are relatively reliable historical data on menarche, a decline in age of menarche of about 3 years has taken place since the end of the last century (19, 21). This decline is associated with an increase in body size and an improved diet. Fourth, socioeconomic status and age at menarche are negatively related in a number of countries. Differences ranging from a few months to about 2 years have been found between urban and rural populations and between high and low income groups (19, 24, 25, 34, 35).

Age at menarche signals the beginning of potential childbearing, but actual reproduction starts at marriage. The mean age at marriage is almost always higher than the mean age at menarche, the difference ranging from about 2 years in some traditional societies to more than 10 years in a number of contemporary European populations. In populations where the mean age at marriage is near 20 or higher, one can hardly expect a fertility effect from nutritional variations in age at menarche, but this fertility effect is quite small even if marriage takes place shortly after menarche and ages at the two events are correlated.

A simple numerical exercise can demonstrate this. Let us assume that in a hypothetical, but not atypical, poorly nourished population the mean age at menarche is 15 years and that a large improvement in nutrition can lower it to 13 years. Let us further assume that marriage is very early and that there is a significant correlation between menarche and marriage so that the mean age at marriage will also decrease—say from 17 to 16 years. This 1-year reduction in age at marriage will lengthen the actual reproductive life-span by about the same amount, thus increasing completed fertility. With a marital fertility rate of 250 per 1000 for 16-year-old women, this additional reproductive time would add 0.25 births per woman on average. Since average completed fertility is typically six or seven births per woman, this implies a fertility increase of about 4 percent. A decrease in adolescent subfertility adds less than 1 percent to this estimate (36). Clearly, substantial changes in age at menarche following improvements in nutrition can be expected to raise fertility by at most a small percentage. The insensitivity of fertility to modification in the age at menarche has also been confirmed by computer simulations (37).

MENOPAUSE

In developed societies the mean age at menopause ranges from 47 to 50 years and the median is 1 or 2 years higher (20, 38). The few reported estimates from developing countries are much less consistent: median ages of 44 in India (39) and 43.7 in a malnourished population in New Guinea (20) are among the lowest observed anywhere. Mean ages of 47.4 in rural Ceylon (24) and 47.5 in poorly nourished mid-19th-century England (2) are nearly the same as in well-nourished populations of today. A relatively high mean of 50.7 years has been found among the Bantu in South Africa (40). The available evidence regarding the determinants of age at menopause is conflicting and inconclusive. A few studies report a time trend in age at menopause or an effect of nutrition or socioeconomic status (20, 24, 38, 41), but other investigations fail to find the same relationships (38, 42, 43). These confusing results are probably due in part to methodological problems, including inappropriate statistical analyses, recall errors in retrospective data, and misreporting of age (20, 38, 43).

No conclusive evidence regarding nutritional variations in age at menopause is provided by these studies. Even if there is such an effect, it would be of demographic interest only if the timing of a woman's final childbirth—and hence her fertility—were significantly affected. The small amount of available evidence suggests very little effect of nutrition on the mean age at last birth. This mean age is 40.9 among the well-nourished Hutterites (9) and—contrary to expectations—slightly higher (41.7 years) in a poorly nourished mid-19th-century English population (2). The use of contraception and induced abortion was virtually absent in both populations. The mean age at last birth is also close to 40 years in a number of other historical natural-fertility populations (44).

PREVALENCE OF PERMANENT STERILITY

Only 3 percent of the married Hutterite women had never borne a child by the time they reached age 50 (5). It has been suggested that that is an unusually low rate of permanent sterility and that higher sterility can be expected in poorly nourished populations (2). Recent demographic surveys in a number of poor developing countries do not support that view. For example, in Bangladesh 2.1 percent of married women aged 45 or over, and in Pakistan and Nepal 2 and 2.6 percent respectively, have never given birth (45).

INHIBITION OF OVULATION BY LACTATION

The term lactation amenorrhea is often used to refer to the temporary absence of menses postpartum, because it is now well established that breast-feeding is the principal determinant of the duration of that amenorrhea. In the absence of breast-feeding the menses return shortly after birth in well-nourished populations (46–48) as well as in poorly nourished ones (14, 49–51). As the duration of breast-feeding increases so does the amenorrheic interval—approximately one additional month of amenorrhea for each 2-month increment in breast-feeding (16, 52). With long lactation mean amenorrheic intervals of 1 to 2 years are observed, not only in the poorest developing countries (14, 53–55) but also in the United States, where a group of women who practiced "natural" (unrestricted) nursing experienced an average of 14.6 months of amenorrhea (56).

An extensive set of data from the WHO Collaborative Study on Breast-feeding (25 subpopulations in nine countries) showed that, at any given time, postpartum variation in proportions of breast-feeding explained, on the average, 85 percent of between-population variance in the proportions of menstruating women (57). Other studies have found high correlations between mean duration of breast-feeding and of amenorrhea when comparing populations (52, 58) or subpopulations within countries (46–49, 55, 59). On the individual level the correlation is somewhat lower. The most plausible explanation for this—aside from measurement error—is that women differ not only with respect to how long they breast-feed but also with respect to their patterns of breast-feeding (60, 61). It has been shown that women who fully breast-feed have a lower probability of resumption of menses than women whose infants receive supplemental food such as fluids by bottle or solids (48, 49, 54, 62). The ovulation- and menstruation-inhibiting effect of breast-feeding and also the differential effect of breast-feeding patterns are believed to be due to a neurally mediated hormonal reflex system initiated by the suckling stimulations of the breast nipple (63, 64).

The question of interest here is whether maternal malnutrition affects amenorrhea independent of breast-feeding practices. Recent studies in relatively poorly nourished rural populations in Bangladesh and Guatemala provide tentative estimates of the importance of moderate malnutrition. In one study in Bangladesh, women were divided into three nutritional status groups on the basis of weight: less than 38.5 kilograms, between 38.5 and 42.4 kg, and over 42.4 kg. The observed mean duration of amenorrhea in these groups was 17.9, 17.5, and 16.8 months, respectively (13). There is a decline with increasing weight, but the differences are not statistically significant. The relation between duration of amenorrhea and other anthropometric measures was also not statistically significant.

In another study in Bangladesh nutritional status was estimated from measures of weight for height. The median duration of amenorrhea in the low, medium, and high nutritional status groups was 21.2, 20.4, and 20.2 months, respectively (54). There was no evidence of a threshold of weight for height necessary for the resumption of menses postpartum (65). It should be noted that these analyses do not control for duration of lactation. However, it is unlikely that this substantially affects the results, because women in rural Bangladesh usually breast-feed their infants until the next pregnancy occurs, and a large majority are still lactating when their menses return.

These results are confirmed in a study in Guatemala in which women were again divided into three nutritional status groups on the basis of anthropometric measures (66). The low and high nutritional status groups had mean weights

Table 2. Mean duration of postpartum amenorrhea (months) in groups differing in caloric intake and in duration of lactation (number in parentheses). Low caloric intake = < 1309 calories a day, middle = 1309 to 1630 calories, high = > 1630 calories. (Data from (*67*)]

Daily caloric intake	Duration of lactation (months)			
	7 to 12	13 to 18	19 to 24	25 or more
Low	6.54 (13)	12.03 (35)	16.44 (45)	19.93 (14)
Middle	6.31 (13)	11.64 (33)	15.47 (57)	18.90 (10)
High	5.47 (14)	11.13 (30)	14.60 (47)	19.64 (11)
High-low difference	1.07	0.90	1.84	0.29

of 43.7 and 55.6 kg and mean amenorrhea duration of 14.8 and 13.2 months, respectively. The difference in amenorrhea was statistically significant and slightly larger than in Bangladesh, possibly because the Guatemalan population is more heterogeneous with respect to nutritional status. Data on total caloric intake were also available, and their relation to postpartum amenorrhea is summarized in Table 2. This table allows direct comparison of the relative importance of lactation and nutrition as determinants of the duration of amenorrhea. Lactation is clearly the primary determinant. There is a fairly consistent, but not statistically significant, difference of the order of 1 month between the amenorrheic periods of women with high and low caloric intake.

These findings seem to be inconsistent with the results of a Mexican study (*68, 69*) of two groups of women, one with and one without dietary supplementation. The group with the supplement had much shorter postpartum amenorrhea than the control group. Wray (*70*) has proposed a plausible explanation for this finding. It appears that the infants of many of the supplemented mothers also received dietary supplements. As a result, these infants needed less milk from their mothers, and the decreased suckling shortened the period of amenorrhea independent of the mother's nutritional status. The validity of this explanation appears to be confirmed by new observations from the same population which show that a small group of supplemented women whose infants receive no supplements had a mean amenorrheic interval of virtually the same duration as the unsupplemented mothers (*71*).

The small differences between nutritional status groups in duration of amenorrhea are not necessarily caused by a direct physiological effect of malnutrition on the mother. It is possible that unmeasured differences in pattern of breast-feeding between the poorly and well-nourished women in these populations are responsible. For example, if malnourished mothers have less food available for supplementing infant diets, or are later in introducing supplementation, their infants will suckle more and thus prolong amenorrhea.

The effect on fertility of variations in amenorrhea duration are easily estimated from the resulting proportional changes in the mean birth interval. The estimates of the studies in Bangladesh and Guatemala are in fair agreement and suggest a difference of approximately 1 month in the amenorrheic intervals of the high and low nutritional status groups. With a typical mean birth interval of 2 1/2 to 3 years, a 1-month change would yield about a 3 percent difference in the marital fertility of the two extreme nutritional status groups.

REGULARITY OF OVULATION AND QUALITY AND QUANTITY OF SPERM

Since it is virtually impossible to estimate directly the regularity of ovulation and the quality and quantity of sperm on a population basis, it is necessary to rely on indirect measures such as the rate of conception among menstruating women. A conception rate is determined also by the frequency of intercourse, but any effect that malnutrition would have on any of these three determinants would be expected to be negative. One can therefore be reasonably sure, if no overall effect of malnutrition on conception rate is found, that it is not because of compensatory effects on any of them.

A convenient indicator of the rate of conception is the mean waiting time to conception. This is simply measured as the number of months between the occurrence of the first postpartum menses—a good indicator of the resumption of ovulation—and the next conception. The two prospective studies of poorly nourished women in Bangladesh and Guatemala discussed in the previous section were specifically designed to test the effect of nutrition status on the mean waiting time to conception (conceptions ending in live births in the Guatemalan case). In both populations contraception and induced abortion are very little used. In Bangladesh the mean waiting times in groups of women with low (< 38.5 kg), medium (38.5 to 42.4 kg), and high (> 42.5 kg) weights were 11.3, 10.7, and 10.0 months, respectively. The differences were not statistically significant after control for the confounding effect of age and absences of husband (13). There was no correlation between other anthropometric measures and mean waiting time. In Guatemala the low, medium, and high nutritional status groups had waiting times of 6.4, 6.1, and 6.3 months, respectively (66). Compared with that of other, mostly better-nourished, populations, the mean waiting time is above average but not unusually long in Bangladesh and relatively short in Guatemala (12, 16).

INTRAUTERINE MORTALITY

Although maternal nutrition is one of the determinants of an infant's birth weight (72, 73), good evidence for a link between moderate malnutrition and fetal mortality does not exist. The study of this subject is hampered by severe methodological problems in measuring the prevalence of intrauterine mortality, especially during the early months of gestation (16). As a consequence, estimates of fetal mortality rates vary widely among populations, even if one restricts comparisons to studies that employ the life table method. Seven independent studies in the Untied States and Sweden yielded estimates ranging from 12.5 to 33.9 fetal deaths per 100 conceptions (16, 74). Similar investigations in underdeveloped countries report figures within this range: 14.9 percent in Matlab Thana, Bangladesh (14); 13.6 percent in the Punjab, India (75); 17.6 percent in Lahore, Pakistan (76); and 16 to 19 percent and 30 percent in two surveys in South India (77). A comparison of reported rates of stillbirths (fetal deaths after week 28 of gestation) among populations indicates a negative trend with modernization, from about 4 percent of conceptions in the least-developed countries to about 1 percent in the Western world (73). However, this trend has only a minor effect on the overall fetal mortality rate, because stillbirths constitute no more than a small fraction of all fetal deaths.

Genetic, health, nutritional, and environmental factors have all been suggested as possible causes of fetal mortality, but it has proved impossible to clearly determine the importance of each factor (78–82). The absence of a statistically significant difference in the fetal mortality rates of the developed and the developing countries suggests that nutrition does not have a large effect. This tentative conclusion is supported by the results of the Guatemalan investigation discussed earlier (66). In that population maternal nutritional status did not affect the mean duration of the interval between the end of postpartum amenorrhea and the next birth. Any increase in intrauterine mortality would have lengthened that interval; the absence of a nutritional differential implies, therefore, that the link between maternal nutrition and the incidence of fetal mortality is either absent or very weak.

FECUNDITY AND FERTILITY IN FAMINE

The discussion up to this point has focused on the effects of chronic malnutrition. We turn now to the impact of acute malnutrition in famines.

Famines are invariably associated with large but temporary reductions in fertility. During food crises in 17th- and 18-century Europe rises in food prices were followed by declines in birthrates (84, 85). Similarly, the rate of conception reached a minimum during famines in recent world wars (86, 87). Perhaps best documented is the Dutch famine which took place from October 1944 to May 1945 in an otherwise well-nourished population (87). The birthrate did not change during the actual famine period, but 9 months later fertility was reduced by more than 50 percent. A fertility decline of nearly the same magnitude was observed after the 1974–1975 famine in Bangladesh. The price of rice began to rise in 1974 and reached a peak in early 1975. Associated with this food shortage was a 50 percent increase in the death rate, predominantly among infants, and a decline in the birthrate from about 45 per 1000 population before the famine to 27.5 for the period from April 1975 to March 1976 (88).

These correlations between the occurrence of extreme food deprivation and fertility provide little insight into the nature of the mechanisms involved. It is evident that fecundity is impaired in famine, because amenorrhea is often reported (*86, 87, 89*) and in severe starvation the gonads atrophy (*89, 90*). However, it is not clear whether this amenorrhea is entirely due to malnutrition or is in part caused by the fear of death and the anxiety that accompanies crisis conditions (*89–91*). Psychological stress alone can induce amenorrhea (*89, 92–94*). A number of other factors have been found to inhibit fertility during some famines: (i) decrease in libido (*88, 89*), (ii) separation of spouses by the search for food or work (*88, 89*), and (iii) voluntary fertility control by contraception, abstention, or induced abortion (*88*). A lack of sufficiently detailed data makes it impossible to estimate accurately the contributions to the fertility decline from each of these factors.

Further evidence regarding the effect of severe malnutrition on fecundity is available from studies of voluntary or self-inflicted starvation. In the classical experiment by Keys, male volunteers were subjected to a 50 percent reduction in caloric intake for 24 weeks; loss of libido was marked, and sperm motility and longevity were significantly reduced (*89*). In females large reductions in weight can produce amenorrhea, which is reversed after restoration of normal weight (*30, 95*), but much of this evidence comes from small samples of patients which may have been self-selected. In patients with anorexia nervosa the influence of psychological or psychotic factors is unclear. Also, amenorrhea frequently precedes major weight loss or persists for long periods after ideal weight has been reestablished (*89, 90, 95*), and significant numbers of severely emaciated women have been found to maintain regular menstruation (*89*). As a consequence, some investigators are reluctant to draw conclusions about the effect of weight on amenorrhea (*89, 96*).

CONCLUSION

Malnutrition can impair the function of the human reproductive process. This effect is strongest and most evident in famine and starvation, when both fecundity and fertility are reduced significantly. The precise causes of this reduction remain to be determined. The change in fecundity is most likely the direct result of severe malnutrition, although it could also be caused by psychological stress and anxiety. The decline in fertility is in part due to the decreased fecundity, but several behavioral changes probably contribute significantly.

Moderate chronic malnutrition has only a minor effect on fecundity, and the resulting decrease in fertility is very small. Among the fecundity components examined here, age at menarche and the duration of postpartum amenorrhea appear to be most affected, but in each case the effect could make a difference of only a few percent between the fertility levels of poorly and well-nourished women with caloric intake differences of the order of several hundred calories a day. Breast-feeding is the principal determinant of postpartum amenorrhea, and unrestricted breast-feeding is associated with lower fertility.

Although the evidence regarding the other fecundity components—age at menopause, prevalence of permanent sterility, regularity of ovulation and quality and quantity of sperm, and probability of intrauterine death—is insufficient to allow close quantitative assessment, it appears that these factors are even less influenced by chronic malnutrition than are age at menarche and amenorrhea, and some of them may not be influenced at all. It may therefore be concluded that a large improvement in the nutrition of mothers in the underdeveloped countries will at most result in a slight increase in fertility. Concern about the effect on fertility of food aid to poor nations (provided this aid does not include large quantities of infant formula) appears to be unwarranted.

REFERENCES AND NOTES

1. R. E. Frisch, *Soc. Biol.* **22**, 17 (1975). A clear distinction should be made between the terms fecundity, fertility, and fecundability. Fecundity is the ability to reproduce. Fertility refers to actual reproductive performance (a fecund woman can be infertile). Fecundability is defined as the monthly probability of conception.
2. ——, *Science* **199**, 22 (1978); in (*3*), p. 91.
3. W. H. Mosley, Ed., *Nutrition and Human Reproduction* (Plenum, New York, 1978).
4. J. Bongaarts, *Popul. Dev. Rev.* **4**, 105 (1978). Frequency of intercourse is another behavioral factor in fertility, but it is a less important determinant of fertility differentials and trends than nonmarriage, deliberate birth control, or breast-feeding.
5. J. W. Eaton and A. J. Mayer, *Hum. Biol.* **25**, 206 (1953).
6. *Selected World Demographic Indicators by Country, 1950–2000* (ESA/P/WP.55, Department of Economic and Social Affairs, United Nations, New York, 1975).
7. H. E. Cross and V. A. McKusick, *Soc. Biol.* **17**, 83 (1970).
8. M. C. Sheps, *Popul. Stud. (London)* **19**, 65 (1965).
9. C. Tietze, *Fertil. Steril.* **8**, 1 (1957).
10. L. Henry, *Eugen. Q.* **8**, 81 (1961).
11. L. T. Rusticka, *Cholera Res. Lab. (Dacca) Sci. Rep. No. 11* (1978). The marital fertility rate is calculated from the total fertility rate for Bangladesh on the assumption that the ratio of marital to general fertility equals the one given by Rusticka.
12. J. A. Menken, thesis, Princeton University (1975).
13. A. K. M. Chowdhury, in (*3*), p. 401.
14. L. C. Chen, S. Ahmed, M. Gesche, W. H. Mosley, *Popul. Stud. (London)* **28**, 277 (1974).
15. S. L. Huffman, A. K. M. A. Chowdhury, W. H. Mosley, *Science* **203**, 922 (1979).
16. H. Leridon, *Human Fertility: The Basic Components* (Univ. of Chicago Press, Chicago, 1977).
17. J. Ganiage, *Trois Villages D'Ile-de-France au XVIII Siecle (Travaux et Documents)* (Institut National d'Etudes Demographiques, Paris, 1963), vol. 40.
18. F. E. Johnston, *Hum. Biol.* **46**, 159 (1974).
19. L. W. Zacharias and R. J. Wurtman, *N. Engl. J. Med.* **280**, 868 (1969).
20. R. H. Gray, in *Patterns and Determinants of Natural Fertility*, J. A. Menken and H. Leridon, Eds. (Ordina, Liege, 1979).
21. J. M. Tanner, *Sci. Am.* **218** (No. 1), 1 (1968).
22. J. Hiernaux, *Eugen. Q.* **15**, 12 (1968).
23. M. Kamat, in *Proceedings of the 6th International Conference, Delhi, India* (Planned Parenthood, New York, 1959), p. 114.
24. S. Chinnatamby, *J. Reprod. Fertil.* **3**, 342 (1962).
25. R. J. Burrell and J. M. Tanner, *Hum. Biol.* **33**, 250 (1961).
26. A. K. M. Chowdbury, S. L. Huffman, G. K. Curlin, *Soc. Biol,* **24**, 316 (1977).

27. R. E. Frisch, *Pediatrics* **50**, 3 (1972).
28. M. Bhalla and J. R. Shrivastava, *Indian Pediatr.* **11**, 487 (1976).
29. R. W. Hillman, P. Slater, M. J. Nelson, *Hum. Biol.* **42**, 570 (1971).
30. R. E. Frisch and J. W. McArthur, *Science* **185**, 949 (1974).
31. L. W. Zacharias, W. M. Rand, R. J. Wurtman, *Obstetr. Gynecol. Surv.* **31**, 4 (1976).
32. W. Z. Billewitz, H. M. Fellowes, C. A. Hytten, *Ann. Hum. Biol.* **3**, 51 (1976).
33. J. Trussel, *Science* **200**, 1506 (1978); J. Reeves, *ibid.* **204**, 881 (1979).
34. T. Laska Murzejewska, *Hum. Biol.* **42**, 2 (1970).
35. S. Madhavan, *Indian J. Med. Res.* **53**, 7 (1965); G. Gopalan and A. N. Naidu, *Lancet*, **1972-II**, 1077 (1972).
36. After menarche there is a period of up to several years during which women experience a relatively high incidence of irregular and anovular cycles. Although clear quantitative evidence is not available, it may be assumed that with the 2-year decline in age of menarche the fecundability of married adolescents rises somewhat. The following crude calculation provides an estimate of the resulting change in fertility: If fecundability increases by 20 percent, fertility will rise by only 6 percent, because the sensitivity of fertility to changes in fecundability is approximately 0.3 [J. Bongaarts, *Popul. Stud.* **30**, 227 (1976)]. Since married adolescents contribute only about 15 percent of completed fertility, the rise in fecundability will add less than 1 percent to completed fertility.
37. J. A. Menken and J. Bongaarts, in (3).
38. B. McMahon and J. Worcester, *Vital and Health Statistics* (National Center for Health Statistics, Washington, D.C., 1966), series 11, p. 19.
39. J. B. Wyon, S. L. Finner, J. E. Gordon, *Popul. Index* **32**, 328 (1966).
40. G. Frere, *S. Afr. J. Med. Sci.* **36**, 21 (1971).
41. N. Wolansky, *Curr. Anthropol.* **13**, 2 (1972).
42. L. Jaszmann, N. D. Van Lith, J. C. A. Zaat, *Int. J. Fertil.* **14**, 2 (1969).
43. S. McKinlay, M. Jefferys, B. Thompson, *J. Biosoc. Sci.* **4**, 2 (1972).
44. H. Charbonneaux, in *Patterns and Determinants of Natural Fertility*, J. A. Menken and H. Leridon, Eds. (Ordina, Liege, 1979).
45. World Fertility Survey, First Reports: *Bangladesh Fertility Survey 1975–1978* (Ministry of Health and Population, Bangladesh, 1978); *Nepal Fertility Survey 1976* (Ministry of Health, Nepal, 1977); *Pakistan Fertility Survey* (Population Planning Council of Pakistan, Pakistan, 1976).
46. E. Salber, M. Feinleib, B. McMahon, *Am. J. Epidemiol.* **82**, 347 (1966).
47. J. Pascal, thesis, University of Nancy, Nancy, France (1969).
48. A. Perez, P. Vela, R. G. Potter, G. Masnick, *Popul. Stud. (London)* **25**, 491 (1971).
49. P. K. Malkani and J. J. Mirchandani, *J. Obstet. Gynecol. India* **11**, 11 (1960).
50. M. Bonte *et al.*, *Int. J. Fertil.* **19**, 97 (1974).
51. R. G. Potter, M. L. New, J. B. Wyon, J. E. Gordon, *J. Chron. Dis.* **18**, 1125 (1965).
52. L. Corsini, in *Patterns and Determinants of Natural Fertility*, J. A. Menken and H. Leridon, Eds. (Ordina, Liege, 1979).
53. M. Singarimbun and C. Manning, *Stud. Fam. Plann.* **7**, 175 (1976).
54. S. L. Huffman, A. M. K. Chowdhury, J. Chakborty, W. H. Mosley, *Popul. Stud. (London)* **32**, 251 (1978).
55. P. Cantrelle and B. Ferry, in (3), p. 353.
56. S. K. Kippley and G. F. Kippley *J. Obstet. Gynecol. Neonatal Nurs.* **1**, 15 (1972).
57. W. Z. Billewitz, *J. Biosoc. Sci.* **11**, 141 (1979).
58. R. Lesthaeghe and H. Page, *Popul. Stud. (London)*, in press.
59. A. K. Jain, T. C. Hsu, R. Freedman, M. C. Chang, *Demography* **7**, 255 (1970).
60. N. Solien de Gonzalez, *Am. Anthropol.* **66**, 873 (1964).
61. B. Winkoff, *Science*, **200**, 895 (1978).
62. T. McKeown and J. R. Gibson, *J. Obstet. Gynaecol. Br. Emp.* **61**, 824 (1954).
63. J. E. Tyson and A. Perez, in (3), p. 11; J. Tyson, *J. Biosoc. Sci. Suppl.*, **4**, 23 (1977).
64. P. Delvoye, J. Delogne-Desnock, C. Robyn, *Lancet* **1976-II**, 269 (1976).

65. S. L. Huffman, A. K. M. A. Chowdhury, W. H. Mosley, *Science* **200**, 1155 (1978).
66. J. Bongaarts and H. Delgado, in *Patterns and Determinants of Natural Fertility*, J. A. Menken and H. Leridon, Eds. (Ordina, Liege, 1979).
67. H. Delgado *et al.*, in (*3*), p. 385.
68. A. Chavez and C. Martinez, *Nutr. Rep. Int.* **7**, 1 (1973).
69. A. Chavez *et al.*, in *Proceedings of the 9th International Conference on Nutrition, Mexico, 1972* (Karger, Basel, 1975).
70. J. D. Wray, in (*3*), p. 197.
71. A. Chavez, data presented at Title XII Workshop on Nutrition and Reproductive Competency, La Jolla, Calif., 1978.
72. A. Lechtig *et. al.*, *Pediatrics* **56**, 508 (1975).
73. *World Health Organization, Technical Report Series. No. 457* (World Health Organization, Geneva, 1970).
74. These estimates of fetal mortality include all intrauterine deaths after the first missed menses (4 weeks from the onset of the last menstrual period).
75. R. G. Potter, G. B. Wyon, M. New, G. E. Gordon, *Hum. Biol.* **37**, 262 (1965).
76. A. K. Awan, *Am. J. Obstet. Gynecol.* **119**, 4 (1975).
77. Unpublished studies cited by C. Gopalan and A. N. Naidu. See also (*36*).
78. *World Health Organization, Technical Report Series, No. 461* (World Health Organization, Geneva, 1970).
79. *Maternal Nutrition and the Course of Pregnancy* (National Academy of Sciences, Washington, D.C., 1970).
80. *World Health Organization, Technical Report Series, No. 302* (World Health Organization, Geneva, 1965).
81. J. Yerushalmy *et al.*, *Am. J. Obstet. Gynecol.* **71**, 1 (1956).
82. D. Baird, in *Public Health and Population Change*, M. Sheps and J. Ridley, Eds. (Univ. of Pittsburgh Press, Pittsburgh, 1965).
83. J. Moustgaard, *J. Reprod. Med.* **8**, 1 (1972).
84. J. Meuvret, *Population* **1**, 643 (1946).
85. E. L. R. Ladurie, *Annales* **24**, 7 (1969).
86. A. Antonov, *J. Pediatr.* **30**, 250 (1947).
87. Z. Stein, M. Susser, G. Saenger, F. Marolla, *Famine and Human Development* (Oxford Univ. Press, London, 1975).
88. W. H. Mosley, in *Patterns and Determinants of Natural Fertility*, J. A. Menken and H. Leridon, Eds. (Ordina, Liege, 1979).
89. A. Keys, J. Brozek, A. Henschel, O. Michelson, H. L. Taylor, *The Biology of Human Starvation* (Univ. of Minnesota Press, Minneapolis, 1950).
90. J. A. Brazel, in (*3*), p. 29.
91. J. M. Moudot-Bernard, *Relationships Between Fertility, Child Mortality and Nutrition in Africa* (OECD Technical Papers, Organization for Economic Cooperation and Development, Paris, 1977).
92. A. Sydenham, *Br. Med. J.* **2**, 159 (1946).
93. P. G. McDonough, *Fertil. Steril.* **30**, 1 (1978).
94. S. L. Israel, *Diagnosis and Treatment of Menstrual Disorders* (Hoeber, New York, 1959).
95. A. H. Crisp and E. Stonehill, *Br. Med. J.* **3**, 149 (1971).
96. A. Levran, *Fertil. Steril.* **25**, 5 (1974).

The Worst Mistake in the History of the Human Race

_____ Jared Diamond _____

To science we owe dramatic changes in our smug self image. Astronomy taught us that our earth isn't the center of the universe but merely one of billions of heavenly bodies. From biology we learned that we weren't specially created by God but evolved along with millions of other species. Now archaeology is demolishing another sacred belief: that human history over the past million years has been a long tale of progress. In particular, recent discoveries suggest that the adoption of agriculture, supposedly our most decisive step toward a better life, was in many ways a catastrophe from which we have never recovered. With agriculture came the gross social and sexual inequality, the disease and despotism, that curse our existence.

At first, the evidence against this revisionist interpretation will strike twentieth century Americans as irrefutable. We're better off in almost every respect than people of the Middle Ages, who in turn had it easier than cavemen, who in turn were better off than apes. Just count our advantages. We enjoy the most abundant and varied foods, the best tools and material goods, some of the longest and healthiest lives, in history. Most of us are safe from starvation and predators. We get our energy from oil and machines, not from our sweat. What neo-Luddite among us would trade his life for that of a medieval peasant, a caveman, or an ape?

For most of our history we supported ourselves by hunting and gathering: we hunted wild animals and foraged for wild plants. It's a life that philosophers have traditionally regarded as nasty, brutish, and short. Since no food is grown and little is stored, there is (in this view) no respite from the struggle that starts anew each day to find wild foods and avoid starving. Our escape from this misery was facilitated only 10,000 years ago, when in different parts of the world people began to domesticate plants and animals. The agricultural revolution gradually spread until today it's nearly universal and few tribes of hunter-gatherers survive.

From the progressivist perspective on which I was brought up, to ask "Why did almost all our hunter-gatherer ancestors adopt agriculture?" is silly. Of course they adopted it because agriculture is an efficient way to get more food for less work. Planted crops yield far more tons per acre than roots and berries.

Just imagine a band of savages, exhausted from searching for nuts or chasing wild animals, suddenly gazing for the first time at a fruit-laden orchard or a pasture full of sheep. How many milliseconds do you think it would take them to appreciate the advantages of agriculture?

The progressivist party line sometimes even goes so far as to credit agriculture with the remarkable flowering of art that has taken place over the past few thousand years. Since crops can be stored, and since it takes less time to pick food from a garden than to find it in the wild, agriculture gave us free time that hunter-gatherers never had. Thus it was agriculture that enabled us to build the Parthenon and compose the B-minor Mass.

While the case for the progressivist view seems overwhelming, it's hard to prove. How do you show that the lives of people 10,000 years ago got better when they abandoned hunting and gathering for farming? Until recently, archaeologists had to resort to indirect tests, whose results (surprisingly) failed to support the progressivist view. Here's one example of an indirect test: Are twentieth century hunter-gatherers really worse off than farmers? Scattered throughout the world, several dozen groups of so-called primitive people, like the Kalahari Bushmen, continue to support themselves that way. It turns out that these people have plenty of leisure time, sleep a good deal, and work less hard than their farming neighbors. For instance, the average time devoted each week to obtaining food is only 12 to 19 hours for one group of Bushmen, 14 hours or less for the Hadza nomads of Tanzania. One Bushman, when asked why he hadn't emulated neighboring tribes by adopting agriculture, replied, "Why should we, when there are so many mongongo nuts in the world?".

While farmers concentrate on high-carbohydrate crops like rice and potatoes, the mix of wild plants and animals in the diets of surviving hunter-gatherers provides more protein and a better balance of other nutrients. In one study, the Bushmen's average daily food intake (during a month when food was plentiful) was 2,140 calories and 93 grams of protein, considerably greater than the recommended daily allowance for people of their size. It's almost inconceivable that Bushmen, who eat 75 or so wild plants, could die of starvation the way hundreds of thousands of Irish farmers and their families did during the potato famine of the 1840s.

So the lives of at least the surviving hunter-gatherers aren't nasty and brutish, even though farmers have pushed them into some of the world's worst real estate. But modern hunter-gatherer societies that have rubbed shoulders with farming societies for thousands of years don't tell us about conditions before the agricultural revolution. The progressivist view is really making a claim about the distant past: that the lives of primitive people improved when they switched from gathering to farming. Archaeologists can date that switch by distinguishing remains of wild plants and animals from those of domesticated ones in prehistoric garbage dumps.

How can one deduce the health of the prehistoric garbage makers, and thereby directly test the progressivist view? That question has become answerable only in recent years, in part through the newly emerging techniques of paleopathology, the study of signs of disease in the remains of ancient peoples.

In some lucky situations, the paleopathologist has almost as much material to study as a pathologist today. For example, archaeologists in the Chilean deserts found well preserved mummies whose medical conditions at time of death could be determined by autopsy (DISCOVER, October). And feces of long-dead Indians who lived in dry caves in Nevada remain sufficiently well preserved to be examined for hookworm and other parasites.

Usually the only human remains available for study are skeletons, but they permit a surprising number of deductions. To begin with, a skeleton reveals its owner's sex, weight, and approximate age. In the few cases where there are many skeletons, one can construct mortality tables like the ones life insurance companies use to calculate expected life span and risk of death at any given age. Paleopathologists can also calculate growth rates by measuring bones of people of different ages, examine teeth for enamel defects (signs of childhood malnutrition), and recognize scars left on bones by anemia, tuberculosis, leprosy, and other diseases.

One straightforward example of what paleopathologists have learned from skeletons concerns historical changes in height. Skeletons from Greece and Turkey show that the average height of hunter-gatherers toward the end of the ice ages was generous 5'9" for men, 5'5" for women. With the adoption of agriculture, height crashed, and by 3000 B.C. had reached a low of only 5'3" for men, 5' for women. By classical times heights were very slowly on the rise again, but modern Greeks and Turks have still not regained the average height of their distant ancestors.

Another example of paleopathology at work is the study of Indian skeletons from burial mounds in the Illinois and Ohio river valleys. At Dickson Mounds, located near the confluence of the Spoon and Illinois rivers, archaeologists have excavated some 800 skeletons that paint a picture of the health changes that occurred when a hunter-gatherer culture gave way to intensive maize farming around A.D. 1150. Studies by George Armelagos and his colleagues then at the University of Massachusetts show these early farmers paid a price for their newfound livelihood. Compared to the hunger-gatherers who preceded them, the farmers had a nearly 50 per cent increase in enamel defects indicative of malnutrition, a fourfold increase in iron-deficiency anemia (evidenced by a bone condition called porotic hyperostosis), a threefold rise in bone lesions reflecting infectious disease in general, and an increase in degenerative conditions of the spine, probably reflecting a lot of hard physical labor. "Life expectancy at birth in the pre-agricultural community was about twenty-six years," says Armelagos, "but in the post-agricultural community it was nineteen years. So these episodes of nutritional stress and infectious disease were seriously affecting their ability to survive."

The evidence suggests that the Indians at Dickson Mounds, like many other primitive peoples, took up farming not by choice but from necessity in order to feed their constantly growing numbers. "I don't think most hunter-gatherers farmed until they had to, and when they switched to farming they traded quality for quantity," says Mark Cohen of the State University of New York at Plattsburgh, co-editor, with Armelagos, of one of the seminal books in the field, *Paleopathology at the Origins of Agriculture.* "When I first started making that argument ten years ago, not many people agreed with me. Now it's become a respectable, albeit controversial, side of the debate."

There are at least three sets of reasons to explain the findings that agriculture was bad for health. First, hunter-gatherers enjoyed a varied diet, while early farmers obtained most of their food from one or a few starchy crops. The farmers gained cheap calories at the cost of poor nutrition. (Today just three high-carbohydrate plants—wheat, rice, and corn—provide the bulk of the calories consumed by the human species, yet each one is deficient in certain vitamins or amino acids essential to life.) Second, because of dependence on a limited number of crops, farmers ran the risk of starvation if one crop failed. Finally, the mere fact that agriculture encouraged people to clump together in crowded societies, many of which then carried on trade with other crowded societies, led to the spread of parasites and infectious disease. (Some archaeologists think it was crowding, rather than agriculture, that promoted disease, but this is a chicken-and-egg argument, because crowding encourages agriculture and vice versa.) Epidemics couldn't take hold when populations were scattered in small bands that constantly shifted camp. Tuberculosis and diarrheal disease had to await the rise of farming, measles and bubonic plague the appearance of large cities.

Besides malnutrition, starvation, and epidemic diseases, farming helped bring another curse upon humanity: deep class divisions. Hunter-gatherers have little or no stored food, and no concentrated food sources, like an orchard or a herd of cows: they live off the wild plants and animals they obtain each day. Therefore, there can be no kings, no class of social parasites who grow fat on food seized from others. Only in a farming population could a healthy, non-producing élite set itself above the disease-ridden masses. Skeletons from Greek tombs at Mycenae c. 1500 B.C. suggest that royals enjoyed a better diet than commoners, since the royal skeletons were two or three inches taller and had better teeth (on the average, one instead of six cavities or missing teeth). Among Chilean mummies from c. A.D. 1000, the élite were distinguished not only by ornaments and gold hair clips but also by a fourfold lower rate of bone lesions caused by disease.

Similar contrasts in nutrition and health persist on a global scale today. To people in rich countries like the U.S., it sounds ridiculous to extol the virtues of hunting and gathering. But Americans are an élite, dependent on oil and minerals that must often be imported from countries with poorer health and nutrition. If one could choose between being a peasant farmer in Ethiopia or a Bushman gatherer in the Kalahari, which do you think would be the better choice?

Farming may have encouraged inequality between the sexes, as well. Freed from the need to transport their babies during a nomadic existence, and under pressure to produce more hands to till the fields, farming women tended to have more frequent pregnancies than their hunter-gatherer counterparts—with consequent drains on their health. Among the Chilean mummies, for example, more women than men had bone lesions from infectious disease.

Women in agricultural societies were sometimes made beasts of burden. In New Guinea farming communities today I often see women staggering under loads of vegetables and firewood while the men walk empty-handed. Once while on a field trip there studying birds, I offered to pay some villagers to carry supplies from an airstrip to my mountain camp. The heaviest item was a 110-pound bag of rice, which I lashed to a pole and assigned to a team of four men to shoulder together. When I eventually caught up with the villagers, the men were carrying light loads, while one small woman weighing less than the bag of rice was bent under it, supporting its weight by a cord across her temples.

As for the claim that agriculture encouraged the flowering of art by providing us with leisure time, modern hunter-gatherers have at least as much free time as do farmers. The whole emphasis on leisure time as a critical factor seems to me misguided. Gorillas have had ample free time to build their own Parthenon, had they wanted to. While post-agricultural technological advances did make new art forms possible and preservation of art easier, great paintings and sculptures were already being produced by hunter-gatherers 15,000 years ago, and were still produced as recently as the last century by such hunter-gatherers as some Eskimos and the Indians of the Pacific Northwest.

Thus with the advent of agriculture an élite became better off, but most people became worse off. Instead of swallowing the progressivist party line that we chose agriculture because it was good for us, we must ask how we got trapped by it despite its pitfalls.

One answer boils down to the adage "Might makes right." Farming could support many more people than hunting, albeit with a poorer quality of life. (Population densities of hunter-gatherers are rarely over one person per ten square miles, while farmers average 100 times that.) Partly, this is because a field planted entirely in edible crops lets one feed far more mouths than a forest with scattered edible plants. Partly, too, it's because nomadic hunter-gatherers have to keep their children spaced at four-year intervals by infanticide and other means, since a mother must carry her toddler until it's old enough to keep up with the adults. Because farm women don't have that burden, they can and often do bear a child every two years.

As population densities of hunter-gatherers slowly rose at the end of the ice ages, bands had to choose between feeding more mouths by taking the first steps toward agriculture, or else finding ways to limit growth. Some bands chose the former solution, unable to anticipate the evils of farming, and seduced by the transient abundance they enjoyed until population growth caught up with increased food production. Such bands outbred and then drove off or killed the bands that chose to remain hunter-gatherers, because a hundred malnourished farmers can still outfight one healthy hunter. It's not that hunter-gatherers abandoned their life style, but that those sensible enough not to abandon it were forced out of all areas except the ones farmers didn't want.

At this point it's instructive to recall the common complaint that archaeology is a luxury, concerned with the remote past, and offering no lessons for the present. Archaeologists studying the rise of farming have reconstructed a crucial stage at which we made the worst mistake in human history. Forced to choose between limiting population or trying to increase food production, we chose the latter and ended up with starvation, warfare, and tyranny.

Hunter-gatherers practiced the most successful and longest-lasting life style in human history. In contrast, we're still struggling with the mess into which agriculture has tumbled us, and it's unclear whether we can solve it. Suppose that an archaeologist who had visited us from outer space were trying to explain human history to his fellow spacelings. He might illustrate the results of his digs by a 24-hour clock on which one hour represents 100,000 years of real past time. If the history of the human race began at midnight, then we would now be almost at the end of our first day. We lived as hunter-gatherers for nearly the whole of that day, from midnight through dawn, noon, and sunset. Finally, at 11:54 P.M., we adopted agriculture. As our second midnight approaches, will the plight of famine-stricken peasants gradually spread to engulf us all? Or will we somehow achieve those seductive blessings that we imagine behind agriculture's glittering facade, and that have so far eluded us?

The Cruel Logic of Our Genes

Jared Diamond

What comfort is it to me that cause follows effect? I must have justice, or I'll destroy myself. All religions are built on this longing, and I'm a believer. But then there are the children: What am I to do about them? That's the question I can't answer. It's beyond all comprehension why children should suffer to pay for a divine system of justice. Justice isn't worth the tears of even a single tortured child. God demands too high an admission price for his divine system. And so, I respectfully give back to God my entrance ticket.
—Dostoyevsky, *The Brothers Karamazov*

The first person I knew who died of a genetic disease was a four-year-old named Sara. I was seven then, and my pediatrician father was caring for Sara and her younger brother, Tommy. Both at first had been normally adorable and happy children, but Sara's life after age two was made increasingly miserable by the blood disease she had inherited. She passed her last months in constant pain from the enlarged liver pressing against her diaphragm. At the time she died Tommy still seemed normal, but eventually he too was hit by the same disease that had taken his sister, he died even more quickly and miserably.

As a youngster I identified with the dying children, not with their parents. I could make no sense of a world in which children died without having done anything to deserve it. Not until more than 40 years later could I feel even part of what Sara and Tommy's parents must have gone through, as I watched my own son Joshua in the hospital, his life in doubt, and the terrified look of a wounded animal in his eyes. Joshua survived, but two of the children in neighboring beds didn't, and I understood then the grief and outrage in the eyes of their parents. As had Dostoyevsky, I found myself wondering how anyone could believe in a system of justice that requires children to suffer.

Genetic diseases uniquely offend us. Yes, we grieve when someone dies for other reasons, from an accident, say, or a contracted illness. But we routinely try to understand such events by asking whether the victim did anything, or neglected to do anything, that led to his death. In genetic diseases that path to understanding is foreclosed. We cannot impute responsibility to the victim, because the cause of his death was present at the time of his conception. Someone with a genetic disease is a walking time bomb, set to explode at any time from infancy until late adulthood, and often there is little or nothing the victim

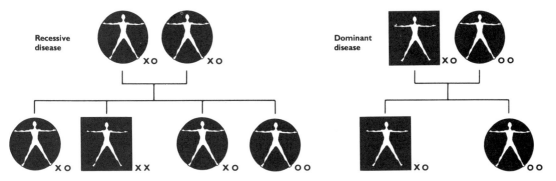

Victims of genetic diseases are represented in the squares. A recessive disease appears only in people who inherit the disease-causing gene (X) from both parents. Such people are called homozygotes (XX). A dominant disease strikes even those with one normal gene (O)—called heterozygotes (XO)—although sometimes not until after the victim has had children.

can do to prevent it. Why does God or fate play these supremely dirty tricks on us?

Our sense that the blow is undeserved is compounded by our sense of its meaninglessness. The death seems to be nothing more than the consequence of a purposeless genetic mistake, a needless mutation blindly passed on to a child who will be summarily disposed of by the relentless workings of natural selection. We can accept the notion of a mistake when we buy a pen that proves defective and we have to discard it in the trash. But we can't face saying, "My child was a mistake, so she ended up in the trash, and there's no more meaning to it than that."

At the root of this anguish lies a big, and unresolved, scientific question: If it's true that the filter of natural selection acts to eliminate deleterious genes, then how is it that genetic diseases persist? The answer may be that, contrary to appearances, genetic diseases are not mere mistakes, that they are in fact sustained by some positive evolutionary purpose. It's an answer that may seem cruel, at least as it pertains to any one victim. And yet it is the only way I've found to make sense of the dilemma that arises when genetic diseases confront our longing to believe in a world of justice.

The term *genetic diseases* conjures up a few rare, genetically simple conditions, such as Duchenne's muscular dystrophy and Tay-Sachs disease, in which everyone affected by the gene invariably dies. But genetic diseases are actually a much broader phenomenon, encompassing the commonest causes of human death. For example, there are very common conditions—such as diabetes, ulcers, heart disease, and probably manic-depression—that depend on multiple genes, and in which only some people bearing those genes fall prey to the disease. Also, we usually think of infectious diseases as being completely different from genetic diseases. In fact, some well-studied infectious diseases—tuberculosis, for one—prove to have a genetic component that affects whether an exposed person will succumb to the infectious agent.

Still other deaths that we don't normally think of as genetic include some of those resulting from miscarriages. Traditionally the frequency of miscarriages was considered to be 15 percent, but this was in pregnancies that lasted long enough to be recognizable by the mother. When hormonal methods for early detection of pregnancy were devised, it became clear that the actual frequency of miscarriages was considerably higher, around 50 percent. Recent studies suggest that many other fertilized embryos don't even implant or survive long enough to become detectable hormonally; adding these to the total yields a miscarriage rate of perhaps 80 percent. That is, for reach person born alive there may have been four phantom brothers or sisters who died before they could be born. Genetic factors contribute to these prenatal deaths also.

So, in the end, genetic diseases are involved in most human deaths. We are all of us time bombs, differing from one another only in the triggering agent, the length of the fuse, and the inevitability of the explosion.

Yet why should this be so? Surely we can't all be merely the unwitting inheritors of past genetic mistakes; for there's no doubt that natural selection does indeed tend to eliminate deleterious genes—a cold-blooded euphemism meaning that people with such genes may well die before having children. Natural selection can't eradicate a deleterious gene permanently, of course, because the gene keeps reappearing in new human embryos by mutation. Could new mutations then account for all cases of a lethal genetic disease?

If this were the case, then each year the number of people dying of that disease would, on average, just equal the number of people in whom that mutation arose independently. Each victim would carry a fresh mutation; the victim's parents wouldn't have carried that genetic mistake, and the victim would have no children to pass it on to. Genetic diseases would then be like scattered fires; each would be extinguished by the fire department, but every day there would be new fires to put out.

Something like this seems to be true for a congenital malformation called Apert's syndrome, in which babies are born with deformed heads, hands, and feet. Most such babies have normal parents, and few grow up to have children of their own. Muscular dystrophy, a more familiar genetic disease, also seems to persist as a result of fresh mutations. However, muscular dystrophy differs from Apert's syndrome in that only men die, while women survive to pass the gene to their children. Still, if fresh mutations ceased, the deaths of all male children inheriting the gene would eventually cause muscular dystrophy to disappear.

Clearly, these and some other diseases really are maintained just by purposeless genetic mutations. But they're all rare diseases, because genetic mutations themselves are rare. Muscular dystrophy is the result of perhaps the most common mutation known in humans, and even it arises only once in every 20,000 births; most other human mutations arise only once in 10 million births. It follows then that any genetic disease that kills many more than one in 20,000 people can't be sustained by mutations alone in the long run and must instead have some other explanation for its persistence.

I said "in the long run" because in certain circumstances a genetic disease can occur frequently for a while without any purposeful factor to sustain it: the gene can become common in a small population as a result of what's known as the founder effect.

Suppose that ten couples settle a sparsely inhabited area and found a new population. Suppose also that, by chance, one member of those ten founding couples carries some rare deleterious gene. If the small group now increases rapidly in numbers, that gene will initially occur in about one-tenth of the population, even though the gene is much rarer in populations that have already reached genetic equilibrium.

Of course, the people carrying the harmful gene will tend to leave fewer descendants than other people, and eventually, after enough generations, the frequency of the gene's appearance will decline to the rate that can be sustained by mutation alone. But that may take centuries, and until then the gene will be present at an above-normal frequency.

There are a number of modern populations with many members descended from a small number of founding couples in the recent past—just think of the white population of Australia. Studies of such populations regularly detect certain genetic diseases that occur frequently in those populations but rarely in the rest of the world. With good genealogical records it's often possible to prove that all known victims of the disease are descended from just one of the population's early founders.

Huntington's chorea, for example, is a fatal inherited neurological disease that occurs with above-normal frequency in southeast Australia. Some painstaking record searching shows that at least 432 Australian victims were directly descended from one English widow named Miss Cundick, who took her 13 children by two marriages and immigrated to Australia in 1848. Evidently Miss Cundick had the gene for Huntington's chorea and passed it on to some of her numerous offspring. They in turn were able to leave many descendants, including hundreds with Huntington's chorea.

As another example, consider a genetic disease called osteodental dysplasia, which causes all one's teeth to fall out by age 20 but otherwise doesn't markedly impair one's ability to attract a mate and have children. While known cases are scattered around the world, a disproportionate number are from South Africa. Is this because something in South Africa's climate makes toothless people especially fertile? Not at all. It turns out that at least 71 known South African cases are descended from a polygamous immigrant named Arnold who, assisted by his seven known wives and 53 grandchildren, propelled the gene to its present high frequency.

Thus the founder effect can explain some locally common genetic diseases—but only under special circumstances. It applies mainly to populations that multiplied greatly from a small number of founding couples in the recent past. And it applies to genes that are eliminated only slowly by natural selection—either because the gene isn't fatal (as in the case of osteodental dysplasia); or because it appears in late adulthood, after the victim could already have had children (as in the case of Huntington's chorea); or because it's recessive, a term I'll explain in a moment.

All this still leaves unexplained the lethal genetic diseases that are widespread in long-established populations. Here, one would think, the frequencies of lethal genes should have long ago declined to the frequencies of mutations. If a fatal genetic disease is nevertheless common, then it's unlikely that the gene's frequency is being maintained by mutations alone. The conclusion seems inescapable that since the gene is not being eliminated by natural selection, it must be fulfilling some positive evolutionary purpose, conveying some benefit that offsets its harmful effect. By that I mean that the gene, while making its bearers more likely than other people to die of condition X, may in fact make them less likely to die of condition Y. Evolution could thus cause the gene to persist, if the children whom it saved at least balanced the children whom it killed.

This conclusion may seem grisly. But this scientific explanation for the persistence of genetic diseases could help us accept the ethical dilemma they pose. The disease gene would not be a pure injustice, since it would also bring advantages—albeit at a price.

There are two ways in which it could actually work. One is that the same person who risks the gene's disadvantages may also stand to reap the gene's advantages: for example, a gene that is bad for you when you're an adult could be good for you when you're a baby. Alternatively, the gene could bestow its harmful effects only upon certain carriers, while blessing others with its benefits: a gene could be good for people who inherit it from just one parent, for example, but bad for people who inherit it from both. That explanation would also help us in our ethical dilemma. The victim's death would not be in vain. In effect, he would be sacrificing his life so that brothers and sisters might reap the benefits of the gene and live.

My guess is that these agonizing bargains are what maintain the high frequencies of our familiar genetic diseases. But its' hard to test this speculation; there's still only one disease—sickle-cell anemia—for which protection at a price is well established. There's suggestive evidence for a few more diseases, speculative theories for several others, and no good clue for most.

To see how these trade-offs might operate, we'll first need a quick review of genetics. Recall that we carry two copies of most of our genes: one that we inherit from our mother, and one from our father. If your maternal and paternal forms of a particular gene are identical, you're termed a homozygote for that gene; if they're different, you're termed a heterozygote.

Suppose that a certain form of a particular gene causes a disease even when you're a heterozygote, with only one copy of that form (your other copy being the normal, non-disease-causing form). We then say that the disease is dominant. If, on the other hand, you get the disease only when you're a homozygote, with both copies of the gene being the disease-related form, then we say the disease is recessive.

Sickle-cell anemia is a recessive disease. It arises from an abnormal form of the hemoglobin pigment, which carries oxygen and gives red blood cells their red color. The abnormal hemoglobin turns red cells from disks into crescents, causing them to be destroyed, and affected homozygotes often die in childhood from a severe red-cell deficiency. Heterozygotes, however, are completely healthy under most circumstances.

The sickle-cell gene is virtually confined to black Africans and their descendants and some peoples of the Mediterranean, the Arabian Peninsula, and India. About 10 percent of U.S. blacks carry the gene, but in some areas of Africa its frequency is as high as 40 percent, which means that in these regions the abnormal form of the gene appears almost as frequently as the normal form and far, far more frequently than could be accounted for just by new mutations.

Until the advent of modern medicine, most sickle-cell homozygotes died without leaving children. Heterozygotes survived and reproduced, but whenever two heterozygotes produced children, one-quarter of their offspring on the average were sickle-cell homozygotes and likely to die. It would seem then that over many generations, natural selection should have caused the frequency of the sickle-cell gene to drop to low levels. Why hasn't it?

The explanation proves to be that the gene is double-edged: while it condemns some to death, it confers life on others. For it turns out that people with a single sickle-cell gene have a significant advantage over normal people in regions where malaria is common. The heterozygotes are less likely to die of the disease because their red cells are poor at supporting the growth of malaria parasites.

In those areas, as a result, more sickle-cell heterozygotes than normal people live long enough to have children of their own. This excess of heterozygous children balances the deaths of homozygous children, such that the sickle-cell gene persists in frequency from generation to generation. In effect, the few homozygotes die of anemia so that the more numerous heterozygotes will have a better chance of surviving malaria. The population as a whole has bought partial protection of many of its children against its worst infectious disease, but at a price. Without consulting them individually, evolution has struck a grim bargain.

Among genetic diseases, sickle-cell anemia is unique in that it offers very strong evidence of an underlying evolutionary trade-off. Many other diseases may involve similar bargains, with homozygotes paying the price and heterozygotes getting the protection, but the evidence is much more speculative. Apparently the protection is either weaker, and thus harder to recognize, or it was amassed against some infectious disease that was important in the past but less common today.

After sickle-cell anemia the most plausible examples are some other blood diseases (such as thalassemias) that may offer Africans, Asians, or Mediterranean peoples weaker protection against malaria. Much more speculative is a theory for the persistence of Tay-Sachs disease, a fatal neurological condition of children that is especially common in Jews of Eastern European origin. The Tay-Sachs gene may formerly have protected heterozygotes against tuberculosis in the days when it was still a leading killer. If so, one could rationalize why the Tay-Sachs gene became most frequent in Eastern European Jews, formerly confined to urban ghettos teeming with tuberculosis. Similarly, the gene for cystic fibrosis, another childhood killer and the most common recessive genetic disease of whites of European descent, may protect heterozygotes against lethal diarrheas from bacterial infections—once a far worse risk of childhood than cystic fibrosis.

There may also be evolutionary bargains in which the costs and benefits are apportioned between the sexes, rather than between homozygotes and heterozygotes. A speculative example is hemochromatosis, which may represent the most common abnormal gene in the United States. The disease arises from unusually rapid intestinal absorption of iron, which can eventually cause body stores of the metal to rise to ten times normal levels. The victim in effect dies of self-inflicted iron poisoning.

Men normally lose very little iron and can't get rid of any excess, unless they're addicted to leeches and bloodletting. Women, on the other hand, are far more likely to suffer from iron deficiency rather than surfeit, because they lose iron through menstrual bleeding, pregnancy, and nursing. Not surprisingly, then, symptoms of hemochromatosis are seen much more often in men than in women.

Perhaps the hemochromatosis gene is actually good for women, by enabling them to absorb iron more efficiently and thus combat their risk of iron deficiency. When, someday, a textbook on genetics comes to be written by a liberated woman physician, the current view of hemochromatosis as a disease may be dismissed as one more distorted product of male chauvinism. Instead, we'll read that a gene for increased iron absorption is a wonderful evolutionary blessing that enables women to overcome one of their leading metabolic problems. A footnote will then mention, by the way, that a few older men bearing the same gene pay with their lives so that women may benefit.

In the cases I've discussed so far, one person reaps the gene's benefits, while a different person bears the risks. But there are at least two examples in which the beneficiary and the victim are one and the same.

Both examples involve diabetes mellitus, a common condition that is often classified as either insulin-dependent or noninsulin-dependent. The insulin-dependent variety is caused by damage to the pancreatic cells that produce insulin, a hormone controlling our blood sugar levels, and it is treated by insulin injections. In contrast, noninsulin-dependent diabetes arises from the body's developing a resistance to its own insulin; treatment usually involves controlling the patient's diet. (These two types of diabetes were formerly known as juvenile-onset and adult-onset diabetes, respectively, because of their tendencies to arise earlier or later in life.) Both forms are genetically influenced, though not in such a simple way as the other diseases I've mentioned.

Only one out of five people genetically at risk actually develops insulin-dependent diabetes (the outcome may depend on infection by a virus that damages the pancreas). Nevertheless, until insulin injections became available, those who did develop diabetes were likely to die, so one would have expected that eventually the frequency of diabetes-related genes would have declined to a level low enough to be sustained by mutations. How did the disease manage to remain common?

Surprisingly, the answer may be that the risk of diabetes is offset by a genetic protection offered to a fetus against the risk of miscarriage. Consider a parent who is heterozygous for a diabetes-related gene. That is, of the parent's two copies of the gene, one is the normal form, while the other is the form that predisposes to diabetes. You'd then expect that half the babies born to such a parent would inherit the normal gene, and half would inherit the diabetes-related gene. In fact, at birth up to 72 percent of the children carry the diabetes-related gene. This suggests that the frequency of miscarriage was higher for fertilized eggs carrying the normal gene than for those carrying the diabetes-related gene. Since four out of the five fetuses with diabetes-related genes will not develop diabetes, the improved chance of prenatal survival keeps the genes common despite the postnatal deaths of one-fifth of the carriers.

Protection against miscarriage will surely prove to be important in explaining the persistence of some genetic diseases, whether or not it proves valid for diabetes in particular. Recall that many or even most conceptions end in miscarriage. Any genetic advantage that helps the fetus survive death before birth is evolutionarily valuable, for its whole childbearing career lies in the future. Evolution may have given us many genes that favor fetuses and babies while causing diseases in adults past childbearing age.

My other example involves the type of diabetes in which the body develops resistance to its own insulin. Normally we release insulin after a meal to help our body store the food we ingest. In this disease, resistance is thought to develop as a result of the body releasing insulin too quickly, too often, or in too large amounts after a meal. While the condition has a genetic basis, it's also obviously influenced by diet. Examples can be found in Pima Indians, Pacific islanders, and Yemenite Jews; in all these peoples the occurrence of diabetes shot sky-high within a decade or two of their rapid transition from an active, low-calorie, low-carbohydrate life to a life of little exercise and a high-calorie, high-carbohydrate diet.

Why would genes that were good for people living meagerly suddenly bring on diabetes when those people became Westernized? It may have something to do with the availability of food. For many people in the West today, food is easily acquired and eaten three or more times daily at scheduled hours. But for many others food is something they eat whenever they are lucky enough to get it. This was certainly true for almost all humans in the past. Our former life was one of feast or famine. Those who could pack away lots of food when it was available, and whose bodies could store it for later use, were able to survive subsequent famines.

Many stories illustrate the ability of people accustomed to a Spartan life to gorge themselves when food was abundant. The British Arctic explorer Sir Edward Parry once did the experiment of offering an Eskimo man named Tooloak as much food and drink as he could consume overnight. In 13 hours Tooloak packed away more than ten pounds of meat and bread, and washed it down with almost two gallons of soup, alcohol, and other liquids.

Throughout most of our evolutionary history, those individuals who released lots of insulin gained an advantage by retaining the calories they gorged.

That enabled them to survive subsequent times of starvation, while their insulin-poor comrades succumbed. But put the same people on a Western diet, where they are challenged to pour out insulin all the time, and they develop resistance to insulin and hence diabetes.

This, then, is the scientific sense we're able to make of genetic diseases. They somehow manage to persist at high frequencies, despite the tendency of natural selection to eliminate deleterious genes. While mutations or the founder effect explains some cases, the main explanation for common, widespread genetic diseases is that the genes somehow help as well as harm our survival. Where genetic diseases differ is in how the costs and benefits are allocated among people. Sickle-cell anemia, and possibly cystic fibrosis and Tay-Sachs disease, help heterozygotes while harming homozygotes. Hemochromatosis may help women while harming men. Insulin-dependent diabetes may help a person as a fetus, then harm him later in life. And non-insulin-dependent diabetes may help a person on a Spartan diet but harm the same person on a generous diet. In all these cases, disease genes bring concealed blessings—at a price.

Do these answers to the scientific paradox suggest an approach to the more difficult ethical paradox? Can they tell us how to maintain our faith in a universe that permits genetic diseases to exist? It's hard to formulate a response that will sound convincing when you're on a pediatric ward, listening to sick children crying. Anyone who has heard those cries understands why Ivan Karamazov spurned God's entrance ticket to his divine system.

But perhaps there is an answer, incomplete though it may be. We live in a world that exposes us to danger at every moment from conception onward. First there is the danger of miscarriage; next, the risk of succumbing to childhood infectious diseases; and then the risks of other infections and starvation throughout all of adult life. In this perilous world we can only try to solve each risk as it arises. Some of our genetic solutions catch up with us later and become labeled as genetic diseases, but that term is a misnomer. Those genes enabled us, or our relatives, to survive earlier dangers. In that sense, genetic diseases are agonizing Faustian bargains in which natural selection plays the role of Mephistopheles.

The Cost of Living

Jared Diamond

Death and aging constitute a mystery we often ask about as children, deny in youth, and reluctantly come to accept as adults. I scarcely reflected on aging when I was a college student. Now that I am 52 years old, I find it decidedly more interesting.

The actuarial tables tell me I can look forward to another 27 statistical years; I'd get an extra four if I were a woman. But it is unlikely that I or many of my contemporaries will survive to be 100, and it's nearly impossible that any of us will live to 120. Why is such longevity so hard for us? Why do humans, even with the best medical care, inevitably grow infirm and die? Aging may be the most obvious fact of life, but there's nothing obvious about what causes it.

Not that science hasn't tried to find out, of course. The why of aging is, after all, an age-old question. In recent years studies of aging have been pursued independently by two separate groups of researchers, each distinguished by its approach to the subject: one group seeks a proximate explanation, the other an ultimate explanation.

To appreciate this difference, consider the question, "Why do skunks smell bad?" You might answer, "It's because skunks secrete chemical compounds with particular molecular structures that result in bad smells. Those chemicals would smell bad no matter what their biological function was." You will have given a perfectly reasonable proximate explanation—that is, you will have described the mechanism immediately responsible for the skunk's bad smell.

But someone else might reason, "It's because skunks would be easy victims for predators if they didn't defend themselves with bad smells. Natural selection ensured that those skunks with the worst smells survived to produce the most babies. The molecular structure of the chemicals is an incidental detail; any other bad-smelling chemicals would suit skunks equally well." This is now an ultimate explanation: it describes the function or chain of events that caused the mechanism immediately responsible for the skunk's smell to be present in the first place.

Research into aging tends to split along similar lines. Physiologists inquire into the cellular mechanisms underlying aging. In general, they believe that something about our physiology makes aging inevitable: for instance, one theory attributes aging to the progressive difficulties our immune system is said to face in distinguishing our own cells from foreign cells. The implicit view among these proximate explainers is that when it comes to aging, evolutionary considerations are irrelevant.

Evolutionary biologists, on the other hand, try to understand how natural selection could ever have permitted those proximate mechanisms, whatever they are, to have evolved. Focused as they are on the ultimate explanation, evolutionary biologists are prone to see the physiologists' quest as shortsighted.

As an evolutionary biologist who has the good fortune to teach physiology, I either have my feet firmly planted in both camps or I am shakily straddling the fence between them, depending on how charitable an observer you are. But it seems to me that aging can't be understood unless we seek both explanations simultaneously.

Let's first consider the subject in the physiological terms of biological repair mechanisms, because aging may be thought of as simply unrepaired damage or deterioration. Our first association to the word *repair* is likely to be those repairs that cause us the most frustration: car repairs. Our cars, we know, will grow old and die, but we spend money to postpone their inevitable fate. We are unconsciously—but constantly—repairing ourselves too, at every level from that of molecules to that of tissues or whole organs. And like the repairs we lavish on our cars, our self-repair mechanisms are of two sorts: damage control and regular replacement.

Fenders are likely targets of automotive damage control. We replace them only if they're bashed in; we don't routinely replace them at every regular oil change. The most visible example of damage control applied to our bodies is wound healing, by which we repair damage to our skin. Many animals can achieve much more spectacular results than we can: lizards can regenerate severed tails, starfish and crabs their limbs, sea cucumbers their intestines. At the invisible molecular level our genetic material, DNA, is repaired exclusively by damage control: we have enzymes that can recognize and fix damaged sites in the DNA helix while ignoring intact DNA.

The other type of repair, regular replacement, is also familiar to every car owner: we periodically change the oil, air filter, and ball bearings to eliminate slight wear, without waiting for the car to break down first. In the biological world teeth are similarly replaced: humans grow two sets, elephants six sets, and sharks an indefinite number during their lifetime. Although we humans go through life with the same skeleton with which we were born, lobsters and other arthropods regularly replace their exoskeleton by molting it and growing a new one.

Regular replacement also goes on at a microscopic level. We replace the cells lining our intestine once every few days, those lining the urinary bladder once every two months, and our red blood cells once every four months. At the molecular level our protein molecules are subject to continuous turnover at a rate characteristic of each particular protein; we thereby avoid the accumulation of damaged molecules. Hence if you compare your beloved's appearance today with that of a month ago, he or she may look the same, but many of the individual molecules forming that beloved body are different. While all the king's horses and men couldn't put Humpty Dumpty together again, nature is taking us apart and putting us back together every day.

Thus, much of an animal's body can be repaired or is regularly replaced anyhow. But the details of how much is replaceable vary greatly with the part and with the species. Judging from the physiological talents of other animals, there seems to be nothing inevitable about our limited repair capabilities.

Since starfish can regrow amputated limbs, why can't we? What prevents us from having six sets of teeth like an elephant, rather than just baby teeth and adult teeth? With four more natural sets, we wouldn't need fillings, crowns, and dentures as we got older. Why don't we protect ourselves against arthritis? All we would need to do is replace our joints periodically, as crabs do. Why don't we guard against heart disease by periodically replacing our hearts? One might suppose that natural selection would favor the man or woman who didn't die of heart disease around age 80 but instead continued to live and produce babies at least until age 200. Why, for that matter, can't we repair or replace everything in our bodies?

The answer surely has something to do with the expense of repair. Here again, the car analogy is helpful. Supposedly, a Mercedes-Benz is so well built that even should you do no maintenance whatsoever—not even lubrication or oil changes—your car will still run for years. At the end of that time, of course, it will fall apart from accumulated irreversible damage. Hence Mercedes owners generally do choose to service their cars regularly. My Mercedes-owning friends tell me that service is very expensive: hundreds of dollars every time they drive into the shop. Nevertheless, they consider the expense worth it: a serviced Mercedes lasts much longer than an unserviced one, and it's much cheaper to service your old Mercedes regularly than to discard it and buy a new one every few years.

At least, that's how Mercedes owners reason in the United States. But suppose you were living in Port Moresby—the capital of Papua New Guinea and, as far as I can tell, the automobile-accident capital of the world—where any car, no matter how well it's maintained, is likely to be totaled within a year. Many car owners in New Guinea don't go to the expense of maintenance: they use the saved money to help buy the next car.

By analogy, how much an animal should invest in biological repair depends on the repairs' expense and on a comparison of the animals' expected life span with and without the repairs. But such questions belong to the realm of evolutionary biology, not physiology.

Evolution, remember, is a game of strategy: the individual whose strategy leaves the most descendants wins. Yet our bodies have many features that seem to reduce rather than maximize our ability to produce offspring. Growing old and dying is just one example; other deterrents seem to be human females' having to wait 12 to 16 years before they can even start to produce babies, then bearing just one baby at a time—and only once every year or so at most—until they undergo menopause. Wouldn't evolution favor the woman who entered puberty at the age of five, completed gestation in a mere three weeks, regularly bore quintuplets, never underwent menopause, lived to 200, and thereby left hundreds of offspring?

I discussed the flaw in this reasoning in my article "Double Trouble" (August 1988), when the birth of my twin sons stimulated me to wonder why twin births remain rare among humans. I concluded then that evolution can't tinker with single characteristics in isolation from the rest of the animal. A woman couldn't simply reduce the length of pregnancy to three weeks, nor regularly give birth to a human litter of five without changing anything else about herself or her babies. Just to make twin births the norm instead of the exception, women would have to double their weight and have four breasts rather than two. And that's just for starters.

Thus, we have to ask not just which traits but which particular combination of traits will result in our greatest evolutionary success. What trade-offs do we have to make? We have only a finite amount of energy available to us; every structure, enzyme, or piece of DNA in our body consumes energy and space that might have gone into something else. Even people doing hard exercise and eating rich food—lumberjacks or marathon runners in training—can't metabolize much more than 8,000 calories per day. So how should we allocate those calories between repairing ourselves and rearing babies, if our goal is to raise as many babies as possible?

At the one extreme, if we were to put all our energy into babies and devote none to biological repair, our bodies would age and disintegrate before we could rear our first child. At the other extreme, if we were to lavish all our available energy on keeping our bodies in shape, we might live a long time but would have no energy left for the exhausting process of making and rearing children. What natural selection must do, then, is adjust an animal's relative expenditures of energy on repair and on reproduction to maximize its reproductive output, averaged over its lifetime.

Several decades ago the evolutionary biologist George Williams cited some striking facts about aging, showing that they become comprehensible only from an evolutionary perspective. Let's consider several of Williams's examples and reexpress them in the physiological language of biological repair, by taking slow aging as an indication of good repair mechanisms.

The first concerns the age at which an animal breeds and produces offspring. That age varies enormously among species: although few humans are so precocious as to produce babies before the age of 12, any self-respecting mouse a mere two months old can already make baby mice. Animal species whose age of first breeding is late, like us, need to devote much energy to repair, in order to ensure that they survive to that reproductive age. Hence we expect investment in repair to increase with age at first reproduction.

For example, we slow-to-reproduce humans age far less rapidly than do mice and are thus presumed to repair our bodies much more effectively. Generally, even with plenty of food and the best medical care, a mouse is lucky to reach its second birthday, while we would be unlucky not to reach our seventy-second. The evolutionary reason: A human who invested no more energy in repair than does a mouse would be dead long before reaching puberty. In these terms, it is more "worthwhile" to repair a human than a mouse.

What might that postulated extra energy expenditure of ours actually consist of? As we've noted, our repair capabilities seem relatively unimpressive. We can't regrow an amputated limb, and we don't regularly replace our skeleton. However, such spectacular but infrequent replacements of a whole structure probably aren't the biggest items in an animal's repair budget. Instead, the biggest expense is all that invisible replacement of so many cells and molecules, day after day. Even if you spend all of every day just lying in bed, you still need to eat about 1,640 calories daily if you're a man—1,430 if you're a woman—just to maintain your body. Much of that maintenance metabolism goes to our invisible scheduled replacement. And so I'd guess that where we cost more than a mouse is in putting a bigger fraction of our energy into self-repair.

A second example involves the risk of irreparable injury. Some biological damage is potentially reparable, but there is also damage that is guaranteed to be fatal—say, being eaten by a lion. If you're likely to be lunch for a lion tomorrow, there's no point paying a dentist to start expensive work on your teeth today. You'd do better to let your teeth rot and start having babies immediately. But if an animal's risk of death from irreparable accidents is low, then there is a potential payoff, in the form of increased life span, from putting energy into expensive repair mechanisms that retard aging. This is the reasoning by which Mercedes owners decide to pay for lubrication of their cars in the United States but not in New Guinea.

Because the risk of death from predators is lower for birds than for mammals (birds can escape by flying), and lower for turtles than for most other reptiles (turtles are protected by a shell), you would expect that birds and turtles stand to gain more from expensive repair mechanisms. And indeed, if you compare longevities of well-fed pets protected from predators, you find that birds do live longer (that is, they age more slowly) than similar-size mammals, and turtles live longer than similar-size shell-less reptiles.

The bird species best protected from predators are seabirds, like petrels and albatross, that nest on remote oceanic islands free of predators. Their leisurely lives rival our own. Some albatross don't even breed until they're ten years old, and we still don't know how long they live; the birds last longer than the metal rings biologists began putting on their legs a few decades ago in order to determine their age. In the ten years it takes an albatross to start breeding, a mouse population could have gone through 60 generations, most of which would already have succumbed to predators or old age.

As our third example, let's compare males and females of the same species. We expect more potential payoff from repair mechanisms and lower rates of aging in that sex with the lower accidental-mortality rate. In many species, males suffer greater accidental mortality than females because they put themselves at greater risk by fighting and through bold displays. This is certainly true of human males today and has probably been so throughout our history. Young men of the twentieth century risk death by daredevil driving; young men of 20,000 B.C. did it by trying to show how they could spear saber-toothed tigers.

Correlated with men's higher accidental-death rate is their higher nonaccidental-death rate. Women's life expectancy is now about four years greater than that of men; some of this difference is because more men than women are smokers, and yet there is a sex-linked difference in life expectancy even among nonsmokers. These differences suggest that evolution has programmed us so that women put more energy into self-repair, while men put more energy into fighting and swagger. I don't mean to denigrate male fighting and swagger, which serve a useful evolutionary purpose: a man engages in such activity to gain wives and secure resources for his children, at the expense of other men and their children. But all the same, it just isn't worth as much to repair a man as it is to repair a woman.

You may wonder, though, why it's worth repairing either a man or a woman past a certain point. Since transmitting one's genes to the next generation is what drives evolution, other animal species rarely survive long past reproductive age. Instead, nature programs death to coincide with the end of fertility, because there is then no longer any evolutionary benefit to gain from keeping one's body in good repair. Yet women are programmed to live for decades after menopause, and most men live to an age when they're no longer siring babies.

The explanation of this apparent exception to evolutionary cost-effectiveness becomes apparent on reflection. The intense phase of parental care is unusually protracted in humans, lasting nearly two decades. Even those older people whose own children have reached adulthood are tremendously important to the survival of not just their children but of their whole tribe. Especially in the days before writing, they acted as the carriers of essential knowledge. Thus, nature has programmed us with the capacity to keep the rest of our bodies in reasonable repair even at an age when the reproductive system itself has fallen into disrepair.

Perhaps the most important conclusion from an evolutionary approach to aging is that it undermines the approach that has long dominated the physiological study of aging. The gerontological literature is obsessed with a search for the Cause of Aging—preferably a single cause, and certainly not more than a few major ones. Within my own lifetime as a biologist, hormonal changes, deterioration in the immune system, and neural degeneration have vied in popularity for the title of the Cause, without compelling support having been adduced for any of the candidates. But evolutionary reasoning suggests that this search will remain futile. There should not be just one, nor even a few, dominant physiological mechanisms of aging. Instead, natural selection should act to match rates of aging in all physiological systems, with the result that aging involves innumerable simultaneous changes.

There's no point doing expensive maintenance on one piece of the body if other pieces are deteriorating more rapidly. Conversely, natural selection should not permit a few systems to deteriorate long before all the others, since the cost of extra repairs on just those few systems would then buy a big increase in life expectancy and would be worth it. By analogy, Mercedes owners shouldn't install cheap ball bearings when they are lavishing expense on all other parts of the car. After all, they could have doubled the life of their $50,000 car by spending just a few dollars more. But it wouldn't pay either to go to the expense of installing diamond ball bearings, when the rest of the car would have rusted away before those ball bearings wore out. Thus, the optimal strategy for Mercedes owners, and for us, is to repair all parts so that everything finally collapses all at once.

The evidence, it seems to me, suggests that we come closer to this evolutionary ideal than to the physiologists' long-sought Cause. Signs of aging can be found wherever one looks. Already I am conscious in myself of tooth wear, considerable decreases in muscle performance, and significant losses in hearing, vision, smell, and taste. Indeed, for all the senses, men's acuity is on the average less than that of equal-aged women. Ahead for me lies the familiar litany: weakening of the heart, hardening of the arteries, increasing brittleness of bones, decreasing kidney filtration rates, lower resistance of the immune system, and loss of memory. The list could be extended almost indefinitely.

Evolution seems indeed to have arranged things such that all our systems deteriorate, and that we invest in repair only as much as we are worth. From a practical standpoint, this conclusion is disappointing. If there were one dominant cause of aging, simply curing it would provide us with a fountain of youth. This thought, operating at a time when aging was considered to be largely a hormonal phenomenon, inspired attempts at miraculous rejuvenation of old people by hormonal injections or implantation of young gonads.

Such an attempt was the subject of Sir Arthur Conan Doyle's story "The Adventure of the Creeping Man," in which the aged Professor Presbury becomes infatuated with a young woman, desperately wants to rejuvenate himself, and instead is found creeping around like a monkey after midnight. The great Sherlock Holmes discovers the reason: the professor has been seeking youth by injecting himself with the serum of black-faced langur monkeys.

I could have warned Professor Presbury that his myopic obsession with proximate causation would lead him astray. Had he thought of ultimate evolutionary causation, he would have realized natural selection would never permit us to deteriorate through a single mechanism with one simple cure. Perhaps it's just as well. Holmes worried greatly about man's desire for a magic elixir of life: "When one tries to rise above Nature one is liable to fall below it. The highest type of man may revert to the animal if he leaves the straight road of destiny. . . . There is danger there—a very real danger to humanity."

Holmes can rest easy; an elixir now seems unlikely to materialize.